S0-BNT-111

CODE

g   gas laser
i   ion gas laser
l   liquid laser
m   molecular gas laser
s   solid-state laser
nm   microwave maser

							H	He
							g, mm	g
			B	C	N	O	F	Ne
			i	g, i	g, i, m	g, i	g, i	g, i
			Al	Si	P	S'	Cl	A
				i	i	g, i	g, i	g, i
Ni	Cu	Zn	Ga	Ge	As	Se	Br	Kr
$^{2+}, mm^{2+}$	g	g, i		i	i	i	g, i	g, i
Pd	Aq	Cd	In	Sn	Sb	Te	I	Xe
		g, i	i	g, i	i	i	g, i	g, i
Pt	Au	Hg	Tl	Pb	Bi	Po	At	Rn
	g	g, i^{2+}	g	g, i				

Eu	Gd	Tb	Dy	Ho	Er	Tm	Yb	Lu
s^{3+}, l^{3+}	mm^{3+}	l^{3+}	s^{2+}	s^{3+}	s^{3+}	s^{3+}, s^{2+}	s^{3+}	
Am	Cm	Bk	Cf	Es	Fm	Md	No	Lw

A. E. SIEGMAN

Professor of Electrical Engineering
Stanford University

AN INTRODUCTION TO LASERS AND MASERS

McGRAW-HILL BOOK COMPANY   NEW YORK   SAN FRANCISCO   ST. LOUIS
DÜSSELDORF   LONDON   MEXICO
PANAMA   SYDNEY   TORONTO

This book was set in Fototronic Bulmer by Graphic Services, Inc., and printed on permanent paper and bound by Von Hoffman Press, Inc. The designer was Janet Bollow; the drawings were done by David A. Strassman. The editors were Basil G. Dandison and Marge Eakins. Charles A. Goehring supervised production. Cover photograph courtesy of Spectra Physics, Inc.

**AN INTRODUCTION TO
LASERS AND MASERS**

Printed in the United States of America.

Library of Congress catalog card number: 79–123189

1234567890   VHVH   7987654321

57362

TO MY FAMILY

The brilliant red star on the cover of this book was created when a camera was placed in the beam of directional monochromatic red light coming from a laser—in this case a helium-neon gas laser with wavelength $\lambda = 6328$ Å or frequency $f = 4.74 \times 10^{14}$ Hz, located more than 20 miles from the camera. Lasers, or optical masers, are now fairly commonplace devices. This particular laser is only one of a very large family of these extraordinary new coherent light sources or optical oscillators, operating in all parts of the electromagnetic frequency spectrum and for the most part invented only within the past ten years.

Before masers were developed slightly over a decade ago, active electronic devices, such as vacuum tubes, transistors, and tunnel diodes, all functioned by means of interactions between applied electric fields and moving charges (most commonly free electrons). The demonstration of the first microwave ammonia maser by C. H. Townes in 1954 introduced a fundamentally new kind of electronic amplification employing interactions between either electric or magnetic fields and the internal resonances of atoms and molecules. From this first device has grown an extraordinarily wide variety of maser and laser devices, using a great variety of maser materials and operating at frequencies ranging from the audio to the ultraviolet.

In terms of frequency range at least, the maser principle is perhaps the most widely applicable electronic-amplification mechanism known (with the parametric-amplifier mechanism running a close second). Yet, despite their sometimes bewildering variety of forms, laser and maser devices all operate by means of essentially the same basic principles. One major objective of this text is to introduce and apply these basic maser principles. A second objective is to explain many of the widely different laser and maser devices in terms of these simple basic concepts.

A third objective of this book is to take the "quantum" out of "quantum electronics." This term has come to be a label applied to lasers and masers, and most people may think of lasers as being basically quantum-mechanical devices. Yet the basic concepts of maser action are actually relatively simple and can be understood almost entirely from a classical viewpoint, with only limited appeals to quantum terms and concepts. As with the physical phenomena underlying the operation of a transistor or any other semiconductor device, the phenomena underlying maser operation can best be explained, understood, and applied on the basis of appropriate semiclassical models and concepts. The classical electron oscillator model can summarize the underlying quantum phenomena in laser physics nearly as well as the concept of a "hole" does in semiconductor physics.

The basic principle of this book, in fact, is that lasers and masers of all types, in all frequency ranges, are simply electronic devices, likely to be of great importance to the electronics engineer. A thorough understanding of these devices is readily accessible to the electronics engineer or student in terms of classical and semi-quantum-mechanical concepts already familiar to him, with no need for an extensive background in quantum theory. No quantum theory is prerequisite for a senior-option or first-year-graduate course based on this book.

The term *maser* originally referred to a microwave-frequency device. However, the more common interpretation now, and the interpretation followed here, is that *maser* is a generic term for all devices that utilize the basic maser principle, in all frequency ranges from audio to optical. The term *laser* refers, then, to an optical-frequency maser. Maser devices in the audio, radio, and microwave portions of the electromagnetic spectrum are not generally competitive with conventional electronic devices such as semiconductors or vacuum tubes, except for a few specialized applications, such as atomic frequency standards and ultralow-noise microwave amplifiers, where they play a limited but important role.

The extension of the maser principle to infrared and optical frequencies, however, in the form of the optical maser, or laser, provides the first (and so far the only) available primary mechanism for coherent amplification and coherent signal generation in the submillimeter, infrared, and optical regions of the electromagnetic spectrum. This technological breakthrough—the term does seem appropriate here—has suddenly added some four or more decades of frequency spectrum to the domain of coherent electronic technology. The electronics engineer can now perform all the familiar functions of signal generation, amplification, modulation, transmission, and detection at frequencies up to 10^4 times higher than previously. In addition, he can perform an almost unlimited variety of new and different functions made possible by the short wavelengths and other unique characteristics of optical signals. In brief, the importance of the laser and its future applications in all areas of science and technology can hardly be overestimated.

This text is intended for use in an introductory course in lasers and masers at the senior or first-year-graduate level. It should be equally adaptable to the requirements of students in physics, electrical engineering, or other branches of science or engineering. I have tried to present a stimulating mixture of basic principles and examples of practical applications. Each chapter concludes with a set of problems and a list of selected references for further reading. As a special feature, the text includes descriptions of many simple and inexpensive experiments and demonstrations that can be carried out to illustrate basic principles or important device characteristics. A surprisingly great variety of inexpensive laser devices and demonstrations can be purchased or fabricated without great difficulty, and in teaching the material in this book I have found it both effective and entertaining (for me at least) to bring many of these demonstrations right into the lecture room.

For complete coverage, all the material in the book can be taken in sequence. If time is limited and the interest is primarily in lasers, Chaps. 4 and 7 may be bypassed, leaving out material primarily relevant to magnetic resonance and microwave masers, without any break in the logical development of the material. Chapter 11 may also be omitted in an abbreviated coverage. The five Appendixes provide supplemental discussions of special points. They are referred to at appropriate points in the text.

Given more time and space this book would have contained chapters on nonlinear optics and optical parametric devices, on light modulation and detection, and on various useful laser applications, particularly holography. Obviously, there is ample room for an instructor to supplement this text in these areas and in other related areas.

The author gratefully acknowledges the assistance of the National Science Foundation, and the efforts of students John Ekstrand, Edward Baardsen, and Ron Selleck, in preparing many of the demonstrations. The encouragement and assistance of Profs. James F. Gibbons, John G. Linvill, Ralph J. Smith, and David F. Tuttle has also been most helpful.

A. E. SIEGMAN

CONTENTS

CHAPTER NINE
DOPPLER BROADENING:
HOMOGENEOUS AND INHOMOGENEOUS TRANSITIONS

346

CHAPTER TEN
OPTICAL MASERS (LASERS)

373

CHAPTER ELEVEN
SPONTANEOUS EMISSION AND NOISE

461

APPENDIXES

499

AN
INTRODUCTION
TO
LASERS
AND
MASERS

AN INTRODUCTION TO LASERS AND MASERS

CHAPTER ONE

1-1 LASERS, MASERS, AND QUANTUM ELECTRONICS

Many familiar electronic devices, such as transistors and vacuum tubes, use moving electric charges, either in semiconductor crystals or in vacuum, to obtain electronic amplification and oscillation. This book, however, is about an important new class of electronic devices that use instead the internal resonances of atoms, or the transitions between quantum energy levels in atoms, to obtain amplification and oscillation. These devices are collectively called *masers*. If they operate at optical frequencies, as many of them do, they are commonly called either *optical masers* or *lasers*.

Figure 1-1 shows the essential elements of a laser device. These essential elements are (1) an appropriate maser material, which may be a gas, a liquid, or a solid; (2) some form of excitation or pumping process, which activates the maser material so that it can provide amplification to an electromagnetic signal; and (3) some type of

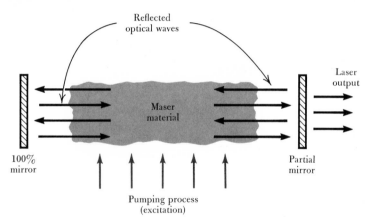

FIG. 1-1   The essential elements of an optical-frequency maser (laser).

structure or electromagnetic circuitry by means of which a signal to be amplified can be applied to the maser material. In the laser oscillator shown in Fig. 1-1, this structure is a pair of mirrors facing each other, so that optical waves may bounce back and forth between the mirrors, passing repeatedly through the active maser material, until they build up into a coherent and monochromatic laser oscillation at an optical frequency.

There is a vast variety of maser and laser materials and pumping processes for these materials, and different maser devices can operate at frequencies ranging from optical frequencies to audio frequencies. Figure 1-2 shows a cavity-type solid-state maser operating in the microwave range and examples of possible low-frequency maser devices using lumped electric circuits. Each of these devices employs some maser material and some pumping process. They differ only in the type of electromagnetic structure employed: lumped circuits for audio- or radio-frequency devices, resonant cavities for microwave devices, and arrangements of mirrors and lenses for optical-frequency devices. All these devices operate on the same basic principles, however, and the explanation of these basic principles is one of the major objectives of this book. We will summarize these basic principles and illustrate them with some important practical examples later in the chapter.

BACKGROUND OF THE MASER PRINCIPLE   ■ The name *maser* was originally an acronym for *m*icrowave *a*mplification by *s*timulated *e*mission of *r*adiation. The first successful maser device operated at a microwave frequency; however, maser action using the same basic principles can now be obtained in almost any frequency range with many different types of atoms, ions, and molecules. Hence the *m* in *maser* is now interpreted more broadly to mean *molecular* rather than microwave. *Laser,* of course, is an acronym for *l*ight *a*mplification by *s*timulated *e*mission of *r*adiation.

The maser process is a very general principle of electronic amplification, probably with broader scope than any other known amplification mechanism. Maser action is possible, at least in principle, with any one of the many internal resonances or transitions of any atom, ion, or molecule in the gaseous, liquid, or solid states. Various practical requirements eliminate most of these transitions for useful maser action, but there are still an enormous number of atomic transitions that permit useful maser action, in every frequency band from the subaudio to the ultraviolet. In particular, a

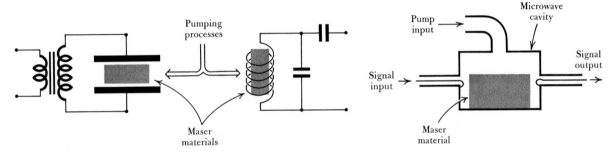

Pumping processes

Maser materials

Low-frequency maser devices

Microwave cavity

Pump input

Signal input

Signal output

Maser material

Microwave maser device

very large number of optical and infrared masers or lasers are possible in numerous atoms and molecules.

FIG. 1-2 The essential elements of resonant-cavity maser devices for microwave and lower frequencies.

The basic physical principles of maser action have been understood since the early days of quantum theory and were clearly stated by Einstein. The practical possibility and the potential importance of the maser principle began to be appreciated, however, only about 1950.[1] The first successful maser device was the gaseous-ammonia maser, or atomic clock, developed (and named) by Charles H. Townes and several of his students at Columbia University in 1954. Townes' original device is still useful as an atomic clock or an atomic frequency standard, at about 23,870 MHz in the microwave range, although newer types of atomic frequency standards now offer strong competition.

■ Since this first maser device, which used certain energy levels of the ammonia (NH_3) molecule, many other maser devices using other types of atomic energy levels have been developed. There are, for example, audio- and radio-frequency maser amplifiers and oscillators which use the nuclear-magnetic-resonance (NMR) energy levels. These masers have very narrow bandwidths and limited power output, and hence they are not of much practical utility, except in a few specialized applications such as magnetometers.

TYPES OF MASER AND LASER DEVICES

There are also microwave-frequency solid-state masers which use electron-paramagnetic-resonance (EPR) energy levels. Microwave solid-state maser amplifiers are somewhat more complex devices than other microwave amplifiers, but they have lower noise figures than any competing microwave amplifiers. Hence they serve limited but important purposes as ultralow-noise receivers for satellite communications, radio astronomy, deep-space telemetry, and certain ultrasensitive radars.

By far the most important and striking use of the maser principle is the optical maser, or *laser*. Lasers are the only known electronic devices that can provide electronic amplification and oscillation at optical and infrared frequencies.[2] The first two successful lasers, developed during 1960, were the pulsed ruby laser, which operates at a visible red wavelength $\lambda = 6943$ Å, or a frequency $f = 4 \times 10^{14}$ Hz, and the first helium–neon gas laser, oscillating at $\lambda = 11,500$ Å, or $f = 3 \times 10^{14}$ Hz. Since then

---

[1] The history of the maser concept is reviewed in Ref. 1-46.

[2] Amplification or oscillation can also be obtained at optical frequencies with parametric amplification. However, every optical parametric amplifier or oscillator requires a pump oscillator at a higher frequency, and this pump oscillator can only be a laser.

laser action has been obtained with atoms, ions, and molecules in gases, liquids, solids, glasses, flames, plastics, and semiconductors, at literally thousands[1] of discrete wavelengths extending from the near-ultraviolet spectral region around $\lambda = 3000$ Å, or $f = 10^{15}$ Hz, through the visible and infrared spectral regions, and out to far-infrared wavelengths as long as $\lambda = 800$ μ, or $f = 4 \times 10^{11}$ Hz. This last laser wavelength is in alternate units $\lambda = 0.8$ mm, or $f \sim 400$ GHz, which is within the upper limit of the frequency range accessible to conventional millimeter-wave electron tubes.

Maser action is now even believed to exist in nature. Certain amplified microwave signals at 1600 MHz have been tentatively attributed to maser action in intergalactic clouds of OH^- ions pumped or excited by light from nearby stars.

IMPORTANCE OF THE LASER   ■ Because the maser principle is the only form of primary electronic amplification available at infrared and optical frequencies, it is almost impossible to overestimate the importance of the optical maser. With lasers used as coherent optical and infrared signal sources and amplifiers, it is now possible to perform at optical frequencies all the electronic functions that electronics engineers are accustomed to performing at conventional radio and microwave frequencies—including amplification, oscillation, amplitude and frequency modulation, pulse modulation, harmonic generation, transmission, and heterodyne detection. In addition to these familiar functions, many novel and unique capabilities arise from the optical nature of radiation and from the extremely small wavelengths involved. The laser is therefore an extraordinarily important outgrowth of the basic maser principle, and an extraordinarily exciting and challenging opportunity for the electronics engineer.[2]

QUANTUM ELECTRONICS   ■ The study of maser principles and devices and related topics, at all frequency ranges, forms the very active field of research and development that has come to be known as *quantum electronics*. This name may be misleading in several ways. For example, despite the implication that a considerable knowledge of quantum theory is required in order to understand lasers and masers, no extensive knowledge of quantum mechanics is required to understand the material in this book. With only a few exceptions, simple and familiar classical ideas are entirely sufficient for our purposes. In fact, a semiclassical discussion rather than a quantum-mechanical one actually provides the clearest approach to quantum electronics.

1-2   BASIC PRINCIPLES OF MASER ACTION

The basic physical principles underlying maser action can be developed in four steps, which will be set down and then explained briefly. The purpose of this section is chiefly to take a quick look at our goals in later chapters, where we will, of course, develop these ideas in much more precise fashion.

The four basic maser principles are as follows:

---

[1] Consider, for example, the opening sentence of the abstract of a recent typical journal article: "We investigated the laser oscillation . . . of carbon disulfide and oxygen and found *270 new lasing lines* . . . ascribed to the P- and R-branch, vibrational-rotational transitions in CO." From D. W. Gregg, and S. J. Thomas, "Analysis of the CS_2-O_2 chemical laser showing new lines and selective excitation," *J. Appl. Phys.*, **39**: 4399 (August, 1968).

[2] For an inexpensive but well-illustrated elementary introduction to laser devices and some of their more important applications, see Ref. 1-2.

1. *Atoms (and also ions and molecules) exhibit internal resonances, at certain discrete characteristic frequencies.* These internal atomic resonances occur at frequencies ranging from the audio up to and beyond the optical regions.

2. *A signal applied to an atom at or near one of its internal resonances will cause a measurable response in the atom.* Depending on circumstances, the atom may absorb energy from the signal, or it may emit energy into the signal.

3. *The strength and the sign of the total response that will be obtained from a collection of many atoms of the same kind depend directly on the population difference, i.e., the difference in population between the lower and upper quantum energy levels responsible for that particular transition.* Under normal positive-temperature thermal-equilibrium conditions, this net response will always be absorptive.

4. *If this population difference can somehow be inverted, so that there are more atoms in the upper energy level than in the lower, then the total response of the collection of atoms will also invert—that is, the total response will change from a net absorptive to a net emissive condition.* The atoms will then give net energy to the signal and thus amplify it.

By building such maser-amplification material into a suitable structure or circuit to carry the signal fields, we can obtain useful amplification, or even coherent oscillation, at the frequency of the particular atomic resonance being used.

   Let us now discuss each of these basic principles in turn.

■ The first basic principle is: ATOMIC RESONANCES

1. *Atoms (and ions, and molecules) exhibit internal or intrinsic resonances at frequencies that are characteristic of the specific atom (or ion, or molecule) involved.*

This statement may be regarded in the first place as a purely experimental conclusion. Figure 1-3 shows a simple experiment by which the reader may observe directly for himself some of the intrinsic resonances of the helium atom by means of an inexpensive and readily available transmission grating.[1] The light from a helium-discharge lamp (or any other available gas-discharge light) is viewed through the transmission grating against a reasonably dark background, as shown. The light emitted by the discharge lamp really consists of a number of sharp, discrete wavelengths, and each of these wavelengths is scattered or diffracted at a different angle by the grating. Thus a number of sharp, brightly colored lines appear to be floating in space against the dark background, more or less as indicated in Fig. 1-3.

   A closer examination with some more precise types of spectrometers will show that these characteristic resonances or spectral lines of the helium atom have the wavelengths indicated in Fig. 1-3. As incidental information, Fig. 1-4 shows the relative response of the average human eye versus wavelength, to indicate the approximate spectral range detected by the eye and the relative response of the eye at certain prominent laser lines. Note that the two outermost red and violet lines in the helium spectrum are far down on the tails of the visual-response curve, although with some care they can still be seen.

■ Although there is a minimum amount of quantum theory in these discussions, we   QUANTUM ENERGY LEVELS
                                                                                   AND TRANSITIONS

---

[1] Every reader should try such an experiment if at all possible. Such transmission gratings are available in cardboard slide mounts at very low cost from Edmund Scientific Company, Barrington, N.J.

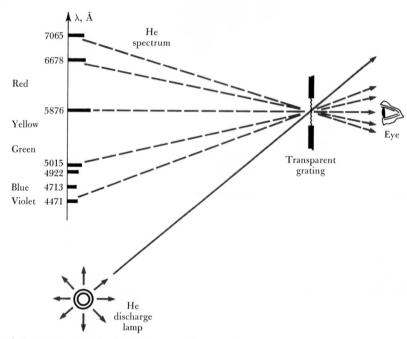

FIG. 1-3   A simple experiment for observing some of the characteristic resonances of the He atom, using an inexpensive transmission grating. The various resonance wavelengths can be seen through the grating as bright colored lines against a dark background.

FIG. 1-4   The relative response of the human eye to different optical wavelengths.

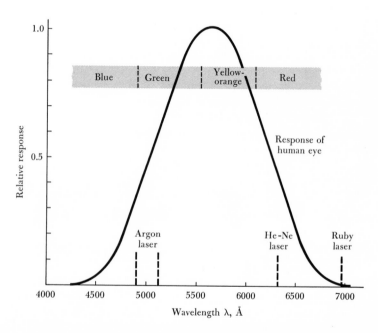

can note here that in quantum-mechanical terms the characteristic resonance frequencies we observe in the helium atom represent transitions between the quantum energy levels of that atom. According to quantum theory, every atom has a set of allowed energy levels located at definite energy values characteristic of that type of atom. If two of these allowed energy levels occur at energy values E_n and E_m (with $E_m > E_n$), then the atom will exhibit a characteristic resonance or transition at the frequency f_{mn}, given by

$$f_{mn} = \frac{E_m - E_n}{h} \qquad (1)$$

where h is Planck's constant, $h = 6.626 \times 10^{-34}$ joule-sec. If the frequency is to be expressed in radians per second, then this is often written in the form

$$w_{mn} = \frac{E_m - E_n}{\hbar} \qquad (2)$$

where $\hbar$ (pronounced "h-bar") is given by $\hbar \equiv h/2\pi = 1.0545 \times 10^{-34}$ joule-sec. Figure 1-5 shows, as an elementary example, an energy-level diagram with three quantum energy levels that might be characteristic of some atom or molecule. The three characteristic resonances or transitions that would then be expected for this atom are shown in the plot of atomic response versus frequency at the right of the figure. The strength and the linewidth of each individual resonance will in general be different, as determined by considerations that we have yet to introduce.

Real atoms have much more numerous and complex arrays of allowed energy levels. For example, Fig. 1-6 shows a large number of the allowed, or characteristic, energy levels for the helium atom. Note that there is a lowest energy level, or *ground energy level,* whose absolute value is arbitrarily chosen to be zero. This is followed by a fairly large gap in energy, and then above the gap a very complex set of higher, or *excited,* energy levels. The collection of numbers, letters, and subscripts and superscripts associated with each level are a spectroscopic notation used to label these energy levels for quantum theorists and to convey certain information about their characteristics for experimental spectroscopists.

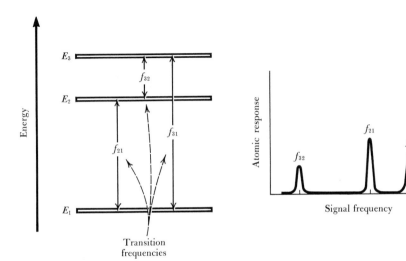

FIG. 1-5 An example of three quantum energy levels and the resonant response that might be expected from an atom having these quantum energy levels.

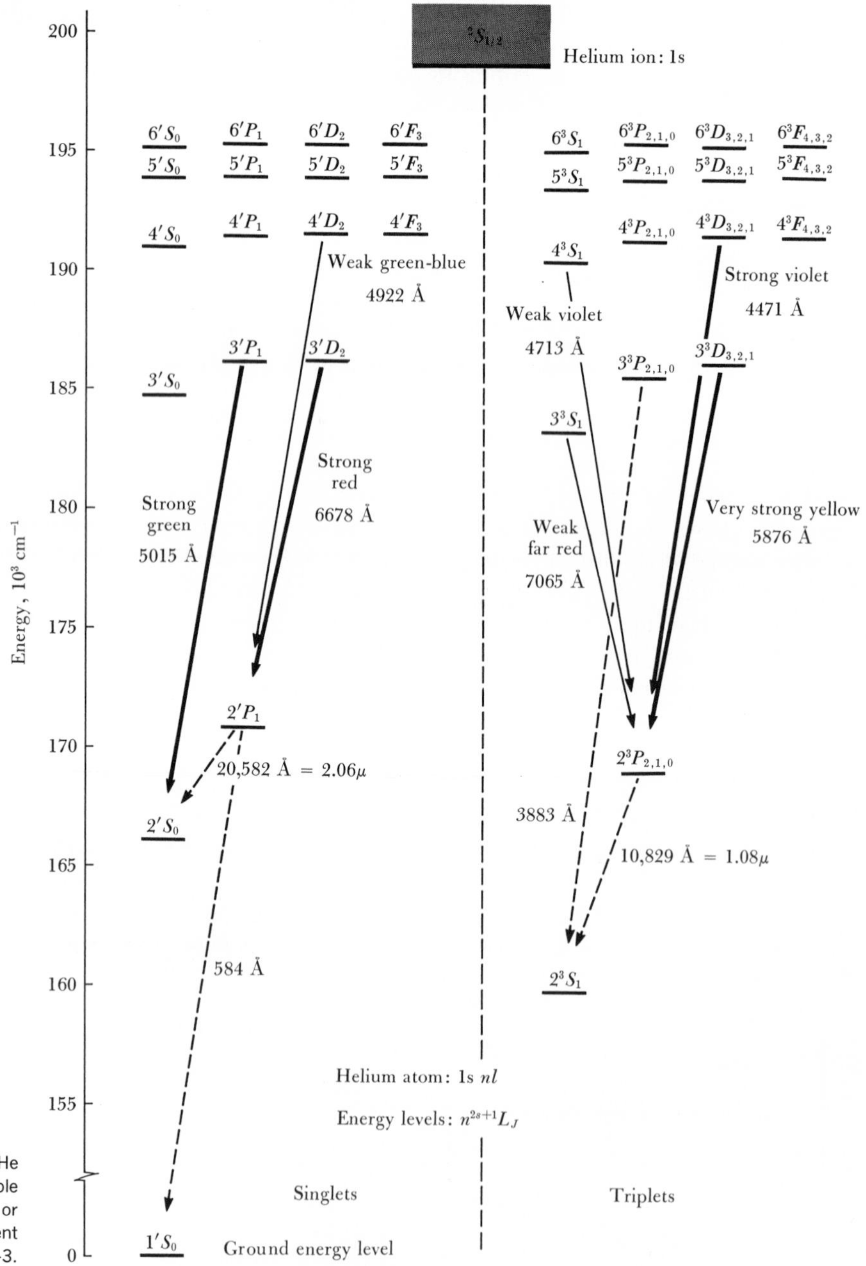

FIG. 1-6 The energy levels of the He atom, showing the transitions responsible for the various resonance frequencies or wavelengths observed in the experiment of Fig. 1-3.

ABSORPTION SPECTROSCOPY   ■ In the experiment of Fig. 1-3 the helium atoms are *excited*, or lifted to their higher energy levels, by collisions with energetic electrons in the discharge lamp. We can then observe some of the characteristic resonance frequencies of the He atoms by measuring the frequencies or wavelengths at which they spontaneously emit radiation. With the aid of some slightly more complicated equipment, it is also possible to observe some of the characteristic resonances of an atom by passing electromagnetic radiation through a collection of these atoms and observing which discrete frequencies or wavelengths are absorbed by the atoms.

Figure 1-7 shows, for example, an elementary optical spectrometer, in which the light source emits a continuum of all possible wavelengths, while the rotatable prism serves to transmit to the atomic sample only a single wavelength, or, more accurately, a very narrow band of wavelengths approximating a single wavelength. By rotating the prism (or, in some spectrometers, rotating a grating instead) the wavelength transmitted through the atomic sample can be tuned across some large range of optical (or infrared or ultraviolet) wavelengths, and the sample's absorption versus wavelength can be measured. Such a device is called an *absorption spectrometer*.

The inset in Fig. 1-7 is an actual recording of a set of closely spaced absorption

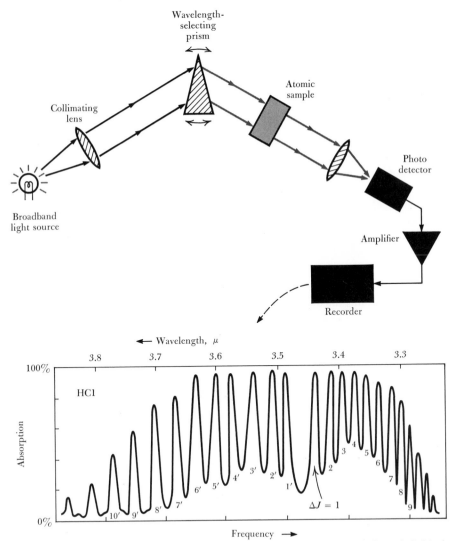

FIG. 1-7 A very elementary optical spectrometer for observing atomic resonances and a typical plot of absorption versus frequency for gaseous HCl molecules at wavelengths near $\lambda = 3.5\ \mu$. The atomic sample in the spectrometer may be a solid, a crystal, or a cell containing a gas or liquid.

lines or characteristic resonances observed when infrared radiation was passed through a sample consisting of HCl vapor. These characteristic resonances, occurring at wavelengths of 3.3 to 3.8 μ (that is, 33,000 to 38,000 Å) are associated with certain internal vibrational motions and vibrational energy levels in the HCl molecules. These same molecules also exhibit a great many other resonances in other spectral ranges not covered by this particular experiment.

ATOMS IN SOLIDS   ■ Atoms in crystals and other solids, as well as in gases, also have characteristic resonance frequencies, and these resonances can be observed in both spontaneous-emission and absorption experiments. Figure 1-8a shows, for example, an experiment in which the Cr^{3+} ions in a crystal of ruby are excited by shining ultraviolet radiation on the crystal. The resulting spontaneous emission from the ruby sample is measured against wavelength by means of a monochromator (in effect a tunable optical bandpass filter) and a photoelectric detector.

The observed spontaneous emission, or *fluorescence*, from ruby will consist almost entirely of a single, very strong, closely spaced pair of resonances, called the R_1 *lines*, as shown by the recorder trace in Fig. 1-8a. These resonances are located near $\lambda = 6934$ Å if the crystal is cooled to liquid-hydrogen temperature ($\sim 20°K$), as it was for the experimental curve shown. The energy-level diagram responsible for this transition will be shown several times later in this chapter, since this transition is the same as that used in the well-known ruby laser. In fact, if a ruby laser rod or ruby sample is excited with a mercury-vapor lamp, a stroboscopic light source, a "mineral light," or any other readily available ultraviolet-light source, the red fluorescent emission is easily seen with the naked eye, and its wavelength can be determined roughly by the method illustrated in Fig. 1-3.

As an additional example, Fig. 1-8b shows the result of the same type of experiment with a crystal of cadmium sulfide (CdS) containing a small percentage of Nd^{3+} ions, where the monochromator is scanned over a much greater wavelength range. There is a pronounced group of resonances at around 9000 Å, associated with certain known energy levels of the Nd^{3+} ion, and another similar but much weaker group around 10,900 Å. That these resonances are indeed associated with the Nd^{3+} ion is verified by repeating the experiment with a crystal of highly pure CdS and noting that the resonances completely disappear.

With proper instrumentation, strong absorption lines due to atomic resonances can also be observed in solids. Such absorption lines are particularly prominent for rare-earth ions, such as neodymium, erbium, gadolinium, in many different crystals. The absorption-vs.-wavelength curves in Fig. 1-9 show some of the characteristic resonances for a small amount of trivalent erbium ions, Er^{3+}, in a crystal of lanthanum fluoride, and for a small doping of trivalent gadolinium ions, Gd^{3+}, in a crystal of strontium fluoride. The existence of sharp, discrete characteristic resonance frequencies is obvious.

MICROWAVE- AND RADIO-   ■ When we plot absorption (or transmission) versus frequency in the immediate
FREQUENCY RESONANCES   vicinity of any of the characteristic resonances of an atom, the resulting plot generally has the appearance of a resonance curve, as we have just seen for optical frequencies. Hence we infer that these frequencies represent characteristic internal resonances for that particular kind of atom. These atomic resonances are by no means limited to optical frequencies, but also occur at microwave and even lower frequencies. The experimental techniques used for observing such resonances must, of course, be considerably different in the various frequency ranges.

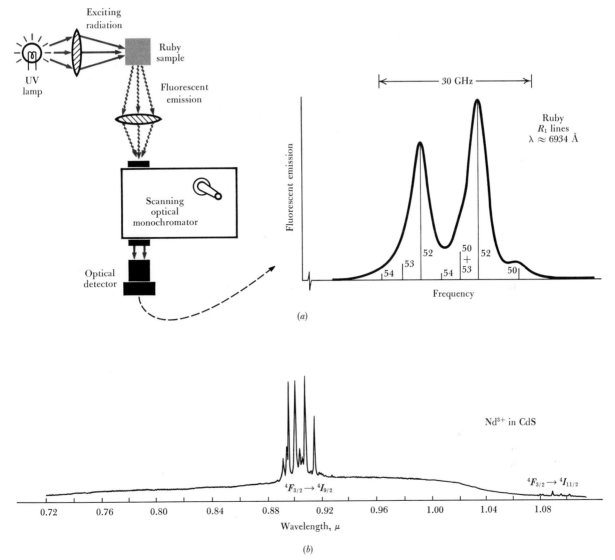

FIG. 1-8 (*a*) A simple fluorescent-emission spectrometer and the two very sharp and narrow fluorescent lines near λ ≈ 6934 Å emitted by a ruby sample excited by ultraviolet radiation. The numbered lines under the ruby spectrum indicate the locations and relative strengths of the resonance for the different isotopes of Cr, taking into account their relative proportions in naturally occurring chromium. (*b*) A similar fluorescent-emission spectrum, measured over a much broader spectral range, for a crystal of CdS containing a small percentage of Nd^{3+} ions.

At very low frequencies, in the audio- and radio-frequency ranges, a variable-frequency electromagnetic signal can be applied to a collection of atoms by placing the atoms inside a coil excited at the appropriate frequency, so that the atoms are subjected to the rf magnetic fields inside the coil, or by placing the atoms between the plates of a capacitor, so that the atoms are subjected to the rf electric field between the plates (the method employed will depend on whether the atomic resonance is excited primarily by magnetic or electric rf fields, with the magnetic case being the

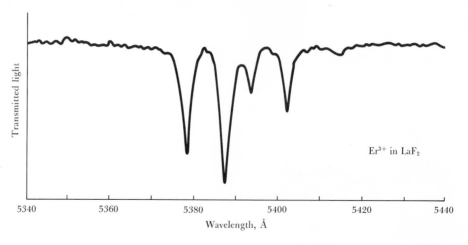

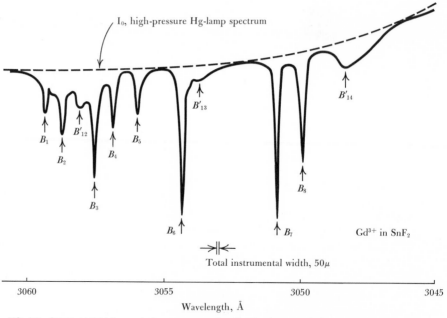

FIG. 1-9 Curves of light transmission versus wavelength, showing several characteristic resonance absorption lines in two different crystals containing small amounts of rare-earth atoms, Er^{3+} in lanthanum fluoride and Gd^{3+} in strontium fluoride.

much more common one). In the microwave range the atoms can be placed inside a tunable microwave cavity, or a microwave transmission-line structure, and appropriate microwave signals applied.

Most, but not all, of the lower-frequency resonances in atoms are observed when a strong dc magnetic field is applied to the collection of atoms, and the observed resonance frequency is usually more or less directly proportional to the strength of the applied dc magnetic field. In such cases the experimental apparatus often takes the form shown in Fig. 1-10. The frequency of the applied signal is held constant at the center frequency of a tuned circuit, and the dc magnetic field strength is varied

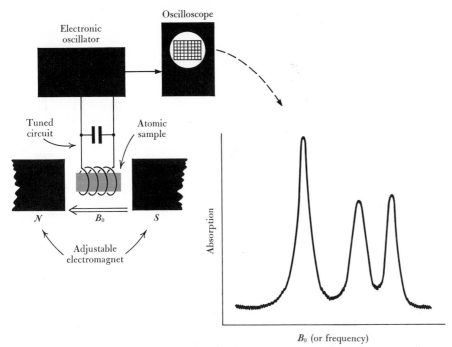

FIG. 1-10   An elementary magnetic-resonance spectrometer and a typical experimental result. The oscilloscope monitors the energy absorbed by the atomic sample. To obtain the display shown, either the oscillator frequency is varied with a fixed magnetic field B_0, or (more commonly) the value of B_0 is varied with a fixed oscillator frequency. The three resonances shown arise from the nuclear magnetic moments of protons located at three different locations in an ethyl alcohol molecule.

to tune the atomic resonance frequency through the applied signal frequency, rather than vice versa. This avoids the necessity for mechanical tuning of the resonant circuit. A microwave-magnetic-resonance spectrometer will have exactly the same form, except that the tuned circuit is replaced by a microwave resonant cavity.

The inset in Fig. 1-10 is a typical result. It shows three closely adjacent resonances that arise at low radio frequencies because of the nuclear magnetic moments of the protons (hydrogen atom nuclei) located at three different positions within the molecular structure of ethyl alcohol. Figure 1-11a shows a different type of microwave-frequency resonance observed in ammonia molecules, in which no dc magnetic field is involved and the resonance is excited primarily by the microwave electric fields. To make this measurement, a variable-frequency microwave signal was passed through a long section of microwave waveguide filled with the ammonia gas, and the very weak absorption owing to the characteristic resonance of the ammonia molecule was measured directly as a function of frequency. This resonance will appear again shortly as the transition employed in the ammonia maser, the first maser device ever to be operated. For comparison, Fig. 1-11b shows a totally different resonance at a much lower frequency, observed in the same ammonia molecules. The three resonances shown are nuclear magnetic resonances observed at a frequency of $\sim$30 MHz, with the ammonia molecules subjected to a dc magnetic field B_0 of a few thousand gauss. The existence of three resonances is associated with the presence of three protons (H nuclei) in the NH_3 molecule.

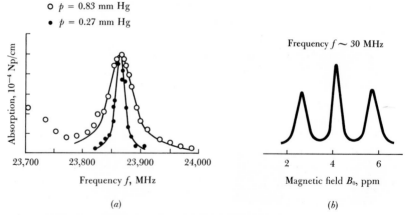

o $p = 0.83$ mm Hg

• $p = 0.27$ mm Hg

Frequency $f \sim 30$ MHz

(a)

(b)

FIG. 1-11 (a) Experimental observation of a characteristic resonance at $f = 23,870$ MHz in the ammonia (NH_3) molecule. The curves show absorption, measured in a long length of waveguide filled with ammonia gas, plotted against microwave signal frequency for two different pressures of the ammonia gas. (b) Nuclear magnetic resonance at $f = 30$ MHz for the three protons in the same NH_3 molecule.

TYPES OF ELECTRONIC AND
MOLECULAR ENERGY LEVELS

■ The energy levels and the associated transition frequencies of atoms, ions, and molecules generally fall into broad classifications determined by the atomic mechanisms responsible for the energy levels and by the frequency ranges in which the resonances occur. For example, a great many resonant frequencies typically occur in the ultraviolet, optical, and near-infrared spectral regions as a result of the different quantum energy levels or allowed quantum states of the *electrons* orbiting about the nuclei of atoms. The He spectra of Figs. 1-3 and 1-6 and the ruby and rare-earth-ion spectra of Figs. 1-8 and 1-9 are examples of such *electronic transitions*. Laser action in the infrared and visible regions can be obtained on a great many such electronic transitions of atoms, ions, or molecules, in gases, liquids, glasses, plastics, and crystals. The ruby laser and the He-Ne laser are only two examples from this very extensive class of lasers.

In addition to these electronic transitions, multiatom molecules also exhibit a very large number of near-infrared and far-infrared (and sometimes even microwave) resonances that arise from the vibrational and rotational motions of the molecule as a whole (the vibrations of the atoms making up a molecule, and the rotation of the whole molecular unit, are quantized according to quantum theory, and do lead to quantum allowed energy levels). The HCl spectrum of Fig. 1-7 is a vibrational spectrum, for example. Laser action at middle- and far-infrared wavelengths can be obtained on many such *vibrational-rotational transitions* in molecular gas discharges. The very powerful CO_2 laser, with its output of many watts or even kilowatts at $\lambda = 10.6$ μ, is a particularly important example of a vibrational-rotational laser transition.

As we noted earlier, in addition to these intrinsic transitions, an atom or molecule placed in a strong dc magnetic field may also exhibit *magnetic-resonance transitions,* with resonance frequencies in the radio- and microwave-frequency ranges. These resonance frequencies can generally be tuned by varying the magnetic field, with the frequency tuning linear with applied field in simple cases. The resonances occurring at radio frequencies in typical magnetic fields of a few thousand gauss arise from the intrinsic magnetic moments possessed by the nuclei of many atoms, leading to the name *nuclear magnetic resonance* (NMR), while the microwave-frequency resonances arise from the magnetic moments associated with the orbital and/or the spin properties of the electrons in certain atoms, leading to the name *electron paramagnetic resonance* (EPR). Maser devices using the radio-frequency NMR resonances are possible and are very interesting as demonstration models, but they are of little practical use because of their complexity compared to transistors and other conventional devices. The ultra-low-noise microwave solid-state maser is a device that makes use of the EPR transitions in certain crystals.

Finally, there are some miscellaneous types of atomic resonances that do not fall cleanly into the above classifications, such as the ammonia transition shown in Fig. 1-11*a*. It is also possible to produce additional (and tunable) transition frequencies in some atoms and molecules by applying very strong dc electric fields to the atoms. The resulting *Stark effect transitions* are well known and well understood, but there do not seem to be any maser devices to date that employ such transitions, primarily because of various practical considerations rather than any barriers in principle.

■ The study of the intrinsic resonance frequencies and the quantum energy levels of atoms constitutes the field of *spectroscopy*, a field with a long and distinguished history and the source of much of our present knowledge of basic physics.[1] Obviously, a knowledge of spectroscopy and of atomic energy levels is basic to the development of new laser devices; and obviously, since the discrete energy levels observed in atoms arise from quantum properties of the atoms, quantum-mechanical calculations are necessary to explain these energy levels fully. Nevertheless, we will discuss spectroscopy and the associated quantum theory only incidentally or in passing. For our purpose, which is to understand the dynamics of how lasers work and something about what they are good for, we may rather cavalierly accept the existence of characteristic atomic resonances and energy levels as readily verified experimental facts, without considering their quantum explanation. As we discuss various laser devices, we will describe the quantum energy levels of some particularly useful maser materials, as obtained by spectroscopists. Our principal interest, however, is the manner in which such resonance transitions, whether found empirically or otherwise, can be used for maser purposes.

SPECTROSCOPY

■ With the existence of characteristic internal atomic resonances reasonably well established, we can now go on to the second basic maser principle:

STIMULATED ATOMIC
RESPONSES

2. *An electromagnetic signal applied to an atom at or very near one of its observed resonance frequencies will (in most cases) elicit a significant and proportional response from that atom.*

Perhaps we should add for completeness that a signal applied to an atom at a frequency not near any of its atomic resonance frequencies will normally elicit no significant response at all.

The first major point here is that the resonant response of the atom will be *significant*. The comparatively strong response (such as strong absorption) that an atom will exhibit to a signal at or near one of its resonance frequencies is basic to maser action, and the dynamics of this response will be one of our major topics in subsequent chapters. It is also important to note that the amplitude of the atomic response will,

[1] For a convenient and inexpensive survey of energy levels and atomic transitions of all varieties see Ref. 1-16. See also Chap. 4 of Ref. 1-6.

under most circumstances, be directly *proportional* to the amplitude of the applied signal. This is a point we will describe in more specific terms later.

We do not actually have any very direct ways of independently monitoring the internal response of a single atom to an applied signal. The fact that an atom—or, in any realistic situation, a collection of many similar atoms—is responding to an applied signal is normally deduced by observing some change or reaction in the applied signal itself. Thus the existence of an atomic response is often inferred by noting a significant absorption of energy by the atoms from the applied signal, as illustrated in Figs. 1-7 to 1-11.

This is, however, only part of the response on an atomic transition. The upper curve in Fig. 1-12 shows the variation in absorption as the transition frequency is scanned through resonance in an NMR experiment of the type diagramed in Fig. 1-10, with the protons in ordinary water as the atomic sample. We see here the absorptive or resistive part of the atomic response, as evidenced by a change in the Q of the tuned-signal circuit due to the atomic resonance. The lower curve in Fig. 1-12, plotted from data taken with exactly the same apparatus, but with a different adjustment of the measuring circuitry, shows the small shift in the exact center frequency of the tuned signal circuit as the transition frequency is scanned through resonance. To put this in another way, this curve shows the small change in apparent inductance of the coil caused by the atomic response as the atomic transition is tuned through resonance. This effect is a *reactive* effect, rather than an absorptive one, associated with the atomic response.

In general, with appropriate experimental techniques it is always possible to observe both absorptive effects and equally significant reactive effects in the response of atoms to applied signals at or near resonances. The reactive effects generally appear

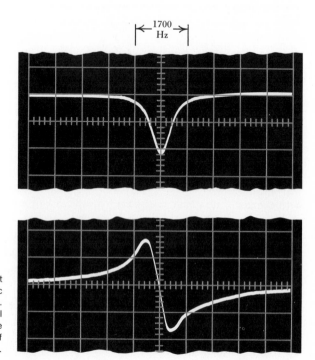

FIG. 1-12 Observations in a nuclear-magnetic-resonance experiment of the type shown in Fig. 1-10, with protons in H_2O as the atomic sample and the transition tuned through resonance by varying B_0. Upper curve: Absorption signal, or change in Q of the tuned signal circuit. Lower curve: Reactive signal, or change in apparent inductance of the coil, as evidenced by a small shift in resonance frequency of the signal circuit when the atoms are tuned through resonance.

as cavity-detuning effects in resonant-cavity experiments or as additional phase-shift contributions near resonance in traveling-wave experiments. Spectroscopists at radio or microwave frequencies can note significant changes in either the loss or the reactance of their experimental circuits when they tune near atomic resonances, and the responses of the atoms can be inferred from either type of measurement. Optical spectroscopists can note either the absorption of waves passing through collections of atoms or added phase shifts which lead to fringe shifts and other effects in optical-interference experiments. We will take pains later to emphasize both the absorptive and the reactive effects associated with atomic responses.

Finally, it is very clear experimentally, and also well understood from atomic theory, that some atomic resonances respond chiefly to the ac electric field of an applied signal, while others respond chiefly to the ac magnetic field of the signal. These two cases form, respectively, the *electric-dipole* and *magnetic-dipole transitions.* We will discuss both cases in later chapters in terms of simple but surprisingly realistic models of an atom. It is also found experimentally that different transitions in atoms exhibit widely differing strengths of response. Some of the potential transition frequencies $f_{mn} = (E_m - E_n)/h$ that we can predict, given the energy levels E_n of an atom, will actually show no response at all to an applied signal near that frequency. As indirect evidence of this, note that the spontaneous-emission spectrum of the helium atoms in Fig. 1-3 lacks a great many of the potential wavelengths that could be predicted from the energy-level diagram of Fig. 1-6, and in general the stimulated-response and spontaneous-emission strengths of an atomic transition are closely related. So-called quantum-mechanical *selection rules* explain these varying strengths of response of atomic transitions. Some transitions, in fact, will show essentially zero response, in which case they are referred to as *forbidden transitions,* in contrast to strongly responding or strongly *allowed transitions.*

■ The preceding discussion leads directly to the third basic maser concept:

DEPENDENCE ON POPULATION DIFFERENCE

3. *The strength of the net resonant response that will be observed on a given transition from a large collection of many similar atoms is directly proportional to the "population difference"—that is, to the difference between the numbers of atoms in the lower and upper quantum energy levels responsible for the transition.*

This important principle arises from the quantum-mechanical analysis of the response of an atom to an applied signal. It cannot be predicted classically, although we will show a close relationship to a classical model in Chap. 4. However, this principle can also be demonstrated experimentally in various ways, and so we can again treat it as an empirical result, independent of its theoretical foundations.

The density of atoms in a maser or laser material will typically be around 10^{18} to 10^{20} atoms/cm^{-3} in solids, and anywhere from 10^{10} to 10^{15} atoms/cm^{-3} in gases. Thus in real laser and maser situations we are dealing not just with single atoms, but with collections of very large numbers of atoms. These individual atoms are, to first order, independent and noninteracting with each other. However, there are a very large number of such atoms present, and it is the average behavior of the collection that is observed in any real experiments.

Consider a collection of some very large number N of identical atoms (or ions, or molecules). Each atom has the same set of characteristic energy levels E_n. In principle it is possible, more or less, to make measurements that will show at a given instant that a certain number N_1 of these atoms are in the lowest energy level E_1, that a certain number N_2 are in the next higher energy level E_2, and that in general N_n of the atoms are in each allowed energy level E_n. The total number of atoms is, of course, the sum over all levels E_n, or

$$\sum N_n = N \tag{3}$$

The number of atoms N_n in each level is called the *population* of that energy level.

There are some important subtleties associated with this description that we will not take time to explain fully at this point. For example, the picture of each atom being located in a single energy level is not fully correct. In a correct quantum description each individual atom must be viewed as being in a complex quantum mixture of states, or as having a certain probability of being found in different energy levels.[1] For our present purposes we may use the concept of an *averaged population of atoms N_n* in each energy level, and this is what is universally done in maser analyses.

Leaving aside these subtleties, the third basic maser principle states that if a signal is applied to some specific atomic transition f_{mn} of a collection of atoms, then the amplitude of the total atomic response is directly proportional to the applied-signal amplitude and to the *population difference* on that particular transition, in the form

$$\begin{aligned} \text{Amplitude of atomic response} &= K \times (N_n - N_m) \times \text{amplitude of applied signal} \\ &= K \times \Delta N_{mn} \times \text{amplitude of applied signal} \end{aligned} \tag{4}$$

where K is an appropriate constant and the quantity $\Delta N_{nm} \equiv (N_n - N_m)$ is the population difference on the $n \to m$ transition. In saying that the amplitude of the atomic response is proportional to the population difference ΔN_{nm}, we mean particularly that the size of the observed absorption effects, as well as the size of any observed reactive or phase-shift effects, is directly proportional to the population difference.

BOLTZMANN'S PRINCIPLE   ■ One simple way of determining this dependence of atomic response on population difference experimentally is by observing some aspect of the atomic response, such as the resonance absorption, while varying the temperature of a collection of atoms. According to a basic principle of statistical mechanics, when a large collection of similar atoms is in thermal equilibrium at temperature T, the relative populations of any two energy levels E_n and E_m must be related by the Boltzmann ratio

$$\frac{N_m}{N_n} = e^{-(E_m - E_n)/kT} = e^{-hf_{mn}/kT} \tag{5}$$

As illustrated in Fig. 1-13, for small energy gaps such that $E_m - E_n \ll kT$ this ratio is close to unity and the two levels of the population are nearly equal (with slightly fewer atoms in the upper level), while for energy gaps large enough that $hf_{mn} \gg kT$ the ratio is close to zero, and there will be very few atoms in the upper energy level at thermal equilibrium.

The energy kT at room temperature ($T \approx 300°\text{K}$) corresponds to an energy gap hf, with $f \approx 6 \times 10^{12}$ Hz, which is equivalent in wavelength to $\lambda \approx 50\ \mu$. There-

---

[1] A fuller explanation of this point is given in Appendix A, which might be read at this point and reviewed at several later stages in our discussions.

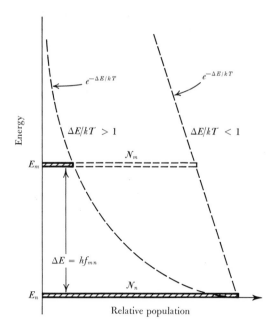

FIG. 1-13 Relative populations in two energy levels E_n and $E_m > E_n$ as a function of energy spacing and temperature, as given by the Boltzmann relation for thermal equilibrium. Note that N_m is shown only in relation to N_n, without keeping the sum of the two populations constant.

fore for any energy gaps whose transition frequencies f_{mn} are in the near-infrared or visible regions the Boltzmann exponent will be $\gg 1$ at normal temperatures. The number of atoms in any upper level will then be very small relative to that in the lower levels. In fact, in any such system, as in the He energy levels of Fig. 1-6, where there is a large energy gap between the ground level and all higher levels, at thermal equilibrium virtually all the atoms will be in the ground level, with very few atoms in the higher energy levels.

In partial confirmation of this, Fig. 1-14 shows the measured absorption spectrum versus wavelength for Nd^{3+} ions in a crystal of yttrium aluminum garnet (commonly called YAG), while Fig. 1-15 shows the Nd^{3+} energy-level structure responsible for the observed transition frequencies. The main point here is that at normal temperatures virtually all the Nd^{3+} ions will be in the lowest available energy level or group of levels (the $^4I_{9/2}$ pair of levels, in spectroscopic jargon); as a result, all the observed absorptions represent transitions from the ground energy level. There are many other strongly allowed potential transitions between other pairs of levels, but since there is virtually no population difference (in fact, no population at all) on these higher transitions, no strong responses are observed at these frequencies.

■ As a small exercise to illustrate these points further, let us calculate the expected energy-level populations and population differences as functions of temperature in some simple three-level system such as that shown in the inset of Fig. 1-16. Here we assume three energy levels, at energies $E_1 = 0$, $E_2 = E$, and $E_3 = 4E$. With the use of the Boltzmann ratios for the various level pairs, finding the populations of these three energy levels as a function of the normalized temperature parameter kT/E is a fairly easy task. Figures 1-16a and 1-16b show both the level populations and the population differences on each pair of levels plotted as a function of the normalized temperature. It is clear that with increasing temperature the strength of the ground-state-connected responses at f_{21} and f_{31} will decrease as the ground-state population

TEMPERATURE DEPENDENCE
IN A THREE-LEVEL SYSTEM

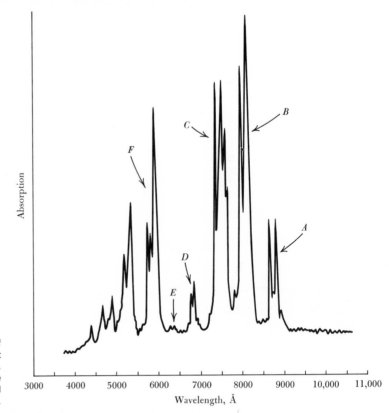

FIG. 1-14   The measured absorption spectrum of a crystal of YAG ($Y_3Al_5O_{12}$) in which a few percent of the Al^{3+} ions have been replaced by Nd^{3+} ions. The various groups of absorption transitions are labelled for comparison with the energy-level diagram of the following figure.

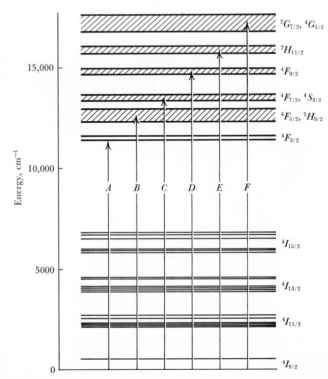

FIG. 1-15   The energy levels of a Nd^{3+} ion in a typical crystal lattice. Energy is measured in units of $cm^{-1} \equiv h \times 30$ GHz. The notations at the right are spectroscopic labels for the energy levels. The higher-lying bands are actually groups of closely spaced levels, and the transitions to these bands are related to Fig. 1-14 by the letters on the arrows.

decreases and the upper-state populations increase. By contrast, the transition f_{32} between two excited states at first increases in strength as the level E_2 begins to be populated before the level E_3, but then eventually decreases in strength as E_1, E_2, and E_3 all become nearly equally populated, and all the population differences tend toward zero at very high temperatures.

We do not have any convenient experimental results to illustrate this general behavior, but observations of transition strengths versus temperature in real atomic systems do agree with the general principles of this simple example. Variable-temperature experiments must take into account that other atomic-resonance properties, particularly the resonance linewidth, may also change with temperature, and it may not be possible in practice to vary temperatures over sufficiently wide ranges to demonstrate the full extent of the Boltzmann effects without either freezing or melting the samples. However, we may take it as an experimental fact that the size of the resonance response from a collection of atoms does indeed vary in direct proportion to the population difference on the transition involved, with change in temperature providing a convenient method to obtain a change in population difference in some of these experiments.

■ The fourth, and final, basic maser principle is really only a straightforward extension of the previous three. However, because of its importance we will state it separately:

POPULATION INVERSION

4. *If it becomes possible, by any means, to achieve a population inversion, in which there are more atoms in a higher energy level than in a lower energy level, then the atomic resonant response on that transition will change sign along with the population difference. In particular, the stimulated absorption normally observed on that transition will change to stimulated emission, i.e., to maser amplification.*

Because of the important, and perhaps somewhat surprising, consequences of this principle, let us examine it in detail.

From the Boltzmann principle, in a collection of atoms at thermal equilibrium there are always fewer atoms in a higher-lying level E_m than in a lower-lying level E_n— at least, if the thermal equilibrium occurs at a *positive* temperature T (this is an important qualification, which we will discuss fully in Sec. 5-1). Therefore the population difference $\Delta N_{nm} \equiv N_n - N_m$ between any two such levels is always positive, that is, $\Delta N_{nm} > 0$, under such conditions. It is also an experimental fact, universally observed, that the resonant response from such a thermal-equilibrium collection of atoms is always absorptive in nature. That is, if an applied signal elicits a response from the collection of atoms at or near any transition frequency, the response is always of such nature that the signal loses energy, with this energy taken up by the collection of atoms.

We have asserted that this resonant response is directly proportional to (among other things) the population difference ΔN_{nm} on the transition being stimulated. The essence of the maser-amplification principle is simply that this proportionality of atomic response to the population difference ΔN_m holds true even if, by some means, the population difference is made to change sign and become negative. Suppose it somehow becomes possible to achieve a temporary situation in which there are more atoms in an upper energy level than in a lower energy level. Then the normally positive

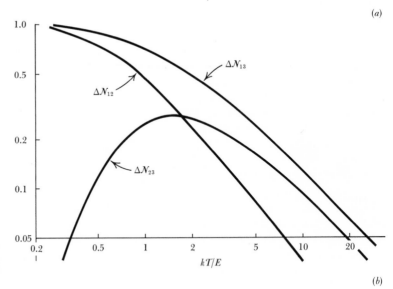

FIG. 1-16   (a) Energy-level populations and (b) population differences versus normalized temperature kT/E for a three-energy-level system with $E_1 = 0$, $E_2 = E$, and $E_3 = 4E$.

population difference on that transition becomes negative, and the normal stimulated absorption as seen from an applied signal on that transition is correspondingly changed to *stimulated emission,* or *amplification* of the applied signal. That is, the applied signal *gains* energy as it interacts with the atoms and hence is amplified (linearly amplified, in fact). The energy for this signal amplification is supplied by the atoms involved in the interaction process. The reactive or phase-shift effects associated with the transition

also change sign under these circumstances, and this leads to measurable and significant effects in maser and laser devices.

The essential condition for maser amplification is thus that somehow we must
have at a given instant more atoms in an upper energy level than in a lower energy
level; that is, for maser amplification

$$\mathcal{N}_m > \mathcal{N}_n \qquad E_n < E_m \qquad \Delta\mathcal{N}_{nm} < 0 \tag{6}$$

as illustrated in Fig. 1-17. The resulting negative sign of the population difference on
that transition is called a *population inversion*. Population inversion is clearly an
abnormal situation; it is never observed in thermal equilibrium, at least not for normal
positive values of the temperature T. However, we will discuss very shortly a number
of different techniques by which the necessary extra atoms can be raised, or *pumped*,
into upper energy levels to obtain population inversion and useful maser amplification
on atomic transitions or resonances at many different frequencies. Depending on the
atomic system involved and the pumping process employed, this inverted population
condition may be obtainable only on a transient basis, yielding intermittent or pulsed
maser action; or it may be possible to maintain the population inversion on a steady-
state basis, yielding continuous-wave (cw) maser action—at least, so long as the pumping process is turned on. There is, in fact, a rather large variety of different practical
solutions to the maser pumping problem.

If we assume, then, that an inverted population condition can somehow be
forced on a given transition, an applied resonant signal will still elicit a strong and
proportional resonant response from the atom. However, this response is of such a
nature that it is the atoms that give energy to the signal, rather than the reverse. The
source of this energy is the atoms themselves. In simplified terms, if $\delta\mathcal{N}$ atoms are
caused to drop from the upper to the lower energy level during the time the signal is
applied, then a total amount of energy $\delta E = \delta\mathcal{N}\, hf$ is made available by the atoms
and is given to the applied signal (just the reverse process occurs, of course, in the
noninverted case, where the atoms absorb energy from the signal). Continued operation of a maser device with continued amplification of applied signals thus tends to
transfer atoms from the upper energy level down to the lower energy level, reducing
the size of the inverted population difference. The surplus of atoms in an upper maser
level tends to be depleted, in fact, both as a consequence of maser amplification and
by natural relaxation processes that always tend to return the energy-level populations

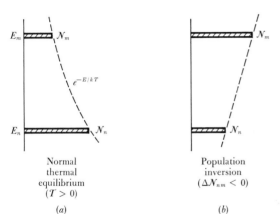

Normal
thermal
equilibrium
($T > 0$)

(a)

Population
inversion
($\Delta\mathcal{N}_{nm} < 0$)

(b)

FIG. 1-17   (a) A normal or absorptive population difference, contrasted
with (b) the inverted population difference required for master amplification.

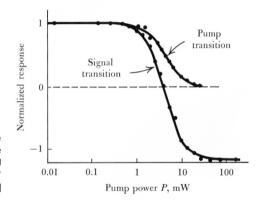

FIG. 1-18   Saturation of the pump transition and maser inversion of the signal transition measured with the maser material potassium chromicyanide (pump ≃ 8000 MHz, signal ≃ 1700 MHz, $T \simeq 2°K$). [From S. Shapiro and N. Bloembergen, "Relaxation effects in a maser material, K_3 (CoCr) (CN)$_6$," *Phys. Rev.* **116**:1453 (1959).]

to their thermal-equilibrium values. If cw maser action is to be maintained, the pumping process must continually replenish the supply of upper-state atoms against both these processes.

EXPERIMENTAL CONFIRMATION   ■ Experimental confirmation of these statements is provided to some degree by the innumerable successfully operating maser and laser devices. We will discuss many of these in more detail shortly, and so at this point we will only consider one piece of experimental evidence to validate our assertions concerning population inversion and maser amplification. Figure 1-18 is a plot of the measured signal absorption on the signal transition of a certain microwave solid-state maser material as the excitation or pumping process for this material is increased from zero to a value sufficient to produce a strong population inversion. In fact, in this particular case the inverted population difference with the pump on is almost exactly equal to the thermal-equilibrium population difference with the pump off, and so the negative absorption in the maser regime is almost exactly equal and opposite to (actually, slightly larger than) the positive absorption at thermal equilibrium.

The behavior of the population difference on the pump transition is shown for this case and is also in agreement with theory, as we will see very shortly in connection with the microwave solid-state maser.

PRACTICAL MASER DEVICES   ■ We have still to discuss the practical considerations of how, given such a maser amplification process, we can use it to obtain a practical maser or laser device in some specific frequency range. This topic is probably best discussed by describing in detail some typical maser and laser devices, and we will do just this in Sec. 1-4. At this point we merely note that a low-frequency maser material can be placed inside a lumped-electric-circuit element such as a coil or a capacitor, and that as a result, a certain amount of negative resistance is added to the equivalent circuit of that element. The same result occurs at microwave frequencies if the pumped maser material is placed in a resonant cavity tuned to the atomic transition involved. At optical frequencies an optical signal wave can simply be transmitted through the maser material (or at microwave frequencies the material can be placed inside a microwave transmission line). Instead of decaying (attenuating) with distance, the signal wave will then grow and be amplified as it travels through the maser material. In brief, the maser amplification process provides a form of *negative-resistance,* or *negative-absorption-coefficient, amplification* in any of the configurations of Figs. 1-1 and 1-2.

We will, of course, discuss in much more detail in later chapters the primary problem of obtaining the necessary population inversion on an appropriate atomic resonance in a collection of atoms as well as the equally important problems of coupling the resulting maser amplification to appropriate electromagnetic circuitry for most effective use.

1.3   SPONTANEOUS VERSUS STIMULATED EMISSION

For completeness let us digress at this point for a brief discussion of spontaneous versus stimulated emission in atoms. The demonstration in Fig. 1-3, or a glance at the colored fluorescent light emitted by a neon tube, a mercury-arc lamp, or an electric discharge or at the fluorescence or colored glow emitted by a mineral or a phosphor under "black light" will illustrate the basic phenomenon of *spontaneous emission*. Closer examination of the emitted light in such examples shows that in most cases it consists of one or a few sharp spectral lines, that is, of characteristic wavelengths or resonance frequencies of the atoms present in the gas or mineral. In an electric discharge or electric arc the atoms in the gas are excited or lifted to various higher energy levels by collisions with electrons or other excited atoms in the discharge. Similarly, in minerals the atoms are excited to higher energy levels by absorbing ultraviolet-light photons. In either case, it is apparent that when such atoms are lifted to higher energy levels they tend to drop back spontaneously to lower energy levels (at a very rapid rate in many cases), getting rid of their excess energy in the process by emitting radiation at the various characteristic resonances f_{mn} of the atomic transitions involved. As we have noted, observation of this fluorescent emission is one very good way of measuring some of the characteristic resonances of atoms, especially at infrared and optical frequencies.

The first point we must make here is that this sort of spontaneous emission by the atoms is not stimulated by any applied signal; it occurs equally well even if the excited atoms are placed in the dark, with no external signals to trigger or stimulate the downward transitions. Moreover, the rate at which the spontaneous emission occurs from an upper level E_m to a lower level E_n is found to depend only on the number of atoms N_m in the upper level, rather than on the population difference $N_n - N_m$, as is the case for stimulated transitions. Thus *stimulated transitions* caused by an applied signal, as in stimulated absorption and emission, and *spontaneous downward transitions*, as in fluorescence emission, are two distinct processes.[1]

The second point is that in any collection of atoms, and specifically in any maser material, both the spontaneous and the stimulated processes occur simultaneously but independently. Stimulated absorption (or emission) occurs at a rate directly proportional to the applied-signal strength and to the population difference on a transition. When the population is inverted, the resulting stimulated emission, or *maser action*, provides a linear and phase-coherent amplification mechanism for an applied signal. Spontaneous emission, by contrast, occurs at a rate that depends only on the upper-level population and on a decay constant characteristic of the particular transition, regardless of whether any signals are present. If signals are present, then spontaneous emission contributes a random emission that essentially adds some narrowband noise to the applied signal. The spontaneously emitted radiation on a given transition has

[1] In a rigorous quantum analysis these processes are actually intimately related, but in such a way that the above statement is still valid. This point is discussed again in Chap. 11.

an average or carrier frequency centered at the atomic resonance frequency, but the spontaneous-emission signal is randomly modulated in both amplitude and phase so as to be essentially narrowband gaussian noise. The linewidth and lineshape of this noise are just equal to the linewidth and lineshape of the atomic transition.

The additive noise contribution from spontaneous emission provides, in fact, the ultimate, or limiting, noise source in any maser amplifier, when all other external or removable noise sources are eliminated. If there is to be a population inversion to permit maser amplification on a given transition, then there must be an upper-level population on that transition. But there will then be at least some unavoidable spontaneous emission on the transition, and this spontaneous emission leads to a limiting maser amplifier *noise figure,* which we will discuss in more detail in Chap. 11.

It is also important to appreciate that the observed spontaneous emission from even a relatively small excited-state population can be bright and intense, particularly at optical frequencies, even though there is no population inversion or maser action on the transition being observed. A transition may fluoresce (spontaneously emit) very strongly, even though the stimulated response to any applied signal is still highly absorptive. Thus there is a sharp distinction between spontaneous emission and maser (or laser) oscillation; the former is essentially noiselike in character, while the latter can have all the coherence characteristics of a true monochromatic, single-mode electronic oscillator.

COHERENCE   ■ We can take the opportunity here for a few additional comments about the coherence and photon properties of spontaneous and stimulated emission. Because of the wave-particle duality often attributed to electromagnetic radiation in quantum theory, spontaneous emission from atoms is often described loosely as the random emission of photons by excited atoms as they drop to lower energy levels. This photon description of the spontaneous-emission process often leads to a similar photon description of the stimulated-absorption or stimulated-emission processes. In particular, the stimulated-emission process in a maser material is sometimes described by saying that the applied signal triggers or stimulates atoms to drop from the upper to the lower maser level, with each atom releasing a photon of energy in the process.

Unfortunately, this mode of description often leads to such questions as: How do we know that the photons emitted in stimulated emission are coherent with the applied signal?[1] Describing spontaneous emission as a random emission of photons seems clear enough, but the stimulated emission of photons does not always seem so clear. Such difficulties arise primarily because the questions are really not properly phrased. The concept of a photon as a billiard-ball-like particle is a limited one, appropriate only in situations where the particlelike nature of light is being observed.[2] To put this more strongly, the concept of light radiation as consisting of little discrete particles called photons is simple and useful in some cases, but causes much confusion in other cases. In discussing masers and lasers, for example, photon concepts can be both misleading and unnecessary. In maser-amplification situations we are dealing essentially with *wavelike* properties of radiation, and hence we should use primarily the *wave* description of radiation.

This entire topic will become much clearer in later discussions. For the present,

---

[1] The question is also often framed as: How do we know that the stimulated photons are in phase with the applied-signal photons?

[2] Photoelectric emission, by the way, is *not* an example of such a situation.

let us simply assert again that when a wave of signal radiation is applied to an inverted maser medium, the applied signal elicits from the atoms a stimulated response that is directly proportional to, and phase coherent with, the stimulating signal's ac electric or magnetic field. This atomic response reacts back on the stimulating signal in such fashion that the amplitude of the signal is increased, but its phase is either unchanged or is shifted by some definite and constant amount (such phase-shift effects occur when the signal is slightly off the center frequency of the atomic line). Thus some energy is added to the applied signal, and we may say that the original signal now "contains more photons," but the amplification process is, in any event, entirely linear and phase preserving. The applied signal and the atomic response are completely and coherently related.

Of course, some spontaneous emission is also added to the signal. Instead of describing this spontaneous emission as a random emission of photons, however, we will emphasize the wave picture of spontaneous emission by describing it as simply the spontaneous emission of narrowband random-noise-like radiation at and near the atomic transition frequency. Both this and the preceding point will be clarified later.

1.4   SOME IMPORTANT PRACTICAL MASER DEVICES

In this section we will briefly discuss, in more or less historical order, a few of the most important examples of maser and laser devices. These descriptions should provide some idea of the variety of ways in which maser action can take place, as well as introducing some practical details concerning energy-level spectroscopy, maser pumping methods, and experimental techniques at various frequencies.[1]

■ The ammonia-beam maser, the first maser device ever to be operated, was developed by Gordon, Zeiger, and Townes[2] at Columbia University in 1954. (The Columbia group, incidentally, also coined the name *maser* for their new device.) This device is also interesting because of its somewhat unusual energy levels and its unique pumping method, although its practical usefulness is now rather limited. The ammonia molecule NH_3, which had been intensively studied by Townes and other spectroscopists, consists of a triangle of H atoms forming the base of a pyramid, with the N atom at the apex, as shown in Fig. 1-19a. This molecule has a mode of vibration in which (in simplified terms) the nitrogen molecule oscillates back and forth through the plane of the H atoms (from position N to position N' in Fig. 1-19a). Actually the H atoms move nearly as much as the N atom, since they are lighter in weight. This mode of vibration of the NH_3 molecule, occurring at $\sim 24,000$ MHz in the high microwave range, is called an *inversion transition* (no connection with population inversion).

In quantum-mechanical terms, there is a double potential well for the N atom in the NH_3 molecule; it can be located on either side of the H atoms. As a result, there is one quantum state in which the molecule's quantum wave function is symmetric (has the same sign on both sides of the triangle) and another quantum state in which the wave function is antisymmetric (has opposite signs on opposite sides of the

THE AMMONIA-BEAM MASER

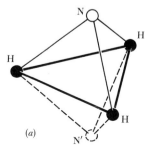

(a)

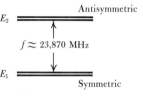

(b)

FIG. 1-19 Simple model of an ammonia (NH_3) molecule. The inversion transition used for maser action corresponds (in a highly oversimplified way) to oscillation of the N atom between the positions N and N' in the model.

---

[1] For some striking photographs of laser devices and a popularized description of laser devices and applications see Ref. 1-47.

[2] Townes, who also played a leading role in the invention of the laser, shared the Nobel Prize in 1965 with two Russian workers, N. G. Basov and A. M. Prokhorov, who had also made important early contributions to low-frequency masers and later to optical masers.

triangle). These two quantum states have slightly different energies, the energy gap corresponding to hf, with $f \approx 23{,}870$ MHz, as shown in Fig. 1-19b.

In the unique pumping scheme of the ammonia maser, a beam of NH_3 molecules from an ammonia source streams from a nozzle into an evacuated chamber, as shown in Fig. 1-20. If we denote ammonia molecules in the upper and lower states as positive and negative, respectively, then this beam will be a nearly equal mixture of positive and negative molecules (since $hf/kT \ll 1$ for this frequency at room temperature, the Boltzmann ratio is very nearly unity). The beam then enters a quadrupole focusing section, as shown in Fig. 1-20. This focuser consists of four (sometimes more) parallel rods to which large dc voltages are applied in an alternating positive and negative sequence, producing a dc field configuration called a *quadrupole field*, with a zero value on the axis and rapidly increasing values off the axis.

Because of their symmetry properties, the upper-level plus molecules experience a net force in the direction of zero E field (toward the axis of the focuser), while the lower-level minus molecules experience a force toward larger E fields, which lie farther out in the focuser. As a consequence, the plus molecules are focused into a confined beam on the axis of the focuser, while the minus molecules are defocused outward until they strike and condense on the focuser structure or the walls of the vacuum chamber (both of which are often cooled to enhance this condensation). Population inversion is thus achieved in the axial beam by physically removing the initial supply of lower-state molecules.

The beam of plus molecules is then directed into a high-Q microwave cavity resonant at 23,870 MHz, with the molecules entering through a small hole in one end and leaving through the opposite end. If enough molecules can be supplied to create a sufficient density of plus molecules in this cavity, these molecules can create a maser amplification, or a negative-resistance effect, larger than the total loss in the high-Q cavity. Under these conditions any initial disturbance will build up into an oscillation

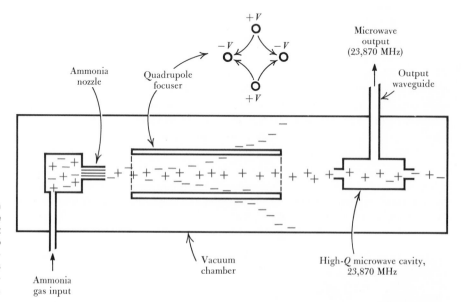

FIG. 1-20 Schematic of an ammonia maser oscillator. The plus and minus signs represent upper-level atoms (focused into the microwave cavity) and lower-level atoms (diverged outwards by the voltages on the quadrupole focuser).

at the resonance frequency of the cavity. This oscillation will persist as long as the supply of plus molecules is sustained.

The flux of plus molecules into the cavity in a practical NH_3 maser may be $\sim 10^{15}$ molecules/sec, and the average number of molecules in the cavity at any instant may be $\sim 10^{10}$. The useful oscillation power output (coupled out through an output waveguide) is extremely small—on the order of 10^{-10} W. The ammonia maser's usefulness arises from the fact that the intrinsic linewidth of the NH_3 molecule's inversion resonance is extremely narrow, corresponding to an equivalent Q for this atomic resonance of $\sim 10^6$. The maser oscillation occurs essentially at the peak of this sharp atomic resonance, $\sim 23,870$ MHz, and is very little affected by the exact tuning of the much broader cavity resonance. Hence the ammonia maser oscillator furnishes an *atomic frequency standard,* at a frequency determined only by the intrinsic and unchanging molecular resonance frequency. With proper design and adjustment, long-term frequency stability of one part in 10^{10} is possible.

The ammonia maser can also be operated as an amplifier by providing both input and output couplings to the maser cavity. However, the power output is so low and the amplification bandwidth so narrow (a few kilohertz) that the device has no practical use. As far as frequency standards are concerned, it appears that other forms of atomic frequency standards are now supplanting the ammonia maser, for various technical reasons.[1] The gaseous-hydrogen maser is one of the newer types of maser atomic clocks.

■ The next useful maser device to be successfully operated was the microwave solid-state maser. A detailed prescription for building a three-level microwave solid-state maser was first given by Bloembergen of Harvard University in 1956.[2] His proposal was very shortly implemented by experimenters at the Bell Telephone Laboratories and elsewhere. There are many materials suitable for microwave solid-state masers. The ruby maser was not the first microwave maser material employed, but it has become one of the most widely used.

THE MICROWAVE SOLID-STATE MASER

Sapphire is aluminum oxide (Al_2O_3) in the form of a hard, transparent, colorless crystal with a hexagonal crystal structure. Ruby (sometimes called corundum) is sapphire in which one out of every 10^2 or 10^3 Al^{3+} ions has been replaced by a chromium Cr^{3+} ion, giving the resulting crystal a characteristic red color which arises from optical absorption bands of the Cr^{3+} ions. In useful maser ruby the concentration of Cr^{3+} ions relative to available Al^{3+} sites is very low, typically ~ 0.05 percent. The red coloring is sufficiently faint that this is often termed *pink ruby*.

Examination of the periodic table shows that the free Cr atom, with atomic number $Z = 28$, has all electron shells filled from $1s$ through $3p$.[3] In addition, there are five electrons in the $3d$ shell ($3d^5$) and one in the $4s$ shell ($4s^1$). The partially filled $3d$ shell makes chromium one of the iron group of elements. When a Cr atom goes into a trivalent site in the ruby lattice it gives up three outer electrons—the single $4s$ and two of the $3d$ electrons—to crystalline bonds with neighboring O^{2-} ions, becoming a Cr^{3+} ion with only three electrons in the unfilled $3d$ shell (which has a total capacity of 14 electrons). The different possible arrangements of these three $3d$ electrons in the

---

[1] For an excellent review of this field see Ref. 1-50.

[2] N. Bloembergen, "Proposal for a new type solid state maser," *Phys. Rev.*, **104**: 324 (October 15, 1956).

[3] Those not familiar with atomic-energy-level jargon may skim over the next paragraph or two.

unfilled $3d$ shell lead, in a fairly complicated way, to the set of Cr^{3+} optical energy levels shown in Fig. 1-21. The importance of these optical levels will become clearer shortly in connection with ruby laser action.[1]

At room temperature or lower all the Cr^{3+} ions will normally be in the lowest or ground optical energy level. This ground optical level, however, actually comprises four energy levels, as shown in the insert in Fig. 1-21. In the ground optical level the three $3d$ electrons are arranged so that the electron spins add, giving a total spin of $S = \frac{3}{2}$ for the Cr^{3+} ion. Therefore there are really $2S + 1 = 4$ energy levels, representing four different allowed orientations of the total spin S in an applied magnetic field. The Zeeman splitting of these levels with an applied dc magnetic field B_0 is indicated in the insert to Fig. 1-21.

The energies of these four Zeeman-split energy levels actually depend in a complicated way on both the strength of the applied magnetic field B_0 and its direction θ with respect to the ruby crystal's symmetry axis. There is, for an example, a zero field splitting into two pairs of levels even at $B_0 = 0$. Figure 1-22 gives a magnified view of these four levels plotted against B_0 for a particular value of θ. For typical laboratory magnetic fields, a few thousand gauss, the transition frequencies between these Zeeman-split ground levels fall in the microwave frequency range, from say 1 to 100 GHz (10^9 to 10^{11} Hz). Hence these levels are candidates for microwave maser action. Bloembergen's maser scheme requires the use of three such energy levels, for example, levels E_1, E_2, and E_3, at the operating point (choice of B_0 and θ) indicated in Fig. 1-22.

THE BLOEMBERGEN THREE-LEVEL MASER SCHEME ■ Figure 1-23a shows the Boltzmann thermal-equilibrium populations of the four ground-state energy levels at this operating point if the ruby crystal is cooled in a bath

[1] These are called *optical* energy levels because the transition frequencies between them are optical frequencies. The allowed energy levels of the Cr^{3+} ion are strongly influenced by the electric fields of the neighboring oxygen ions in the crystal lattice; hence these levels are very different from the levels characteristic of an isolated Cr^{3+} ion in a gas. Variations in the surroundings smear some of the levels into broad bands rather than sharp levels.

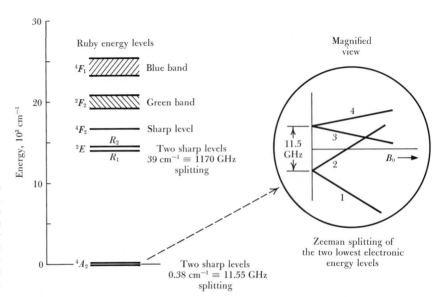

FIG. 1-21 The optical energy levels of the Cr^{3+} ion in Al_2O_3 (ruby), with an insert showing the microwave paramagnetic-resonance levels of the ground optical level. The ruby laser works between the $R_1(^2E)$ level and the ground level. The ruby microwave maser uses the Zeeman-split ground levels.

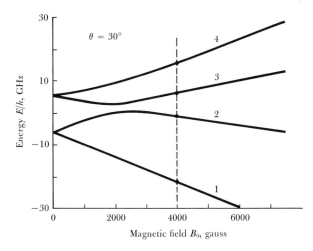

FIG. 1-22 The Zeeman-split ground-state energy levels of the Cr^{3+} ion versus B_0 for a particular direction of B_0, $\theta = 30°$ between the magnetic field direction and the ruby-crystal axis. The energy is plotted in frequency units, E/h, so that transition frequencies can be read easily. The energy levels at the indicated value of $B_0 = 4000$ gauss would provide a good operating point for a microwave solid-state maser, as shown in the following figures.

of liquid helium at $4.2°K$. Suppose now that a strong microwave pump signal is applied to the ruby crystal at the transition frequency f_{31}. As long as the population $\mathcal{N}_1$ exceeds $\mathcal{N}_3$, some of this pumping radiation will be absorbed by Cr^{3+} ions, causing a net transfer of these ions out of level E_1 and into level E_3. If this forced transfer is strong enough, the population $\mathcal{N}_1$ will be reduced and the population $\mathcal{N}_3$ increased to the point where these two populations may become essentially equal. This forced equalization of the E_1- and E_3-level populations by a strong applied pump is called *saturation* of the $1 \leftrightarrow 3$ transition; we will discuss this in more detail later. To achieve saturation the pumping radiation must be intense enough to override relaxation effects, which tend to return the populations to their thermal-equilibrium values. The existence of saturation on the pump transition is clearly shown in the experimental results of Fig. 1-18.

When the populations $\mathcal{N}_1$ and $\mathcal{N}_3$ are equalized, the populations of the remaining levels $\mathcal{N}_2$ and $\mathcal{N}_4$ may also readjust themselves because of altered relaxation rates among all energy levels. However, as Figs. 1-23b and c indicate, the new steady-state

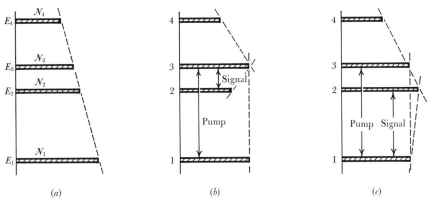

FIG. 1-23 Population of four microwave maser levels under various conditions: (a) thermal equilibrium; (b) pump on the $1 \rightarrow 3$ transition saturated, with population readjustments such that $N_3 > N_2$; (c) pump on and saturated, with population readjustments such that $N_2 > N_1$. With energy levels as shown, condition (b) is considerably more likely than condition (c).

value of N_2 must in general be either less than or greater than the equalized values of N_1 and N_3. In other words, the result must be a condition of population inversion either on the $3 \leftrightarrow 2$ transition or the $2 \leftrightarrow 1$ transition. This achievement of a steady-state population inversion on one transition by saturating a higher-frequency transition is the essence of Bloembergen's three-level maser pumping scheme. As a practical matter, the inversion usually occurs on whichever of the two transitions, f_{32} or f_{21}, has the smaller energy gap. The development of signal inversion in this fashion is also clearly shown in Fig. 1-18.

The essential elements of a microwave maser are shown in Fig. 1-24. A suitable crystal, such as ruby, is placed in a microwave cavity, which is in turn placed between the poles of an electromagnet.[1] The microwave cavity must have two resonant frequencies, one at the pump frequency, say, 10 GHz, and one at the signal frequency, say, 3 GHz. A pump input transmission line must be provided, as well as a signal input-output line or lines to carry the signals to be amplified. Application of a proper dc field together with a sufficiently strong pump input then results in cw maser action at the appropriate signal frequency.

CHARACTERISTICS OF
MICROWAVE MASERS

■ The entire maser cavity must in practice be cooled, usually to liquid-helium temperature. This cooling in part slows down relaxation processes and permits saturation to be obtained at reasonable pump power levels, say, a few milliwatts of microwave power. The most important reason for cooling, however, is illustrated by the population diagrams of Fig. 1-23. The strength of maser action obtained on the signal transi-

[1] In more modern designs the heavy electromagnet is replaced by a superconducting solenoid to supply the dc magnetic field.

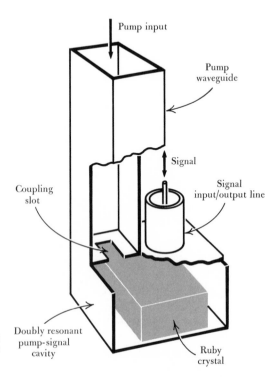

FIG. 1-24 A typical cavity-type microwave solid-state maser. For good pumping efficiency the microwave cavity should have a resonant mode at the pump frequency as well as at the signal frequency.

tion is directly proportional to the inverted signal population difference when the pump is on, but this difference is clearly more or less of the same order as the thermal-equilibrium population difference before the pump is applied (see Fig. 1-18, for example). This depends in turn on temperature through the Boltzmann factors; in fact the $\Delta \mathcal{N}_{nm}$ in such a system vary inversely with temperature from helium temperature upward. Although weak maser action is possible in special cases at liquid-nitrogen temperature ($77°K$), large enough population differences for useful three-level microwave maser action almost invariably require liquid-helium cooling.[1] This requirement is awkward from a practical standpoint, since it requires fairly elaborate refrigeration techniques, but it does help to achieve the microwave solid-state maser's extremely low noise figure.

The principal utility of the microwave solid-state maser, in fact, is an ultralow-noise preamplifier for specialized microwave applications. A well-designed microwave maser can have 20 to 30 dB of gain, with a useful bandwidth not exceeding a few, or at most a few tens of megahertz in traveling-wave versions. The noise figure of a microwave maser is, however, lower than any other known amplifier, typically <0.2 dB, or an equivalent input noise temperature $\leq 10°K$. The maser contains no hot cathodes, shot noise, or other usual noise sources, and the only relevant internal noise sources are spontaneous emission in the maser material itself and thermal noise from any losses in the cavity and input line, which are at helium temperature. Most modern microwave masers are of the traveling-wave variety, in which a propagating circuit replaces the narrowband resonant cavity, as illustrated in Fig. 1-25. The maser action then causes the signal wave to grow with distance along the special ruby-filled slow-wave circuit. Advantages of the traveling-wave maser include larger bandwidth and greater stability, with the same ultralow-noise performance.

Microwave solid-state masers have been operated with a dozen different maser crystals at frequencies from a few hundred megahertz to ~ 100 GHz, with the practical applications concentrated in the 1- to 10-GHz range. There are only a limited number of applications in which background noise levels are low enough that the added complexity of a microwave maser receiver is worth while. Most of these are applications in which a receiving antenna (which must itself be a low-noise component) is pointed at a cold sky background, as in radio-astronomy applications, satellite communication

[1] Note that the increase from helium ($4.2°K$) to nitrogen ($77°K$) cooling reduces the population differences, and hence the available gains, by a factor of almost 20.

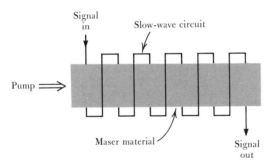

FIG. 1-25 A traveling-wave microwave solid-state maser. The signal propagates along a special slow-wave circuit, interacting with the maser crystal. The pump energy travels as a waveguide type of mode in the surrounding envelope. The signal enters one end of the circuit and leaves, amplified, at the other end.

links, deep-space telemetry, and some specialized radar applications. The microwave solid-state maser is thus a useful but fairly limited example of the maser principle.[1]
■ The Cr^{3+} ions in ruby play a double role: the sublevels of the ground optical level are used for microwave maser action, while the ground and higher optical levels are used for optical maser (laser) action. The possibilities of optical maser action were discussed in some detail by Townes and Schawlow of the Bell Telephone Laboratories in 1958; they suggested various gases and rare-earth ions in crystals as potential laser systems.[2] The first successful optical-maser action was achieved in 1960, however, by Maiman at the Hughes Research Laboratories, with ruby, a crystal not previously considered a particularly promising candidate. The ruby laser still remains one of the most important practical laser devices.

Maiman achieved laser action in ruby by the following straightforward approach. As we noted earlier, the three electrons in the unfilled $3d$ shell of a Cr^{3+} ion can arrange themselves in various orbits within this shell, corresponding to the different optical levels of Fig. 1-21 (these are different *electronic* levels). At thermal equilibrium at any reasonable temperature, essentially all the ions will be in the ground energy level, since the thermal energy kT is much less than the transition energy hf to any of the higher levels.

Maiman placed a cigarette-sized ruby rod inside a powerful spiral photographic flashlamp filled with xenon gas, as shown in Fig. 1-26. This flashlamp was connected to a capacitor bank of a few hundred microfarads charged to a few kilovolts. When a high-voltage trigger pulse from a spark coil is applied to such a lamp, the xenon gas is ionized and becomes conducting. The energy of several thousand joules stored in the capacitors is then discharged through the lamp in a millisecond or so. The power input to the flashlamp during this pump pulse is thus on the order of megawatts of

---

[1] A good summary and description of a traveling-wave maser in a typical practical application is given in Ref. 1-42. An extensive coverage of all aspects of microwave masers is given in Ref. 1-12.

[2] A. L. Schawlow and C. H. Townes, "Infrared and optical masers," *Phys. Rev.*, **112**: 1940 (1958).

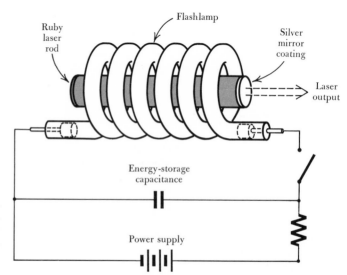

FIG. 1-26 The essential elements of a pulsed ruby laser oscillator. In its simplest form the ruby rod has silver mirrors evaporated directly on its polished ends and is placed inside a powerful xenon-filled spiral flashlamp. The laser is fired by discharging a large high-voltage capacitance through the flashlamp.

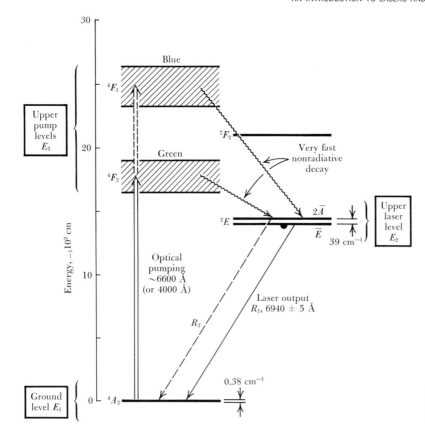

FIG. 1-27 In the course of laser action the Cr^{3+} ions traverse the paths indicated through the ruby energy levels.

electrical power. A very large fraction of this is converted into light output.[1] When the light from this pulse strikes the ruby rod, some of it is absorbed by the Cr^{+3} ions, and many of the ions are excited or pumped to their higher optical levels.[2] Many of them are pumped in particular to the bands of levels labeled $^4F_2$ and $^4F_1$ in Fig. 1-21, redrawn as Fig. 1-27. We will call these upper levels, collectively, E_3, for short. It is the case in ruby that virtually all ions excited to the energy levels E_3 will decay or relax almost immediately to the lower ^2E levels, which we will call level E_2. This very fast relaxation is of the so-called *nonradiative* type, which means simply that the energy $E_3 - E_2$ spontaneously released by each ion in dropping down goes not into a radiated photon of light, but into heating up the surrounding ruby crystal lattice.

The closely spaced pair of R_1 and R_2 levels (which, for simplicity, we are considering as a single level E_2) are metastable levels; that is, an ion entering these levels will remain there for a relatively long time—about 4 msec, on the average—before it decays to the ground level by spontaneously emitting a fluorescent photon at[3]

---

[1] These same flashlamps are normally employed in photoflash photography, flashing airport runway lamps, lighthouse beacons, and similar applications.

[2] It is only a choice of words whether we speak of the *ions* or the *electrons in the ions* as being excited to the higher energy levels; the physical meaning is the same.

[3] The exact wavelength varies somewhat with temperatures, from $\lambda \approx 6943$ Å at $300°$K to $\lambda \approx 6934$ Å at $77°$K (see Sec. 9-2).

$\lambda \simeq 6943$ Å. A short pulse of intense pump light on a ruby crystal will thus lift a number of ions up into the E_3 level, from which they drop down into the metastable E_2 or R levels. The ruby crystal will then spontaneously emit 6943-Å fluorescent radiation. This fluorescent emission will decay in intensity in exponential fashion, with a time constant of $\sim$4 msec, as shown in Fig. 1-28a. The pumping efficiency of ruby has the desirable characteristic of being nearly unity; i.e., nearly every pump photon absorbed by the ruby leads to the subsequent emission of a fluorescent photon.

Figure 1-28a illustrates the energy-level populations at the end of a pump flash whose intensity is below laser threshold. Virtually no atoms collect in levels E_3 at any time, because of the exceedingly fast downward relaxation from these levels, but some fraction (less than one-half) of the atoms originally in E_1 have been pumped through E_3 and into the metastable level E_2. If the pump-flash intensity is increased, this pumping process occurs more rapidly. Figure 1-28b shows a stronger pump flash, and the resulting greater fraction (nearing 50 percent) of the total atoms in level E_2 at the end of the pump flash. Finally, Fig. 1-28c shows that for a pump-flash intensity that exceeds the laser threshold value, at a certain point during the pump flash more than half the ions will be lifted from E_1 to E_2, and a temporary condition of population inversion will thereby be obtained between levels E_2 and E_1. This is the essential basis of laser action in ruby.

BUILDUP OF LASER OSCILLATION ■ When such population inversion is obtained, amplification of an optical signal at or near 6943 Å can be obtained simply by passing this optical signal through the ruby rod. In addition, spontaneous 6943-Å fluorescence emitted from anywhere in the ruby crystal will experience a net maser amplification in traveling out through the surrounding ruby crystal. Radiation traveling in the axial direction will experience particularly large amplification because of the longer interaction length. If both ends of the ruby rod are polished flat and made into mirrors with silver or dielectric coatings, then waves traveling exactly along the rod can bounce back and forth many times between the mirrors, being further amplified on each pass. In fact, if the round-trip maser am-

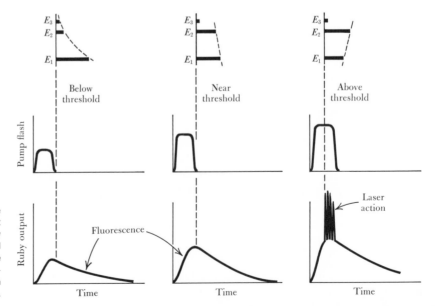

FIG. 1-28 Examples of the fluorescence plus laser output from a ruby laser at three different pump levels: (a) below threshold, (b) near threshold, and (c) above threshold. The fluorescence comes out randomly and in all directions, while the laser output forms an intense, highly collimated beam.

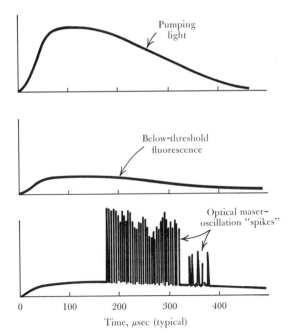

FIG. 1-29 Time development of typical optical maser operation in ruby. The top trace is the light output from the xenon flashlamp, the middle trace is fluorescent-light output from the ruby without laser oscillation, and the bottom trace (at greatly reduced sensitivity) is the fluorescent-light output plus optical maser oscillations. The laser oscillation typically occurs in the form of "spikes," or bursts of laser output a few microseconds apart (such spiking can be eliminated under proper operating conditions).

plification of such a wave in one complete circuit exceeds the total round-trip energy losses due to imperfect mirrors and other causes, then this situation is essentially a feedback amplifier with a net closed-loop gain greater than unity; the maser process provides the amplification and the end mirrors provide the feedback. Coherent optical oscillations can then build up between the mirrors at a rapid rate in exactly the same fashion as the buildup of coherent oscillations in any electronic system. As a result, an intense burst of 6943-Å laser oscillation will be obtained from the ends of the laser rod, either through coupling holes in the mirrors, or more usually through a partial transmittance of the end mirrors. Figure 1-28c illustrates this result. The upper curve shows the pump flash, and the lower curve shows the intense laser output, which does not begin until near the middle of the pump flash, after the condition of population inversion has been achieved. Figure 1-29 shows much the same results in more detail.

The laser oscillations are extremely directional along the laser-rod axis, because the feedback is highest, and hence the pump threshold lowest, for waves traveling exactly perpendicular to the end mirrors. The oscillations are also highly monochromatic, because there are only certain discrete optical frequencies, or *axial modes,* at which the feedback loop (the round-trip path between mirrors) is exactly an integral number of wavelengths. The laser oscillation output is thus much more *collimated* or *directional,* and also much more *monochromatic,* than any incoherent light-emission process such as spontaneous emission or emission from a purely thermal light source. These two properties, directionality and monochromaticity, together with very great intensity, are the major features of the laser-oscillation light output.

The characteristic "spiking" of the laser output evident in Figs. 1-28 and 1-29 is a type of relaxation oscillation or blocking oscillation which modulates the laser action in ruby and in many other solid-state lasers. It occurs because the laser oscillation very rapidly builds up to such a level that all the excess atoms in the upper laser level E_2 are used up by the laser action. The laser oscillation then ceases for a few microseconds, until the pump flash again builds up a population inversion, causing another spike of laser oscillation. Laser action finally ceases altogether when the pump flash drops below the level necessary to sustain population inversion. In practice, perhaps 1 percent of the initial electrical energy input to the pump lamp in a ruby laser can be converted to laser oscillation output. For an electrical input of 1000 joules—and many ruby lasers have much larger inputs than this—this means $\sim$10 joules of laser output in a period of $\sim$100 μsec, or a laser-oscillation power level of $\sim$100 kW (the peak power is actually higher because of the spiking behavior). This is an incredible amount of power to be concentrated in a highly directional and monochromatic optical beam. It permits such feats as detecting optical radar echoes from the moon, burning through a $\frac{3}{8}$ in. steel plate in a single shot, or causing nonlinear optical effects and optical harmonic generation in many other materials.

OTHER OPTICALLY PUMPED
SOLID-STATE LASERS: THE
NEODYMIUM LASER

■ The pumping methods in the three-level microwave ruby maser and the three-level optical ruby laser have much in common. The chief difference is that $hf/kT \ll 1$ for all transitions in the microwave case and $hf/kT \gg 1$ in the optical case. As a result, the optical maser's pump transition need not be saturated as in the microwave case. In addition, the higher-frequency pumping radiation in the optical case is supplied by an incoherent lamp rather than by a coherent pump oscillator. An alternative design for this type of laser places the ruby rod and a straight flashlamp at the two focal lines of an elliptic cylindrical reflector, as shown in Fig. 1-30. This arrangement is considerably more efficient, since nearly all the light from the flashlamp is focused directly

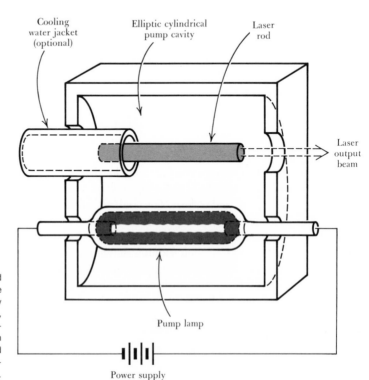

FIG. 1-30 For greater pumping efficiency the laser rod and a straight pumping lamp can be placed along the parallel focal lines of an elliptic cylindrical pump cavity with highly reflecting walls. Some solid-state lasers, such as the Nd-YAG laser, can then operate continuously as well as pulsed, using a cw Hg-arc lamp or even a high-intensity tungsten-filament lamp. The laser rod or the pump lamp may be surrounded by a transparent jacket for cooling water.

into the ruby laser rod. With this more efficient pumping geometry, continuous as well as pulsed laser action can be obtained in ruby (although only with considerable difficulty and rather poor performance) by replacing the pulsed flashlamp with a powerful (several kilowatts) cw arc lamp.

Ruby is, in fact, theoretically a poor laser material. Because it is a three-level system, at least half the ground-state atoms must be lifted to the upper level E_2 before any population inversion between E_2 and E_1 can occur at all. Figure 1-31 shows that if a four-level laser system is used instead, with pumping from E_1 to E_4 and fast relaxation to a metastable level E_3, then population inversion between levels E_3 and E_2 is obtained as soon as only a few ions are accumulated in level E_3. There are, in fact, many four-level laser systems using rare-earth ions (neodymium, erbium, dysprosium, etc.) in various crystals. The pump thresholds of these systems for either pulsed or cw operation are typically much lower than for ruby. Unfortunately, all these systems oscillate at longer infrared wavelengths (between 1 and 3 μ), beyond the visible region and beyond the range of the most convenient types of photodetectors.

The neodymium Nd^{3+} ion is a particularly useful example of such an optically pumped rare-earth laser system. The energy levels of the Nd^{3+} in almost any crystalline-lattice surrounding are essentially the same as shown in Fig. 1-15, and the $^4F_{3/2}$ level (level A in Fig. 1-15) is almost always metastable, with a fluorescent lifetime of 100 μsec to 1 msec. Thus the Nd^{3+} ion can be pumped on all the transitions A to F of Figs. 1-14 and 1-15, and laser action obtained from level A to one of the lower-lying levels. Laser action most commonly occurs from the lowest $^4F_{3/2}$ level to the lowest $^4I_{11/2}$ level, at a wavelength $\lambda \approx 1.06 \ \mu = 10{,}600$ Å in the near infrared. The Nd^{3+} ion in the YAG ($Y_3Al_5O_{12}$) lattice gives good cw laser action at 1.06 μ, with a cw threshold to the pumping lamp of a few hundred watts and a cw laser power output of a few watts. However, good-quality Nd-YAG crystals are difficult to grow in larger than birthday-candle sizes. High-power pulsed laser action at 1.06 μ can also be obtained with the Nd^{3+} ion in glasses. Glass laser rods of very high quality can be fabricated in broomhandle sizes. Energy outputs of several thousand joules per millisecond can be obtained with such very large laser rods.

■ Shortly after the invention of the ruby laser an ingenious technique was developed for greatly increasing the peak power output from a pulsed solid-state laser. One of the two end mirrors of the laser is rotated very rapidly by a high-speed motor, as shown in Fig. 1-32. During most of the rotation cycle this mirror is thus tilted at an angle, so that the two mirrors are not facing each other, and the laser is pumped very strongly with a pulsed flashlamp. Near the end of the pump pulse a very large population inversion will have been built up in the maser material, but no laser action can start because the mirrors are not in parallel. At this point the rotating mirror is suddenly restored to parallelism. Because of the large population inversion, the gain and the available stored energy in the laser rod are very high, and the round-trip gain in the laser cavity at that instant is very much greater than unity. As a consequence, the laser oscillation builds up much more rapidly than in normal operation and will rise very rapidly to a peak power level much higher than normal. The laser will "dump" all its available stored energy in a very short, very high-power pulse, with much higher peak power than in normal laser operation.

Because the essential feature of this technique entails first spoiling the Q of the resonator formed by the two mirrors, and then suddenly switching the cavity Q back

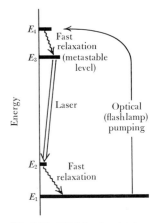

FIG. 1-31 Obtaining four-level laser action between levels E_3 and E_2, where E_3 is a metastable level, is relatively easy, since the lower level E_2 is initially almost unpopulated if $E_2 - E_1 \gg kT$.

Q SWITCHING

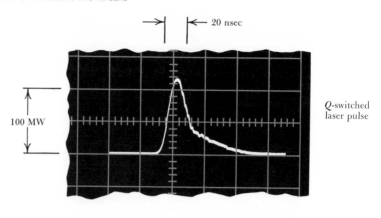

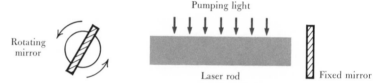

FIG. 1-32 Diagram of a simple Q-switched solid-state laser and an oscilloscope tracing of a typical Q-switched laser-output pulse in ruby.

to a relatively high value, the technique is known as *Q spoiling* or *Q switching*.[1] Laser pulses with lengths of 10 to 100 nsec and peak powers from 10 MW to over 1 GW (10^9 W) are conveniently obtained by this technique, from both ruby and Nd^{3+} lasers. These short intense pulses are very useful in laser radar applications, laser rangefinders, high-power optical experiments, and many other applications. Figure 1-32 shows a typical Q-switched ruby-laser pulse waveform.

GASEOUS OPTICAL MASERS:
THE HELIUM-NEON LASER

■ The next type of laser to be successfully demonstrated was the helium-neon gas laser, developed by Ali Javan and co-workers at the Bell Telephone Laboratories in 1960. A free atom in a gas has a complex set of characteristic energy levels, as illustrated in Fig. 1-6, representing different allowed orbits for the outer electrons of that particular atom. These energy levels in gaseous atoms are generally quite sharply defined, and the transitions between them have narrow resonance linewidths, since there are no crystalline surroundings to perturb the atoms. These levels can be used for laser action in many gases, often at many different wavelengths, with different transitions in the same atom. The atoms in a gas laser are most commonly pumped or excited to upper energy levels by collisions with electrons or with other atoms in a gas discharge. The mixed He-Ne laser is an excellent example of the gas laser. It was also the first successful gas laser and the first continuously operating laser of any sort. Since it is still one of the most important practical lasers, we will examine it in some detail.

Figure 1-33 shows the essential elements of a typical gas laser, with the key element being the gas-discharge or plasma tube. A glowing electric discharge can be excited in almost any gas either by passing dc current through the gas or by applying rf

---

[1] In practice the rotating mirror is often motor driven at a constant rotation rate, and the pump pulse is timed so that the mirror comes into parallelism just as the population inversion reaches a peak. Several other techniques (Kerr cells, saturable dyes) for Q switching a laser cavity have more recently become available, and the rotating-mirror technique is now much less used than it was.

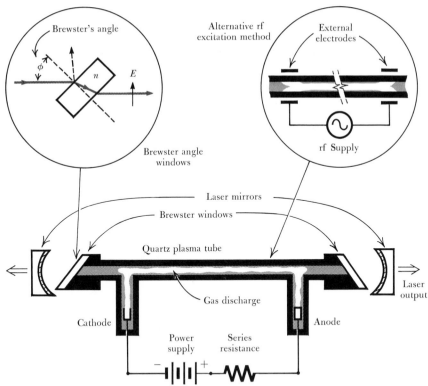

FIG. 1-33 The essential elements in a gas laser are the plasma tube, the laser mirrors, and the power supply. The gas discharge may be obtained with internal electrodes, or with external rf electrodes (upper right). The Brewster-angle windows transmit vertically polarized light with zero surface reflections (upper left).

electric fields to the gas. In such a discharge some fraction of the gas atoms are ionized, creating a mixture of neutral atoms, positively charged ions, and free electrons—the *plasma*. Applied electric fields accelerate the electrons and ions, the electrons much more effectively because they are lighter. Accelerated electrons then collide energetically with atoms and ions, exciting them into higher energy levels. The atoms and ions decay back to lower energy levels partially by spontaneous (fluorescent) emission, which creates the light emitted by the plasma tube. For a dc discharge, an emitting cathode and an anode are placed inside the discharge tube, and a current is passed between them, as shown (the series resistance is required because the voltage-current characteristic of the gas discharge usually has a negative-resistance slope in the normal range of operation). For an rf discharge, ac electric fields are applied to the plasma by rf electrodes, which may be either inside or outside the glass envelope of the discharge tube, as shown in the insert to Fig. 1-33. The discharge region between the electrodes furnishes part or all of the capacitance for a tuned-tank circuit at the rf frequency (which may typically be in the 15- to 30-MHz range). Either type of discharge, dc or rf, may be used for laser purposes.

Figure 1-34 shows some of the important energy levels of neutral He and Ne atoms. When atoms are struck by electrons in a discharge, they are excited preferentially to certain levels. As the diagram indicates, He atoms are rather efficiently excited

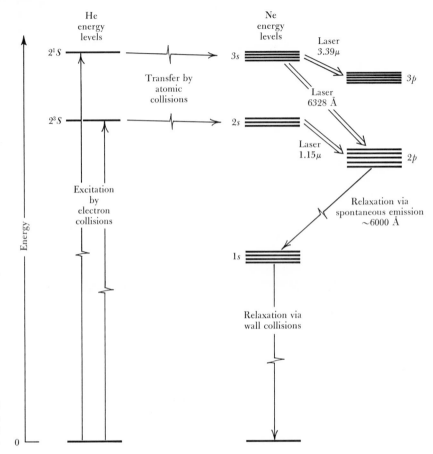

FIG. 1-34 Mechanism of operation of the He-Ne gas-discharge laser. Laser operation can be obtained on several different Ne transitions.

to the 2^3S and 2^1S levels by electron impact, while Ne atoms are not very strongly excited by electron impact at all. The two He levels excited by electrons are metastable; that is, they have relatively long lifetimes against downward relaxation. They also happen to have almost exactly the same energies as the $2s$ and $3s$ excited levels of Ne. As a result, once an He atom has been lifted to the 2^3S or 2^1S levels, there is a fair chance that before it decays downward by other means, it will collide with, or at least brush past, an unexcited Ne atom. If this occurs, there is a good chance that an energy transfer between the He and Ne atoms may take place; that is, the He atom may drop back to the ground state, giving up its energy of excitation, while the Ne atom simultaneously absorbs the energy and is excited upwards. This transfer can occur efficiently only if the two levels are nearly perfectly matched. In this chain of events, therefore, the electrons pump the He atoms, and the He atoms pump the Ne atoms. This mechanism in effect pours a continuous supply of Ne atoms preferentially into the Ne $2s$ and $3s$ levels, and as a consequence, these levels acquire a steady-state population which, though small, can be larger than the populations of several lower levels.

Once again the basic requirement for maser amplification is fulfilled. As Fig. 1-34 indicates, if the pumping action is strong enough, and depending on details of mirror reflectivities and excitation rates, the Ne atoms may provide laser action on several different transitions—at 6328 Å in the red region, at 1.15 μ (11,500 Å) in the near infrared region, at $3.39\,\mu$ farther into the infrared region, or simultaneously in combinations of these and still other wavelengths.[1]

The laser pumping mechanisms described were first worked out by Javan at the Bell Telephone Laboratories, leading in 1960 to the first gas laser oscillation (at $1.15\,\mu$). As in many other instances, the first successful laser action was a considerable triumph, achieved only with great difficulty. Now dozens of gases are made to produce laser action at thousands of different wavelengths, and it seems quite easy.

As Fig. 1-34 shows, a typical laser tube has end windows oriented at the Brewster angle, at which waves with the proper (vertical) polarization can enter and leave the window with no reflection at the air-dielectric interface. The maser gains in many gas lasers are quite low, and even small unnecessary losses cannot be tolerated. The laser mirrors are often of the multiple-dielectric-layer type, giving very high reflectivity at the desired wavelength, again to minimize internal losses.[2]

■ Pulsed solid-state lasers, although they possess a comparatively high degree of coherence, still display substantially less than perfect characteristics of monochromaticity and directionality, owing in large part to crystalline imperfections and scattering and to thermal distortions of the laser crystal during the powerful pump pulse. In contrast, cw gas lasers as a class are generally longer, much more monochromatic and stable, considerably more directional, and much less powerful than solid-state lasers. Gas lasers are used in optical testing and optical alignment, scientific measurements of many types, and accurate length and distance measurements, both in surveying and at small distances; a possible future application is in optical-frequency communications.

CHARACTERISTICS OF GAS LASERS

The He-Ne red (6328-Å) laser is by far the most common type of laser device. Typical commercial models of this laser require 5 to 10 W of excitation power and produce from 0.5 to 50 mW of cw laser output. The laser tubes typically have an inner bore diameter of a few millimeters and are 10 cm to 1 m long. Tube lives are several thousand hours. Several manufacturers supply inexpensive self-contained low-power He-Ne lasers, such as the typical example shown in Fig. 1-35, for less than $200. A small gas laser is a considerably simpler device than a television tube, or even a small radio tube, and such lasers could undoubtedly be mass produced at much less cost. The $3.39\text{-}\mu$ transition in He-Ne and another very strong laser transition at $3.51\,\mu$ in He-Xe operate at inconveniently long wavelengths for use in photodetectors and other related accessories. However, these two transitions are characterized by extraordinarily high laser gains per unit length, making laser action very easy to obtain (although the power outputs are not particularly large). Hence they are often used when a middle-infrared laser wavelength is required.

There are also scores of other gas-discharge lasers, producing outputs at thousands of wavelengths, from the near-ultraviolet through the far-infrared regions. One notable example is the ionized-argon laser. If an extremely large dc (or rf) current is passed through an He-Ar mixture, the argon becomes sufficiently ionized, and the ions

---

[1] Each of the levels shown in Fig. 1-34 is actually a group of closely spaced levels, and each transition a cluster of closely adjacent transitions. One transition in each cluster is usually strongest and oscillates preferentially, while others can be made to oscillate with increasing degrees of difficulty.

[2] Javan's first lasers had internal mirrors, inside the gas discharge tube itself. Such mirrors are difficult to adjust and impossible to change once the laser is assembled, but they do give better laser action than external mirrors. Research lasers generally have Brewster windows, but many inexpensive self-contained gas lasers are now being made with internal mirrors.

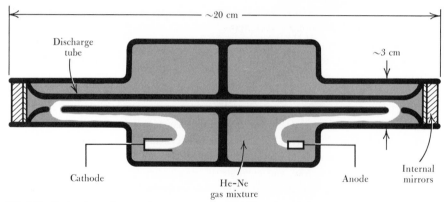

FIG. 1-35 Design for an inexpensive self-contained He-Ne laser tube (University Laboratories, Inc., Berkeley, Calif.). The internal mirrors are cemented into place after alignment. Typical power-supply requirements are 2000 V dc at 60 mA.

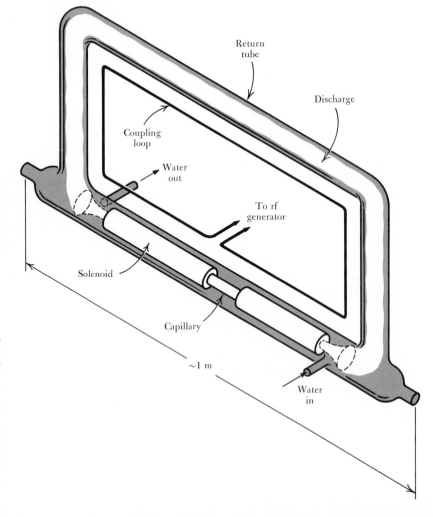

FIG. 1-36 Sketch of one type of high-power ionized-argon gas laser. In the pumping arrangement shown the gas discharge forms a closed loop which acts as a single-turn secondary coil magnetically excited by the primary coil, which in turn is connected to an rf generator. With this arrangement no rf electrodes are required either internally or externally. The rf drive power to this type of laser may exceed 10 kW cw, producing a laser output of only 1 W in the green or blue regions. The focusing solenoid helps confine the discharge inside a narrow capillary bore in the laser region.

sufficiently excited, to permit laser oscillation with considerable intensity on several transitions of the argon Ar^+ ion. Ion laser action of the same sort is also obtained from several other of the rare gases, such as krypton. Figure 1-36 shows a typical ion laser of this type. Continuous laser outputs of several watts can be obtained, for example, at 4880 or 5140 Å in the blue-green region of the visible spectrum using argon. This high power output in the middle of the visible spectrum is very useful, since the human eye, photoemissive cathodes, and photographic film all have peak responses at these wavelengths. Argon lasers are at present, however, very inefficient and require very high pump power (several kilowatts). As a consequence, the laser tubes are expensive, require water cooling, and have short lifetimes because the large currents rapidly deteriorate the laser tubes.

A great many gas-laser transitions operate on a pulsed basis, although for various reasons they will not operate on a continuous basis. A useful example is the pulsed mercury laser, which oscillates at 6150 Å in the red region, using a transition in the Hg^+ ion. Although this laser system will operate only in very short pulses (a few microseconds), the pulses can recur at a high rate, so that the output appears continuous to the human eye. A useful characteristic of this laser is that it provides very high gain even in large-bore discharge tubes.

■ There is another class of gas lasers which are sufficiently new, interesting, different, and important to warrant separate discussion. These are the molecular vibrational-rotational lasers, of which the carbon dioxide laser is the principal example. Molecules are more complex than atoms and have correspondingly more complex energy-level structures. Not only can the electrons in molecules be excited to higher energy levels, in close analogy with single atoms, but the constituent atoms in the molecule can also vibrate in relation to each other, and the molecule as a whole can rotate. Both these types of motion are quantized in quantum theory. Hence molecules have many vibrational-rotational energy levels not found in single atoms. The vibrational levels are generally more closely spaced (lower vibrational frequencies) than electronic levels, and the rotational sublevels are still more closely spaced. The associated vibrational-rotational transition frequencies thus lie in the middle- and far-infrared spectral ranges. Figure 1-37 shows, as a typical example, the three possible modes of vibration, and Fig. 1-38 shows some of the lowest vibrational-rotational levels of the CO_2 molecule when the electrons of the molecules are in the lowest electronic state. Figure 1-38 also shows that each vibrational level is in turn further split into a collection of closely spaced rotational sublevels associated with rotational spinning of the complete CO_2 molecule.

When a gas discharge is created in a molecular gas such as CO_2, electron impacts excite the molecules to higher electronic and vibrational-rotational levels. The excited molecules then trickle down by relaxation through the complex array of levels shown in Fig. 1-38. Patel at Bell Telephone Laboratories discovered in 1965 that in the case of CO_2 the result of this process was a population inversion between the 00°1 level and the lower 02°0 and 10°0 levels[1] in the CO_2 electronic ground state, leading to laser oscillations in two multiple groups of transitions near 9.6 and 10.6 μ. Adding

MOLECULAR GAS LASERS: THE CARBON DIOXIDE LASER

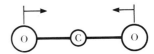

f_1 Symmetric stretch

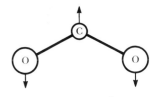

f_2 Bending mode

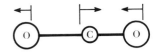

f_3 Antisymmetric stretch

FIG. 1-37 The vibrational energy levels of the CO_2 molecule come out of a quantum-mechanical analysis of these three fundamental modes of vibration of the molecule. The fundamental vibration frequencies for CO_2 are $f_1 = 1337$ cm^{-1}, $f_2 = 667$ cm^{-1}, and $f_3 = 2349$ cm^{-1} (1 cm^{-1} = 30 GHz).

---

[1] This notation is spectroscopic jargon telling which modes of molecular vibration are involved in each energy level. The label *nml* means, for example, *n* quanta of frequency f_1 (from Fig. 1-37), *m* quanta of frequency f_2, and *l* quanta of frequency f_3.

various other gases, such as H_2O, N_2, and He, to the discharge increases the pumping efficiency. The 10.6-μ transition in particular can give cw power outputs from watts to multiple kilowatts, with power efficiencies approaching an extraordinary 30 percent from electric input to laser power output. This is far more efficient than any other laser system. Good results, although not equal to those for CO_2, have also been obtained in other molecules.[1]

The 10-μ spectral region is at present a somewhat difficult one, in that convenient detection methods have not been developed. The available photodetectors are insensitive and expensive and require awkward low-temperature cooling. Nonetheless, because of its power and efficiency, the CO_2 laser is of great practical importance. The destructive effects of a CO_2 laser beam with even a few tens of watts of power are very impressive: such a beam burns easily through a wooden plank, an asbestos sheet, or a metal plate. It is also interesting to note that the earth's atmosphere has one of its "windows" of high-infrared transmission centered just at the 10-μ wavelength. The CO_2 laser should find important applications in cutting, welding, heating, evaporating, sealing, and similar industrial processes, and possibly also in optical-frequency radar and communication systems. The CO_2 laser is particularly easy to construct, since the operating conditions are not critical, the gain is high, the vacuum requirements are

[1] Typical results for CO_2 lasers are summarized in Ref. 1-53 and the following papers in that issue.

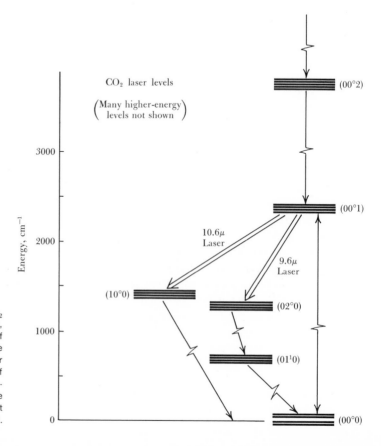

FIG. 1-38 Some of the lower energy levels of the CO_2 molecule. The levels shown are vibrational levels, each of which is split into a very large number of *rotational* levels (not shown to scale). Many of the higher vibrational levels are not shown, and still higher levels representing electronic transitions would lie off the figure at the top. The label (*n, m*) on each vibrational energy level tells how many quanta of each of the fundamental vibration modes are involved in that energy level.

very simple, and the longer wavelength makes optical tolerances much less stringent.[1] Figure 1-39 shows a typical simple CO_2 laser. This ease of construction is perhaps a disadvantage, since the hazards to eyes and other damage associated with this powerful but totally invisible beam are extremely serious. Stringent safety precautions must be followed in working with even a low-power CO_2 laser.

■ The great variety of available laser devices is further emphasized by the semiconductor laser, which employs considerably different energy levels and pumping mechanisms and generally has different performance characteristics from the lasers we have considered so far. A semiconductor laser consists essentially of a very small sample or chip of semiconductor material, often (though not always) in the form of a *p-n*-junction diode. When some of the electrons in a semiconductor sample are excited from the valence band into the conduction band (for example, by shining light on the sample, bombarding it with an electron beam, or passing current through it), it is often possible to observe a *band-gap emission,* or radiative recombination, from the semiconductor, at wavelengths more or less corresponding to the energy gap between valence and conduction bands. This radiation is fluorescence, or spontaneous emission, caused by some of the excess electrons in the conduction band dropping back down to the valence band and giving up their excess energy as light in the process. If such a semiconductor sample can be pumped strongly enough, by bombarding it strongly or by passing very large forward currents through the *p-n* junction, it becomes possible to obtain a population inversion between certain of the valence and conduction levels and thus to observe a genuine laser action at these same wavelengths.

Laser action can now be obtained in this way in a dozen or more semiconductor materials, at numerous wavelengths ranging from the visible and ultraviolet to about

SEMICONDUCTOR LASERS: THE GALLIUM ARSENIDE DIODE LASER

---

[1] For the first CO_2 laser built in the author's student laser laboratory (by graduate student John P. Markiewicz) the mirrors were mounted internally with a machined section of red rubber hose; the output window was Saran-Wrap (good only at very low powers), the N_2 supply was the atmosphere, and the CO_2 supply was a plastic shirt bag inflated by a quick squirt from the fire extinguisher on the laboratory wall.

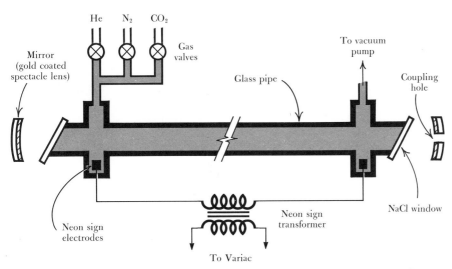

FIG. 1-39 Schematic of a simple CO_2 laser. Such a laser can easily be constructed with glass pipe, rubber hose, and gold-coated spectacle lenses for mirrors, but safety precautions must be carefully followed in working with this particularly dangerous laser beam.

10 μ in the infrared region, depending on the semiconductor band gaps available. Pumping with a high-voltage electron beam is the most effective excitation method and leads to laser action in the largest number of materials. However, we will concentrate chiefly on the dc-current-excited *p-n*-junction type of semiconductor laser, since it is by far the simplest and most useful type. This form of semiconductor laser is sometimes called the *injection* or *diode-injection laser,* since the laser action is created by charge carriers injected into a semiconductor diode.

Figure 1-40 shows the structure of a typical diode-injection laser. The diode itself is a tiny chip of semiconductor material such as gallium arsenide (GaAs), typically between 0.3 and 1 mm (12 to 40 mils) long and with even smaller transverse dimensions, soldered onto a small gold-plated mounting post or tab. The sample is cut from heavily doped *n*-type material, but only after *p*-type impurities have been diffused into the top of the sample, so that the top layer becomes *p*-type with a thin, planar *p-n* junction created a short distance below the top surface. Contact to the *p* region is made by means of a fine wire. When a large forward current is passed through this diode, population inversion and laser action are created in a very thin layer, perhaps only 10 μ thick, located at or very close to the junction plane. If the ends of the diode sample are cut by cleaving the semiconductor crystal, they provide extremely smooth parallel surfaces without further preparation, and since the laser gain in the junction layer is very high, the normal reflection ($\sim$30 percent) at the semiconductor-air end surface provides sufficient feedback for laser oscillation without further mirror coating. The laser output then emerges from the junction plane through the ends of the small chip. The sides of the sample are usually rough sawn to inhibit undesired reflections from the side surfaces of the crystal.

THEORY OF DIODE INJECTION
LASERS

■ In discussing the general principles of semiconductor recombination radiation and injection laser action we will assume some familiarity from semiconductor theory with the allowed energy levels for electrons in semiconductors. These levels are grouped into broad bands, generally with energy gaps between certain bands; in particular, there is normally a valence band, separated by an energy gap from higher-lying conduction bands. Under normal conditions in an intrinsic or *undoped semiconductor,* virtually all the available energy levels in the valence band are occupied by electrons, and the con-

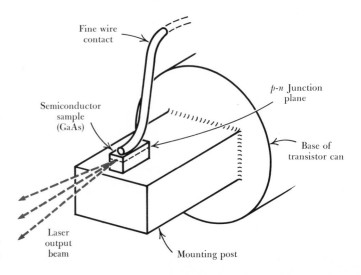

FIG. 1-40 A typical *p-n* diode-injection laser or semiconductor laser (greatly magnified).

duction band is virtually empty; i.e., very few electrons have sufficient energy from thermal or other sources to occupy levels in the conduction band. If there are any unfilled energy levels near the top of the valence band, the vacancy or deficit of a negatively charged electron in such an energy level acts as a mobile positive-charge carrier and is called a *hole*. The energy gap between the valence and conduction bands is the characteristic energy gap or band gap of the semiconductor. The band gap generally corresponds, by Planck's law, to a frequency or wavelength in the visible or infrared region of the spectrum.

In a nonintrinsic or *doped semiconductor*, there will be a limited number of additional rather sharply defined energy levels located within the energy gap, due to the presence of various added impurities or doping atoms in the semiconductor. If these added energy levels are located just above the top of the valence band and can accept additional electrons, the impurities are called *acceptors* and the semiconductor becomes a *p* type. If the added levels are located just below the bottom of the conduction band and have electrons to give up, the impurities are called *donors* and the semiconductor becomes an *n* type. In lightly doped semiconductors the acceptor or donor levels form rather sharp and distinct energy levels within the band gap. Injection lasers, however, more commonly use heavily doped materials, in which the acceptor and donor energy levels broaden and more or less merge with the closely adjacent valence or conduction bands, respectively.

Figure 1-41 shows energy-level diagrams describing the valence band and conduction bands in the *p-n*-junction region of a heavily doped sample. An important parameter in a semiconductor at thermal equilibrium is the *Fermi energy level*. This energy value is a parameter in the Fermi-Dirac statistical distribution of electrons among the available energy levels, but it also represents physically the energy level below which essentially all available levels are occupied and above which essentially all available levels are empty. With no voltage applied, the Fermi level must be constant everywhere throughout a semiconductor sample. The top diagram in Fig. 1-41 shows the resulting energy-level diagram near a *p-n* junction between heavily doped *n* and *p* regions at equilibrium with no voltage applied. On the *n* side, both the conduction band and the occupied donor energy levels are filled, and hence on an absolute energy scale the entire energy-level structure must be depressed slightly below the Fermi level E_F, as shown. Conversely, on the *p* side, the acceptor-created energy levels at the top of the valence band are not filled, and the entire band structure must be located slightly above the Fermi level. The intervening region between the *p* and *n* regions is the *transition* or *junction region*. The absolute energy difference between the *p* and *n* regions is the *built-in voltage* or *contact potential* of the *p-n* diode.

The lower diagram in Fig. 1-41 shows the changes that occur when a forward voltage is applied to such a diode. The absolute energy difference, measured in electron volts, between the *p* and *n* regions is reduced by the applied potential in volts (the Fermi level is no longer strictly applicable, since the diode is not in equilibrium). It is now possible for both electrons from the *n* region and holes from the *p* region to move into the junction region from opposite sides and overlap in at least part of the junction region. In the overlap region, where both electrons and holes are present, it becomes possible for an electron in the conduction band to drop into and fill a vacancy, or hole, in the valence band. The hole and electron then recombine. The excess energy of the electron in this process may go into excitation of acoustic vibrations, which simply heat the surrounding semiconductor crystal lattice (called *non-*

radiative recombination or *spontaneous emission of a phonon*), or it may go into the spontaneous emission of a photon of light at or very near the band-gap wavelength. This light is called the *recombination radiation*.

Because the probabilities of either nonradiative or radiative recombination are always rather large, neither electrons nor holes can spill very far outside their respective regions before such recombination occurs. Thus the recombination region is limited to a thin layer in the immediate vicinity of the junction (this region is biased somewhat to the *p* side in Fig. 1-41 because we have assumed a relatively heavier doping on the *n* side than on the *p* side, as is often the case in practical GaAs devices). There is, of course, an associated forward current flow through the diode (positive current moving from right to left) because positive holes flow to the left in the *p* region and negative electrons flow to the right in the *n* region. These carriers then combine and annihilate each other in the overlap region of the junction.

If the radiative (light-emitting) recombination rate dominates the nonradiative (photon-emitting) recombination rate, as can be the case in optimum materials (direct-band-gap semiconductors), then very nearly one photon of recombination radiation will be emitted for every electron of charge that flows through the diode. If the band gap of the semiconductor in volts is V_g (typically $V_g \sim 0.1$ to 1 V), then every emitted

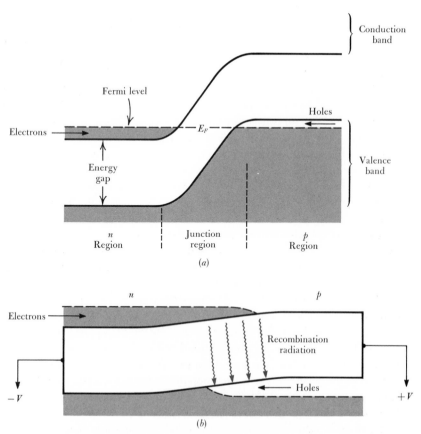

FIG. 1-41 Energy levels versus distance along a cross section through a *p-n* junction with heavily doped *p* and *n* regions, for (a) equilibrium with no voltage applied, and (b) with a forward voltage applied to cause current flow and radiative-recombination emission.

photon carries away energy eV_g. The power-supply energy required to send one electron through the diode is eV_d, where V_d is the voltage drop across the diode. This voltage drop will be slightly larger than V_g and will also include contributions due to ohmic voltage drops across the p and n regions of the diode and in the diode leads. Thus the energy efficiency of the radiative-recombination process will be

$$\frac{\text{Light-energy output}}{\text{Electric-energy output}} = \frac{\text{radiative recombination rate}}{\text{total recombination rate}} \times \frac{V_g}{V_d}$$

The first factor on the right is sometimes called the *internal radiative quantum efficiency*. The important point is that in optimum situations both of the right-hand factors can approach unity, and the energy efficiency can thus approach 100 percent. An additional consideration is that the p- and n-type regions surrounding the junction region are highly absorbing for the emitted radiation, and in the below-threshold, or nonlaser, case only about 10 percent of the radiated light may be able to escape from the semiconductor sample without being internally reflected and reabsorbed. Even so, this process can furnish an extremely efficient and bright narrowband infrared light source. Diodes designed for this purpose are commercially available at low cost.

■ Laser action will also occur in the overlap region near the diode junction when the current flow through the diode becomes sufficiently large and exceeds a certain threshold value. When electrons from the n side and holes from the p side are injected into the junction region at a sufficiently high rate, an electron-population inversion is created between filled levels near the bottom of the conduction band and empty levels (holes) near the top of the valence band. Laser action near the band-edge wavelength then occurs in this thin layer, and laser oscillations can build up between the reflecting ends of the semiconductor sample, as shown in Fig. 1-40. If the forward current is increased to a few times the threshold value, virtually all the injected current goes into the laser oscillation. Thus the oscillation output compared to electric-energy input can have the same near-100 percent efficiency characteristic of the below-threshold recombination radiation described above. The p and n regions surrounding the junction layer are still lossy to the laser wavelength, so that the laser action is confined to the very thin, planar junction region. However, the laser-oscillation waves travel largely in the axial direction along this layer and escape into free space through the ends of the diode. Laser efficiencies exceeding 60 percent are possible in low-temperature diodes, although 10 percent or less is more common for room-temperature operation, where the p- and n-region losses have more serious effects.

CHARACTERISTICS OF
INJECTION LASERS

The physical size of the resulting laser device could hardly be smaller—a tiny semiconductor chip, mounted, perhaps, in a transistor package with a window on one end—and the pumping requirement is extremely simple—a low-voltage dc current source. Thus the semiconductor laser offers unique advantages of small size, simplicity, and extraordinarily high efficiency. It can also be a very inexpensive device, well suited to mass fabrication, and its output can be directly modulated even up to gigahertz modulation frequencies simply by modulating the pumping current through the diode. However, this type of laser also has some compensating disadvantages. Because of the extreme thinness and generally small size of the laser region, as well as transient heating and other effects that occur during the laser action, it is very difficult to control the mode pattern and mode structure of the laser action. The laser beam usually emerges in a rather wide beam, perhaps 5 to 15°. This beam can be much more narrowly collimated by passing it through a small telescope, but not to nearly the degree possible with, say, gas lasers (although it still far exceeds the capabilities of ordinary nonlaser light sources). The laser action in the semiconductor laser originates, not between two sharp and well-defined energy levels, but between the edges of two broad bands. Partially as a result of this, the spectral purity and monochromaticity of the injection-laser output is also much poorer than in other types of lasers (although, again, it is still much better than any incoherent light source).

Gallium arsenide provided the first successful semiconductor laser in late 1962, with successful experiments reported nearly simultaneously by three independent research groups at the General Electric and IBM research laboratories and at MIT Lincoln Laboratory. Gallium arsenide, with a band-gap energy of 1.4 to 1.5 eV and a transition wavelength $\lambda = 8400$ to 9100 Å (depending on temperature), is still the most widely used diode laser system, although a half-dozen other semiconductors have since been made to operate as diode lasers, and many additional materials will exhibit laser action under high-voltage electron-beam excitation. The near-infrared transition wavelengths from GaAs can be shifted down to as short as ~6500 Å in the visible-red spectrum by employing a mixed semiconducting alloy of GaAs and GaP, although at some cost in performance. Efficient radiative recombination, as well as diode laser action, appear to be possible only in semiconductors having what is known as a *direct-gap* energy-band structure. As a result, the semiconductors most widely employed in conventional electronic devices, silicon and germanium, are not suitable for diode laser action, since they are indirect-gap semiconductors.

Figure 1-42*a* is a plot of light output versus current input for one of the earliest successful laser diodes, showing the transition from radiative recombination or in-coherent light emission below threshold to laser action above threshold. The change-over from the below-threshold incoherent emission to the above-threshold true laser oscillation is evidenced by the steep rise in the light output versus current input, with greatly increased efficiency; the simultaneous changeover to a highly directional char-acter of the laser radiation from the ends of the diode, accompanied in many cases by distinctive mode patterns on the ends of the junction region; and a sudden, sharp narrowing of the spectral width of the emitted light above threshold. Figure 1-42*b* contrasts the broad fluorescent linewidth of the below-threshold radiative recombina-tion with the sharp-line emission characteristic of the laser output (parts *a* and *b* of the figure represent data on two quite different types of diodes, but the results shown are both entirely characteristic of either type of diode). Closer examination of the laser output spectrum with a higher-resolution instrument shows that the sharp line actually consists of a series of evenly spaced and even sharper lines, corresponding to a set of discrete cavity resonance frequencies, as we will discuss in later chapters.

Although the shape and temperature dependence of the curves for light output versus current in Fig. 1-42*a* are typical, the threshold current requirements have been somewhat reduced by diode improvements. Threshold currents as low as 50 mA at 4°K and cw power outputs up to 1 W at 77°K have been demonstrated. The threshold current increases rapidly with temperature, however, varying roughly as T^3 above 20°K. Room-temperature threshold currents are then ~10 A in typical diodes, although the applied voltage required is only a few volts. Because of power-dissipation limitations in the tiny diode structure, room-temperature operation is limited to low-duty cycles, typically with short pulses (100 nsec to 1 μsec) at moderately rapid line-pulse rates (~10^4 pulses/sec). Peak pulse power outputs of several watts at room temperature and up to 100 W at 77°K can be obtained. Note that, in view of the very

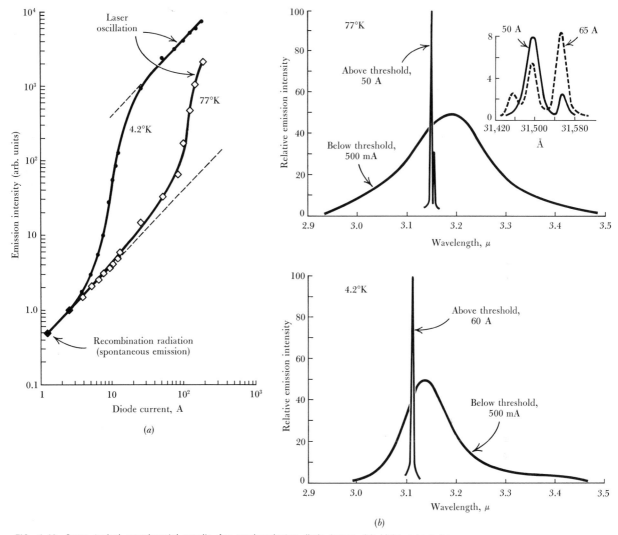

FIG. 1-42 Some typical experimental results for semiconductor diode lasers. (a) Light output (at ~ 8500 Å) versus diode current for one of the earliest GaAs diode-injection lasers. The sudden sharp rise at about 4 A represents the laser threshold point. [From Quist et al., *Appl. Phys. Letters*, **1**:91 (1962).] (b) Typical spectra of infrared output near 3.1 μ from one of the earliest InAs diode-injection lasers, show-ing typical spectra below and above the threshold current value at two different temperatures. The spon-taneous-emission spectra are drawn to an expanded intensity scale compared to the laser emission, since the below-threshold emission is very much weaker than the laser emission. [From Melngailis, *Appl. Phys. Letters*, **2**:176 (1963).] Although these results are taken from two different kinds of diode lasers, each result is actually typical of both kinds of lasers.

small area of the junction region, the currents mentioned above correspond to current densities in the diode from 10^2 A/cm² at low temperature up to 10^4 to 10^5 A/cm² at room temperature.

Injection lasers appear to have promise in such systems as small hand-held or portable optical radar and ranging units and pulse-modulated line-of-sight communi-cation links. Potential space applications include compact and efficient radars for rendezvous, docking, and soft landings, as well as astronaut communications. Less exotic terrestrial applications that are under consideration include land surveying, electric-eye surveillance units, an inexpensive collision-warning radar system for automobiles, and an obstacle-avoidance laser cane for the blind. There may be many other opportunities to take advantage of the light weight, small size, simplicity, and low cost of this type of laser device.[1]

1-5 SOME ADDITIONAL MASER SYSTEMS

The lasers and masers described above include most of the important types currently in use. There are a number of additional types of maser systems, both proposed and in operation, that are to some extent exotic, either in the materials employed or in the pumping scheme or method of operation of the device. However, they serve to illustrate further the great generality of the maser principle.

ACOUSTIC MASERS ■ With recently developed techniques it has become feasible to generate and transmit microwave-frequency acoustic waves through the interior of various crystals. These waves are generated by a microwave resonant cavity in contact with a tiny transducer, or ultraminiature microphone, which is usually a thin piezoelectric film evaporated directly onto the side of the crystal. It is then possible to transmit from a microwave-signal generator into a microwave acoustic beam, and also to receive and detect microwave acoustic signals by the reverse process, although usually with some losses in the coupling process into or out of the acoustic waves.

If a microwave acoustic signal tuned to any of the microwave transition frequencies of a ruby microwave maser crystal is transmitted through that crystal—and sapphire or ruby does transmit acoustic waves quite well—then this microwave acoustic signal will excite a stimulated response in the Cr^{3+} ions and will interact with the atomic transition in the same fashion as a microwave electromagnetic signal. The acoustic signal will be absorbed if the transition is in thermal equilibrium, or it will be amplified by acoustically stimulated emission or acoustic maser amplification if the transition is inverted. All the general maser concepts and principles we have discussed so far also apply to both acoustic and electromagnetic atomic interactions.

It therefore is possible, at least in principle, to construct an all-acoustic maser of the Bloembergen three-level type, with an acoustic pump on one transition and an acoustic signal to be amplified on another transition. As a practical matter, acoustic pumping is likely to be inefficient because of the poor coupling from signal generators to acoustic waves (and possibly because of nonlinear effects that occur with acoustic waves at higher power levels). However, the ruby microwave maser system (or a system employing any other suitable microwave maser crystal) can just as well be pumped in the usual fashion by the usual microwave electromagnetic pump signal. The inverted transition can then be used to amplify a microwave acoustic signal. Exactly this technique has, in fact, been used to make successful *phonon masers* that amplify acoustic waves propagating through the crystal and also produce regenerative oscillation in the acoustic modes of the crystal. Typical experiments have been done with a microwave electromagnetic pump frequency of $\sim$23 GHz and a microwave acoustic-signal fre-

---

[1] Several articles on semiconductor lasers are listed in the references at the end of the chapter. Simple descriptions of semiconductor laser action and of some potential practical applications are given in Refs. 1-48, 1-49, and 1-52. Much more detailed reviews of the entire semiconductor laser field are given in Ref. 1-39 and the article by Nathan in Ref. 1-20. One specific laser radar experiment is described in Ref. 1-41.

quency of $\sim$9.3 GHz. A practical use for this type of maser is not yet evident, but it does clearly demonstrate the extension of the maser principle to a totally different and nonelectromagnetic type of signal radiation.[1]

■ If the rare-earth ions commonly used for laser action in crystals are dissolved in solution, the rare-earth energy levels associated with the unfilled inner $4f$ electron shell remain almost unchanged. Hence there is at least the possibility that optically pumped laser action might be obtained in liquids as well as in crystals and in glasses. In fact, despite some major obstacles to laser action in liquids, several good liquid laser "crystals" have been demonstrated to lead to liquid laser action on a transition of the europium Eu^{3+} ion at 6131 Å and on the familiar Nd^{3+} ion at 1.06 μ.

LIQUID LASERS

There are a number of reasons to be particularly interested in liquid laser materials. In general, good laser crystals are expensive and very difficult to grow, particularly in larger sizes. They contain optical strains, defects, and imperfections that are very difficult to eliminate, and these defects cause mode distortion, scattering losses, and serious internal damage at higher power levels. By contrast, a homogeneous liquid can have nearly perfect optical quality. A liquid will not, of course, crack or shatter, as do costly laser rods when the power input becomes just a bit too high. If the liquid laser material can be prepared at all, then a laser "rod" of any desired size can be prepared simply by filling a suitable tube with the liquid, as shown in Fig. 1-43. Liquids do show considerably larger thermal-expansion coefficients and thermal changes in index of refraction than do solids, but in a really high-power laser it would be possible to cool and recirculate the laser solution through the active region.

The major difficulty with liquid lasers incorporating rare-earth ions seems to be that typical liquids offer an excited rare-earth ion a great variety of ways to relax back to its ground level via fast nonradiative processes in which vibrational energy is transmitted to surrounding atoms in the liquid. It thus becomes difficult to achieve and maintain the needed population inversion between upper laser levels. One successful solution to this problem has been to use some rather complicated organic liquids called *chelates,* in which the rare-earth ion (such as Eu^{3+}) becomes locked in the center of a complex organic molecule, or cage. This cage then shields the ion from the agitation of the surrounding liquid molecules and essentially encloses it in a small pseudo-crystalline shield.

Another more recent approach is to use a liquid solvent consisting entirely of heavier atoms, eliminating in particular the usual hydrogen content, since the rate of loss of atomic excitation to the solvent decreases rapidly for heavier solvent atoms. The elimination of hydrogen rules out virtually all ordinary organic liquids, and there are also other restrictions, since the liquid must be transparent to the laser and pump-

[1] A recent summary of phonon maser experiments is given at the end of Ref. 1-54.

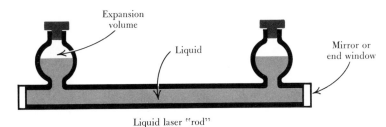

Expansion volume

Liquid

Mirror or end window

Liquid laser "rod"

FIG. 1-43 Schematic of a typical liquid laser "rod."

ing wavelengths and have other reasonable characteristics. The best solution to date is the liquid selenium oxychloride ($SeOCl_2$) containing dissolved Nd^{3+} ions which laser at 1.06μ. Except for the fact that it is highly toxic, this liquid has generally good characteristics, including a low refractive index, good optical transmission, and a density comparable to glass. The fluorescent intensity of the dissolved Nd atoms is high, and the pumping bands are equivalent to or better than those in crystalline host lattices. Very strong laser action has been obtained from this system, and it may become quite important in the future.[1]

ORGANIC-DYE LASERS

■ Very recently another type of liquid laser has been developed—the organic-dye laser—which makes use of the excited electronic energy levels of organic molecules in various liquids and dyes. Because they have fast relaxation times, dyes generally require very intense and rapid pumping, and in many cases the organic-dye laser is itself pumped by another high-power laser, such as a ruby laser. Dye lasers are presently the subject of considerable research effort, since they can yield high peak powers in short pulses, although it seems unlikely that they can ever provide low-power cw laser action. Interesting possibilities also exist for shifting the wavelengths in these lasers by making slight changes in the chemical composition of the dye.[2]

CHEMICAL LASER PUMPING:
THE FLAME LASER

■ The primary objective of laser pumping is to excite atoms or molecules to upper energy levels. In most conventional lasers this is accomplished by optical pumping or by an electric discharge in a gas. Another potential energy source for producing excited atoms, however, is chemical reactions. The conversion of chemical energy into atomic excitation is graphically illustrated, for example, by the large number of excited atoms and the large amount of light produced by the chemical reactions occurring in a flame or an explosion. Chemical energy is generally the least expensive form of energy and it is available in large amounts per unit volume or per unit weight (energies of combustion or of chemical reaction per unit volume or unit weight of fuel are generally orders of magnitude greater than the purely electrical energy that can be stored in comparable volumes or weights). There is much interest, therefore, in exploring ways in which an inverted population might be created during or after a chemical reaction, for example, in gases reacting in a flame or in a controlled explosion.

Several laser systems pumped by entirely chemical (or at least entirely non-electrical) methods have already been demonstrated. However, these are all what might be called "chemioptical" laser systems, since they use the light emitted by a chemical reaction to pump the laser action in a separate atomic system. For example, on a clear day the sun can provide a moderately intense cw pumping lamp, with a power density at the earth's surface of ~ 1 kW/m^2 and a spectral distribution equivalent to a black-body source at $\sim 6000°$K. With the aid of appropriate polished reflectors to collect the sunlight, laser rods of several different crystals as well as glass rods containing Nd^{3+} and other rare-earth ions have been successfully operated as cw sun-pumped laser systems.

When the shock wave generated by the detonation of a small shaped explosive charge is passed through certain gases, such as argon, the extreme compression of the gas in the shock front rapidly heats and excites the gas, causing intense light emission. In several experiments the light from such an "argon bomb" has been used as a rapid

---

[1] An excellent review of this subject is given in Ref. 1-32. See also A. Heller, "Laser action in liquids," *Physics Today*, **35** (November, 1967).

[2] For a good introduction to organic-dye lasers see Ref. 1-38.

and intense pump source for pulsed ruby and Nd lasers. The light coming directly from a flame or explosion has also been used to pump various laser rods (with appropriate precautions, so that the explosive shock wave does not shatter the laser rod itself). Cyanogen gas burning in oxygen generates an extremely energetic flame which has been used to pump ruby rods for brief periods. A small pulsed Nd-glass laser has been successfully pumped with an ordinary photographic flashbulb, and "Gatling-gun" lasers have been proposed in which a single laser rod would be pumped repeatedly by small light-source cartridges containing an explosive light-emitting mixture. Weak cw laser action on the 10.6-μ CO_2 laser transition has also been successfully excited by pumping the CO_2 gas with a surrounding flame from gas jets supplied with CO and O_2.

■ There is even greater interest in finding systems in which the chemical energy source and the laser action can be contained in the same gaseous system. The general principle is that an atom or molecule of, say, type A will react with another molecule of type BC according to the formula

PURELY CHEMICAL LASERS

$$A + BC \xrightarrow{\text{chemical reaction}} (AB)^* + C + \text{energy}$$

The asterisk on $(AB)^*$ indicates that at least some of the energy released in the chemical reaction is to be used to form the new molecule AB in one of its excited levels rather than its ground state. Laser action is then theoretically possible on some appropriate transition in the AB molecule.

A number of systems of this type have been made to operate; for example, the system

$$H + Cl_2 \longrightarrow (HCl)^* + Cl$$

gives laser emission on an HCl transition at $\lambda = 3.77\ \mu$. Unfortunately, to date the only way to create the necessary free H atoms for this reaction is to dissociate the molecules in an initial H_2-Cl_2 mixture with a priming flash from a flashlamp, and the electric energy required for the priming flash far exceeds the energy output from the laser. The system is a true chemical laser reaction, but it cannot yet be operated with purely chemical energy input. Other chemical laser systems have also been made to operate, but only with initial electrical priming or exciting inputs that considerably exceed the laser output. It seems very likely, however, that further research may lead to successful lasers in which the pumping excitation comes entirely from chemical reactions in the laser system, and in which the only required inputs are suitable chemical fuels.[1]

■ A major advance in the science of radio astronomy some years ago was the observation of radio emission at 1420 MHz originating from interstellar clouds of hydrogen gas. This particular radio emission represents spontaneous emission, or what might be called *microwave atomic fluorescence*, on a particular transition in atomic hydrogen, coming from hydrogen atoms in thermal equilibrium at a fairly low temperature. As such, it possesses none of the characteristics of maser amplification, but only the usual characteristics of fluorescent emission.

MASER ACTION IN NATURE

More recently, however, surprising observations have been made of radio emission at ~1670 MHz coming from OH molecules located near certain stars. This

---

[1] The article on chemical lasers, Ref. 1-30, is very readable. Many excellent detailed theoretical discussions and surveys are to be found in Ref. 1-18, although no experimental chemical lasers have yet been reported.

emission actually consists of four known OH transitions located at 1616, 1665, 1667, and 1720 MHz. If the emission on these lines originated spontaneously, the four lines should have strengths in the ratios of $1:5:9:1$, as predicted by well-known transition strengths for the four transitions. In fact, however, the observed intensity ratios are quite different, and they change fairly rapidly with time (a time scale of weeks). The emission profile of each line is not a smooth profile in frequency, but sometimes contains several very sharp spectral components. The linewidths are such that the temperature of the source must be less than $50°K$ to make the doppler broadening as small as observed. At the same time, the intensity of the emission is so strong as to correspond to source temperatures $\gtrsim 10^8°K$, and the emission apparently originates from extremely small point sources or in the form of highly direct beams. The different spectral lines are also often polarized in very definite ways, with polarizations that change with time and are generally different from the expected results for spontaneous emission.

The only reasonable explanation of these results is that the radiation originates from spontaneous emission somewhere in an OH cloud and is then strongly and selectively amplified by maser amplification as it passes through other regions of the OH cloud. Such amplification would account for the anomalous intensity ratios and the greatly increased brightness and high directionality of the emission. Appropriate Zeeman splittings due to intergalactic magnetic fields could also account for the polarization properties. It is also reasonable that the maser-gain properties might change rapidly with time, although changes in the total amount of OH and the associated spontaneous emission would not be expected on the time scales observed. The mechanism of pumping responsible for the apparent population inversion is not yet clear, but a number of suggestions center on selective optical pumping of the OH molecule by intense stellar ultraviolet radiation. The observed emissions all come from OH clouds closely adjacent to very intense stars, where there is no shortage of radiation or of other available energy mechanisms that might excite the OH molecules and cause population inversion.

The gains of certain gas-laser transitions are very high, and many researchers have suggested that laser action must actually have been achieved inadvertently on many occasions in numerous gas-discharge and plasma experiments carried out for completely different purposes. It now appears that maser action must also have been occurring for many eons in nature, and our laboratory experiments are only now catching up with the interstellar facts.[1]

RANGE OF MASER MATERIALS ◼ To provide some idea of the total range of available maser materials and maser transitions, the periodic table on the inside covers of this book shows all, or nearly all, the elements with which maser or laser action has been obtained in one form or another. It is not possible, of course, to indicate all the additional molecular species and compounds, such as CO_2 and GaAs, in which laser action has also been obtained. Maser and laser materials now include 50 of the elements, and it is impossible to say how many of the remaining elements could be made to produce some kind of laser activity if the attempt were to be made (it is very likely that pulsed gas or ion laser action could be obtained in the high-temperature vapors of a great many of the remaining elements,

---

[1] A general survey of these observations and their interpretation is given in Ref. 1-40. One recent calculation of a proposed pumping mechanism, with extensive references to earlier papers, is Ref. 1-43. For an introductory description see Ref. 1-37.

for example). However long laser action may have awaited discovery, it is now known to be a very widespread phenomenon.

1-6 SPECIAL PROPERTIES OF LASER LIGHT

Laser light, the light emitted by an oscillating laser, is simply electromagnetic radiation and is fundamentally no different from that emitted by another source. However, the beam of light emitted by a well-controlled laser does differ in its detailed properties from the light emitted by other luminous sources or hot bodies, particularly with respect to directionality, monochromaticity, and statistical or waveform characteristics. In fact, the differences in these properties between laser light and ordinary thermal light are so large and so remarkable that it would almost be correct to say that laser light differs in basic character from other light.

■ The power output from even a small gas laser is typically in the range $P \geq 1\,\text{mW} \equiv 10^{-3}\,\text{W}$, while pulsed solid-state laser oscillator-amplifier combinations generate peak power outputs as high as $P \sim 1\,\text{GW} \equiv 10^9\,\text{W}$ (although only in exceedingly short pulses). Since one photon of visible light represents $\sim 10^{-19}$ joules of energy, the photon outputs of typical lasers range over

LASER LIGHT INTENSITY VERSUS THERMAL LIGHT INTENSITY

$$\text{Laser photons/sec} \equiv \frac{P}{hf} \sim 10^{16} - 10^{28} \tag{1}$$

However, the thermal photon output within a bandwidth Δf centered at frequency f (or wavelength $\lambda = c/f$) emitted from an area ΔA on a hot body or hot surface may be written as

$$\text{Thermal photons/sec} = \frac{2\pi}{\lambda^2} \frac{1}{e^{hf/kT} - 1} \Delta A \, \Delta f \tag{2}$$

where T is the temperature of the hot body (we are assuming that the emissivity of the hot body has its maximum possible value, unity). This output is distributed over all possible states of polarization. If we consider output only in a certain fixed polarization, as in the output from a typical laser, then the expression in Eq. (2) must be divided by 2.

To gain some feel for the numbers involved here, let us first note that the quantity hf/k in the Boltzmann exponent has the value $hf/k \sim 25,000°\text{K}$ for visible light ($\lambda = 6000\,\text{Å}$), so that

$$\frac{1}{e^{hf/kT} - 1} \approx \frac{1}{e^{25,000/T} - 1} \approx e^{-25,000/T} \tag{3}$$

The factor $(e^{hf/kT} - 1)^{-1}$ (which, as we will see in Chap. 11, is essentially the number of thermal photons in a resonant mode at thermal equilibrium) will be $\ll 1$ for visible light frequencies, unless the temperature of the hot body approaches $T \sim 25,000°\text{K}$.

Now, the output aperture of a typical laser may be a few millimeters, or perhaps a centimeter, in diameter, and the laser output beam will be essentially monochromatic, $\Delta f \to 0$. Let us consider a hot body with a surface area $\Delta A = 1\,\text{cm}^2$ and, to favor the broadband thermal source, a bandwidth Δf corresponding to the width of the visible spectrum, or $\Delta \lambda \sim 1000\,\text{Å}$. Then, for a hot-body temperature of $T = 1000°\text{K}$, with $\Delta \lambda = 1000\,\text{Å}$ and $\Delta A = 1\,\text{cm}^2$, the thermal photon output in the visible range will be

$$\text{Thermal photons/sec} \sim 10^{12} \tag{4}$$

We can conclude that it takes a fairly large and fairly hot body to generate as much visible light as is produced by even a fairly small laser.

DIRECTIONALITY   ■ The thermal source just described will, of course, be radiating as a lambertian source into all possible directions from its surface, while a typical laser radiates all its output into a single, highly collimated and directional beam, as shown in Fig. 1-44a. In fact, in a well-designed laser which oscillates in a *single lowest-order transverse mode*, the laser output beam will consist essentially of an ideal uniform plane wave such that the output has a uniform and constant phase distribution across the entire output aperture.[1] The laser's optical wavefront is then comparable to the microwave wavefront obtained from a large high-quality dish or horn type of microwave antenna.

When a beam with planar wavefronts radiates from an aperture of diameter d or area A, the beam propagates as essentially a parallel beam for a distance[2] of about d^2/λ and then begins to spread linearly with distance because of the unavoidable effects of diffraction. The angular spread $\Delta\theta$ of the far-field beam is related to the aperture diameter d and wavelength λ by $\Delta\theta \approx d/\lambda$; or the far-field solid angle into which the laser radiates is given by $\Delta\Omega \approx (\Delta\theta)^2 \approx A/\lambda^2$. Obviously, lasers can emit such highly directional beams, with such small far-field angles, because the laser oscillation can be made to occur in a lowest-order mode in which the phase is uniform across the entire laser aperture.

A hot surface, by contrast, radiates its thermal energy into an entire 2π steradians, or one hemisphere, of solid angle, as shown in Fig. 1-44b, although, because the radiation falls off as $\cos\theta$, where θ is polar angle from the normal to the surface, the effective solid angle is only π steradians. Thus the number of photons per second that a hot surface would radiate into the same small solid angle as the laser (and into only a single polarization) is

$$\text{Thermal photons/sec} = \frac{\Delta f}{e^{hf/kT} - 1} \tag{5}$$

Even for a bandwidth of 1000 Å and a temperature of 1000°K, this number is only $\sim 10^3$ photons/sec, compared with $\geq 10^{16}$ photons/sec for typical lasers.

In physical terms, someone standing in the beam of a laser in the far field and looking back toward the laser would see it as a brilliant point source of light (as on

FIG. 1-44 Directional characteristics of the output radiation from (a) a single-lowest-transverse-mode laser and (b) a thermal (hot-body) source.

[1] The output distribution will, in fact, have some amplitude variation across the aperture (usually gaussian; see Chap. 8) but will still be close to uniform. Also, the output wavefront will often be spherical rather than planar but can be readily converted to planar by a collimating lens on the laser's output mirror.

[2] This distance is sometimes called the *Rayleigh range* (see Chap. 8).

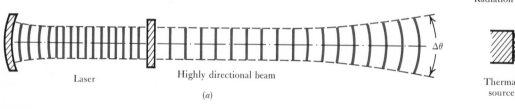

Laser

Highly directional beam

$\Delta\theta$

(a)

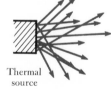

Radiation into all directions

Thermal source

(b)

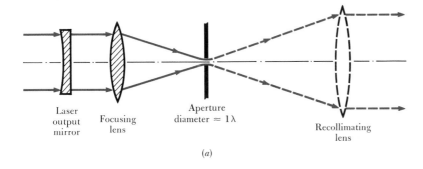

Laser output mirror   Focusing lens   Aperture diameter ≈ 1λ   Recollimating lens

(*a*)

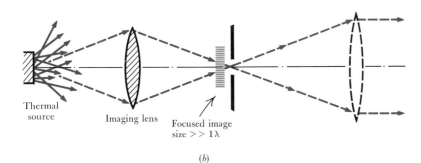

Thermal source   Imaging lens   Focused image size >> 1λ

(*b*)

FIG. 1-45 Focused beams from (*a*) laser and (*b*) thermal sources.

the jacket of this book), with a brightness far exceeding that of any thermal source at any reasonable temperature.

■ These same conclusions can be arrived at by another approach. The beam from a laser can be focused with a lens to a tiny spot, or waist, as in Fig. 1-45*a* (and then allowed to expand again and be recollimated, if desired). If the lens is of good quality and free from serious aberrations, the size of the focused spot will be equal to the diffraction limit or resolution limit of the focusing lens. If an $f/1$ lens (focal length = beam diameter) is employed, the focused spot will be approximately a wavelength in diameter. All the power in the laser output may then be focused into a spot one wavelength in diameter or through a pinhole of the same size.

FOCUSED LIGHT BEAMS

By contrast, if we try to focus the radiation from a thermal source into a small spot, as in Fig. 1-45*b*, the size of the focused spot will be determined by the demagnified image size of the thermal source. This will generally be much larger than a wavelength. There is, in fact, a basic theorem which says that we can never achieve an effective temperature in a focused spot, as in Fig. 1-45*b*, that is any hotter than the original thermal source (there is no way to focus sunlight with a lens or in a solar furnace to achieve a temperature any hotter than the apparent radiation temperature of the sun, which is ~6000°K).[1]

[1] In the case shown in Fig. 1-45*b*, the only way to make the focused or demagnified image of the thermal source very small is to move the thermal source itself back from the lens by a large distance. However, as the thermal source is moved back, the lens collects an ever-smaller fraction of the total thermal radiation emitted by the source.

To produce a "searchlight beam" from a thermal source having the same degree of collimation as a laser we must use a lens plus a pinhole aperture of diameter $d \approx \lambda$, but we can then collect only the radiation from a surface area $\Delta A \approx \lambda^2$, and the very small number of photons per second from an area this small is given by Eq. (5) above.

MONOCHROMATICITY   ■ The output from a laser is very nearly a perfectly monochromatic sine wave, with very nearly zero bandwidth. The minimum value of this bandwidth is limited, in theory, by quantum noise effects, as described in Chap. 11. In practice the bandwidth is usually considerably larger (although still very small), as determined by mechanical vibrations, microphonics, and similar disturbances, which change the length of the laser cavity slightly and thus cause the laser oscillation frequency to fluctuate by small amounts.

The output from a high-quality stable gas laser can be confined within a bandwidth $\Delta f \sim 10$ kHz $\sim 10^4$ Hz, which means $\Delta \lambda \sim 10^{-7}$ Å, or even less in special cases (note that this means a spectral purity $\Delta f/f \sim 2 \times 10^{-11}$). Even a rather poor-quality solid-state laser can have a bandwidth of $\Delta f \sim 10^9$ Hz (which means $\Delta \lambda \sim 10^{-2}$ Å). Obviously, if we were to use bandwidths of this order instead of $\Delta \lambda \sim 1000$ Å, as in the sample calculations above, the number of photons per second from any thermal source would become enormously smaller.

BRIGHTNESS AND EQUIVALENT TEMPERATURE   ■ Instead of making further calculations of thermal photon outputs, let us simply ask: If we were able to collimate a thermal source with lenses, as in Fig. 1-45, and also to filter that thermal source down to a very small bandwidth Δf by means of optical filters, so that the resulting beam had the same far-field angular spread and the same bandwidth as a typical laser, how hot would the thermal source have to be to have the same power output as the laser power P in the same bandwidth and angular beamwidth? The required condition for this case is

$$\text{Laser photons/sec} \equiv \frac{P}{hf} = \text{thermal photons/sec} \equiv \frac{\Delta f}{e^{hf/kT} - 1} \qquad (6)$$

which inverts to

$$\frac{hf}{kT} = \ln\left(1 + \frac{hf\,\Delta f}{P}\right) \approx \frac{hf\,\Delta f}{P} \qquad (7)$$

or, finally, if $P = 10^{-3}$ W and $\Delta f = 10^4$ Hz,

$$T \approx \frac{P}{k\,\Delta f} \approx 10^{16}\,°\text{K} \qquad (8)$$

Obviously, from this viewpoint even a small laser corresponds to an incredibly hot thermal radiation source.

The key to the special nature of laser light is its *brightness*, by which we mean the power output per steradian of solid angle per hertz of bandwidth. Within its very narrow beam angle and in its very narrow spectral range, a laser is brighter than any conceivable thermal source by a really enormous factor.

STATISTICAL AND WAVEFORM CHARACTERISTICS   ■ The output from a laser differs in still another important way from an incredibly bright, collimated, and narrowband thermal source. Suppose that we could generate a filtered thermal source which had all the directional and extremely narrowband properties of a laser.[1] Suppose also that we could somehow measure and record the instantaneous waveform emerging from such a filtered thermal source, cycle by cycle, say, on an oscilloscope screen. Then the output, having come from a gaussian random thermal source through purely linear filtering processes, would still be gaussian random noise—even though it would be extremely narrowband gaussian noise. A sample of the thermal-source waveform might be as in Fig. 1-46a. The waveform would be a quasi-sine wave at a carrier frequency equal to the laser frequency, with slowly but widely varying amplitude and phase. The amplitude and phase would vary randomly, with a maximum rate of variation equal to the (very small) bandwidth Δf of the filtered source.

By contrast, the output from a real laser oscillator would be as in Fig. 1-46b; it would differ from the thermal source in having a highly stabilized amplitude, just like the output from any other type of sinusoidal electronic oscillator at any frequency. The spectral bandwidth of the laser results almost entirely from random *phase* or *frequency modulation*, caused by various sources as mentioned above.

A specified bandwidth and power spectral density for a signal can be obtained from many different kinds of waveforms, representing many different combinations and mixtures of amplitude and/or frequency modulation of the signal. Thus, even if a laser and a thermal source have the same bandwidth and the same power spectrum the output of the laser will differ from that of the thermal source in its detailed waveform and

[1] Instead of beginning with a broadband thermal source and filtering out by absorption all the unwanted wavelengths, a much more efficient procedure would be to control the emissivity versus wavelength of the hot body so that the emissivity was maximum ($\epsilon \to 1$) in the very narrow wavelength range desired and negligible ($\epsilon \to 0$) at all other wavelengths. This is, of course, to some extent what occurs in gas discharges, such as the He discharge shown in Fig. 1-3, which emit only at discrete wavelengths. The discharge is quite hot, but it is essentially transparent and hence has zero emissivity at most wavelengths, except for the few strong spectral lines where the He atoms absorb (and hence also emit) radiation strongly.

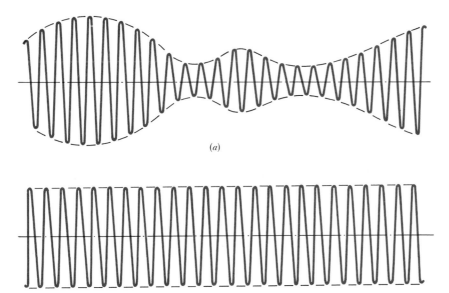

(a)

(b)

FIG. 1-46 The waveforms characteristic of (a) narrowband gaussian noise from a filtered thermal source and (b) the amplitude-stabilized output from an electronic oscillator such as a laser.

statistical properties. This difference has been verified in recent years by many detailed and subtle experiments, and the stabilized-amplitude aspect of laser radiation is of importance in many communications and interferometric applications.

COHERENCE   ■ The directionality properties of laser beams are often described loosely as *spatial coherence,* and the narrowband properties as *temporal* or *spectral coherence.* The special waveform properties are sometimes included simply as part of coherence. These usages are, however, very loose and imprecise. There is an area of optics (or electromagnetic theory) known as coherence theory, in which certain types of coherence functions are rigorously defined. The purist will insist that the term "coherence" be limited strictly to applications in this field, others may continue to refer to lasers as "coherent light sources," but they should at least recognize that without a more precise formulation the meaning is only very loosely defined.

CHARACTERISTICS OF REAL   ■ Not all real lasers have ideal characteristics. Many real lasers may oscillate, not in
LASERS   one mode, but perhaps in 5 or 10 or 100 transverse modes at once. The far-field beam spreading and the focused-spot sizes of such lasers will then be correspondingly larger than for a well-controlled single-transverse-mode laser.

Also, many real lasers oscillate in multiple axial modes, so that they may emit perhaps 5 or 10 or even 100 closely spaced frequencies at once. Such lasers are obviously less monochromatic than an ideal single-frequency laser. However, their output is still confined to a very narrow spectral range, not much wider than about a linewidth of the atomic transition. The laser output may also exhibit such imperfections as spiking or envelope relaxation oscillations which make the output waveform less than perfectly sinusoidal.

Some of these imperfections can be minimized or eliminated with sufficient care in design and construction. This may be difficult, if not impossible, in certain types of lasers (semiconductor lasers, for example, generally have very bad spatial and spectral properties), but the existence of less-than-perfect lasers should not obscure the fact that some lasers can be built with very nearly perfect spatial, spectral, and temporal properties. Moreover, even a very bad laser will still be enormously brighter than almost any thermal light source.

PROBLEMS

1-1. On a large sheet of paper lay out a logarithmic frequency–wavelength scale extending from the audio range ($f = 10$ Hz, say) to the far ultraviolet ($\lambda = 1000$ Å, say). On parallel scales indicate the frequency in powers of 10 (10^n Hz) over the entire scale, as well as on separate scales of 1 to 100 kHz, 1 to 10,000 MHz, and 1 to 1,000 GHz. Show the wavelength on scales of 1 to 100 m, 1 to 100 cm, 0.1 to 10 mm, 0.1 to 1000 μ, and 1000 to 10,000 Å. Above this scale indicate the following "landmarks":

(a) Audio-frequency range (human ear)

(b) Broadcast am and fm bands

(c) Television channels 2 to 11

(d) Microwave radar S and X bands (2 to 4 GHz and 8 to 12 GHz, respectively)

(e) The deep-space satellite telemetry band (2200 MHz)

(f) The visible-light range (human eye)

(g) Wavelengths of the NH_3 maser, the ruby laser, the He-Ne laser (6328 Å, 1.15 μ, 3.39 μ), Nd-YAG and Nd-glass lasers (1.06 μ), argon-ion lasers (4880 and 5140 Å), CO_2 and H_2O lasers (119 μ), HCN lasers (337 μ), and pulsed Ne^{3+} ion UV lasers (2358 Å)

1-2. In optical *absorption* spectroscopy a wide range of optical frequencies is sent through a material and the wavelengths absorbed by the material are noted; in fluorescent *emission* spectroscopy the material is excited in some fashion (such as ultraviolet light or electric current) and the wavelengths of fluorescent emission that appear are noted. Experiments by these two methods on the same material generally yield quite different sets of wavelengths (although there are some matching pairs). Why are the two sets of characteristic wavelengths different?

1-3. Evaluate the number of atoms per second that must make stimulated downward transitions if a maser device is to have a cw power output of 1 W at $f = 3000$ MHz, $\lambda = 10\ \mu$, and $\lambda = 5000$ Å.

1-4. Pink ruby of the type commonly used in ruby lasers contains approximately 2×10^{19} chromium Cr^{3+} ions/cm^3. Under optimum pumping and Q-switching conditions, almost all these ions can be lifted into the upper laser level just before the burst of Q-switched laser action occurs. What is the maximum possible energy output in a single Q-switched laser burst from a ruby rod 7.5 cm long and 1 cm in diameter ($\sim$3 by $\frac{3}{8}$ in.)? What is the peak power output if this burst lasts for approximately 100 nsec?

1-5. When two quantum energy levels, E_1 and E_2, of an atom are separated by an energy gap $\Delta E \equiv E_2 - E_1$, and a large number of such atoms are in thermal equilibrium at temperature T, then the relative numbers of atoms N_1 and N_2 in the two levels are given by the Boltzmann ratio $N_2/N_1 = e^{-\Delta E/kT}$. Evaluate this ratio for the following cases:

(a) The energy gap $\Delta E = hf$ corresponds to an electron-paramagnetic-resonance transition in the microwave range, say, $f = 3000$ MHz, and the temperature is $T = 300°$K (about room temperature). What is the fractional population difference $(N_2 - N_1)/N_1$?

(b) Consider the same situation, except that $f = 10,000$ MHz and the temperature is $T = 4.2°$K (liquid-helium temperature). What is $(N_2 - N_1)/N_1$?

(c) Let $T = 300°$K and ΔE correspond to an optical-frequency transition, say, $\lambda = 6000$ Å. What is the Boltzmann ratio N_2/N_1?

(d) What temperature T would be required to make N_2 equal to 10 percent of N_1 in part (c)?

1-6. Using the Boltzmann principle, find analytic expressions for the energy-level populations N_1, N_2, and N_3 in Fig. 1-16 as a function of the parameter E_0/kT.

1-7. The total energy content of the atomic system of Fig. 1-16 and Prob. 1-6, as a function of temperature, is given by

$$E(T) = N_1(T)E_1 + N_2(T)E_2 + N_3(T)E_3$$

The specific heat of the atomic system is then $C(T) = dE/dT$. Write a short computer program to evaluate $E(T)$ and $C(T)$ and plot these quantities against temperature T. *Note:* In earlier days, when spectroscopic methods at radio and optical frequencies were not so well developed as they are now, experimental measurements of C versus T were used to deduce the energy-level structure of materials. Can you explain from your results in this problem how this method might work?

REFERENCES

BOOKS

1-1. G. Birnbaum, *Optical Masers,* Academic Press, New York, 1964.

1-2. R. Brown, *Lasers: Tools of Modern Technology,* Doubleday Science Series, New York, 1968 (paperback).

1-3. A. L. Bloom, *Gas Lasers,* Wiley, New York, 1968.

1-4. C. C. Eaglesfield, *Laser Light,* Macmillan, New York, 1967.

1-5. D. Fishlock (ed.), *A Guide to the Laser,* American Elsevier, New York, 1967.

1-6. M. Garbuny, *Optical Physics,* Academic Press, New York, 1965.

1-7. G. C. B. Garrett, *Gas Lasers,* McGraw-Hill, New York, 1967.

1-8. P. Grivet and N. Bloembergen (eds.), *Quantum Electronics III,* Columbia University Press, New York, 1964 (2 vols.).

1-9. O. S. Heavens, *Optical Masers,* Methuen Monographs, London, 1964.

1-10. B. A. Lengyel, *Introduction to Laser Physics,* Wiley, New York, 1966.

1-11. A. K. Levine (ed.), *Lasers: A Series of Advances,* vol. 1, Marcel Dekker, New York, 1966.

1-12. A. E. Siegman, *Microwave Solid-state Masers,* McGraw-Hill, New York, 1964.

1-13. W. V. Smith and P. P. Sorokin, *The Laser,* McGraw-Hill, New York, 1966.

1-14. P. R. Thornton, *The Physics of Electroluminescent Devices,* Barnes and Noble, New York, 1967.

1-15. A. Vuylsteke, *Elements of Laser Theory,* Van Nostrand, Princeton, N.J., 1960.

1-16. D. H. Whiffen, *Spectroscopy,* Wiley, New York, 1966 (paperback).

1-17. A. Yariv, *Quantum Electronics,* Wiley, New York, 1967.

JOURNAL SPECIAL ISSUES

1-18. John N. Howard, K. E. Shuler, and W. R. Bennett, Jr. (eds.), *Applied Optics Supplement on Chemical Lasers,* Optical Society of America, Inc., Washington, D.C., 1965.

1-19. *Proc. IEEE,* Special Issue on Quantum Electronics, vol. 51 (January, 1963).

1-20. *Proc. IEEE/Appl. Optics,* Special Joint Issue on Optical Electronics, vols. 54/55 (October, 1966). Useful review papers in this issue include A. L. Bloom, "Gas lasers"; Z. J. Kiss and R. J. Pressley, "Crystalline solid lasers"; E. Snitzer, "Glass lasers"; M. I. Nathan, "Semiconductor lasers."

ARTICLES FROM SCIENTIFIC AMERICAN

1-21. H. Lyons, "Atomic clocks," February, 1957, p. 51.

1-22. J. P. Gordon, "The maser," December, 1958, p. 42.

1-23. A. L. Bloom, "Optical pumping," October, 1960, p. 72.

1-24. A. L. Schawlow, "Optical masers," June, 1961, p. 52.

1-25. A. L. Schawlow, "Advances in optical masers," July, 1963, p. 34.

1-26. J. A. Giordmaine, "The interaction of light with light," April, 1964, p. 38.

1-27. O. R. Frisch, "Molecular beams," May, 1965, p. 58.

1-28. E. N. Leith and J. Upatnieks, "Photography by laser," June, 1965, p. 24.

1-29. S. E. Miller, "Communication by laser," January, 1966, p. 19.

1-30. G. C. Pimentel, "Chemical lasers," April, 1966, p. 32.

1-31. F. A. Morehead, Jr., "Light-emitting semiconductors," May, 1967, p. 108.

1-32. A. Lempicki and H. Samelson, "Liquid lasers," June, 1967, p. 80.

1-33. S. R. Hartmann, "Photon echoes," April, 1968, p. 32.

1-34. C. K. N. Patel, "High-power carbon dioxide lasers," August, 1968, p. 22.

1-35. A. L. Schawlow, "Laser light," Special Issue on Light, September, 1968, p. 120.

1-36. D. R. Herriott, "Applications of laser light," Special Issue on Light, September, 1968, p. 140.

1-37. A. H. Barrett, "Radio signals from hydroxyl radicals," December, 1968, p. 36.

1-38. P. Sorokin, "Organic (liquid dye) lasers," February, 1969, p. 30.

JOURNAL ARTICLES

1-39. G. Burns and M. I. Nathan, "*P-N* junction lasers," *Proc. IEEE,* 52:770 (July, 1964).

1-40. A. H. Cook, "A maser in the sky," *New Scientist,* April, 1967, p. 26.

1-41. B. S. Goldstein and G. F. Dalrymple, "Gallium arsenide injection laser radar," *Proc. IEEE,* 55:181 (February, 1967).

1-42. M. L. Hensel and E. B. Treacy, "Twenty-one centimeter traveling-wave maser for the Harvard radio telescope," *Rev. Scientif. Instruments,* 35:970 (August, 1964).

1-43. C. V. Heer and R. A. Settles, "Theory for the anomalous polarization of cosmic OH-18-cm radiation and for hyperfine lasers," *J. Molecular Spectroscopy,* 23:448 (August, 1967).

1-44. H. F. Evey, "Electroluminescence and semiconductor lasers," *IEEE J. Quantum Electron.,* **QE-2**:713 (November, 1966).

1-45. C. G. Lehr, "The generation of coherent light," *IEEE Student Quart.,* September, 1962, p. 2.

1-46. B. A. Lengyel, "History of masers and lasers," *Am. J. Phys.,* 34:903 (October, 1966).

1-47. Thomas Meloy, "The laser's bright magic," *National Geographic,* 130:858 (December, 1966).

1-48. M. I. Nathan, G. Burns, and C. M. Johnson, "Injection lasers: state of the art," *Electronics,* Dec. 6, 1963, p. 61.

1-49. M. I. Nathan, G. Burns, and C. M. Johnson, "Injection laser systems for communications and tracking," *Electronics,* Dec. 13, 1963, p. 34.

1-50. A. O. McCoubrey, "A survey of atomic frequency standards," *Proc. IEEE,* 54:116 (February, 1966).

1-51. R. A. Paananen, "Progress in ionized-argon lasers," *IEEE Spectrum,* June, 1966, p. 88.

1-52. R. Rediker, "Infrared and visible light emission from forward-biased *p-n* junctions," *1963 IEEE Intern. Conv. Rec.;* also published in *solid/state/design,* August, 1963, p. 19.

1-53. J. D. Rigden and G. Moeller, "Recent developments in CO_2 lasers," *IEEE J. Quantum Electron.,* **QE-2**:365 (September, 1966).

1-54. E. B. Tucker, "Interaction of phonons with iron-group ions," *Proc. IEEE,* Special Issue on Ultrasonics, 53:1547 (October, 1965).

CHAPTER TWO

ELECTRIC-DIPOLE TRANSITIONS: THE CLASSICAL ELECTRON-OSCILLATOR MODEL

In this chapter we will develop a simple physical model, the *classical electron-oscillator model*, which is a surprisingly good representation of the internal dynamics of many atomic transitions. With this model we will be able to analyze and understand many of the important effects of an applied signal on an atom, and also the effects of the atom back on the applied-signal circuit. Since useful maser amplification requires not only that a signal act on the maser atoms, but also that the atoms react back on the signal, it is important to understand both aspects of this interaction.

2.1 THE CLASSICAL ELECTRON-OSCILLATOR MODEL

We saw in Chap. 1 that atoms exhibit sharp internal resonances at certain discrete, characteristic transition frequencies. In most cases these atomic resonances are not accompanied by any related resonances at higher harmonics. From this we infer that the atomic motion associated with each resonance is purely sinusoidal, without any higher harmonic components, so that each observed resonance represents some sort of internal *simple harmonic motion* of the atom. In many cases, moreover, these internal resonances can be excited experimentally only by an applied ac *electric* field at or near the resonant frequency. This suggests that the resonance consists of some sort of forced oscillatory motion of the electric charges inside the atom.

From atomic physics we may have an image of the atom as a small but massive positively charged nucleus, surrounded by one or more lightweight negatively charged orbiting electrons. These electrons may be viewed as discrete point charges traveling in orbits about the nucleus, as in Fig. 2-1*a*, or they may be viewed in more fuzzy fashion as simply a "cotton-candy" cloud of diffuse negative electronic charge surrounding the nucleus, as in Fig. 2-1*b*. This latter picture is, in fact, quite compatible with the quantum-mechanical view of an atom.

In a classical description, an external electric field applied to the quantum-mechanical model of an atom will cause the positive nucleus to move slightly in one direction and the negative electron cloud to move slightly in the opposite direction (perhaps also with some distortion of the electron orbits or of the shape of the charge cloud). It also seems clear that if the nucleus and the charge cloud are given an initial relative displacement from their equilibrium positions and are then released, they will execute some sort of oscillatory motion about their equilibrium positions. In other words, this model exhibits precisely *an oscillatory or resonant behavior* and *a response to an applied electric field.*

With these points in mind, we shall use the model of Fig. 2-1*b* as a simple classical model for describing those atomic resonances that respond strongly to an applied electric field. Such atomic resonances, or transitions, are called *electric-dipole transitions.* In this chapter we will compute the response of our model to an applied ac electric field near resonance. We will then connect the model with a particular electric-dipole transition in a real atom by equating the oscillation frequency and other characteristics of the model (such as the resonance linewidth or Q) to the observed oscillation frequency and Q of the real atom.

Our hope is, of course, that the response of the simple model will show many of the same important features as the response of a real atom on any one of its resonance transitions. This is, in fact, a realistic expectation. The classical electron-oscillator

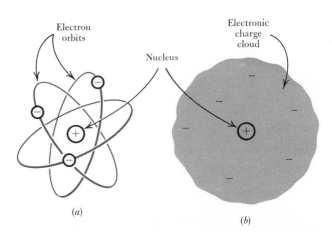

FIG. 2-1 Two different semiclassical models for an atom. The atom is described as a small massive nucleus surrounded by either (*a*) point electrons traveling in orbits or (*b*) a fuzzy, roughly spherical cloud of electronic charge.

(*a*)

(*b*)

model that we are developing turns out to be a very good model for the response of a real atom on any single one of its electric-dipole transitions. A real atom, of course, has numerous electric-dipole transitions, at different transition frequencies, while our model has only one resonance frequency. The model is limited, therefore, to describing or modeling the behavior of only one selected transition at a time. It is not sufficiently complicated to model all the transitions of an atom at once.[1]

■ We take as our analytical model, therefore, a single electron, assumed to be bound to its equilibrium position by a linear restoring force which gives it an oscillation frequency ω_a for small displacements $x(t)$ from equilibrium. We may even visualize this electron as a point electron suspended by springs, as in Fig. 2-2. The equation of motion for this electron,[2] given an applied electric field $e_x(t)$, is then

EQUATION OF MOTION: DAMPING

$$\ddot{x}(t) + \omega_a{}^2 x(t) = -\frac{e}{m} e_x(t) \tag{1}$$

where $x(t)$ is the displacement of the electron from its equilibrium position and the $\omega_a{}^2$ term represents the assumed linear restoring spring force on the electron.

However, we must also expect our model to have some sort of *damping*, or *loss*, in it, although this damping may be quite small. Without some damping, the Q of the model would be infinite and its response to an applied signal exactly at resonance would also be infinite, whereas we know from experience that real atomic transitions have finite linewidths and a finite response at resonance. Therefore we add to the equation of motion a phenomenological[3] damping term $\gamma \dot{x}(t)$, obtaining the result

$$\ddot{x}(t) + \gamma \dot{x}(t) + \omega_a{}^2 x(t) = -\frac{e}{m} e_x(t) \tag{2}$$

This equation is, of course, just the familiar equation for a simple harmonic oscillator or *RLC* electric circuit with damping. The natural solutions to the equation in the absence of any driving term $e_x(t)$ will have the damped sinusoidal form

$$x(t) = \exp[-\gamma t/2 \pm j\sqrt{1 - (\gamma/2)^2}\,\omega_a t] \approx \exp(-\gamma t/2 \pm j\omega_a t) \tag{3}$$

where the damping coefficient γ is a parameter to be determined by experiment, i.e., by comparison with the observed linewidth or decay rate of a real atomic transition.

It is important to note that the amplitude $x(t)$ of the natural solution decreases with time as $e^{-\gamma t/2}$, so that the energy $W(t) \propto x^2(t)$ attenuates in the form

$$W(t) = W_0 e^{-\gamma t} = W_0 e^{-t/\tau} \tag{4}$$

The time constant τ, defined by

$$\tau \equiv \gamma^{-1} \tag{5}$$

is thus the energy-decay time for the model, and γ is the energy-decay rate.

■ Our discussion of damping in the classical electron oscillator, and also in real atomic

CLASSICAL RADIATIVE DAMPING

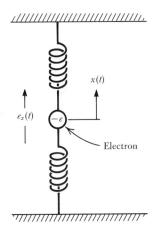

FIG. 2-2 A purely mechanical model for an atom or a classical electron oscillator. The springs give the electron an oscillation frequency ω_a for displacements $x(t)$ from its equilibrium position.

---

[1] The classical electron-oscillator model (often called the *Lorentz* model of an atom) has a long and productive history. An original reference (but one not too difficult to read) is reprinted as Ref. 2-3; see especially chap. III, secs. 77–81. For additional background material see Refs. 2-2, 2-8, and 2-11.

[2] Since the nucleus is so much heavier than the electron, we assume that it is only the electron that moves, and we assume only a single electron (atomic number $Z = 1$) for simplicity.

[3] "Phenomenological" is a multisyllable jargon word meaning that we add some more or less reasonable mathematical term to the equation of motion for a system in order to make the mathematical predictions agree more closely with the actual phenomena observed in the real system.

transitions, must now proceed with some caution. There are a great many different damping processes and damping rates, with different characteristics, that may be significant in real atoms. Some care will be needed to keep these different damping processes clear as we develop them in this and later chapters. At this point we will discuss one damping mechanism that is fundamental to any classical electron oscillator, *classical radiative damping*. One reason for the importance of this damping process is that the damping it predicts for the classical oscillator is closely analogous to a similar quantum damping process that occurs in real atoms. A strongly allowed electric-dipole transition in a real atom will have a radiative damping rate of approximately the same value as the classical radiative damping rate in a classical electron oscillator at the same frequency. There are many additional damping processes which may or may not be present in a real atomic resonance, but radiative damping is always present.

Classical electromagnetic theory asserts that any accelerating or oscillating electric charge will act as a miniature antenna and will continuously radiate away electromagnetic energy to its surroundings. This radiation provides an unavoidable damping mechanism for the oscillating charge in our model, since it continuously extracts energy from the stored kinetic and potential energy in the electron's motion. Deriving the correct form for this classical radiative-damping term is beyond the scope of this text,[1] and we will simply assert that the effect of radiative damping is taken into account by adding to the electron's equation of motion a force term of magnitude $(e^2/6\pi\epsilon_0 c^3)\dddot{x}$, so that the equation of motion for the classical oscillator becomes

$$\ddot{x}(t) - \frac{e^2}{6\pi\epsilon_0 mc^3}\dddot{x}(t) + \omega_a{}^2 x(t) = -\frac{e}{m}e_x(t) \tag{6}$$

In anticipation of future results, let us define a radiative damping rate γ_{rad} as

$$\gamma_{\mathrm{rad}} \equiv \frac{e^2\omega_a{}^2}{6\pi\epsilon_0 mc^3} \tag{7}$$

so that the equation of motion becomes

$$\ddot{x}(t) - \frac{\gamma_{\mathrm{rad}}}{\omega_a{}^2}\dddot{x}(t) + \omega_a{}^2 x(t) = -\frac{e}{m}e_x(t) \tag{8}$$

Now, in looking for the natural frequencies of this system, if we drop the forcing term on the right-hand side and assume solutions of the form e^{st}, the resulting secular equation is the cubic

$$s^2 - \frac{\gamma_{\mathrm{rad}}}{\omega_a{}^2}s^3 + \omega_a{}^2 = 0 \tag{9}$$

For all frequency ranges of interest to us (ultraviolet and all longer wavelengths) it is always true that the radiative-damping term is small, $\gamma_{\mathrm{rad}} \ll \omega_a$. This equation will then have two of its roots close to the resonance frequencies; that is, $s \approx \pm j\omega_a$. Using this as a starting point, we can find that the system in fact has two roots, or two natural resonance frequencies, given to a very good approximation by

$$s_1, s_2 \approx -\gamma_{\mathrm{rad}}/2 \pm j\omega_a \tag{10}$$

---

[1] Good discussions of the radiative-damping term are given in Ref. 2-5, chap. 21, and Ref. 2-11, chap. 12; Ref. 2-7 gives a very advanced-level discussion, and another approach is taken in Ref. 2-4.

The damping rate given by these two roots is just γ_{rad}, making it clear why we chose to define this particular quantity above.

The third root of the cubic secular equation can now be found. It is given to an equally good approximation by

$$s_3 \approx + \frac{\omega_a{}^2}{\gamma_{rad}} \tag{11}$$

This root will give a term that expands or diverges, and at a very rapid rate. It is obviously a nonphysical term, since it would lead among other things to an energy radiation approaching infinity in a time very much shorter than one oscillation cycle. Since the transient term corresponding to this root is obviously not physical, we will not consider this root further.[1]

If only the two roots s_1 and s_2 are physically significant, then the analysis will be simplified if we extract and discard the s_3 root. In fact, the significant roots s_1 and s_2 are essentially the same if the secular equation is reduced to

$$s^2 + \gamma_{rad}s + \omega_a{}^2 = 0 \tag{12}$$

This is the same as saying that the equation of motion may be reduced to the simpler resonant form

$$\ddot{x}(t) + \gamma_{rad}\dot{x}(t) + \omega_a{}^2 x(t) = -\frac{e}{m} e_x(t) \tag{13}$$

The radiative-damping term is thus reduced to the usual simple form for a damped resonant system.[2]

The radiative damping rate γ_{rad} and damping time τ_{rad} for the classical oscillator are then given by

$$\gamma_{rad} \equiv \frac{1}{\tau_{rad}} = \frac{e^2 \omega_a{}^2}{6\pi\epsilon_0 mc^3} \tag{14}$$

This is an important result, which we will use in later chapters. Substituting numbers

---

[1] Readers trained in engineering may be suspicious of this casual dismissal of the third root as "nonphysical." In usual engineering analyses, if the equations of a linear system yield a set of roots s_n, then the transient terms associated with each of those roots will usually be excited by almost any set of initial condition; in fact, it usually takes some very special set of initial conditions to avoid exciting any given transient term. In the present case, the appearance of the growing s_3 root, without the corresponding term ever appearing in reality, seems to argue that something must be wrong with the basic analysis, perhaps in the form of the $\dddot{x}$ term. However, the conclusion reached in much more sophisticated analyses of the classical electron oscillator still seems to be that the $\dddot{x}$ radiative-damping term is correct, but that there is simply no combination of initial conditions under which the associated transient term can be excited. See, for example, Ref. 2-6.

[2] These same results can be obtained much more quickly by arguing at the outset that the $\dddot{x}$ radiative-damping term is going to be small, so that the natural motion will still be very nearly of the form $x(t) \sim e^{\pm j\omega_a t}$. If so, then to a first approximation the time-differentiation operation is $d/dt \approx \pm j\omega_a$. Replacing two out of the three time differentiations in the $\dddot{x}$ term by $-\omega_a{}^2$ then yields

$$-\frac{e^2}{6\pi\epsilon_0 mc^3}\dddot{x}(t) \approx \frac{e^2 \omega_a{}^2}{6\pi\epsilon_0 mc^3}\dot{x}(t) = \gamma_{rad}\dot{x}(t)$$

which is the same result as above. The weakness in this approach is, of course, that it is not at all clear, without going through the more exact analysis above, why we should replace just these two differentiation operations, and not any others in the overall equation, by $-j\omega_a$.

into this expression will show that if ω_a is an optical frequency, the classical radiative decay time is $\tau_{\text{rad}} \sim 10^{-8}$ to 10^{-9} sec. Since this is still very long compared to the period of an optical frequency ($\sim 10^{-14}$ sec), the radiative damping rate of the classical oscillator can properly be described as small. Because of the $\omega_a{}^2$ dependence of γ_{rad}, the radiative-damping effects become even smaller at lower frequencies.

2-2 RESPONSE OF THE CLASSICAL OSCILLATOR MODEL TO AN APPLIED SIGNAL

In this section we will examine the induced response of the classical electron-oscillator model to an applied signal. The reaction back on the applied-signal circuit resulting from this oscillator response will be the subject of a later section. Since maser problems generally involve sinusoidal or near-sinusoidal signals applied to an essentially linear system at or near a resonance, we will calculate the forced response of the classical oscillator model by considering its response to sinusoidal applied signals in particular.

FORCED SINUSOIDAL RESPONSE   ■ Our first step is to find the forced or steady-state response when a sinusoidal field $e_x(t)$ is applied to our classical model. The basic equation of motion is

$$\ddot{x}(t) + \gamma \dot{x}(t) + \omega_a{}^2 x(t) = -\frac{e}{m} e_x(t) \tag{1}$$

where γ is the total damping rate, including radiative damping and any other damping mechanisms that are present. If $e_x(t)$ is sinusoidal, then the steady-state $x(t)$ will also be sinusoidal, since the equation is linear. Hence we write both quantities in the form

$$\begin{aligned} e_x(t) &= \text{Re}\,(\tilde{E}_x e^{j\omega t}) = \tfrac{1}{2}[\tilde{E}_x(\omega)e^{j\omega t} + \tilde{E}_x^*(\omega)e^{-j\omega t}] \\ x(t) &= \text{Re}\,[\tilde{X}(\omega)e^{j\omega t}] = \tfrac{1}{2}[\tilde{X}(\omega)e^{j\omega t} + \tilde{X}^*(\omega)e^{-j\omega t}] \end{aligned} \tag{2}$$

The complex quantities $\tilde{E}_x(\omega)$ and $\tilde{X}(\omega)$ are sometimes called *phasors*, since their phase and magnitude give the phase and magnitude of the corresponding real quantities. For example, if we write $\tilde{X}(\omega)$ in terms of its magnitude and phase angle as

$$\tilde{X}(\omega) \equiv |\tilde{X}|e^{j\theta_x} \tag{3}$$

then we have for the real time function

$$x(t) = |\tilde{X}| \cos\,(\omega t + \theta_x) \tag{4}$$

We write the phasors as functions of frequency ω because our answers will depend strongly on the frequency of the applied signal.

As long as only linear operations are involved, we can substitute the Re form of Eqs. (2) for $e_x(t)$ and $x(t)$ on both sides of the equation of motion (1), replace the d/dt operation by $j\omega$, and then drop both the Re operation and the $e^{j\omega t}$ factors for simplicity, leaving these quantities as implicit. The equation of motion thus becomes

$$(-\omega^2 + j\gamma\omega + \omega_a{}^2)\tilde{X}(\omega) = -\frac{e}{m}\tilde{E}_x(\omega) \tag{5}$$

The solution for the sinusoidal forced motion $\tilde{X}(\omega)$, in terms of the forcing field $\tilde{E}_x(\omega)$, is then

$$\tilde{X}(\omega) = j\frac{e}{m}\frac{1}{\gamma\omega + j(\omega^2 - \omega_a{}^2)}\tilde{E}_x(\omega) \tag{6}$$

The collection of factors in front of $\tilde{E}_x(\omega)$ gives the phase and amplitude relationship—the *electromechanical admittance*—between $\tilde{E}_x(\omega)$ and $\tilde{X}(\omega)$.

The solution in the form (6) predicts the response of our model to an applied signal at any frequency ω, whether close to or far from resonance. We are chiefly interested, however, in applied signals exactly at or reasonably near to the resonance frequency, i.e., signals for which $\omega \approx \omega_a$. For these signals we may make the simplifying approximation

$$\omega^2 - \omega_a{}^2 = (\omega + \omega_a)(\omega - \omega_a) \approx 2\omega(\omega - \omega_a) \tag{7}$$

With this approximation the steady-state response (6) takes the form

$$\tilde{X}(\omega) \approx j\frac{e}{m\gamma\omega}\frac{1}{1 + 2j(\omega - \omega_a)/\gamma}\tilde{E}_x(\omega) \tag{8}$$

We will use this approximate, but still very accurate, form for the solution at frequencies near resonance in all our future discussions. Remember, however, that to find the solution for frequencies far from resonance, the more exact form (6) must be used for the frequency dependence.

■ When the frequency response of the forced sinusoidal motion in a system has the form

THE LORENTZIAN LINESHAPE

$$\frac{1}{1 + 2j(\omega - \omega_a)/\gamma} = \frac{1}{1 + j\delta} \tag{9}$$

where δ is the normalized frequency detuning, then the amplitude squared or power response has the form

$$\frac{1}{1 + [2(\omega - \omega_a)/\gamma]^2} = \frac{1}{1 + \delta^2} \tag{10}$$

This form for the power response is commonly called in atomic resonance physics the *Lorentz* or *lorentzian lineshape*, and the complex-amplitude-response form $1/(1 + j\delta)$ is called the *complex lorentzian lineshape*. This form of resonance-frequency response will appear repeatedly in all our later discussions.

The magnitude of the complex amplitude response is down by 0.707 from its peak value, or the power response is down to half the peak value ("3-dB-down points"), when the signal frequency ω is detuned from resonance on either side by an amount $\delta = 1$ or $\omega - \omega_a = \pm\gamma/2$. Therefore the full linewidth of the atomic resonance between half-power or 3-dB points, which we will denote by $\Delta\omega_a$ in circular or radian frequency units, is just equal to the damping coefficient γ; that is, the full resonance linewidth is

$$\Delta\omega_a = \gamma \tag{11}$$

Note that in the literature the term *linewidth* and symbols such as $\Delta\omega$, Δf, and $\Delta\nu$ are often used to indicate the half-width of a line, from line center to the half-power point. However, we will use *linewidth* consistently to mean the *full bandwidth* between half-power points.

It is useful to note by way of comparison that the response (e.g., the admittance or impedance) of a tuned electric circuit with quality factor Q has the general form

$$\frac{1}{1 + jQ(\omega/\omega_0 - \omega_0/\omega)} \tag{12}$$

With the same approximation (7) for signals not too far from resonance, that is, $|\omega - \omega_0| \ll \omega_0$, this response can be well approximated by

$$\frac{1}{1 + jQ(\omega/\omega_0 - \omega_0/\omega)} \approx \frac{1}{1 + 2jQ(\omega - \omega_0)/\omega_0} \tag{13}$$

Thus a resonant electric circuit also has an essentially lorentzian response, with a full radian-frequency bandwidth $\Delta\omega$ which corresponds to an atomic-resonance bandwidth through

$$\Delta\omega = \frac{\omega_0}{Q} \qquad \leftrightarrow \qquad \Delta\omega_a = \gamma$$

It is important to understand that the near-resonance approximation we have used requires only the relatively mild restriction that $|\omega - \omega_0| \ll \omega_0$. By contrast, to be well within the linewidth or resonant region of a resonant response, the much stiffer restriction $|\omega - \omega_0| \ll \Delta\omega = \omega_0/Q$ must be satisfied. In general, therefore, we can consider frequencies that are well outside the linewidth of a high-Q resonance but are still well within the range of validity of the near-resonance approximation used above.

INDUCED POLARIZATION   ■ In the remainder of this section we will often refer to our classical electron oscillator as a model atom, or simply an atom. The concepts we will discuss all apply in exactly the same way, in fact, to induced transitions or internal motions in real atoms as they do to the motions of the classical-oscillator-model atom. Thus the induced response $x(t)$ or $\tilde{X}(\omega)$ given above may be viewed as the internal response of a single model atom to an applied E field. In practical maser problems, however, we are not concerned with the response of a single atom, but with the overall response from a collection containing a very large number of similar atoms per unit volume, and with the electrical aspects of the response associated with the induced motion in the atoms. This electrical response, for either the classical oscillator model or a real atom, is in the form of an induced macroscopic electrical *polarization,* as we will now see.

When the negatively charged electron in our model (or, if you like, the center of gravity of the electronic charge cloud) is displaced by an amount $x(t)$ from the positively charged nucleus, our model atom becomes a small electric dipole. The dipole moment $\mu_{ex}(t)$ of this dipole in the x direction is the electronic charge (which is $-e$ for an electron) times the displacement $x(t)$ of that charge, or

$$\mu_{ex}(t) = -ex(t) \tag{14}$$

This is an *induced* electric-dipole moment in the model atom, since it is caused by the applied electric field.

In electromagnetic theory the electric field $\mathbf{e}(t)$ and the electric displacement $\mathbf{d}(t)$ at any point in space are related by

$$\mathbf{d} = \epsilon_0 \mathbf{e} + \mathbf{p} \tag{15}$$

where $\mathbf{p}(t)$ is the electric polarization at that point. In physical terms, the electric polarization $\mathbf{p}$ is the electric-dipole moment per unit volume; that is, $\mathbf{p}$ is the net electric-dipole moment in any little unit volume surrounding the point of observation. For example, suppose one of these unit volumes contains a very large number N_v of our model atoms, each reacting similarly but independently to the applied E field. Then the x component of electric polarization, or total electric-dipole moment per unit volume, in this collection of atoms will be

$$p_x(t) = \sum_{\substack{\text{all atoms in} \\ \text{unit volume}}} \mu_{ex}(t) = -N_v e x(t) \tag{16}$$

The subscript v is a reminder that N_v is not a number, but a number *density*, i.e., the number of atoms per unit volume. We are thus asserting here that a collection of electric-dipole atoms is, in effect, a *material medium*. If there is a very large number of atoms present in even a small unit of volume,[1] then we can add up all the individual *microscopic* atomic moments $\boldsymbol{\mu}_e$ in that volume to create a net *macroscopic* polarization $\mathbf{p} = \Sigma\boldsymbol{\mu}_e$ in that volume.

  This process of adding together the very small individual dipole moments from a great many microscopic atoms to create a net macroscopic electric polarization (or, in magnetic materials, adding together a great many individual magnetic dipoles to create a macroscopic magnetic polarization) is basic to the interaction between electromagnetic signals and atomic transitions. This is how we establish a bridge between the microscopic dynamics of a single atom and the macroscopic or bulk properties of a laser crystal or other maser material containing many atoms per unit volume. This approach is also applied in other situations, such as determination of the dielectric constant or index of refraction of a dielectric or the magnetic properties of a magnetic material. In direct analogy to the electric-polarization–electric-dipole case, the macroscopic magnetic polarization or magnetization in, say, an iron bar is the summation of the microscopic magnetic-dipole moments of the individual iron atoms in the bar.

ELECTRIC SUSCEPTIBILITY $\chi(\omega)$

■ For sinusoidal electromagnetic field quantities the general relationship of D, E, and $\mathcal{P}$ becomes, in phasor form,

$$\tilde{\mathbf{D}}(\omega) = \epsilon_0 \tilde{\mathbf{E}}(\omega) + \tilde{\boldsymbol{\mathcal{P}}}(\omega) \tag{17}$$

In any *linear* medium the polarization $\tilde{\boldsymbol{\mathcal{P}}}(\omega)$ is linearly related to the electric field $\tilde{\mathbf{E}}(\omega)$ in the form

$$\tilde{\boldsymbol{\mathcal{P}}}(\omega) = \tilde{\chi}(\omega)\epsilon_0 \tilde{E}(\omega) \tag{18}$$

where $\chi(\omega)$ is the *electric susceptibility* of the linear medium.[2] The relationship between $\tilde{\mathbf{D}}$ and $\tilde{\mathbf{E}}$ then becomes

$$\tilde{\mathbf{D}}(\omega) = \epsilon_0[1 + \tilde{\chi}(\omega)]\tilde{\mathbf{E}}(\omega) = \epsilon(\omega)\tilde{\mathbf{E}}(\omega) \tag{19}$$

where

$$\tilde{\epsilon}(\omega) \equiv \epsilon_0[1 + \tilde{\chi}(\omega)] \tag{20}$$

is the dielectric constant of the medium.

  In particular, in a medium consisting of a collection of classical oscillators we have established linear relationships between $p_x(t)$ and $x(t)$, and in turn, between $x(t)$ and $e_x(t)$. If also we write $p_x(t)$ in phasor form as

$$p_x(t) = \tfrac{1}{2}[\tilde{\mathcal{P}}_x(\omega)e^{j\omega t} + \tilde{\mathcal{P}}_x^*(\omega)e^{-j\omega t}] \tag{21}$$

then, from our results above, we can write

$$\tilde{\mathcal{P}}_x(\omega) = -N_v e \tilde{X}(\omega) = -j\frac{N_v e^2}{m\gamma\omega}\frac{1}{1 + 2j(\omega - \omega_a)/\gamma}\tilde{E}_x(\omega) \tag{22}$$

---

[1] There are in fact a very large number of atoms per unit volume in any real maser material—perhaps 10^{10} to 10^{12} atoms/cm^3 in gas lasers, and up to 10^{20} atoms/cm^3 in solid-state masers.

[2] Strictly speaking $\tilde{\chi}(\omega)$ should be a tensor quantity connecting the two vectors $\tilde{\mathcal{P}}$ and $\tilde{\mathbf{E}}$.

Our collection of classical-model atoms thus forms, at least so far as x-directed components are concerned, a linear material medium with a finite dielectric constant different from free space and with a macroscopic electric susceptibility given by

$$\tilde{\chi}(\omega) \equiv \frac{\tilde{P}(\omega)}{\epsilon_0 \tilde{E}(\omega)} = -j\frac{N_v e^2}{m\epsilon_0 \omega \gamma} \frac{1}{1 + 2j(\omega - \omega_a)/\gamma} \tag{23}$$

This step, in which we make a transition from individual microscopic atoms (or classical oscillators) to a macroscopic electric susceptibility, is simply a rephrasing of the microscopic-macroscopic discussion above, but it is also perhaps the most important single step in the entire analysis of maser action.[1] Once the microscopic atomic response has been converted to a macroscopic electromagnetic susceptibility, all questions of atomic physics and quantum theory can be left behind. Any laser or maser problem is reduced to the purely electromagnetic problem of inserting the macroscopic susceptibility $\tilde{\chi}(\omega)$ into Maxwell's equations and finding appropriate solutions for the electromagnetic fields, or the ac voltages and currents, in the structures or circuits of the maser device under study.

TENSOR SUSCEPTIBILITIES ■ We may note here as an aside that in the general case the response of a so-called *anisotropic material* to an applied electric field will be different for different directions of the applied field. Hence the susceptibility $\tilde{\chi}(\omega)$ will be a tensor quantity; i.e., it will have different values for different directions. We have considered here only field components along a rather vaguely defined x direction, and hence the susceptibility $\chi(\omega)$ we derived above really represents only what would be the $\tilde{\chi}_{xx}(\omega)$ element of a susceptibility tensor in general. The symmetric charge-cloud model of Fig. 2-1 should presumably have the same response to an applied E field in any direction, and so its susceptibility should be the same in any direction, or completely isotropic; the linear oscillator model of Fig. 2-2 could be considered to have a strong response in the x direction and no response in any other direction, making it highly anisotropic. The tensor susceptibilities of real atomic transitions are definitely anisotropic, with the magnitude of the response depending strongly on the direction, or polarization, of the applied fields. We need not consider tensor properties in detail at this point, since we can discuss other more important aspects without including polarization properties. We will return to them, however, in a later chapter.

FREQUENCY RESPONSE: REAL AND IMAGINARY PARTS ■ The atomic susceptibility $\tilde{\chi}(\omega)$ is a complex quantity, with real and imaginary parts,

$$\tilde{\chi}(\omega) = \chi'(\omega) + j\chi''(\omega)$$
$$= -\frac{N_v e^2}{m\epsilon_0 \gamma \omega}\left[\frac{2(\omega - \omega_a)/\gamma}{1 + [2(\omega - \omega_a)/\gamma]^2} + j\frac{1}{1 + [2(\omega - \omega_a)/\gamma]^2}\right] \tag{24}$$

The distinction between the real and the imaginary parts, $\chi'(\omega)$ and $\chi''(\omega)$, will be extremely important in all our subsequent discussions. It will turn out that the imaginary part $\chi''(\omega)$ represents the *lossy*, or *absorptive*, part of the atomic response (which in the maser case becomes the emissive or amplifying part of the response), while the real part $\chi'(\omega)$ represents the *reactive*, or *phase-shifting*, part of the response (which also changes sign in going from a normal to a maser situation).

We can write the induced ac polarization in the form

$$p(t) = \text{Re}\,[\tilde{P}(\omega)e^{j\omega\tau}] \tag{25}$$

---

[1] For a more rigorous discussion of this, including the Lorentz-Lorenz correction, see Ref. 2-10, chap. 4.

and then write $\tilde{\mathcal{P}}(\omega)$ as

$$\tilde{\mathcal{P}}(\omega)e^{j\omega t} = \tilde{\chi}(\omega)\epsilon_0\tilde{E}(\omega)e^{j\omega t} = [\chi'(\omega) + j\chi''(\omega)]\epsilon_0\tilde{E}(\omega)e^{j\omega t}$$
$$= \chi'(\omega)\epsilon_0\tilde{E}(\omega)e^{j\omega t} + \chi''(\omega)\epsilon_0\tilde{E}(\omega)e^{j(\omega t+\pi/2)} \qquad (26)$$

Note the $\pi/2$, or $90°$, phase shift of the second term. To put this another way, note that if the applied E field is

$$e(t) = E \cos(\omega t + \theta) = \mathrm{Re}\,(Ee^{j\theta}e^{j\omega t}) \qquad (27)$$

then the induced polarization is evidently

$$p(t) = \epsilon_0\left[\chi'(\omega)E \cos(\omega t + \theta) + \chi''(\omega)E \cos\left(\omega t + \theta + \frac{\pi}{2}\right)\right]$$
$$= \epsilon_0[\chi'(\omega)E \cos(\omega t + \theta) - \chi''(\omega)E \sin(\omega t + \theta)] \qquad (28)$$

The real part $\chi'(\omega)$ gives the component of the induced polarization $\mathcal{P}$ that is *in phase* with the applied field E, while $\chi''(\omega)$ gives the *quadrature component*, the component of $\mathcal{P}$ that is $90°$ out of phase with the applied field.

The frequency dependence of $\chi'(\omega)$ and $-\chi''(\omega)$ is plotted in Fig. 2-3. Since

$$\tilde{\epsilon}(\omega) = \epsilon_0[1 + \tilde{\chi}(\omega)] = \epsilon_0[1 + \chi'(\omega) + j\chi''(\omega)]$$

the $\chi'(\omega)$ part represents an in-phase addition to the real part of the dielectric constant $\epsilon(\omega)$, or an additional reactive contribution given by

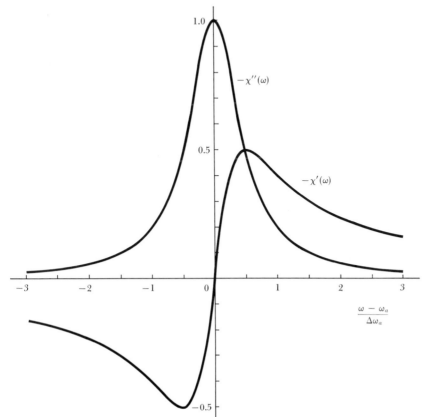

FIG. 2-3 Frequency dependence of the real and imaginary parts of the complex susceptibility $\chi(\omega) \equiv \chi'(\omega) + j\chi''(\omega)$ versus frequency deviation on either side of resonance. Compare these theoretical curves with the experimental curves shown in Fig. 1-12.

$$\chi'(\omega) = -\frac{N_v e^2}{m\epsilon_0\omega\gamma} \frac{1}{1 + [2(\omega - \omega_a)/\gamma]^2} \tag{29}$$

This contribution is zero exactly on resonance. It varies linearly with frequency for small displacements away from resonance on either side, leading up to a broad displaced peak of opposite sign on opposite sides of the resonance line center. The $\chi''(\omega)$ component of the susceptibility, representing the quadrature or lossy component of the susceptibility, is

$$\chi''(\omega) = -\frac{N_v e^2}{m\epsilon_0\omega\gamma} \frac{1}{1 + [2(\omega - \omega_a)/\gamma]^2} \tag{30}$$

As shown in Fig. 2-3, this has a strongly resonant response, with maximum value at resonance, dropping away symmetrically on either side. The lineshape of this component is, in fact, just the (real) lorentzian lineshape characteristic of the resonance response of the model atom.

The calculated curves of Fig. 2-3 should be compared with the excellent experimental curves of χ' and χ'' versus ω shown in Fig. 1-12.

POWER ABSORPTION BY THE
DRIVEN OSCILLATORS

■ We will study the significance of $\chi'(\omega)$ and $\chi''(\omega)$ later in connection with equivalent circuits and traveling-wave interactions. We can gain some further understanding at this point, however, by calculating the average power delivered to a collection of classical oscillators by an applied sinusoidal field at steady state. If the oscillating electron in our model has a motion $x(t)$, then its instantaneous velocity is $\dot{x}(t)$. The instantaneous rate at which work is done on the moving electron by the applied electric field, i.e., the instantaneous power flow from field to atom, is

$$\text{Instantaneous power per atom} = \text{force} \times \text{velocity} = -e[e_x(t)\dot{x}(t)] \tag{31}$$

To obtain the time-average power per unit volume delivered to a collection of such oscillators we must multiply this by the density of atoms N_v and average the instantaneous power over one full cycle. In phasor notation, this leads to

$$\begin{aligned}
\text{Average power} &= -\overline{N_v e[e_x(t)\dot{x}(t)]} \\
\text{per unit volume} &= -\tfrac{1}{4}N_v e\overline{(\tilde{E}_x e^{j\omega t} + \tilde{E}_x^* e^{-j\omega t})(j\omega\tilde{X}e^{j\omega t} - j\omega\tilde{X}^* e^{-j\omega t})} \\
&= -\tfrac{1}{4}j\omega N_v e(\tilde{E}_x^*\tilde{X} - \tilde{E}_x\tilde{X}^*)
\end{aligned} \tag{32}$$

but by relating $\tilde{X}$ to $\tilde{\mathcal{P}}_x$ we may also write this as

$$\text{Average power per unit volume} = \tfrac{1}{4}j\omega[\tilde{E}_x^*(\omega)\tilde{\mathcal{P}}_x(\omega) - \tilde{E}_x(\omega)\tilde{\mathcal{P}}_x^*(\omega)] \tag{33}$$

In this form the average-power expression is closely related to a well-known result in electromagnetic theory, that a time-varying polarization $p(t)$ is essentially equivalent to bulk polarization current density, $j_p(t) \equiv (d/dt)p(t)$. The instantaneous power per unit volume delivered to this current density by an accompanying E field is $e(t)j_p(t)$, and averaging this form over time leads to the same average-power expression.

At this point, however, we are more interested in noting that if $\tilde{\mathcal{P}}(\omega)$ and $\tilde{E}(\omega)$ are related by $\tilde{\mathcal{P}}(\omega) = \tilde{\chi}(\omega)\epsilon_0\tilde{E}(\omega)$, then the average power per unit volume delivered by the field to the model atoms is

$$\begin{aligned}
\text{Average power} &= -\tfrac{1}{2}\omega\epsilon_0\chi''(\omega)\tilde{E}_x(\omega)\tilde{E}_x^*(\omega) \\
\text{per unit volume} &= -\tfrac{1}{2}\omega\epsilon_0\chi''(\omega)|\tilde{E}_x(\omega)|^2
\end{aligned} \tag{34}$$

Thus the average power-dissipation density in a medium with complex electric suscepti-bility $\tilde{\chi} = \chi' + j\chi''$ is directly proportional to the *imaginary* part χ'' of the suscepti-bility. The real part χ' represents additional reactance, while the imaginary part χ'' represents dissipation or loss (gain in the maser case, as we will see later).[1] The power given by expression (34) represents power absorbed by the collection of oscillators from an applied electromagnetic signal. At steady state, of course, the oscillators must pass this power on in turn to their surroundings, or to some other energy sink, through the damping mechanism γ. The minus sign in front of the final expression for power dissipation may be confusing; note, however, that the expression for $\chi''(\omega)$ given earlier also had a minus sign in front, so that the power dissipated in the collection of oscillators is indeed positive.[2]

■ We have just shown that in a medium with a complex susceptibility $\tilde{\chi}(\omega)$, the imaginary part of this susceptibility corresponds to a loss or power-dissipation mecha-nism in the medium. We will illustrate this general result by showing that another (and perhaps more familiar) type of loss in a medium, *ohmic loss,* can also be considered as simply an imaginary component added to the susceptibility or dielectric constant of the medium.

OHMIC LOSSES

Recall that one of the two basic Maxwell electromagnetic equations is

$$\nabla \times \mathbf{h}(t) = \frac{d}{dt}\,\mathbf{d}(t) + \mathbf{j}(t) \tag{35}$$

where $\mathbf{j}(t)$ means the real current density, if any exists, in a given volume [this real current density must be distinguished from the equivalent polarization current density $\mathbf{j}_p(t) \equiv (d/dt)\mathbf{p}(t)$ discussed earlier; the latter is already included in the $\mathbf{d}(t)$ term]. The sinusoidal form of this equation is

$$\nabla \times \tilde{\mathbf{H}}(\omega) = j\omega\tilde{\mathbf{D}}(\omega) + \tilde{\mathbf{J}}(\omega) \tag{36}$$

Suppose that the medium under study has a real dielectric constant ϵ and also a finite linear conductivity σ, so that

$$\mathbf{D} = \epsilon\mathbf{E} \qquad \text{and} \qquad \mathbf{J} = \sigma\mathbf{E} \tag{37}$$

often called *ohmic conductivity,* since the medium in question obeys Ohm's law. The Maxwell equation then becomes

$$\nabla \times \tilde{\mathbf{H}} = j\omega\epsilon\tilde{\mathbf{E}} + \sigma\tilde{\mathbf{E}} = j\omega\epsilon\left[1 - \frac{j\sigma}{\omega\epsilon}\right]\tilde{\mathbf{E}} = j\omega\epsilon'\tilde{\mathbf{E}} \tag{38}$$

The second and third equalities point out that the conductivity σ, which is responsible for the ohmic losses in the material, can be completely absorbed into an extended (and now complex) dielectric constant ϵ', given by

$$\epsilon' \equiv \epsilon - \frac{j\sigma}{\omega} \tag{39}$$

---

[1] The power-dissipation question becomes slightly more complicated when the susceptibility $\tilde{\chi}(\omega)$ is an anisotropic tensor quantity. In this case reactance and dissipation are no longer associated quite so straight-forwardly with the real and imaginary parts of the susceptibility, but rather with what are called the *hermitian* and *antihermitian* parts of the susceptibility tensor.

[2] In order to avoid these double minus signs, some writers use the convention that χ' and χ'' are to be defined from the beginning by $\tilde{\chi} = \chi' - j\chi''$. Since we will have further confusion with susceptibilities chang-ing sign in going from absorption to maser action, we have retained the more familiar convention $\tilde{\chi} = \chi' + j\chi''$.

which we can compare with

$$\tilde{\epsilon}(\omega) = \epsilon_0[1 + \tilde{\chi}(\omega)] = \epsilon_0[1 + \chi'(\omega) + j\chi''(\omega)] \tag{40}$$

Obviously, the ohmic-loss term is like an imaginary component χ'' in the expanded dielectric constant; this term has a *negative* sign for a positive conductivity σ, and hence for positive loss.

We can draw two conclusions from the foregoing discussion. First, ohmic conductivity σ represents one kind of loss mechanism which can clearly be represented by a negative imaginary term $j\chi''_{\text{ohmic}} \equiv -j\sigma/\omega$ added to the extended dielectric susceptibility. Second, a collection of oscillators or atoms with internal resonances will also have quite separate losses due to the internal resonances themselves. These losses can be represented by an imaginary atomic component χ''_a, which will be present in the extended dielectric constant or electric susceptibility. To put this another way, if χ''_a is the component of electric susceptibility due to atomic internal resonances, as computed above, this component will have the same effect as an additional equivalent conductivity $\sigma_{\text{eq}}(\omega)$ (over and above any ohmic conductivity) given by

$$\sigma_{\text{eq}}(\omega) \equiv -\omega\epsilon_0\chi''_a(\omega) \tag{41}$$

There will, of course, also be reactive effects associated with the real χ'_a component added to the dielectric constant of the medium.

2.3   THE RESPONSE OF REAL ELECTRIC-DIPOLE ATOMS

The classical electron-oscillator model we have discussed in Secs. 2-1 and 2-2 provides a surprisingly accurate and nearly complete analytical model for the properties of any single electric-dipole transition in a real atom. In fact, only a few simple modifications are required to make the results we have obtained applicable to real transitions in real atoms, including the quantum-mechanical properties of the atomic transitions. This section outlines the steps by which we may go from the classical electron oscillator results to the quantum results for real atoms.

CLASSICAL ELECTRON
OSCILLATORS AND REAL
QUANTUM ATOMS

■ The electric susceptibility $\tilde{\chi}(\omega)$ is one way of expressing the final results of our analyses that will be generally useful in further discussions and calculations. We can use this expression, for example, to illustrate the conversion from classical-oscillator to quantum-atom results.

The expression developed in Sec. 2-2 for the susceptibility of a collection of classical oscillators is

$$\tilde{\chi}(\omega) = -j\frac{N_v e^2}{m\epsilon_0\omega\gamma}\frac{1}{1 + 2j(\omega - \omega_a)/\gamma} \tag{1}$$

Since in this elementary case the total decay rate γ and the atomic linewidth $\Delta\omega_a$ are the same, we can also write the classical susceptibility as

$$\tilde{\chi}(\omega) = -j\frac{N_v e^2}{m\epsilon_0\omega\,\Delta\omega_a}\frac{1}{1 + 2j(\omega - \omega_a)/\Delta\omega_a} \tag{2}$$

Now, we noted in Sec. 2-1 that a classical electron oscillator, regardless of whatever other damping or line-broadening rates it may have, will always have at least a purely radiative damping rate γ_{rad} or a purely radiative lifetime τ_{rad} given by

$$\gamma_{\text{rad}} = \frac{1}{\tau_{\text{rad}}} = \frac{e^2 \omega_a{}^2}{6\pi\epsilon_0 m c^3} \tag{3}$$

Note also that at least part of the collection of constants on the right-hand side of Eq. (3) also appears in much the same form in expression (2) for $\tilde{\chi}(\omega)$. This is suggestive (but hardly compelling) evidence that we might substitute the radiative decay rate $1/\tau_{\text{rad}}$ for this collection of constants in the susceptibility expression (2). If we do this, and make use of the fact that $c = f\lambda$, the classical-oscillator result then takes the particularly simple form

$$
\begin{aligned}
\tilde{\chi}(\omega) &= -j\frac{3}{4\pi^2}\frac{N_v \lambda^3}{\Delta\omega_a \, \tau_{\text{rad}}}\frac{1}{1 + 2j(\omega - \omega_a)/\Delta\omega_a} \\
&= -j\frac{3}{8\pi^3}\frac{N_v \lambda^3}{\Delta f_a \, \tau_{\text{rad}}}\frac{1}{1 + 2j(\omega - \omega_a)/\Delta\omega_a}
\end{aligned} \tag{4}
$$

where λ is the wavelength corresponding to the resonance frequency ω_a, $\Delta\omega_a$ is the linewidth in radian-frequency units, and $\Delta f_a \equiv \Delta\omega_a/2\pi$ is the same quantity in conventional frequency units (cps or Hz). Note that in this simple result the constant factor in front contains only the number of atoms per cubic wavelength, $N_v\lambda^3$, and the dimensionless product $\Delta\omega_a \, \tau_{\text{rad}}$. In fact, if purely radiative damping is the only damping or line-broadening mechanism present in some particular collection of model atoms, then we have the particularly simple result that $\Delta\omega_a \, \tau_{\text{rad}} \equiv 1$. However, in other cases other mechanisms will make $\Delta\omega_a$ larger than its value due to radiative damping alone, and as a result, the product $\Delta\omega_a \, \tau_{\text{rad}}$ will be larger, and the peak magnitude of the susceptibility will be smaller.

■ The reason for converting the classical-electron-oscillator susceptibility to the form of Eq. (4) now becomes apparent: if we replace all the parameters in Eq. (4) with the corresponding parameters for a real atomic transition, we will have an expression that predicts the exact susceptibility for a real electric-dipole transition in a real quantum-mechanical atom. The classical result in (4) can be converted to the correct quantum result for a real electric-dipole atomic transition by the following steps:

REAL QUANTUM ATOMS

1. The classical-oscillator resonance frequency ω_a and wavelength λ are replaced by the *actual transition frequency* $\omega_{mn} \equiv (E_m - E_n)/h$ and actual wavelength λ_{mn} of the $m \rightarrow n$ atomic transition involved.

2. The linewidth $\Delta\omega_a$ or Δf_a of the classical oscillator is replaced by the *real linewidth* $\Delta\omega_{mn}$ or Δf_{mn} of the real atomic transition, including any and all line-broadening mechanisms that may be important in real atoms.

3. The radiative damping time τ_{rad} characteristic of the classical oscillator is replaced by a corresponding *actual radiative damping time* τ_{mn} characteristic of the real atomic transition.

4. Finally, the total number (or number density) N_v of the classical oscillator is replaced by the *population difference* (or, really, the *population-difference density*) $(N_n - N_m)_v$ of the atomic transition involved.

The first of these steps seems obvious; the second is also fairly obvious and should become even more understandable after we discuss some additional resonance-line-broadening mechanisms in Chap. 3. The third step, replacing the radiative lifetime, has a quantum-mechanical background, which we will discuss somewhat further below. The final step, replacing the classical-oscillator population $\mathcal{N}_v$ with the atomic population *difference* $(\mathcal{N}_n - \mathcal{N}_m)_v$, is purely quantum mechanical in origin. This fundamental quantum-mechanical result was, in fact, introduced as the third basic maser principle of Sec. 1-2.

The final expression for the complex susceptibility $\tilde{\chi}(\omega)$ produced by a collection of real atoms at or near one of their resonance frequencies is thus

$$\tilde{\chi}(\omega)_{mn} = -j\frac{3}{8\pi^3}\frac{(\mathcal{N}_n - \mathcal{N}_m)_v\lambda_{mn}{}^3}{\Delta f_{mn}\,\tau_{mn}}\frac{1}{1 + 2j(f - f_{mn})/\Delta f_{mn}} \tag{5}$$

Note again that $(\mathcal{N}_n - \mathcal{N}_m)_v$ is the population-difference *density*, i.e., the difference in populations per unit volume in the two atomic energy levels E_n and E_m responsible for the f_{mn} transition.

All the parameters in Eq. (5) will in general differ for each different atomic transition in a collection of atoms. The atomic resonance frequency f_{mn} and wavelength λ_{mn} are, of course, determined by the quantum energy-level structure of the atoms in question. The resonance linewidth Δf_{mn} will be determined by a number of factors, some of which we will examine in Chap. 3 and later on in Chap. 9. The energy-level populations $\mathcal{N}_n$ and $\mathcal{N}_m$ will be determined by temperature, as well as by all the pumping and excitation processes and other signals that may be applied to the collection of atoms. Finally, the radiative damping time τ_{mn} will have a value characteristic of the particular atom and transition.

ATOMIC RADIATIVE DAMPING
TIMES AND OSCILLATOR
STRENGTHS

■ Different atomic transitions in real atoms exhibit different strengths of response to an applied signal, ranging from a response nearly as strong as that of a classical electron oscillator (which we call a *strongly allowed transition*) to responses that are still observable but many orders of magnitude weaker (which we call *weakly allowed* or *nearly forbidden transitions*), and even to transitions exhibiting no significant response at all (which we call *strictly forbidden transitions*). The strength of the response of a given atom on a given transition depends on the quantum-mechanical properties of that atom, and in particular on the quantum properties of the two quantum energy levels involved in the transition.

If an atom responds only weakly on a given transition, then it seems apparent that the internal motion of the atom on that transition must not be strongly coupled to an applied electric field. Since an oscillating ensemble of charges couples to an applied electric field through the net electric-dipole moment of the ensemble, a weak coupling to the field must mean that the internal atomic motion on that transition does not generate much net electric-dipole moment. The internal structure and internal motions of a real quantum atom are, of course, considerably more complex than the simple charge-cloud model of Fig. 2-1, and it is not surprising that some of these motions generate only a weak or even a zero electric-dipole moment.

From considerations of reciprocity, it would seem that if an electric field only weakly excites a certain characteristic motion in a collection of charges, then that characteristic motion of the charges should in turn only weakly excite any electric fields; i.e., the characteristic motion should be a poor or inefficient radiator for electromagnetic radiation. Specifically, if a certain atomic transition responds only weakly to applied signals near its transition frequency, then it should also radiate only weakly at that frequency; in other words, it should be characterized by a long radiative damping time τ_{mn}.

This is, in fact, exactly the result we have just seen: the response of either a classical oscillator or an atomic transition is inversely proportional to the radiative damping time of that oscillator or transition. From reciprocity, if applied signals do not couple well to a system, then that system does not couple well back to the applied fields. Real atomic transitions may have radiative damping times that range from values close to that of a classical oscillator at the same frequency up to very much longer values. The response strengths of these different transitions then vary in inverse proportion to the radiative damping times.

The strength of response of an atomic transition in relation to the response of a classical electron oscillator at the same frequency is often expressed by a parameter called the *oscillator strength* F_{nm} of the given transition.[1] The strength of an atomic transition in quantum theory is expressed in terms of a *quantum-mechanical matrix element* r_{nm} evaluated between the two quantum states involved in the transition.[2] The oscillator strength is then defined as

$$F_{nm} \equiv \frac{4\pi}{3} \frac{m\omega_{mn} r_{nm}^2}{h} \tag{6}$$

However, it can be shown that this definition of oscillator strength is also equivalent to

$$F_{nm} \equiv \frac{1}{3} \frac{\tau_{\text{rad}}}{\tau_{mn}} \tag{7}$$

Thus F_{nm} is the real atomic radiative damping rate compared to the radiative damping rate of a classical oscillator with the same frequency. The factor ⅓ enters because of some complexities, not explained here, having to do with the polarization response or the variation with direction of applied field of the classical oscillator compared to the real atom.

Strongly allowed electric-dipole transitions have oscillator strengths on the order of unity. The atomic transitions used in laser and maser systems, however, usually have much smaller oscillator strengths, even as small as $F_{nm} \sim 10^{-3}$ to 10^{-6}. In fact, a metastable optical transition with a very long lifetime, and hence a slow decay rate must, by definition, have a very low oscillator strength; such transitions are widely used in practical lasers.[3]

In terms of the oscillator strength, the susceptibility presented by a collection of real atoms on a given transition can be written as

$$\tilde{\chi}(\omega)_{mn} = -j3F_{nm} \frac{(N_n - N_m)_v e^2}{m\epsilon_0 \omega_{mn} \Delta\omega_{mn}} \frac{1}{1 + 2j(\omega - \omega_{mn})/\Delta\omega_{mn}} \tag{8}$$

Note that this expression now has exactly the same form as our original expressions (1) and (2) for a collection of classical oscillators, except for the multiplying factor

---

[1] The conventional notation in the literature for oscillator strength is f_{nm}, but since we are already using this for frequency, we will use the capital letter instead.

[2] If $\psi_n(\mathbf{r})$ and $\psi_m(\mathbf{r})$ are the normalized quantum states or eigenstates corresponding to the lower and upper energy levels, then the matrix element r_{nm} is given by evaluating the integral

$$r_{nm} = |\int \psi_n^*(\mathbf{r})\mathbf{r}\psi_m(\mathbf{r}) \, dr|$$

between these two quantum states.

[3] A good discussion of oscillator strengths, with references, may be found in Ref. 2-1, pp. 7-48–7-58.

$3F_{nm}$ representing the oscillator strength and the substitution of population-difference density for classical-oscillator density.

In later chapters we will make good use of expressions (5) and (8) for the susceptibility of a real atomic transition in analyzing different types of laser and maser devices. At this point, however, it is sufficient to note that all the quantum-mechanical theory for a real atomic transition can be condensed into the simple macroscopic susceptibility expression (5) or (8), and the real atomic results are remarkably well predicted by the simple, classical electron-oscillator model developed in this chapter.

EXPERIMENTAL
DEMONSTRATIONS

■ The absorptive contribution $\chi''(\omega)$ of an atomic transition can be observed at optical frequencies by measurements of the absorption (or transmission) versus wavelength when radiation is passed through a collection of atoms. The basic spectroscopic techniques for such measurements and some examples of typical experimental results were presented in Chap. 1. The reactive contribution $\chi'(\omega)$ of such transitions is somewhat more difficult to demonstrate, simply because it seems to be less convenient to measure optical phase or phase shift than to measure optical intensity or optical absorption. However, some ingeniously simple demonstrations of $\chi'(\omega)$ effects in gas atoms were developed by Wood and others as early as 1901. Wood's classic book[1] contains descriptions of these experiments and their results, and a great deal of other rewarding and stimulating material besides. (Note that the phase-shifting effects of $\chi'(\omega)$ are referred to in physical optics literature as *dispersion,* or sometimes *anomalous dispersion.*)

2.4 REACTION BACK ON THE ELECTROMAGNETIC FIELD: EQUIVALENT CIRCUIT

Our next major problem is to evaluate the *back reaction* which our excited oscillators or atoms will exert back on the electromagnetic circuit that provides the applied fields. It is only through this back reaction, in fact, that we can know that applied ac fields are eliciting a response in an atom.

There are several ways of carrying through the derivation presented in this section. The most general approach would be to use the result we have just obtained, that the presence of a collection of atoms creates in a volume a net electric susceptibility, or a frequency-dependent change in dielectric constant, having both real and imaginary parts. This susceptibility can then be fed into Maxwell's equation for the electromagnetic circuitry, in order to derive various results of greater or lesser complexity. We will, however, first allow a more elementary approach. Since we are discussing electric-dipole response, we should presumably consider our individual electron oscillators to be placed in some region of strong ac electric field—for example, between the plates of a capacitor to which an ac voltage is applied. When we speak of capacitor plates and voltages, we are obviously employing low-frequency concepts that are directly appropriate only at audio or radio frequencies, and not at microwave or optical frequencies. The conclusions we will reach from this low-frequency approach, however, are much more general and are in fact entirely valid at microwave and even optical frequencies.

LOW-FREQUENCY APPROACH:
INDUCED CAPACITOR CURRENT

■ To begin such an analysis, let us consider a capacitor, as in Fig. 2-4a, with a voltage $v(t)$ across it and a plate spacing d, so that the instantaneous E field in the capacitor is

---

[1] Ref. 2-12; see especially chap. XV, figs. 293–299, and the striking color photographs in the frontispiece.

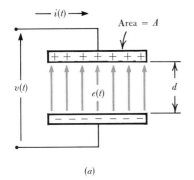

(a)

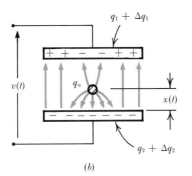

(b)

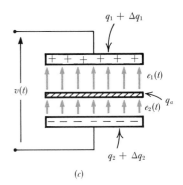

(c)

$$e(t) = -\frac{v(t)}{d} \tag{1}$$

FIG. 2-4 (a) A parallel-plate capacitance, into which is inserted a test charge which may be considered as either (b) a point charge or (c) a planar sheet charge.

Associated with this voltage and field is a total surface charge $q_1(t)$ on the capacitor plate, given by

$$q_1(t) = \frac{\epsilon_0 A}{d} v(t) = Cv(t) \tag{2}$$

where A is the area of the capacitor plates and C is the total capacitance (for simplicity we will assume a uniform parallel-plate capacitance and neglect edge effects). There will, of course, be an equal and opposite charge $q_2(t) = -q_1(t)$ on the lower capacitor plate.

Suppose now that a movable *test charge* q_a is introduced between the capacitor plates while the capacitor voltage remains fixed at $v(t)$. This charge will induce an additional surface charge Δq_1 on the upper plate, as well as a surface charge Δq_2 on the lower plate. If all the electric field lines from q_a terminate on either the upper or the lower capacitor plates, the total additional induced surface charges must be equal and opposite to the inducing charge, or

$$\Delta q_1(t) + \Delta q_2(t) = -q_a \tag{3}$$

By superposition, the total surface charges on the plates caused by $v(t)$ and the test charge q_a will be simply additive. Figure 2-4b illustrates these surface charges.

If q_a is located close to the *lower* capacitor plate, almost all of its electric field lines will terminate on the lower plate, and so the induced surface charges will be $\Delta q_1(t) \approx 0$ and $\Delta q_2(t) \approx -q_a$. If q_a moves across the gap to the upper plate, then the opposite situation prevails; that is, $\Delta q_1(t) \approx -q_a$ and $\Delta q_2(t) \approx 0$. The point here is that as the test charge q_a moves from one side of the gap to the other, a net charge equal to $-q_a$ moves around through the external circuitry from the lower plate to the upper. In fact, if the gap field is uniform, as we have assumed, the net amount of charge transferred from Δq_2 to Δq_1 is linear in the position of q_a in the gap; that is, if the instantaneous position of q_a in the gap is $x(t)$, $0 \le x \le d$, then

$$\Delta q_1(t) = -\frac{q_a x(t)}{d} \qquad 0 < x(t) < d \tag{4}$$

and

$$\Delta q_2(t) = -q_a\left[1 - \frac{x(t)}{d}\right] \tag{5}$$

One way of deriving this result is to assume that the test charge q_a, rather than being in the form of a point charge, is in the form of a thin charge layer or sheet, as shown in Fig. 2-4c. From elementary concepts of electrostatics, especially Gauss' law, we can readily derive the electric field strengths above and below the sheet charge and the resulting surface charges on the upper and lower capacitor plates as a function of the vertical position of the sheet charge, provided that the capacitor voltage remains fixed at a value $v(t)$. The point-charge model can also be handled without much difficulty by applying the method of image charges. For the semi-infinite parallel-plate-capacitor case the result is exactly the same as the sheet-charge mode.

Suppose now that, instead of a test charge, our electron-oscillator model, consisting of a positive nucleus with charge $+e$ and a negative electron cloud with charge $-e$, is placed at a position x_0 within this capacitor. Then, in the absence of any internal oscillation, the resulting total induced charge on the upper plate due to both the positive nucleus and the negative electron will be

$$\Delta q_1(t) = -\left[\frac{ex_0}{d} + \frac{(-e)x_0}{d}\right] = 0 \tag{6}$$

Suppose, however, that the atom is oscillating in such fashion that while the nucleus remains fixed at x_0, the center of the electron cloud is displaced to $x_0 + x_1(t)$, where $x_1(t)$ is the motion we have been analyzing. Then we have

$$\Delta q_1(t) = -\left[\frac{ex_0}{d} + (-e)\frac{x_0 + x_1(t)}{d}\right] = \frac{ex_1(t)}{d} = -\Delta q_2(t) \tag{7}$$

Thus we see that the time-dependent internal motion $x(t)$ of the atom induces a net time-dependent charge $\Delta q_1(t)$ on the capacitor plates. Moreover, within the limits of our uniform assumption, the net ac charge induced is independent of the position x_0 of the atom in the gap.

The total charge on the upper capacitor plate with the atom present is thus

$$q(t) = q_1(t) + \Delta q_1(t) = Cv(t) + \frac{e}{d}x_1(t) \tag{8}$$

Let us drop the subscript on $x(t)$, since this particular $x(t)$ means the internal oscillatory motion of an electron oscillator placed between the capacitor plates. The total ac current flowing into the capacitance is then

$$i(t) \equiv \frac{d}{dt}q(t) = C\dot{v}(t) + \frac{e}{d}\dot{x}(t) \tag{9}$$

or, if all quantities are sinusoidal,

$$\tilde{I}(\omega) = j\omega C\tilde{V}(\omega) + j\frac{\omega e}{d}\tilde{X}(\omega) \tag{10}$$

The $\dot{x}(t)$ and $j\omega\tilde{X}(\omega)$ terms on the right-hand side in these equations are very important. They express, in fact, the entire reaction of the oscillators (or atoms) back on the source of the applied electromagnetic signal.

If the entire volume of the capacitance is filled with a collection of atoms with number density $\mathcal{N}_v$, there will be a total of $\mathcal{N}_v A d$ atoms present, all subjected to the same applied field $e_x(t)$ due to the voltage $v(t)$ or $\tilde{V}(\omega)$ across the capacitor. The forced steady-state motion $x(t)$ will then be the same for each oscillator, and their total induced charges $\Delta q_1(t)$ will simply add. Using our previous results (Sec. 2-2) for $\tilde{X}(\omega)$, $\tilde{E}_x(\omega)$, or $\tilde{V}(\omega)$, we may write

$$\tilde{I}(\omega) = j\omega C \tilde{V}(\omega) + \mathcal{N}_v A d j \frac{\omega e}{d} \tilde{X}(\omega)$$

$$= j\omega C \tilde{V}(\omega) - \frac{\mathcal{N}_v A e^2}{m\,\Delta\omega_a} \frac{1}{1 + 2j(\omega - \omega a)/\Delta\omega_a} \tilde{E}_x(\omega)$$

$$= \left[j\omega C + \frac{\mathcal{N}_v C e^2}{m\epsilon_0\,\Delta\omega_a} \frac{1}{1 + 2j(\omega - \omega_a)/\Delta\omega_a} \right] \tilde{V}(\omega) \qquad (11)$$

The second term inside the brackets evidently gives the effect of the collection of oscillators or model atoms, or the reaction of these atoms back on the applied field circuit.

■ We will now see how this analytical expression for the back reaction of the atoms can be converted into a simple equivalent-circuit model that will have very important applications in later chapters. Let us denote the total admittance as viewed into the combination of the capacitance plus atoms by $\tilde{Y}(\omega)$, so that

$$\tilde{I}(\omega) = \tilde{Y}(\omega) \tilde{V}(\omega) \qquad (12)$$

Then it is evident from the last line of Eq. (11) that $\tilde{Y}(\omega)$ for the capacitance plus atoms is given by

$$\tilde{Y}(\omega) = j\omega C + \frac{\mathcal{N}_v C e^2}{m\epsilon_0\,\Delta\omega_a} \frac{1}{1 + 2j(\omega - \omega_a)/\Delta\omega_a} = j\omega C + \tilde{Y}_a(\omega) \qquad (13)$$

The apparent or effective total admittance as viewed into the capacitance plus atoms evidently consists of the original capacitance C in parallel with a complex shunt *atomic admittance* $\tilde{Y}_a(\omega)$ which represents the back-reaction effects of the classical oscillators or atoms.

Figure 2-5 shows this equivalence schematically. Consider in particular a shunt admittance $\tilde{Y}_a(\omega)$ consisting of a resistance R_a, an inductance L_a, and a capacitance C_a, together forming a series resonant circuit tuned to $\omega = \omega_a$. The shunt admittance presented by this particular circuit is

LOW-FREQUENCY APPROACH:
EQUIVALENT CIRCUIT

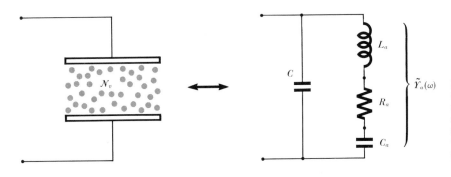

FIG. 2-5 A capacitance filled with a density N_v of resonant atoms can be very accurately represented by the equivalent circuit on the right, where C is the capacitance in the absence of the atoms and $\tilde{Y}_a(\omega)$ is the additional admittance due to the resonant atoms.

$$\tilde{Y}_a(\omega) = \frac{1}{R_a + j(\omega L_a - 1/\omega C_a)} = \frac{1}{R_a} \frac{1}{1 + jQ_a(\omega/\omega_a - \omega_a/\omega)}$$

$$= \frac{1}{R_a} \frac{1}{1 + 2jQ_a(\omega - \omega_a)/\omega_a} \tag{14}$$

The last equality is valid within our usual approximation that $\omega - \omega_a \ll \omega_a$. Then this series-resonant admittance has exactly the same form as the atomic admittance $\tilde{Y}_a(\omega)$ derived above, provided only that the series-resonant equivalent circuit has the same resonance frequency, the same Q or linewidth, and the same net conductance on resonance as does the atomic admittance. That is, the equivalent-circuit admittance and the atomic admittance are equal if the following three conditions are satisfied:

$$\sqrt{\frac{1}{L_a C_a}} = \omega_a$$

$$\frac{\omega_a L_a}{R_a} = Q_a = \frac{\omega_a}{\Delta\omega_a} \tag{15}$$

$$\frac{1}{R_a} = \frac{N_v C e^2}{m\epsilon_0 \, \Delta\omega_a} = \frac{N_v A e^2}{md \, \Delta\omega_a}$$

The dominant frequency dependence of $\tilde{Y}_a(\omega)$ is in the resonant-circuit denominator, and for any reasonable value of Q_a there is no significant difference in using ω or ω_a in the constant term in front. Therefore, upon inversion of the above three relations, the three equivalent-circuit elements become

$$R_a = \frac{m\epsilon_0 \, \Delta\omega_a}{N_v C e^2}$$

$$L_a = \frac{R_a}{\Delta\omega_a} = \frac{m\epsilon_0}{N_v C e^2} \tag{16}$$

$$C_a = \frac{1}{\omega_a^2 L_a} = \frac{N_v C e^2}{m\omega_a^2 \epsilon_0}$$

Thus the equivalent-circuit elements shown in Fig. 2-5 can be completely expressed in terms of the original capacitance C and the parameters of the model atoms themselves, ω_a, $\Delta\omega_a$, and N_v.

The major result of this section, in fact, is the conclusion that the capacitance plus the atoms it contains can be completely represented by the equivalent circuit of Fig. 2-5. The back reaction of the atoms on the signal circuit is completely accounted for by the series resonant circuit connected in shunt with the empty capacitance, with the circuit elements R_a, L_a, and C_a given by the expressions above. Many important maser calculations can be carried through with nothing more than this simple equivalent circuit.

Note that if we write the conductance $\tilde{Y}_a(\omega)$ in terms of its parallel components, i.e., its conductance and susceptance, we obtain

$$\tilde{Y}_a(\omega) = G_a(\omega) + jB_a(\omega)$$

$$= \frac{1}{R_a} \frac{1}{1 + [2Q_a(\omega - \omega_a)/\Delta\omega_a]^2} + j\frac{1}{R_a} \frac{2Q_a(\omega - \omega_a)/\Delta\omega_a}{1 + [2Q_a(\omega - \omega_a)/\Delta\omega_a]^2} \tag{17}$$

The conductance or loss element $G_a(\omega)$ clearly has exactly the same lorentzian lineshape as does $\chi''(\omega)$, as plotted in Fig. 2-3, while the reactance contribution $B_a(\omega)$ has exactly the same frequency dependence as the real susceptibility component $\chi''(\omega)$. This is another aspect of the identification of $\chi'(\omega)$ and $\chi''(\omega)$ with the reactive and resistive parts of the atomic response, respectively. Note also that both the loss and reactance effects are directly proportional to $\mathcal{N}_v$, the density of atoms placed in the ac electric-field region—or to the population-difference density $(\mathcal{N}_n - \mathcal{N}_m)_v$ in the quantum atomic case.

■ The equivalent-circuit elements just derived may be expressed in a slightly different form which will be useful in later discussions. Let us rewrite the electric susceptibility $\tilde{\chi}(\omega)$ of Eq. (2), Sec. 2-3, in the form

ALTERNATE FORM FOR EQUIVALENT-CIRCUIT ELEMENTS

$$\chi(\omega) = -j\frac{\mathcal{N}_v e^2}{m\epsilon_0 \,\Delta\omega_a}\frac{1}{1 + 2j(\omega - \omega_a)/\Delta\omega_a} = -j\chi_0''\frac{1}{1 + 2j(\omega - \omega_a)/\Delta\omega_a} \tag{18}$$

where the quantity

$$\chi_0'' = \frac{\mathcal{N}_v e^2}{m\epsilon_0 \omega \,\Delta\omega_a} \tag{19}$$

is the magnitude of the (purely imaginary) susceptibility at midband. The circuit elements R_a, L_a, and C_a representing the atomic response may then be written as

$$\begin{aligned} R_a^{-1} &\equiv G_a = \chi_0'' \omega_a C \\ L_a^{-1} &= \chi_0'' \omega_a C \,\Delta\omega_a \\ C_a &= \chi_0'' \frac{\Delta\omega_a}{\omega_a} C = \frac{\chi_0'' C}{Q_a} \end{aligned} \tag{20}$$

In this form it is clear that the atomic admittance elements may be expressed entirely in terms of the original capacitance C and the resonance frequency ω_a, the linewidth $\Delta\omega_a$, and the peak (midband) susceptibility χ_0'' of the atomic transition.

■ The basic result we have just obtained can be derived in several other ways. One simple way, based on electromagnetic theory, is to note that the capacitance C' of a parallel-plate capacitor containing a medium other than free space is given by

ALTERNATE DERIVATION: NONPLANAR CAPACITANCES

$$C' = \frac{\epsilon A}{d} = \frac{\epsilon}{\epsilon_0} C = [1 + \chi(\omega)]C \tag{21}$$

where $\chi(\omega)$ is the dielectric constant of the medium between the plates and C is the capacitance without the medium. However, as we saw in preceding sections, a collection of classical oscillators or atoms forms a dielectric medium, with a susceptibility $\tilde{\chi}(\omega) = \chi'(\omega) + j\chi''(\omega)$ given by Eq. (18). Therefore the admittance presented by a capacitance filled with a collection of classical oscillators should become

$$\begin{aligned} \tilde{Y}(\omega) = j\omega C'(\omega) &= j\omega C[1 + \chi'(\omega) + j\chi''(\omega)] \\ &= j\omega C - \omega C\chi''(\omega) + j\omega C\chi'(\omega) \\ &= j\omega C + G_a(\omega) + jB_a(\omega) \end{aligned} \tag{22}$$

Substitution of $\chi''(\omega)$ and $\chi'(\omega)$ from (18) will then lead to exactly the same expressions for $\tilde{Y}_a(\omega)$ that we have just obtained from our more physical derivation. This briefer derivation makes it very clear, however, that $G_a(\omega)$ is indeed directly related to $\chi''(\omega)$ and $B_a(\omega)$ to $\chi'(\omega)$.

The above relationship between C' and C in terms of ϵ and ϵ_0 should hold, in fact, for any arbitrary shape of capacitor plates (provided that the entire medium between and around the plates is filled with the dielectric medium ϵ, so that the field shape is not perturbed when the medium is added). Therefore this derivation should also be correct for any type of capacitance, not just the elementary parallel-plate geometry. This conclusion is correct.

ALTERNATE DERIVATION:
FIELD-ENERGY APPROACH

■ It is also relatively easy to extend our earlier derivation to the case of capacitor electrodes of arbitrary shape, and we can gain some further insight into the physics of the atomic back reaction from this derivation. Figure 2-6 shows one possible form of nonplanar capacitance geometry for purposes of illustration. Suppose that an oscillator (or a real atom) is placed at some point $\mathbf{x}_0$ near the electrodes of this capacitance, as shown. We must now use a three-component vector $\mathbf{x}_0 \equiv (x_0, y_0, z_0)$ to describe the position of the test charge or atom. We also suppose that if a voltage $v(t)$ is applied to the electrodes, the resulting electric-field vector at the position $\mathbf{x}_0$ is given by $\mathbf{e}(\mathbf{x}_0)$.

Associated with any applied voltage $v(t)$ there is a total charge $q(t)$ on the upper electrode of this capacitance, given by

$$q(t) = Cv(t) \qquad (23)$$

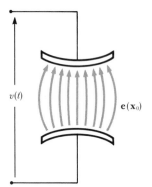

FIG. 2-6 Example of a non-parallel-plate capacitance.

where C is the capacitance between the two electrodes (this capacitance for any complicated electrode geometry can presumably either be calculated by more sophisticated formulas or simply measured). There is also a total induced charge $\Delta q(t)$ on the upper plate caused by the presence of the atom. Calculating the magnitude of this induced charge $\Delta q(t)$ due to a point test charge at any arbitrary location $\mathbf{x}_0$ near the electrodes would be a complicated electromagnetic problem, but fortunately we are not so much interested in the magnitude of $\Delta q(t)$ as we are in how $\Delta q(t)$ changes when the electron in an oscillator or atom moves in its oscillatory motion. This current, or time rate of change of $\Delta q(t)$, is obtained as follows.[1] Suppose that a constant-voltage source (battery) is applied across the electrodes, so that $v(t)$ is held at a fixed value V. Note also that $\Delta q(t)$ is identically zero if the oscillator is at rest, $x(t) = 0$, since the positive nucleus and negative electron then have equal and opposite effects. Suppose that the electron then moves from its equilibrium position $\mathbf{x}_0$ by a small amount $\Delta \mathbf{x}_0$. The work that will be done on the electron by the electric field $\mathbf{e}(\mathbf{x}_0)$ during this small motion will be

$$\Delta W = -e[\mathbf{e}(\mathbf{x}_0) \cdot \Delta \mathbf{x}_0] \qquad (24)$$

This is work done, or energy delivered, by the electric field $\mathbf{e}(t)$. This energy must come from the battery that creates the electric field. Since the battery voltage is fixed (for purposes of derivation), the battery must supply this energy by delivering a small amount of additional charge Δq to the capacitance. The work done by the battery must then be

$$\Delta W = V \Delta q = -e[\mathbf{e}(\mathbf{x}_0) \cdot \Delta \mathbf{x}_0] \qquad (25)$$

where Δq is the charge delivered by the battery to the upper (positive-voltage) electrode.

Equating the two expressions for ΔW, since they must be equal, then gives

$$\Delta q = -e \frac{\mathbf{e}(\mathbf{x}_0) \cdot \Delta \mathbf{x}_0}{V} \qquad (26)$$

[1] For a longer and more rigorous discussion of the following derivation and some of its subleties see Ref. 2-9.

Dividing both sides by the time Δt required for these small changes and then going to the limit of vanishing small Δt converts this result into

$$i_a(t) = -\frac{\mathbf{e}(\mathbf{x}_0) \cdot \dot{\mathbf{x}}(t)}{V} \tag{27}$$

for the additional current $i_a(t)$ into the capacitance due to the internal motion $\dot{\mathbf{x}}(t)$ of the electron oscillator.

The voltage $v(t)$ was assumed constant in this derivation in order to simplify the arguments. However, by superposition, if we allow both $v(t)$ and $\mathbf{x}(t)$ to vary, then the effects of these two quantities should simply be additive. Changes in $\mathbf{x}(t)$ will lead to the induced current $i_a(t)$, as above, while changes in $v(t)$ will lead to the usual capacitive current flow $C\dot{v}(t)$. Therefore the total current flow into the capacitance will take the form

$$i(t) = C\dot{v}(t) - e\left[\frac{\mathbf{e}(\mathbf{x}_0)}{V} \cdot \dot{\mathbf{x}}(t)\right] \tag{28}$$

If the motion $\mathbf{x}(t)$ is an induced response in an oscillator or atom caused by the field $\mathbf{e}$ at that atom's location, then the field $\mathbf{e}$ and the motion $\dot{\mathbf{x}}$ are likely to be parallel. We can then simplify the dot product in (28) to an ordinary scalar product and write

$$i(t) = C\dot{v}(t) - \frac{e}{d_{\text{eq}}(\mathbf{x}_0)}\dot{x}(t) \tag{29}$$

where $d_{\text{eq}}(\mathbf{x}_0)$ is an equivalent plate spacing for the specific case being considered. That is, the ratio of the electric field at any position near the electrodes to the voltage applied across the electrodes depends only on the shape of the electrodes—the geometry of the situation—and not on time or voltage. By writing

$$\frac{|\mathbf{e}(\mathbf{x}_0)|}{V} \equiv \frac{1}{d_{\text{eq}}(\mathbf{x}_0)} \tag{30}$$

we summarize all the geometry of the equivalent plate spacing d_{eq}. For the simple planar case, d_{eq} equals the actual spacing d as might be expected. For more complicated electrode geometries this quantity must presumably be calculated from knowledge of the electric field patterns between the electrodes, or perhaps measured somehow.

The fact that the induced current or the back reaction of the atom on the circuit depends on the electric field strength at the location of the test charge or atom is interesting. This means that both the maximum induced response in the atom and the maximum back reaction on the circuit will be obtained by locating the atom in a region of maximum electric field strength. This is equally true for low-frequency lumped capacitances, in fact, and for microwave or optical resonant cavities. The latter may have much more complicated electromagnetic field patterns than a simple lumped capacitance, but maximum response for an electric-dipole atomic transition will always be obtained by locating the atoms in regions of strong electric field.

If a capacitance is to be filled with a collection of atoms, it is presumably useful to place atoms only in regions where the electric field per unit applied voltage has at least some reasonably large value. The total induced response in the capacitance is then found by integrating expression (28) over all the volume occupied by atoms. Regions where the field per unit voltage is weak contribute relatively less to this integration, and there is no point in placing atoms in such regions.

2.5 THE COMPLETE SYSTEM: CAVITY PLUS ATOMS

The lumped equivalent circuit of Fig. 2-5 provides an important model for many real laser and maser devices. It might seem at first that this model would be useful only for low-frequency maser devices (such as audio- and radio-frequency devices). However, it actually provides a realistic and accurate analytical model for laser and maser devices operating at microwave and optical frequencies. The equation of motion for the signal mode in any resonant maser or laser structure at any frequency can always be cast into the same form as the circuit equation for a low-frequency lumped resonant circuit, including the back-reaction effects of atoms contained in the circuit, which will appear in the same fashion as in Sec. 2-4. Hence expressions for such measurable properties as input impedance, reflection coefficient, power gain, phase shift, and bandwidth can be calculated in terms of low-frequency lumped circuitry, and these calculations will give equally accurate answers for real systems such as a microwave resonant cavity, or even an optical resonant cavity consisting of two mirrors facing each other.

Our simple lumped-circuit model is thus of very wide applicability, and we will develop its properties further in later chapters. In this section we will extend the capacitance model of Fig. 2-5 slightly by converting it into a resonant-circuit or cavity model, with the effects of the atoms included. The relationship between a real resonant-cavity device and its lumped equivalent circuit will then be emphasized.

LUMPED-CIRCUIT MODEL FOR A RESONANT CIRCUIT OR CAVITY

■ The maximum interaction with the atoms in a capacitance, as in Fig. 2-5, will be obtained when there is the maximum possible ac voltage across the capacitance, and hence across the atomic admittance $\tilde{Y}_a(\omega)$. A large ac voltage across a capacitance can be obtained most easily if the capacitance is connected in parallel with a shunt inductance L to form a parallel-resonant circuit tuned to the desired ac signal frequency. In a great many practical applications, therefore, a capacitance filled with resonant atoms, as in Fig. 2-5, will be made part of a parallel tuned circuit, as shown in Fig. 2-7, with a resonant frequency ω_c which is equal to, or at least near to, the atomic resonance frequency ω_a. A circuit resistance R (or a conductance $G \equiv 1/R$) has also been included in Fig. 2-7 to account for the presumably finite $Q \equiv Q_c$ of this parallel resonant circuit.

The resulting total circuit model shown in Fig. 2-7, consisting of a tuned parallel-resonant circuit representing the signal-circuit elements without atoms, in parallel with

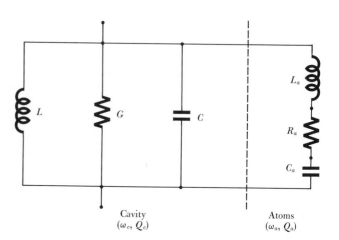

FIG. 2-7 In practice the capacitance C containing the atoms is often itself part of a tuned circuit or cavity having resonant frequency ω_c and quality factor Q_c, in addition to the resonant frequency ω_a and quality factor Q_a of the atomic equivalent circuit. There is also a molecular or maser quality factor Q_m which expresses how strongly the atomic circuit loads down the cavity circuit, or vice versa.

a series-resonant circuit representing the atoms themselves, will provide an accurate analytical model for calculating the behavior of a resonant-cavity maser device in any frequency range, including microwave and optical masers. We will often refer to the *LRC* portion of the circuit, representing the circuit elements without atoms, as the *cavity* portion of the equivalent circuit, since these elements do represent the resonant cavity of a maser device without atoms present. The combination of the resonant cavity plus the separately resonant atoms yields the doubly resonant circuit shown in Fig. 2-7. Later we will examine some of the interesting results that arise from the doubly resonant nature of this circuit.

The values of the circuit elements in Fig. 2-7 can be related to known or measurable properties of the real cavity and atoms in any real device. We have already seen in Eqs. (20) of Sec. 2-4 how the atomic circuit elements L_a, R_a, and C_a may be related to the capacitance C, the atomic resonance frequency ω_a, the damping rate or linewidth $\gamma \equiv \Delta\omega_a$, and the peak susceptibility χ_0'' of an atomic transition. Similarly, the circuit elements L, R, and C of the cavity portion may be related to the cavity resonance frequency ω_c and the cavity $Q \equiv Q_c$ through the expressions

$$\omega_c{}^2 = \frac{1}{LC} \qquad Q_c = \frac{R}{\omega_c L} = \omega_c RC \tag{1}$$

Inverting these expressions leads to the results

$$G \equiv R^{-1} = \frac{\omega_c C}{Q_c} \qquad L = (\omega_c{}^2 C)^{-1} \qquad C = C \tag{2}$$

These results, together with Eq. (20) of Sec. 2-4, determine all the other circuit elements in Fig. 2-7 in relation to the capacitance C.

If we are given any real resonant cavity at any frequency, containing a collection of real resonant atoms, then the two resonance frequencies (ω_c and ω_a) and the two resonant Q terms ($Q_a \equiv \omega_a/\Delta\omega_a$ and Q_c) are significant measurable physical properties of the cavity alone and of the atoms alone. The only remaining significant factor in the combined cavity-plus-atoms system is some measure of how heavily the cavity resonance is loaded by the presence of the atoms (or vice versa). The peak susceptibility χ_0'' furnishes this information, and given the five physically measurable parameters ω_c, Q_c, ω_a, Q_a, and χ_0'' for any real system, we can calculate the values of all the circuit elements in a lumped equivalent circuit for that real system in relation to the one element C.

■ We will now introduce a slightly different way of describing the strength of the interaction between cavity and atoms. We have the cavity $Q \equiv Q_c$, which is the Q of the parallel *LRC* part of the lumped circuit, and the atomic linewidth $Q \equiv Q_a = \omega_a/\Delta\omega_a$, which is the Q of the series $L_a R_a C_a$ part of the circuit. We will now consider the Q that is obtained if we consider the *cavity* reactance elements L and C loaded by the *atomic* conductance element $G_a \equiv R_a{}^{-1}$. Figure 2-8 illustrates the definitions of these three different Q values. The new hybrid or interaction Q, which we will denote as Q_m, is thus

MASER OR MOLECULAR Q_m

$$Q_m \equiv \omega_a R_a C = \frac{R_a}{\omega_a L} \tag{3}$$

(If ω_a and ω_c are close enough to each other, as they will be in any useful real device, then it makes little or no difference whether we use ω_a or ω_c in defining the Q_m.) We

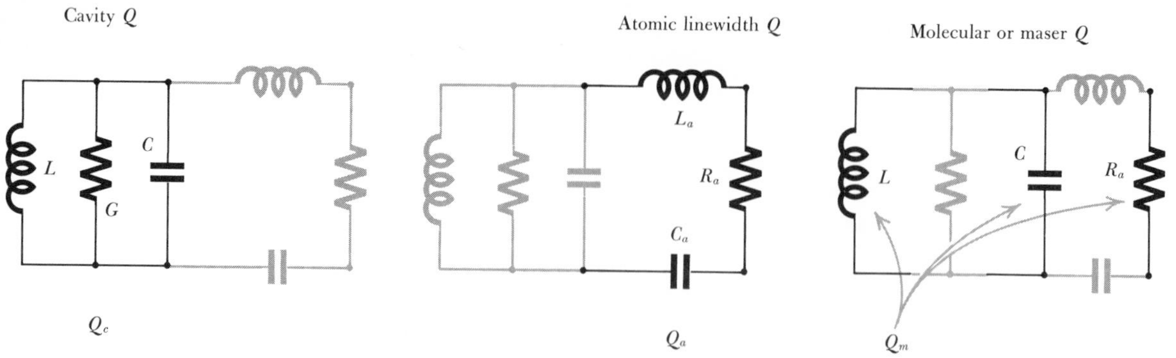

Cavity Q Atomic linewidth Q Molecular or maser Q

Q_c Q_a Q_m

FIG. 2-8 Diagrams illustrating the physical significance of the empty cavity Q_c, the atomic linewidth Q_a, and the interaction or molecular Q_m.

call this parameter Q_m because we will later be able to interpret it as a kind of *maser Q*. It will be of considerable importance later on in determining the strength of maser action and the performance limitations of maser devices. For the time being, however, we may call it the *molecular Q*, since it is a Q factor which determines how strongly the cavity is loaded by the atoms or molecules that are placed in it.

From our earlier results in Sec. 2-4 we find immediately that

$$Q_m = \omega R_a C = \frac{1}{\chi_0''} \tag{4}$$

That is, Q_m is simply the reciprocal peak midband susceptibility χ_0'' of the atomic collection, so that Q_m is simply another way of expressing this factor. Note that in usual circuit discussions a high Q value generally means a low level of unwanted losses in a circuit, and so there is a tendency to consider large Q values as desirable. It is important to realize, however, that in this instance a *low* value of the molecular Q_m is desirable because it implies a strong atomic response χ_0'' and a generally desirable heavy coupling or loading of the circuit by the atoms. In maser applications a low value of Q_m, and hence a high value of the reciprocal $1/Q_m$, will mean the largest gain-bandwidth product and the best performance for a practical maser device.

SUMMARY OF THE COMPLETE EQUIVALENT CIRCUIT ▪ We can now summarize all these results by rewriting the five basic relations connecting the physical parameters for any real cavity maser device with the circuit elements for the lumped equivalent circuit of Fig. 2-7:

$$\omega_c^2 = \frac{1}{LC} \qquad Q_c = \omega_c RC = \frac{\omega_c C}{G}$$

$$\omega_a^2 = \frac{1}{L_a C_a} \qquad Q_a^2 = \frac{\omega_a L_a}{R_a} \qquad Q_m = \omega R_a C \tag{5}$$

We have here only five real device parameters (ω_c, Q_c, ω_a, Q_a, and Q_m), whereas there are six circuit elements (L, R, C, L_a, R_a, and C_a) to be determined in the equivalent circuit. However, there is always an arbitrary impedance scaling factor involved in representing any real device by a lumped equivalent circuit. That is, to obtain correct experimental predictions from an equivalent circuit (for example, predictions of the stability or the growth rate of the system), all that is needed are the values of the lumped-circuit elements relative to some arbitrarily chosen reference element (we used the capacitance C in our earlier expressions). The five parameters above provide all the information that is necessary to represent any real device by an accurate lumped equivalent circuit. There will always be the arbitrary impedance scaling factor or choice of impedance reference level (choice of C value), which does not enter into any experimental predictions obtained from the equivalent circuit.

We will develop these ideas further and make extensive use of the equivalent circuit in Chap. 5 and subsequent chapters.

■ There are unfortunately no strong electric-dipole transitions in any real atoms in the microwave frequency range or lower (most strong electric-dipole transitions are in the optical frequency range). Hence there are no convenient ways to demonstrate the ideas above in terms of electric-dipole atoms with real lumped electric circuits, or even with microwave resonant cavities. There are, however, strong atomic resonances that occur at microwave and lower frequencies due to *magnetic-dipole transitions.* As we will see in Chap. 4, the induced atomic motion in a magnetic-dipole transition differs in detail from that in an electric-dipole transition, but the general $\chi'(\omega)$ and $\chi''(\omega)$ properties and the resulting equivalent circuits are essentially the same. Thus the following experiment, conducted at microwave frequency with a strong magnet-dipole transition, could in principle be carried out with an electric-dipole transition if one were available. The lumped-circuit model of Figs. 2-7 and 2-8 really turns out to be valid also for *optical*-frequency experiments, but for a first demonstration a lower-frequency experiment will provide a closer parallel.

Figure 2-9a shows the basic experiment. A resonant circuit—to be specific, a microwave resonant cavity with a resonance frequency in the range of ~9000 MHz— is driven by a swept-frequency signal generator whose output is swept in frequency about the resonance frequency ω_c of the tuned circuit. By means of a microwave component known as a *directional coupler,* the power reflected back from the resonant cir-

EXPERIMENTAL
DEMONSTRATION

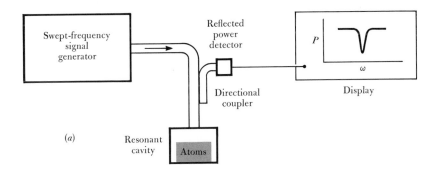

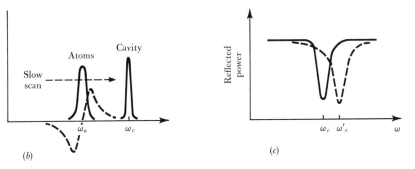

FIG. 2-9 An experiment to show the reactive effects of $\chi'(\omega)$ on the resonant frequency of a tuned circuit. The apparatus sketched in (a) displays reflected power from the tuned circuit versus frequency, showing the usual cavity dip. When the atomic resonance frequency ω_a is tuned near the cavity frequency ω_c as in (b), the observed cavity dip shifts, or pushes, to one side, to a shifted resonant frequency ω'_c, as shown by the dashed line in (c).

cuit is monitored, detected, and displayed against the swept signal frequency on an oscilloscope screen or other display unit. Since the resonant circuit absorbs power in its internal losses when driven at its resonance frequency but reflects most of the incident power when the incident frequency is off resonance on either side, the result is the usual *cavity dip,* corresponding to the cavity resonance curve, as illustrated in Figs. 2-9a and 2-9c.

Suppose that this cavity dip is monitored continuously while the resonance frequency ω_a of the atoms inside the cavity is slowly scanned from well below ω_c to well above ω_c, as illustrated in Fig. 2-9b. In a real device these atoms might be the Cr^{3+} ions in a large sample of dark ruby filling the microwave cavity, and the tuning of the resonance frequency ω_a would be accomplished by changing the magnitude of the dc magnetic field B_0 applied to the ruby sample (the resonance frequency ω_a of magnetic-dipole or magnetic-resonance transitions of this type can generally be tuned by varying the strength of a dc magnetic field applied to the atoms).

The reactive effects of the atomic transition then show up very clearly as follows. When the atomic resonance frequency ω_a increases to within an atomic linewidth or two of the unperturbed cavity frequency ω_c, the reactive effects of the atomic transition (as shown by the dashed line in Fig. 2-9b) contribute some additional reactance to the cavity tuned circuit, and the resonance frequency of the tuned circuit appears to shift to a slightly displaced apparent frequency ω_c' (as shown by the dashed line in Fig. 2-9c). In other words, the cavity dip as seen on the swept-frequency display appears to shift or push slightly to one side when the atomic resonance comes near the unperturbed cavity resonance. When the atomic and cavity resonances become exactly coincident, however, there is no cavity frequency shift, since the reactive effects are zero at the atomic line center. However, as the atomic frequency moves on to the other side of the cavity frequency, the cavity dip pushes in the opposite direction, since the reactive contribution of the atomic transition is then opposite in sign.

When the atomic and cavity resonances are exactly coincident, although there is no cavity frequency shift, there is a change in the cavity losses because of the absorptive part $\chi''(\omega)$ of the atomic response, and so the depth of the cavity dip changes. As we will see in Chap. 5, this change in depth of the cavity dip may be either upward or downward, depending on whether the resonant circuit is undercoupled or overcoupled to the external measuring circuitry.

The shift in apparent cavity resonance frequency caused by the atomic reactive effects is not large. However, in an X-band microwave cavity (~ 9000 MHz) of fairly high Q, filled with a sample of dark ruby so as to have a fairly high density of Cr^{3+} ions, the shift can readily be observed on an oscilloscope screen even with the cavity and sample at room temperature. Cooling the ruby sample to, say, liquid-nitrogen temperature will make the observed effect approximately four times stronger. This observed frequency shift can also, with a little effort, be analyzed with the equivalent circuit of Fig. 2-7 (see Prob. 2-11 for details). The amount of frequency push turns out to be proportional to the reciprocal molecular Q_m^{-1}, as might be expected, since this is a measure of the strength of the atomic effects on the resonant circuit. As we will see in Chaps. 5 and 10, this cavity pushing effect for an absorptive transition is very closely related to some important atomic frequency-pulling effects observed in real maser and laser amplifiers and oscillators.

PROBLEMS

2-1. Discuss the magnitude and the phase of the forced response $x(t)$ of the classical electron-oscillator model to a sinusoidal applied electric field $e_x(t)$ as a function of the driving frequency ω, from well below resonance to well above resonance. Explain in mechanical terms the power transfer from the applied signal to the oscillator for frequencies at and near resonance, and describe the behavior of the oscillator in the reactive regime off resonance.

2-2. Suppose we expand the semiclassical atomic model of Fig. 2-1 by assuming that the electronic charge cloud is a rigid, uniform, spherical distribution of negative charge with total mass Zm, total charge $-Ze$, and diameter $2a$, surrounding a point nucleus of mass ZM and charge $+Ze$, where Z is the atomic number, m is the electron mass, M is the proton mass, and e is electronic charge. Suppose that this rigid electronic charge cloud is displaced slightly from a concentric position about the nucleus (the charge cloud is assumed to be "transparent" to the nucleus). Find the net restoring force on the displaced charge cloud (or, alternatively, find the resulting change in total potential energy of the system) for small displacements. Find the resonance frequency at which the charge cloud will oscillate about the nucleus (it may be assumed that only the electronic charge cloud will move appreciably, since $M \gg m$). Using the radius of the first Bohr orbit in the Bohr model of an atom as a first guess for the outside radius a of the charge cloud, compute a numerical value for the resonance frequency derived above.

2-3. Consider a *two-dimensional* classical electron oscillator (a point electron free to move in two dimensions on an xy plane) with a linear central restoring force such that the restoring force terms are $f_x = -Kx$ and $f_y = -Ky$. Assume that there is also a dc magnetic field B_0 normal to the xy plane and that there are equal damping factors γ_a for both the x and y components of motion.

For a sinusoidal E field $e_x(t)$ applied in the x direction, find the resulting steady-state displacements $x(t)$ and $y(t)$ of the oscillator as a function of the applied frequency (you will have to solve two coupled equations of motion, and there may be two resonances). Discuss, with appropriate sketches, the nature of the electron motion as a function of the various parameters involved (since the analytic expressions become somewhat complicated, it will be useful to consider a large enough value of B_0 that the Zeeman splitting of the two resonances is large compared to their individual linewidths). Explore in particular the form of the electron motion near each resonance peak.

2-4. At what frequency (and what wavelength) will the Q_a of a classical electron oscillator be reduced to unity, provided that purely radiative decay is the only decay or line-broadening mechanism that is operative?

2-5. Evaluate the radiative decay rate and the radiative lifetime for a classical electron oscillator with the same resonance frequency as the He-Ne 6328-Å laser line. Also evaluate the atomic linewidth Q_a that would apply if this were the only damping or line-broadening effect present. *Note:* The actual 6328-Å transition in neon is much weaker, i.e., it has a much slower radiative decay rate; also, other broadening mechanisms, such as collision and doppler broadening, are present in the real He-Ne laser.

2-6. The decay mechanism for the 6934-Å laser transition of the Cr^{3+} ion used in the ruby laser is known to be almost purely radiative, especially at lower temperatures, with a measured lifetime $\tau \approx 4.3$ msec. Approximately what is the oscillator strength for this transition?

2-7. Consider a complex-plane plot of the locus of the complex lorentzian susceptibility $\tilde{\chi}(\omega)$ of a classical electron oscillator with frequency ω as a parameter. Using a coordinate system in which χ' is plotted along the x axis and χ'' is plotted along the y axis, plot a contour showing how $\tilde{\chi}(\omega)$ varies as the frequency ω is varied, from well below to well above resonance. What is the geometric or analytical form of this contour?

2-8. Some types of spectrometers used to study atomic resonances yield as their output signal, not the susceptibility components $\chi'(\omega)$ or $\chi''(\omega)$, but a plot of the first derivative $(d/d\omega)\chi''(\omega)$ versus ω. This derivative of $\chi''(\omega)$ has two peaks of opposite sign and looks much like $\chi'(\omega)$. Find the full linewidth $\Delta f_a'$ between these two peaks for a lorentzian transition, and relate this width $\Delta f_a'$ to the atomic linewidth Δf_a as we have chosen to define it.

2-9. At what distance from resonance, on either side, will the difference between the exact form and the approximate lorentzian form for the classical electron-oscillator response become as large as 10 percent? Assume high-Q resonances.

2-10. Assume that a sinusoidal voltage $v(t)$ with peak value V is applied across the capacitance-plus-atoms model of Fig. 2-5. Evaluate the reactive stored energy $\frac{1}{2}L_a i_a^2$ that this voltage creates in the inductance of the atomic equivalent circuit. Also evaluate the total kinetic energy $\frac{1}{2}mu_x^2$ summed over all the model atoms in the system under these same conditions. Do these two reactive stored energies have the same value? Why?

2-11. Section 2-5 describes how the apparent resonance frequency ω_c' of a tuned circuit or cavity shifts, or is pushed first in one direction and then in the other, as the resonance frequency ω_a of an absorptive atomic transition is slowly scanned from somewhat below to somewhat above the unshifted cavity resonance frequency ω_c. Analyze this effect with the cavity-plus-atoms equivalent circuit of Fig. 2-7 by calculating the total admittance $\tilde{Y}(\omega) = G(\omega) + jB(\omega)$ into this circuit, assuming that in general $\omega_a \neq \omega_c$. Find the resonance frequency ω_c' of this input admittance if *resonance* is defined here as that frequency $\omega = \omega_c'$ at which the input susceptance $B(\omega) = 0$. Sketch and discuss how this apparent resonance frequency ω_c' shifts away from the unperturbed resonance frequency ω_c as the atomic frequency ω_a is varied over a range of several atomic linewidths above and below the empty-cavity resonance frequency. Does the atomic effect actually *push* or *pull* the apparent cavity frequency?

Hint: This problem becomes a bit involved, but it can be solved, at least implicitly. It may be easier to calculate $\omega_a - \omega_c$ as a function of $\omega_c' - \omega_c$, rather than the reverse. All resonance terms should be approximated by the general lorentzian form, and the answers should come out in terms of only the various resonance frequencies and Q parameters. Strictly speaking, resonance might be more accurately defined as that frequency at which $|\tilde{Y}(\omega)|$ is a minimum, but for high-Q circuits it is much easier and almost as accurate to calculate instead the frequency at which $B(\omega)$ is zero.

REFERENCES

2-1. L. Allen, "Atomic Line Strengths," in E. V. Condon and H. Odishaw (eds.), *Handbook of Physics*, part 7, chap. 3, McGraw-Hill, New York, 1958.

2-2. M. Garbuny, *Optical Physics*, Academic Press, New York, 1965.

2-3. H. A. Lorentz, *The Theory of Electrons*, 2d ed., Dover Publications, New York, 1952 (paperback).

2-4. R. G. Newburgh, "Radiation and the classical electron," *Am. J. Phys.*, **36**:399 (May, 1968).

2-5. W. K. H. Panofsky and M. Phillips, *Classical Electricity and Magnetism*, Addison-Wesley, Reading, Mass., 1955.

2-6. G. N. Plass, "Classical electrodynamical equations of motion with radiative reaction," *Rev. Mod. Phys.*, **33**:37 (January, 1961).

2-7. F. Rohrlich, *Classical Charged Particles*, Addison-Wesley, Reading, Mass., 1965.

2-8. B. Rossi, *Optics*, Addison-Wesley, Reading, Mass., 1957.

2-9. M. D. Sirkis and N. Holonyak, "Currents induced by moving charges," *Am. J. Phys.*, **34**:943 (October, 1966).

2-10. J. C. Slater, *Quantum Theory of Molecules and Solids*, vol. III, *Insulators, Semiconductors, and Metals*, McGraw-Hill, New York, 1967.

2-11. J. M. Stone, *Radiation and Optics*, McGraw-Hill, New York, 1963.

2-12. R. W. Wood, *Optical Physics*, 3d ed., Macmillan, New York, 1934.

LIFETIME
AND
COLLISION BROADENING
OF
ATOMIC TRANSITIONS

The linewidth of a given transition in a collection of atoms is an important property of that transition, especially for laser and maser applications. We found in Chap. 1 that a nonzero energy-damping rate for a classical oscillator caused a corresponding nonzero line-width for its resonance behavior. We also saw that radiative damping is one energy-damping mechanism that is always present in any classical oscillator or in any real atomic transition. There are, however, several additional energy-damping mechanisms that can increase the total energy-damping rate, and hence further broaden the total resonance linewidth of an oscillator or an atom. More important, there are also several physical mechanisms that can broaden the resonant response of a transition still further without increasing the energy-damping rate. In this chapter we will discuss one of the most important of these additional broadening mechanisms.

We will first review the *lifetime broadening* of atomic resonances, that is, the broadening caused by energy-damping or decay mechanisms of all sorts. We will then discuss the important concept of *collision broadening,* caused by *random dephasing processes* which lead to broadening of an atomic or oscillator response without changing the energy-damping rate at all. An understanding of collision broadening and dephasing is basic to an understanding of the general resonance behavior of many real atomic transitions. Other major line-broadening mechanisms, including the *doppler-broadening* of many optical transitions in gases, will be discussed later, in Chap. 9.

3-1 LIFETIME BROADENING OF AN ATOMIC RESONANCE

As we have seen, for a classical electron oscillator with energy-decay rate γ and energy-decay lifetime $\tau \equiv \gamma^{-1}$ the full radian-frequency linewidth $\Delta\omega_a$ of the oscillator response is

$$\Delta\omega_a \equiv \gamma \qquad \text{or} \qquad \Delta\omega_a \tau = 1 \tag{1}$$

Every $m \leftrightarrow n$ transition or internal resonant motion of a real atom will similarly have a total energy-decay rate γ_{mn} and an energy-decay lifetime $\tau_{mn} \equiv \gamma_{mn}^{-1}$, representing the total rate at which that internal resonant motion loses energy. If no line-broadening mechanisms other than energy damping are operative, the real atomic transition will exhibit a complex lorentzian resonance response exactly like that in the classical electron-oscillator model (with the appropriate changes stated in Sec. 2-3). The resulting lifetime-broadened atomic-resonance linewidth will be

$$\Delta\omega_{mn} = \gamma_{mn} = \tau_{mn}^{-1} \tag{2}$$

The resonance broadening caused by energy damping or decay is referred to in general as *lifetime broadening* of the atomic transition. Lifetime broadening is the most fundamental type of line broadening, although it is by no means always the strongest broadening mechanism present.

PURELY RADIATIVE LIFETIME BROADENING

■ In the absence of any other damping mechanisms, a classical oscillator (or a real atomic transition) will always lose energy at a purely radiative damping rate $\gamma_{\text{rad}} \equiv 1/\tau_{\text{rad}}$ through emission of electromagnetic radiation to its surroundings. The radiative damping rate for a classical electron oscillator was given in Chap. 1. We also saw that the radiative damping rates for real atomic transitions are widely different for different transitions, depending on the oscillator strength of the particular transitions. Note that what we are here calling *radiative damping* in real atoms is exactly the same physical process as the *spontaneous emission* or *fluorescence* described in Sec. 1-3. The lifetime τ_{rad} associated with this process is called the (purely) *radiative lifetime,* and the associated broadening of an atomic resonance due to this process alone is called the *radiative linewidth* of the transition. For example, the radiative lifetime of a classical oscillator (or of a strongly allowed electric-dipole atomic transition) in the optical frequency range is $\tau_{\text{rad}} \sim 10^{-8}$ sec, and so the associated purely radiative linewidth is $\Delta f_a \equiv \Delta\omega_a/2\pi \sim 15$ MHz.

NONRADIATIVE DAMPING

■ Atomic transitions may also be damped (in the sense of losing internal energy) by other decay mechanisms. An atom in a crystal or solid, for example, can lose internal energy by giving energy to the thermal lattice vibrations of the surrounding solid.[1]

---

[1] The random thermal vibrations of a crystal lattice or of the atoms in a solid can equally well be described as the *heat energy* or *thermal energy* of the solid, as *random acoustic vibrations* in the solid, or as *thermal phonons,* where a *phonon* refers to one quantum of acoustic energy, in analogy with the photon as one quantum of electromagnetic energy. These names all refer to the same physical quantity in the solid.

This damping of the atom's internal motions by energy loss to the surrounding solid is referred to as *nonradiative damping*. The term "nonradiative" is something of a misnomer here, since this type of damping simply means that the atom spontaneously radiates acoustic phonons as well as electromagnetic photons to its surroundings. Both the radiative and the nonradiative processes represent a form of spontaneous emission, with a very similar quantum-theoretical interpretation. However, the radiative, or electromagnetic, spontaneous emission consists of radiation that can in general be readily measured or observed, whereas the nonradiative, or acoustic, spontaneous emission is radiation that is less readily detected.

Other forms of nonradiative damping or energy dissipation are also available to atoms. For example, an atom in a gas may lose internal energy through *inelastic collisions* with the walls of the container or with other atoms. In such inelastic collisions the atom gets rid of internal energy by transferring it to the walls or to the other atoms. In general, we are interested in any mechanism by which an atom can damp the internal energy associated with its internal oscillatory motions.

The total damping rate γ_{mn} for a given transition is then the sum of the radiative and all the nonradiative damping rates, since these decay mechanisms operate simultaneously and in parallel. That is, we may write the total damping rate as

$$\gamma_{mn,\text{total}} = \gamma_{mn,\text{rad}} + \gamma_{mn,\text{nonrad}} \tag{3}$$

This total γ_{mn} is the damping rate that should be used in computing the full lifetime broadening of a transition. It always includes some radiative contribution; the nonradiative contribution may or may not be significant, depending on the physical circumstances. Where significant nonradiative damping does occur, it may be much stronger than the purely radiative contribution. This will, of course, considerably broaden the associated resonance line.

■ If we associate a lifetime τ_i with each damping rate γ_i by writing $\gamma_i \equiv 1/\tau_i$, we must combine the effects of different decay mechanisms by adding the reciprocal lifetimes: that is,

COMBINING DIFFERENT DECAY MECHANISMS

$$\frac{1}{\tau_{mn,\text{total}}} = \frac{1}{\tau_{mn,\text{rad}}} + \frac{1}{\tau_{mn,\text{nonrad}}} \tag{4}$$

where the total τ_{mn} represents the actual or observed lifetime that will be measured for the transition. If nonradiative damping is present, this observed lifetime will inevitably be shorter than the purely radiative lifetime. For example, in observing the fluorescent emission from an atomic system after some sort of initial excitation pulse, the radiation we will see represents the purely radiative part of the decay, but the lifetime with which the observed emission decreases is the total decay lifetime, including radiative and nonradiative processes.

Optical-frequency transitions among levels of atoms in very-low-pressure gases and gas discharges can be predominantly radiatively damped if nonradiative damping mechanisms are weak or absent. As a consequence, the resonances of atoms in very-low-pressure gases can be very sharp and narrow.[1] Transitions of atoms in crystals and solids, by contrast, often show rapid nonradiative decay, because the coupling of the internal atomic oscillations to the surrounding lattice is strong, and nonradiative decay

---

[1] The doppler broadening mechanism to be described in Chap. 9 is usually very important for such transitions, however.

processes can occur readily. Such transitions will have short lifetimes and broad line-widths. A few transitions of selected atoms in solids do turn out to be decoupled from the lattice vibrations and to have more or less predominantly radiative decay. These transitions, with their relatively long lifetimes and narrow linewidths, are preferred for solid-state lasers. The R_1 and R_2 laser lines in ruby and selected narrow fluorescent lines of rare-earth ions in crystals, such as the 1.06-μ Nd^{3+} line, are examples of such transitions. Thus the 6943-Å laser line in ruby[1] has a lifetime of $\tau \approx \tau_{\text{rad}} \sim 4.3$ msec, or $\gamma_{\text{rad}} \approx \mathcal{N}_{\text{rad}} \approx 230$ sec^{-1}.

Examination of the classical radiative-damping expression will show that radiative decay rates become vanishingly small at microwave and lower transition frequencies, and hence radiative decay becomes an insignificant damping mechanism (lower frequency implies smaller acceleration for the same peak oscillation amplitude, and radiative damping is related to acceleration). Most microwave-frequency and lower magnetic-resonance transitions lose their energy entirely by nonradiative relaxation. This is often called *spin-lattice relaxation*, since the energy is transferred from the magnetic spins to the surrounding lattice.

LIFETIME BROADENING AND THE UNCERTAINTY PRINCIPLE

■ The *uncertainty principle* of quantum theory can be stated in many different ways, one of which is

$$\Delta E \, \Delta t \geq \tfrac{1}{2} \hbar \tag{5}$$

In this form the principle says that if the energy of a quantum system is measured in an experiment which takes a length of time $\sim \Delta t$ to perform, then the energy cannot possibly be measured to an accuracy much better than $\sim \Delta E$, where $\Delta E \geq \hbar / 2 \, \Delta t$.

In the case of an atomic transition between two quantum levels in an atom we might propose to measure the energy E of the upper level in relation to the lower level by measuring the frequency ω of the transition between the levels, since the energy gap is $E = \hbar \omega$. However, if the transition has a finite linewidth $\Delta \omega = \gamma = 1/\tau$, this will set a limit of, say, $\Delta \omega / 2$ on how accurately the transition frequency can be measured. The resulting energy uncertainty will be of order of magnitude

$$\Delta E \approx \frac{\hbar \, \Delta \omega}{2} = \frac{\hbar \gamma}{2} \tag{6}$$

where γ is the damping rate of the lifetime-broadened transition. However, if an atom remains in the upper level for only about one lifetime τ before dropping to the lower level, an experiment on that atom cannot possibly last longer than about $\Delta t \approx \tau \equiv \gamma^{-1}$, on the average. We therefore obtain

$$\Delta E \, \Delta t \approx \frac{\hbar \gamma}{2} \gamma^{-1} \approx \frac{\hbar}{2} \tag{7}$$

In other words, lifetime broadening and the uncertainty principle applied to this particular example say the same thing. We can list lifetime broadening as an example of the working of the uncertainty principle if we like, although we have certainly derived it without any use of the uncertainty principle or of quantum mechanics.

[1] The full linewidth of this ruby transition is very, very much broader than the lifetime-broadened value, however, because of another broadening mechanism described in Chap. 9.

3-2   BROADENING OF AN ATOMIC RESONANCE BY DEPHASING COLLISIONS

At this point we are faced with an important new concept: the broadening of an atomic resonance due to random collisions between atoms, or random *dephasing* of the resonant response. Such processes can broaden the resonant response of a classical oscillator or an atomic transition, over and above the lifetime broadening, without changing or increasing the energy-damping rate of the transition.

■ In the following discussion we will assume that our classical electron-oscillator model of Chap. 2 has some damping rate γ and an applied ac signal as before. However, we will now suppose in addition that at irregular, randomly occurring intervals each oscillator or atom undergoes a dephasing process we may call a *collision*. The essential characteristic of a dephasing collision is that it suddenly interrupts the internal oscillatory motion of the oscillator or atom in such a way that the atom restarts its driven motion after the collision with a completely random initial phase. That is, we suppose that the initial phase of the oscillatory motion just after the collision may have any value between 0 and 2π with equal probability; all "memory" of the phase of the motion just before the collision is destroyed. Figure 3-1 illustrates this type of randomly interrupted sinusoidal motion.

THE BASIC COLLISION OR DEPHASING PROCESS

It may be helpful to picture this collision process in exactly the mechanical fashion suggested by the common meaning of the word—that is, as a jarring mechanical impact of the oscillator as a whole with another atom (or with the walls of a container), such that the oscillator loses all memory of its previous motion and starts on a new section of forced oscillation. Just such mechanical collisions between atoms do occur in gases and have just the effects we will derive in this section. Hence this collision description furnishes a realistic picture for real atoms in gases. Simple expressions for the rates at which such collisions occur can even be predicted from kinetic theory as functions of the pressure and temperature of the gas (see Sec. 3-4). Dephasing processes which are, in effect, very much like collisions also occur with atoms fixed in position in a crystal lattice or a solid. Each atom in a solid is subjected to ac electromagnetic fields due to the internal oscillations of other similar atoms near it in the solid. These ac fields are weak, but they are also very close in frequency to the resonances of the atom. Each atom couples randomly to its neighboring atoms through these so-called *dipolar interactions* (as well as in other ways not explained in detail here). The net result of these interactions among neighboring atoms is very much as if repeated dephasing collisions occurred between the atoms. The net effects of dipolar and other related interactions among atoms are enough like the effects of collisions that collision termi-

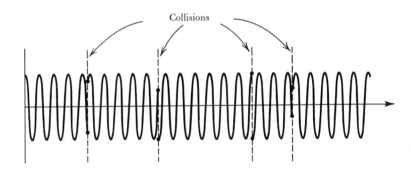

FIG. 3-1 Example of a sinusoidal oscillation interrupted by randomly occurring dephasing events, or collisions. Note the random phases with which the oscillation restarts after each collision.

nology and collision results are also applicable to a considerable extent even in solids. Collision concepts are thus often applied to solids, even though actual physical collisions do not occur. We will use the easily visualized term *collision* to refer to any sort of random dephasing event in general.

ELASTIC AND INELASTIC COLLISIONS

■ The collisions experienced by an atom may be either elastic or inelastic. If the atom does not lose any of its internal oscillatory energy during a collision (or if two similar atoms collide and exchange internal energy with no net loss), the collision is said to be an *elastic collision*. Although the internal motion of the atom has the same amount of energy after an elastic collision, the phase of this motion (relative to the applied ac field or to the precollision motion) is randomly altered. Elastic collisions thus provide a dephasing mechanism without contributing to the energy-decay or damping rate γ of a transition.

An *inelastic collision* is one in which an atom loses some or all of the energy associated with its internal oscillatory motion. The internal energy may be transformed during the collision into kinetic energy of the same atom or of the recoiling partner in the collision, or given to a wall with which the atom collided, or transformed into other excitations of the colliding atoms. In any event, inelastic collisions not only have dephasing effects on the atomic internal motion, but also contribute to the overall or total damping rate γ for the internal motion. Elastic and inelastic collisions can occur simultaneously, at different collision rates, in the same collection of atoms.

COLLISION STATISTICS

■ In order to analyze the broadening effects caused by collisions, we must first derive some simple statistical properties of collisions. Consider some large group of n atoms in a collection. The basis of our derivation is the reasonable assumption that the individual atoms in this group will undergo collisions randomly and independently. Hence we suppose that the small number Δn of atoms in this large group that will suffer collisions during a short time interval Δt is directly proportional to the total number of atoms n in the group and to the length Δt of the time interval; that is, we assume that

$$\Delta n \equiv k_c n\,\Delta t = \frac{n\,\Delta t}{T_2} \tag{1}$$

The constant k_c must have the dimension per unit time. The conventional notation is to write $k_c \equiv 1/T_2$, where T_2 is a characteristic time called the *collision time* or *dephasing time*. The constant k_c is often called the *collision frequency*. It can be shown that if we follow the career of any single atom through many successive collisions, then T_2 is the average interval between collisions for that single atom.

Let us next consider a large initial group of n_0 atoms at $t = 0$ and ask how many of these—call the number $n(t)$—will have suffered *no collisions at all* at a time t later. From our assumption above, given a group of $n(t)$ atoms still uncollided at time t, the number Δn from that group that will suffer collisions during the ensuing interval Δt (between t and $t + \Delta t$) will be

$$\Delta n = T_2^{-1} n(t)\,\Delta t \tag{2}$$

Since these Δn atoms are thereby lost from the uncollided group $n(t)$, the number remaining in the uncollided group after the interval Δt is $n - \Delta n$. Thus the differential equation governing the time variation of the uncollided number $n(t)$ is simply

$$\frac{d}{dt}\,n(t) \equiv \lim_{\Delta t \to 0} \frac{-\Delta n}{\Delta t} = -\frac{1}{T_2}\,n(t) \tag{3}$$

The solution to this equation with the initial condition $n(t) = n_0(t = 0)$ is, of course,

$$n(t) = n_0 e^{-t/T_2} \tag{4}$$

which is shown in Fig. 3-2.

Thus, out of a group of n_0 initial atoms at $t = 0$, only $n_0 e^{-t/T_2}$ atoms will still have suffered no collisions at all after time t (all the others will have suffered one or more collisions). To put this another way, if we observe any single atom beginning at $t = 0$, the probability that after a time interval t this atom will have suffered no collisions at all is e^{-t/T_2}. This probability of no collisions of course approaches zero after a few collision times T_2.

■ We can now derive an expression for the resonance-like broadening that results from these random collisions. Let us consider the motion $x(t)$ at time t of a driven oscillator and assume that this oscillator suffered its last previous collision at an earlier time t_0 and began with an initial motion $\tilde{X}_0$ just after this collision. To find the motion at time t we must solve the equation of motion for the classical electron oscillator, as given in Secs. 2-1 and 2-2, with both the transient and steady-state terms included in the solution. This problem is straightforward, and the resulting motion may be written to a close approximation as

$$x(t: \tilde{X}_0, t_0) = \tilde{X}(\omega)e^{j\omega t} + [\tilde{X}_0 - \tilde{X}(\omega)e^{j\omega t_0}]e^{(-\gamma/2 + j\omega_a)(t-t_0)} \tag{5}$$

The notation $x(t: \tilde{X}_0, t_0)$ means that this is the internal motion $x(t)$ of the atom, given that it started with initial motion $\tilde{X}_0$ just after a collision at $t = t_0$. Taking the real part of the right-hand side of the equation is, of course, understood.

The first term in the solution is the forced or steady-state motion with the steady-state response calculated in Chap. 2,

$$\tilde{X}(\omega) = j\frac{e}{m\omega\gamma}\frac{1}{1 + 2j(\omega - \omega_a)/\gamma}\tilde{E}_x(\omega) \tag{6}$$

where $\tilde{E}_x(\omega)$ is, as before, the sinusoidal applied electric field. The second term is the transient term, necessary to satisfy the specified initial conditions $\tilde{X}_0$ just after the collision at t_0. To verify the initial conditions we note that if we set $t = t_0$ in the total solution, then we have for the initial displacement

$$x(t_0) = \text{Re } \tilde{X}_0 \tag{7}$$

where the Re operation is indicated explicitly. If we differentiate both sides of the total solution, set $t = t_0$, and take the real part, we obtain for the initial velocity

$$\dot{x}(t_0) = \text{Re}\left\{\left(j\omega_a - \frac{\gamma}{2}\right)\tilde{X}_0 + \left[j(\omega - \omega_a) - \frac{\gamma}{2}\right]\tilde{X}(\omega)e^{j\omega t_0}\right\} \tag{8}$$

But we are considering only frequencies for which $|\omega - \omega_a| \ll \omega_a$, and for reasonably sharp resonances $\gamma/2 \ll \omega_a$ also, so that to a good approximation the initial velocity becomes simply

$$\frac{\dot{x}(t_0)}{\omega} \approx \text{Im } \tilde{X}_0 \tag{9}$$

Thus the real and imaginary parts of $\tilde{X}_0$ essentially give the initial displacement and the initial velocity of the oscillator or atom just after the last previous collision.

DERIVATION OF COLLISION BROADENING

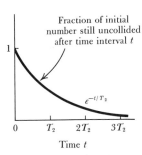

FIG. 3-2 The number of atoms not having yet suffered any collision at all after a time interval t decreases exponentially, with a time constant T_2.

■ The analysis of the line-broadening effects of collisions now proceeds as follows. Consider all the oscillators (a large number) in a collection, or even in a little unit volume within that collection, at a specific instant of time t. Each of these oscillators will have suffered its last previous collision at some different earlier time t_0 and will have started out after that collision with some different initial motion $\tilde{X}_0$. Figure 3-3 indicates some of the possible motions $x(t)$ for different oscillators in the collection. Our problem now is to calculate the average motion at time t of all the oscillators in the collection, where we mean by *average* the result of averaging over all the different earlier collision times t_0 and all the different possible initial conditions $\tilde{X}_0$. The motion $x(t: \tilde{X}_0, t_0)$ of a single oscillator depends, of course, on $\tilde{X}_0$ and t_0, as well as on t and on $\tilde{E}_x(\omega)$. To find the average motion we must average this result over the quantities $\tilde{X}_0$ and t_0, which are different for each atom in the collection. Evaluating these averages is our next task.

The phase and amplitude of $\tilde{X}_0$ give the phase and amplitude of the initial motion of any given oscillator in the collection just after its last collision. The essence of our random-phase assumption for the collision process, or the essence of what we mean by dephasing, is that the phase of the postcollision motion $\tilde{X}_0$ for different atoms is random and uniformly distributed over all possible values. But the average of many different sine waves with different phases, where any phase is equally probable, is just zero. If $\tilde{X}_0$ is equally likely to have any possible phase angle, then averaging over all possible phases of $\tilde{X}_0$ will entirely eliminate the $\tilde{X}_0$ term in the solution for $x(t: \tilde{X}_0, t_0)$. Hence the result of averaging over all phases of $\tilde{X}_0$ is

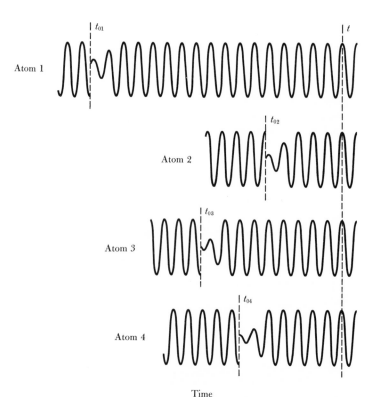

FIG. 3-3 We wish to find the average motion at time t of a collection of individual atoms, each of which had its last previous collision at a different earlier time t_0.

$$x_{\mathrm{av}}(t: t_0) = \tilde{X}(\omega)(e^{j\omega t} - e^{j\omega t_0}e^{(-\gamma/2+j\omega_a)(t-t_0)}) \tag{10}$$

Note that $\tilde{X}_0$ has entirely disappeared from the averaged result solely on the basis of its randomly distributed phase. The distribution of the postcollision amplitudes or energies, i.e., the postcollision distribution of $|\tilde{X}_0|$ or $|\tilde{X}_0|^2$, is irrelevant. We may deduce from this that dephasing collisions are equally effective whether the collisions are elastic or inelastic. Inelastic collisions contribute to energy damping, while elastic collisions do not, but the broadening effects of both are the same.

We must now consider all the oscillators at time t and ask how many of these had their last previous collisions at various earlier times t_0. One way of stating the collision probability results we derived earlier is to say that if we consider a number n_0 of oscillators at time $t = 0$, the number $\Delta n(t)$ of those that will experience their next collision within the small interval Δt between time t and $t + \Delta t$ is given by

$$\Delta n(t) = \frac{n_0 e^{-t/T_2}}{T_2} \qquad 0 \leq t \leq \infty \tag{11}$$

Most of the oscillators will have their next collisions within about one collision time or so, and very few of them will have their first collisions at times later than a few collision times T_2. But the random sequences of collisions and intervening periods for a collection of oscillators or atoms will be exactly the same statistically if we run time backward, i.e., if we examine the history of collisions for the atoms going backward in time. From this we may argue that if we consider a group of n_0 oscillators at $t = 0$, the number $\Delta n(t)$ that will have had their last previous collisions during a time interval Δt between the earlier (and hence negative) times t and $t + \Delta t$ will be given by the same distribution; that is,

$$\Delta n(t) = \frac{n_0 e^{-|t|/T_2}}{T_2} \Delta t \qquad -\infty \leq t \leq 0 \tag{12}$$

The absolute value appears in the exponent because the t values are now negative. This result tells us, among other things, that very few oscillators will have had their last previous collision more than a few collision times earlier.

Suppose we examine the collection of oscillators at a given time t and ask how many of these, $\Delta n(t_0)$, had their last previous collision during the time interval Δt_0 between t_0 and $t_0 + \Delta t_0$, that is, during an interval that occurred $t - t_0$ sec earlier. This is the same problem as above, except for a change in notation and a shift along the time scale. The number of oscillators (out of a total of n_0) that had their last collision in the range Δt_0 will be given by

$$\Delta n(t_0) = \frac{n_0 e^{-(t-t_0)/T_2}}{T_2} \Delta t_0 \qquad -\infty \leq t_0 \leq t \tag{13}$$

The average motion for an oscillator at time t must now be found by setting down the $\tilde{X}_0$-averaged motion $x(t: t_0)$ for an oscillator whose last collision was in the range Δt_0 about t_0, weighting this motion by the relative number of oscillators whose last collisions occurred in that range Δt_0, and averaging over all earlier values $t_0 \leq t$. In other words, we will obtain our final value, fully averaged over $\tilde{X}_0$ and t_0, by writing

$$x_{\mathrm{av}}(t) = \frac{\displaystyle\sum_{t_0 < t} x(t: t_0)\, \Delta n(t_0)}{\displaystyle\sum_{t_0 < t} \Delta n(t_0)} = \frac{\displaystyle\int_{-\infty}^{t} x(t: t_0)\, dn(t_0)}{\displaystyle\int_{-\infty}^{t} dn(t_0)} \tag{14}$$

If we convert Δn and Δt_0 into dn and dt_0, these sums become integrals over dt_0 for $-\infty \leq t_0 \leq t$, and with some minor algebraic manipulations this expression becomes

$$x_{\text{av}}(t) = \tilde{X}(\omega) T_2^{-1} \int_{t_0=-\infty}^{t_0=t} \left[e^{j\omega t_0} e^{(-\gamma/2 + j\omega_a)(t-t_0)} \right] e^{-(t-t_0)/T_2} \, dt_0 \tag{15}$$

The necessary integration is a bit lengthy, but straightforward. The final result of the averaging process is

$$x_{\text{av}}(t) = \frac{1 + 2j(\omega - \omega_a)/\gamma}{1 + 2/\gamma T_2 + 2j(\omega - \omega_a)/\gamma} \tilde{X}(\omega) e^{j\omega t} = \tilde{X}_{\text{av}}(\omega) e^{j\omega t} \tag{16}$$

The phasor amplitude of the average atomic motion $\tilde{X}_{\text{av}}(\omega)$, averaged over all the colliding atoms, is evidently

$$\tilde{X}_{\text{av}}(\omega) = \frac{1 + 2j(\omega - \omega_a)/\gamma}{1 + 2/\gamma T_2 + 2j(\omega - \omega_a)/\gamma} \tilde{X}(\omega) \tag{17}$$

However, with our previous results for $\tilde{X}(\omega)$ in terms of $\tilde{E}_x(\omega)$, this becomes

$$\tilde{X}_{\text{av}}(\omega) = j \frac{e}{m\omega(\gamma + 2T_2^{-1})} \frac{1}{1 + 2j(\omega - \omega_a)/(\gamma + 2T_2^{-1})} \tilde{E}_x(\omega) \tag{18}$$

This is the major result of our collision-broadening analysis.

RESULTS OF COLLISION
BROADENING

■ The most important feature of this result is immediately evident: *the collision-averaged result has exactly the same lorentzian form as the original response without collisions, except that the original damping rate γ is everywhere replaced by the expanded quantity $\gamma + 2T_2^{-1}$*. That is, the collision-broadened response may be written exactly as before in the form

$$\tilde{X}_{\text{av}}(\omega) = j \frac{e}{m\omega \, \Delta\omega_a} \frac{1}{1 + 2j(\omega - \omega_a)/\Delta\omega_a} \tilde{E}_x(\omega) \tag{19}$$

except that, whereas the linewidth $\Delta\omega_a$ in the case of lifetime broadening only was given by

$$\Delta\omega_a = \gamma \tag{20}$$

in our collision-broadened results the complete linewidth is given by the more general expression for collision plus lifetime broadening,

$$\Delta\omega_a = \gamma + \frac{2}{T_2} \tag{21}$$

The presence of collisions evidently increases the linewidth of the oscillators' averaged response without any necessary increase in the energy-damping rate γ. The shorter the mean time T_2 between collisions, the larger the collision broadening; in fact, the additive contribution of collisions to the radian-frequency linewidth $\Delta\omega_a$ is just $2T_2^{-1}$, just twice the collision rate.

The same substitution of $\Delta\omega_a = \gamma + 2T_2^{-1}$ for $\Delta\omega_a = \gamma$ may be made in the susceptibility expression $\tilde{\chi}(\omega)$, which becomes

$$\tilde{\chi}(\omega) = -j \frac{N_v e^2}{m\omega\epsilon_0(\gamma + 2T_2^{-1})} \frac{1}{1 + 2j(\omega - \omega_a)/(\gamma + 2T_2^{-1})} \tag{22}$$

and in any other related expressions in our analysis. Hence from now on we will not bother to carry along the subscript av on these results. Note also that as the width of the response is broadened by increased collisional effects, the peak value at line center decreases in inverse proportion because of the $\Delta\omega_a^{-1}$ factor in the collection of constants in front. It can readily be shown, in fact, that the area under the lorentzian resonance curve for $\chi''(\omega)$ remains constant as the linewidth $\Delta\omega_a$ of the resonance increases or decreases.

We have seen that both elastic and inelastic collisions will have equal line-broadening effects. However, the inelastic collisions also represent a damping mechanism which contributes part of the total damping rate γ. The rigorous treatment of elastic versus inelastic collisions in quantum theory becomes somewhat complex, but we may assert here that if the effects of inelastic collisions are included in the linewidth calculation both as a part of γ and as a part of the $2T_2^{-1}$ contribution, then the inelastic-collision effects will incorrectly be counted twice. If both elastic and inelastic collisions are present in a given atomic system, it is probably best to include the inelastic-collision effects as part of the total damping rate γ and to include in the $2T_2^{-1}$ term only the elastic-collision rate or the mean time between elastic collisions.

In many practical situations the collision rate $2T_2^{-1}$ is much faster than the energy-damping rate γ; in other words, $T_2 \ll \tau$. The average atomic response may then be written as

$$\tilde{X}(\omega) \approx j\frac{e}{4m\omega}\frac{2T_2}{1 + jT_2(\omega - \omega_a)}\tilde{E}_x(\omega) \qquad T_2 \ll \gamma^{-1} \tag{23}$$

or

$$\tilde{\chi}(\omega) \approx -j\frac{N_v e^2}{4m\omega\epsilon_0}\frac{2T_2}{1 + jT_2(\omega - \omega_a)} \qquad T_2 \ll \gamma^{-1} \tag{24}$$

Note that the decay rate γ and the lifetime τ actually *disappear entirely* from these expressions. When collision broadening is dominant the exact decay rate γ is not significant in so far as the atomic lineshape is concerned, and very often only the parameter T_2 is stated in giving the response of an atomic transition, with the damping rate γ remaining unknown or at least unspecified.

Depending on circumstances, and on the exact mechanisms responsible for the value of T_2, the parameter T_2 is referred to variously as the *collision time*, the *dephasing time*, the *transverse relaxation time*, or the *dipolar* or *spin-spin relaxation time* (especially in magnetic resonance, as discussed in Chap. 4).[1]

■ The collision-broadening results we have just obtained analytically can also be described in the following physical terms. Instead of considering the randomly interrupted oscillating motion of an atom as observed in a laboratory, let us consider the apparent electric field $e_x'(t)$ as it might be seen by a hypothetical observer riding on the oscillating electric charge in our model. To an observer on the randomly colliding atom the applied signal $e_x'(t)$ would appear, not as an uninterrupted monochromatic sine wave at frequency ω, but as a randomly interrupted sine wave with a random phase jump at each interruption, as indicated in Fig. 3-4a. Such a random type of phase modulation, at intervals of $\sim T_2$ sec, would spread the spectrum of the signal as seen from the atom out over a frequency range of $\Delta\omega \sim 1/T_2$, as shown in

ALTERNATE DESCRIPTION OF COLLISION BROADENING

---

[1] It also corresponds in more sophisticated quantum analyses to the so-called "relaxation time for the off-diagonal elements of the density matrix."

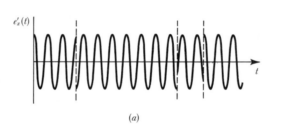

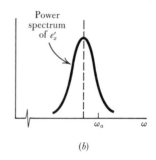

FIG. 3-4 (a) The randomly phase-interrupted signal field $e_x'(t)$ as seen from the colliding atom. (b) The power spectrum of the randomly dephased signal $e_x'(t)$.

(a)

(b)

Fig. 3-4b (see also Prob. 3-2). Therefore, even though the applied-signal frequency ω as measured in the laboratory may be separated from the oscillator's resonant frequency ω_a by a frequency shift of this order, the apparent signal as seen from the atom still has some frequency components at and near the resonance frequency. Hence the atom will respond even to applied signals as much as $\Delta\omega \sim 1/T_2$ away from ω_a in frequency.

This viewpoint also explains the reduced peak response with collision broadening. Even when the laboratory signal is tuned exactly to ω_a, the random phase modulation shifts much of the signal energy to frequencies outside the intrinsic (lifetime-broadened) linewidth of the oscillator. Hence the response even at line center is reduced, more or less in proportion to the collisional "smearing out" of the applied-signal spectrum as seen from the atoms.

Line broadening due to collisions or random dephasing is a most important concept, and we will use the above results repeatedly in subsequent chapters. Although actual collisions do not occur for real atoms in solids, other random interactions between the oscillations of individual atoms can lead to essentially the same dephasing results. Thus collision concepts are often useful in describing atomic transitions in solids.

3-3 COLLISION-BROADENING AND ENERGY-DECAY EFFECTS IN REAL ATOMS

By including the dephasing effects of collisions in a collection of oscillators or real atoms we have made our model of the properties of such a collection much more realistic. In this section we will discuss further the effects of energy decay and of collisions on both the steady-state time-averaged behavior and the transient behavior of collections of atoms in order to improve our understanding of the relaxation processes in real atoms.

STEADY-STATE BEHAVIOR: RANDOMNESS VERSUS ORDER

■ Dephasing or collision effects obviously act to scramble, or randomize, the oscillatory motions of individual oscillators or atoms. As a result, different oscillators tend to have randomly phased displacements $x_i(t)$ and velocities $\dot{x}_i(t)$. When we add up the displacements of individual oscillators in order to calculate the macroscopic polarization in a collection of oscillators, according to

$$p_x(t) = - \sum_{\text{all atoms}} e x_i(t) \tag{1}$$

then if dephasing effects predominate, the individual displacements $x_i(t)$ will add with random phases, giving an essentially zero macroscopic or bulk electric polarization p_x.

Conversely, an applied-signal field $e_x(t)$ acts as a coherent *ordering* mechanism, tending to make all the individual oscillators come into oscillation with the same forced phase. This leads to a coherent summing of the individual contributions $x_i(t)$, all in phase, and thus to a finite induced macroscopic polarization p_x in the collection of atoms.

As a homely analogy, consider a group of mothers attempting to push a long line of childrens' swings in a park all in phase, so that all the swings will go back and forth together, while the children are pulling at each other's swings and jerking them away from smooth oscillation. The net result of this conflict between randomizing collisions, as measured by T_2, and the ordering effect of the applied field is a broadened linewidth and a reduced midband or peak response, with these effects being enhanced as the randomizing effects of the collisions become stronger.

■ In most practical laser and maser situations the ordering effects of the normal applied-signal fields are relatively weak compared to the randomizing effects of the dephasing collisions. As a result, even with an applied signal present, the phases of the individual motions of the oscillators are largely random, and the applied-signal field $e_x(t)$ succeeds in causing only a small average amount of ordering in the atomic motions.

The individual oscillator motions shown in Fig. 3-3 are useful in giving a graphic idea of how an applied field will pull individual atoms toward synchronism following phase-randomizing collisions. However, they do not really apply in the typical case. The applied field is usually not strong enough to pull individual atomic motions into phase with the applied field nearly as completely as shown in Fig. 3-3 before the next dephasing collision occurs. Hence individual atomic motions are largely random in phase, even with an applied signal present. Applying a small field $e_x(t)$ creates only a small amount of average ordering, and thus a small amount of macroscopic polarization $p(t)$. Applying a larger field creates a proportionally larger degree of ordering and a proportionally larger macroscopic polarization. However, for usual signal levels the fractional degree of ordering still remains small, and the macroscopic polarization thus remains small compared to the value it could have if all atoms oscillated completely in phase. In most situations, then, the average induced motion $\tilde{X}_{av}(\omega)$ is very much smaller than the maximum motion $\tilde{X}(\omega)$ that could be induced if dephasing effects were not present.

There can be some unusual situations, particularly in pulsed or transient experiments, in which the applied-signal fields become strong enough to produce more or less complete ordering of the individual oscillatory motions of atoms, even against the randomizing effects of collisions. Various complicated and interesting transient effects occur in this limit, including such phenomena as $90°$ pulses, $180°$ pulses, spin echoes, and photon echoes. Such effects are rather easily produced in nuclear-magnetic-resonance experiments, for example, where the dephasing processes are often very weak (long T_2 or very narrow Δf_a). However, they occur in optical-frequency experiments only in rather unusual, very-high-power situations.[1]

■ In a real atom an applied signal creates an internal oscillatory motion or electric-dipole moment, just as in a classical electron oscillator, and the relative phases of the individual atomic motions determine whether or not a macroscopic polarization is produced in a large collection of atoms, just as in a collection of classical oscillators. In a collection of real atoms there may be real atomic collisions between the atoms

TYPICAL STEADY-STATE BEHAVIOR

BROADENING IN REAL ATOMS: QUANTUM DESCRIPTION

[1] For an example see Ref. 3-5.

(as in gases), or so-called "dipolar interactions" due to overlapping dipolar fields of the atoms (particularly in solids), or other types of interactions between adjacent atoms, sometimes through the medium of the surrounding crystal lattice. All these atomic interactions can produce dephasing effects, with some characteristic dephasing time T_2 which will play exactly the same role in the real atomic case as in the classical electron-oscillator analysis.

If we wish to consider any more rigorous and complete quantum-mechanical analysis of atomic line-broadening effects, we must take into account the basic fact that the broadening of transitions is caused by interactions either among the very large number of nearly independent atoms themselves or between the atoms and their very complex surroundings. Hence any such rigorous quantum analysis will immediately become a multibody type of problem involving a very large number of mutually inter-acting systems, all of which must be treated at once. In this type of problem progress toward any sort of solution can be made only with the greatest difficulty.

As a result, broadening effects are almost invariably introduced even into quantum analyses by means of simple phenomenological broadening terms, which are added to the single-atom quantum equations of motion at some convenient point. These broadening terms are chosen in whatever way seems most likely to give a reasonable approximation of the broadening process, on the basis of physical insight and experimental comparison. Being able to solve the resulting equations of motion without too much difficulty is another factor in choosing the form of the broadening terms.

There is, as a result, no really rigorous quantum analysis of either lifetime or collision broadening against which our simple classical arguments can be compared. In fact, the most commonly used quantum broadening expressions are simply our classical arguments rephrased in quantum terminology.[1] Thus, except for some slight extensions for multilevel atoms, the classical discussions of this chapter are equally valid for the quantum case.

THERMAL EQUILIBRIUM:
THERMAL MOTION VERSUS
INDUCED MOTION

■ A collection of oscillators or atoms in thermal equilibrium has a certain amount of thermal energy associated with it; that is, each individual oscillator will have a small but finite random amount of energy in the form of oscillatory motion (unless the collection is cooled to $0°K$). To take this into account, we must expand our discussion and write the displacement of an individual oscillator or atom in the form

$$[x_i(t)]_{\text{total}} = [x_i(t)]_{\text{stim}} + [x_i(t)]_{\text{spon}} \tag{2}$$

In this equation the stimulated term is just the motion $x_i(t)$ that we have been analyzing up to this point. As we have noted before, in a collection of real atoms the average induced motion is proportional to the following important factors:

$$[x_i(t)]_{\text{stim}} \propto \text{oscillator strength } F_{mn} \times \text{lineshape function } (\gamma, T_2) \times$$
$$\text{population difference } \mathcal{N}_m - \mathcal{N}_n \times \text{applied signal } e_x(t) \tag{3}$$

The thermal motion represents the additional effects of thermal agitation, independent of any applied signals. We will see in Chap. 11 that the spontaneous or thermal motion in a collection of real atoms is proportional only to the following factors:

$$[x_i(t)]_{\text{spon}} \propto \text{oscillator strength } F_{mn} \times \text{lineshape function } (\gamma, T_2) \times$$
$$\text{upper-level population } \mathcal{N}_m \tag{4}$$

[1] See, for example, Breene, Ref. 3-1.

Note in particular that the spontaneous motion is proportional only to the *upper-level* population of the atomic transition involved, and is totally independent of any applied field or signal.

The spontaneous or thermal type of internal atomic motion that we are introducing here is exactly the same as the spontaneous emission discussed in Chap. 1. It is also the same as the thermal noise (or quantum noise) that inevitably occurs whenever atomic absorption effects are present. In most practical situations this thermal motion and its measurable effects are quite small, and the thermal part of the atomic motion can be completely disregarded in calculating the stimulated or induced part of the atomic motion, as we have done thus far. The thermal motion can be entirely neglected, for example, in calculating the induced response, the macroscopic susceptibility, the net atomic absorption, and the gain of a maser device. Spontaneous or thermal motion does have to be included when we want to talk about fluorescence, or thermal-noise voltages in equivalent circuits, or the noise figure of a maser amplifier. It is introduced at this point partly as a foundation for future discussions and partly because we need these ideas in describing some illustrative experiments.

■ Consider a collection of real atoms placed between a pair of capacitor plates, as in Fig. 3-5*a*, for the moment with no signal applied. The atoms will be oscillating at their various transition frequencies because of the thermal part of their motion. However, because of the existence of dephasing processes, the thermal motions of the individual atoms will have random phases. Thus there will be no coherence to the thermal motions of the individual atoms, and no coherent macroscopic polarization in the collection as a whole.

THERMAL NOISE AND FLUORESCENCE

If there were any macroscopic polarization in the collection of atoms, due to oscillation of the atoms with some coherence among their phases, then this macroscopic polarization would produce a macroscopic induced charge on the capacitor plates and a macroscopic sinusoidal open-circuit voltage across the capacitor terminals. This is most unlikely; we do not expect a macroscopic sinusoidal voltage, with a definite phase and amplitude, to appear across the terminals of a purely passive capacitor in thermal equilibrium, even if the capacitor is filled with a collection of atoms also in thermal equilibrium. However, if we examine the voltage across the capacitor terminals with a sufficiently sensitive low-noise receiver, we will in fact find a finite (but very small) thermal-noise voltage across the terminals. This voltage consists of narrowband noise

FIG. 3-5 Thermal-noise or spontaneous-emission effects in atoms.

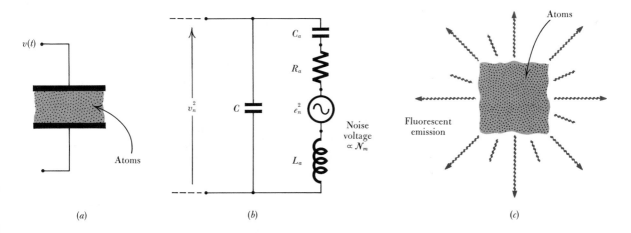

(*a*)   (*b*)   (*c*)

at each of the atomic transition frequencies, with a bandwidth and lineshape exactly equal to the bandwidth and lineshape of each corresponding transition. As we will see in Chap. 11, this voltage represents exactly the thermal-noise voltage associated with the resistance R_a in the atomic equivalent circuit, as shown in Fig. 3-5b. For each given atomic transition, the magnitude of this noise voltage squared is directly proportional to the upper-level population N_m of the transition involved (and this population in turn depends on the temperature of the atomic collection through the Boltzmann population ratios).

This is the description of the thermal-noise effects in lumped-equivalent-circuit terms. If we consider the same effects in optical-frequency terms, then we simply have a collection of atoms in free space, as in Fig. 3-5c. With no signals applied, and with no mirrors present or laser action taking place, we certainly would not expect any beams of coherent light to emerge from this collection of atoms in any sharply defined direction or at any sharply defined frequency. However, if there are atoms excited to upper energy levels (which requires a rather elevated temperature at optical frequencies), we can expect fluorescent emission at the various transition frequencies to emerge from the collection of atoms in all directions. This emission will be proportional to the upper-level population on each transition and will be essentially a noise signal, with a bandwidth and lineshape equal to those of the corresponding transition. This fluorescence is the optical version of, and is exactly the same physical process as, the thermal-noise voltage in the lumped-circuit case. We will make all these points more definite in Chap. 11.

ENERGY DECAY IN
REAL ATOMS

■ In a real atomic system we are concerned, of course, with quantum-mechanical energy levels and with the populations or numbers of atoms $N_n(t)$ in those energy levels. The energy-decay rate γ which we introduced in the classical oscillator model then has the following analog in the real quantum case. If we consider for simplicity a collection of atoms having only two energy levels, E_1 and E_2, and hence only a single transition frequency $f_a \equiv f_{21}$, then the internal energy $W(t)$ of this collection of atoms is given by (see Fig. 3-6)

$$W(t) = N_1(t)E_1 + N_2(t)E_2 \tag{5}$$

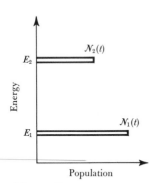

FIG. 3-6   The populations of two atomic energy levels.

The energy-decay rate for $W(t)$ must then correspond to the decay rate at which the energy-level populations $N_1(t)$ and $N_2(t)$ revert back to their thermal-equilibrium values if they are initially perturbed from these values. We will discuss this energy-decay or longitudinal relaxation process in more detail in our discussion of rate equations in Chap. 6. However, the major point is that the energy-decay rate γ of the classical model becomes in the real atomic case the decay rate or relaxation rate at which the energy-level populations of $N_1(t)$ and $N_2(t)$ on the relevant transition recover to their equilibrium values following any initial disturbance. The associated decay time γ^{-1} has been denoted by τ in this and the preceding chapter, but it will also often be denoted by T_1 in later chapters.

DEMONSTRATION OF ENERGY
DECAY

■ The amount of fluorescence or spontaneous emission on an atomic transition is directly proportional to the upper-level population on the transition, and this fluorescence is often apparent on optical transitions (it is much weaker and more difficult to observe on microwave and lower-frequency transitions). Observing the fluorescent emission on a transition is thus a good way to monitor the upper-level population, and particularly the decay or relaxation of that population following an initial disturbance, which gives a direct measure of the energy-decay rate γ.

Figure 3-7 shows one simple experiment for observing directly the decay rate γ for the upper level of the 6943-Å laser transition in ruby (see Figs. 1-27 and 1-28). The stroboscopic light source[1] provides repeated short intense light pulses a few tens of microseconds long which are absorbed by the ruby sample, lifting some of the Cr^{3+} ions out of their ground energy level and into the higher energy levels, particularly into the metastable ruby R_1 level. From this upper level the atoms decay back to the ground state by fluorescent emission at the transition wavelength of 6943 Å, with a comparatively long energy-decay time of $\tau \sim 4$ msec. This radiation is detected by a photodetector and displayed as a decaying exponential on an oscilloscope. The narrowband 6943-Å filter in front of the photodetector filters out most (but not all) of the exciting radiation from the stroboscopic source, so as to avoid overloading the photodetector with the initial excitation pulse.

Ruby is a particularly convenient material for this demonstration because it has an unusually long fluorescent lifetime or energy-decay time on this transition, and because it has an unusually high quantum efficiency, in the sense of fluorescent energy reradiated compared to excitation energy absorbed, thus giving a readily detectible signal. However, the same sort of experiment can be carried out with many other types of atoms at their appropriate wavelengths. Note also that the atomic linewidth $\Delta\omega_a$ of this ruby transition is many orders of magnitude larger than the energy decay, that is, $\Delta\omega_a = \gamma + 2/T_2 \gg \gamma$, so that obviously $T_2 \ll \gamma^{-1}$ for this system.

■ Now as an illustration of dephasing effects, in contrast to energy-decay effects, consider the experiment shown in Fig. 3-8a. A capacitance containing a collection of atoms is resonated with an inductance and a shunt resistance to form a low-Q tuned circuit whose resonant frequency coincides with the transition frequency of the atoms between the capacitor plates. This circuit is first connected to a signal voltage generator and is then switched over to a signal receiver, both of which are tuned to the atomic transition frequency ω_a.

DEMONSTRATION OF
DEPHASING EFFECTS

---

[1] These sources are usually pulsed xenon flashlamps. Their intensity is far too low to produce laser action, at least in the simple configuration shown in Fig. 3-7.

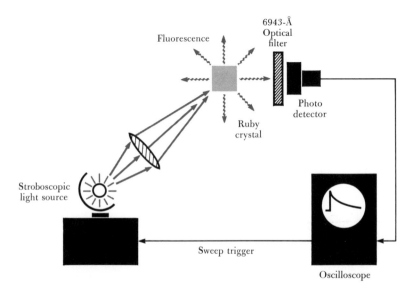

FIG. 3-7 An experiment for demonstrating energy decay by measuring the fluorescent lifetime of a ruby (or other atomic) sample.

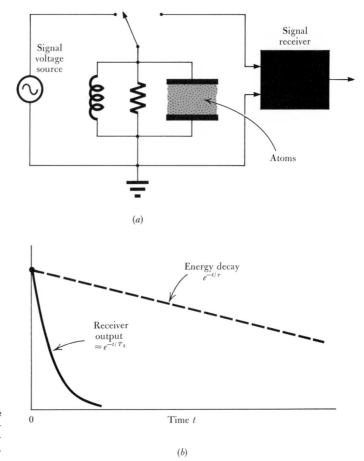

(a)

(b)

FIG. 3-8 A possible experiment to demonstrate the fast decay due to dephasing of the coherent polarization set up in a collection of atoms by an applied-signal field.

Suppose that the on-resonance signal voltage is first applied across the tuned circuit, and hence the capacitor plates, at a fairly large voltage level, so that the atoms between the capacitor plates are set into oscillation fairly strongly and a certain amount of ordering is created in their oscillation phases. A significant macroscopic ac polarization $p(t)$ is thus created in the volume occupied by the atoms. Following this excitation, the circuit is rapidly disconnected from the signal source and connected to the signal receiver, which will measure the ac voltage level across the circuit. Figure 3-8b illustrates the resulting transient sequence of events.

First of all, applying the signal voltage to the tuned circuit creates a certain amount of stored signal energy in the inductance and capacitance of the tuned circuit. After the switch this energy will decay with time in the form $v(t) \approx e^{-(\omega/2Q_c)t}$. We suppose that the tuned circuit has a sufficiently low Q_c that the cavity decay time $\tau_c \equiv Q_c/\omega_c$ is short compared to the dephasing time T_2 of the atoms. Hence this cavity transient will die out very rapidly; in fact, this particular transient is not shown in Fig. 3-8b.

Now, once the atoms in the capacitor plate have been set in oscillation by an applied signal, if the applied voltage is turned off, the atoms will still continue to oscillate and the associated macroscopic polarization will continue to exist until the relaxation effects of dephasing and/or energy decay have time to act. In this case we assume that the energy-decay time is long compared to the dephasing time. Therefore, because of the dephasing effects among the atoms, the phases of the individual atomic oscillations will become progressively more random, and the magnitude of the macroscopic polarization will die out toward zero with an exponential decay constant T_2.

However, as long as there is any macroscopic polarization $p(t)$ remaining in the volume between the capacitor plates, a finite back-reaction ac voltage proportional to this polarization will appear across the capacitor terminals, and the signal receiver will measure this voltage (the size of the ac voltage across the terminals depends on the magnitude of the polarization, the dimensions of the capacitance, and the values of the lumped-circuit elements, as pointed out in Prob. 3-3). The result will be a transient ac voltage at frequency ω_a appearing between the capacitor terminals, with an envelope that decays as $v(t) \approx e^{-t/T_2}$, as shown in Fig. 3-8b. This induced voltage disappears with the more rapid time constant T_2 even though the energy associated with the atomic motions decays only with the longer time constant $\tau \equiv \gamma^{-1}$. That is, the macroscopic polarization can decay with time in the form

$$p(t) = -\sum ex_i(t) = p_0 e^{-t/T_2} \tag{6}$$

even though the oscillation energy decays in the form

$$W(t) = \tfrac{1}{2}m\sum |\dot{x}_i(t)|^2 + \omega^2 |x_i(t)|^2 = W_0 e^{-t/\tau} \tag{7}$$

(the energy expression for the classical oscillator model). Note that the phases of the individual atomic oscillations do not enter into this energy expression.

This particular experiment makes it clear that there are two quite different time constants in this situation, the dephasing or collision time T_2 and the energy-decay time τ. Where collision broadening or other dephasing effects are important (which includes many, but not all, laser and maser materials) the dephasing time T_2 will be considerably shorter than the energy-decay time τ, and the atomic linewidth will be correspondingly wider than the lifetime-broadened value alone.

During the time that the signal voltage is applied in this experiment, the signal delivers a certain amount of energy to the atoms, so that they have the initial energy W_0 at the time the voltage source is disconnected. This energy is over and above the ordinary reactive stored energy in the cavity circuit elements and corresponds to the reactive stored energy in the circuit elements L_a and C_a of the atomic equivalent circuit. After the circuit is switched, a very small portion of this energy comes out in the form of the coherent voltage discussed above. However, the bulk of W_0 decays through energy-decay mechanisms, which means that this energy must go into heating (very slightly, in most cases) the surroundings of the atoms. For example, if the energy decay of the atoms is largely by nonradiative relaxation, then the energy goes largely into additional heat energy in the lattice vibrations of the crystal containing the atoms. If the atoms relax largely by purely radiative relaxation, then this energy comes off as fluorescence or thermal noise, which is absorbed somewhere in the circuitry or the surroundings of the atoms, leading eventually to a very slight warming of these surroundings.

The transient voltage observed in this experiment may be described as a coherent voltage in several senses. First of all, it arises from the phase-coherent portion of the atomic oscillatory motions in the collection of atoms. Second, it is a clean decaying sinusoid, rather than a noiselike emission, as in the energy-decay experiment described earlier. Third, it has a definite and coherent phase relationship to the sinusoidal signal voltage applied before the switching time. It would be possible with a more sensitive receiver also to observe the incoherent thermal-noise emission from this same circuit after the coherent voltage has died out, and possibly to measure the energy-decay time of the atoms as in the energy-decay demonstration described earlier. However, as a practical matter, an experiment of this type is feasible only at infrared or optical frequencies, where the fluorescent emission is stronger and can be observed without great difficulty.

There is no indication in Fig. 3-8 of any specific atomic system for carrying out this proposed experiment. The reason is the same as at the end of Chap. 2: there are no conveniently available strong electric-dipole transitions in any real atoms having transition frequencies in the microwave-frequency range or lower. Hence there are no convenient ways to conduct this experiment with real lumped-circuit elements and electric-dipole type atoms. However, electric-dipole atoms behave in exactly this way in higher frequency ranges, and would also do so at lower frequencies if suitable transitions existed. Essentially the same behavior also takes place in magnetic-dipole-type transitions at frequencies as low as the audio-frequency range. We will discuss this type of behavior and describe an exactly analogous magnetic-dipole experiment in the following chapter.

ENERGY DECAY AND COLLISION BROADENING IN MULTIPLE-ENERGY-LEVEL ATOMS

■ The broadening effects in a system having more than just two energy levels become somewhat more complex. There will generally be several time constants associated with the decay of atoms among the various energy levels, and there may also be different collision rates for the various levels. For example, in the multiple-energy-level system shown in Fig. 3-9, let us examine the lifetime-plus-collision broadening of the $E_m \rightarrow E_n$ transition specifically. For simplicity, let this be an optical-frequency case in which the Boltzmann factor is $E_n/kT \gg 1$ for all the upper energy levels. In this case the thermal-equilibrium populations of all the upper levels are essentially zero. We can then talk about the relaxation rates γ_{kl} at which atoms drop from any upper level E_k to any lower level E_l (we will extend this discussion to the general nonoptical case in Chap. 6).

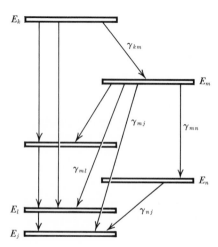

Fig. 3-9 Some of the energy-decay or relaxation routes among levels in a multiple-energy-level atomic system.

If there are $N_m(t)$ atoms in level E_m at a given instant, the total rate of relaxation or energy decay from level E_m to all lower energy levels E_l may be written as

$$\frac{d}{dt} N_m(t) = -\sum_{E_l < E_m} \gamma_{ml} N_m(t) = -\gamma_m N_m(t) \tag{8}$$

The relaxation rates γ_{ml} may include radiative and nonradiative relaxation processes, depending on circumstances. The total decay rate γ_m or lifetime $\tau_m \equiv \gamma_m^{-1}$ of level E_m is thus the sum of all the decay processes from E_m to lower levels; that is,

$$\gamma_m \equiv \frac{1}{\tau_m} = \sum_{l<m} \gamma_{ml} = \sum_{l<m} \frac{1}{\tau_{ml}} \tag{9}$$

We can write a similar expression for each of the energy levels of the atom. Figure 3-9 shows some of the individual decay rates involved.

We can also suppose that there is a certain *collision rate* k_m that is characteristic of the atoms in the E_m energy level. This rate may in general be different from the collision rate k_n associated with atoms in some E_n energy level (the atom may appear to have a different "size" so far as collisions are concerned, depending on which quantum energy level it is in).

Given all these constants, a semi-quantum-mechanical analysis then predicts that the linewidth $\Delta\omega_{mn}$ of the $E_m \to E_n$ transition due to the combined effects of lifetime and collision broadening should be given by

$$\Delta\omega_{mn} = \gamma_m + \gamma_n + k_m + k_n \tag{10}$$

This quantum result is, in fact, little more than a slight extension of our previous classical results. We might think, for example, of a simple two-level transition in which E_n is the ground level E_1, and the upper level $E_m \equiv E_2$ decays only into the ground level, so that $\gamma_m = \gamma_{21} = \gamma$ and $\gamma_n = \gamma_1 = 0$. If we also assume that the collision rate is the same for the upper and lower levels $k_2 = k_1 = T_2^{-1}$, then we convert the quantum result back to our classical result,

$$\Delta\omega_a = \gamma + \frac{2}{T_2} \tag{11}$$

Even in more complicated multilevel cases, as a practical matter we are seldom in a position to know accurately all the different decay and collision rates γ_{ml} and k_m that may be involved, and so the simplified classical result is used in any case.

3-4   COLLISION RATES IN REAL GASES

In this section we will consider briefly the collision rates among atoms in real gases as a function of pressure, temperature, and the sizes, or collision cross sections, of the atoms, and discuss some experimental results showing collision broadening effects on real laser transitions.

■ From the kinetic theory of gases it is possible to derive expressions for the rates at which collisions will occur in a volume of gas due to the thermal kinetic motion, or *brownian motion,* of the gas atoms or molecules; we will then know the dephasing time T_2. In a gas containing a mixture of two different kinds of atoms or molecules—say, types a and b with concentrations N_{va} and N_{vb} (atoms per unit volume)—the average

COLLISION RATES AND
COLLISION CROSS SECTIONS

number of collisions Z_{ab} per unit volume per unit time between atoms of type a and type b is given by[1]

$$Z_{ab} = \mathcal{N}_{va}\mathcal{N}_{vb}Q_{ab} \sqrt{\frac{8kT}{\pi}\left(\frac{1}{M_a} + \frac{1}{M_b}\right)} \tag{1}$$

The quantity Q_{ab} has the dimensions of area and is called the *collision cross section* for the atoms. It measures the size of the atoms so far as the collision process is concerned, that is, how big an a atom appears to an approaching b atom, or vice versa. The collision rate is also rather naturally proportional to the average thermal velocities of the atoms, given by $\sqrt{8kT/\pi M_a}$ and $\sqrt{8kT/\pi M_b}$, where T is the temperature associated with the kinetic motion of the atoms[2] and M_a and M_b are the molecular masses of the a and b atoms or molecules.

The average number of collisions per second for a single atom of, say, type a will be the total rate Z_{ab} per unit volume divided by the total number of a atoms per unit volume; that is, the cross-collision frequency is

$$\frac{1}{T_2} = \frac{Z_{ab}(T)}{\mathcal{N}_{va}} = \mathcal{N}_{vb}Q_{ab} \sqrt{\frac{8kT(M_a^{-1} + M_b^{-1})}{\pi}} \tag{2}$$

We can also use this formula to calculate the rate at which the atoms in a gas will collide with the other atoms of the same type. If we single out one atom and think of it as the only type-a atom, with all the other identical atoms being called type-b atoms, then the collision frequency of that one type-a atom with all the other atoms is evidently

$$\frac{1}{T_2} = \mathcal{N}_v Q \sqrt{\frac{16kT}{\pi M}} \tag{3}$$

where the subscripts are no longer needed, since $a \equiv b$.

From our earlier discussion, the collision broadening of a transition in an a atom due to collisions with b atoms will be given by

$$\Delta\omega_a = \frac{2}{T_2} = 2\mathcal{N}_{vb}Q_{ab} \sqrt{\frac{8kT(M_a^{-1} + M_b^{-1})}{\pi}} \tag{4}$$

The broadening is thus directly proportional to the concentration (and hence the partial pressure) of the type-b gas, the collision cross section Q_{ab}, and the square root of the gas kinetic temperature T and is inversely proportional to the atomic or molecular masses M. The concentration of atoms in a gas may be related to the partial pressure and temperature of each particular species by[3]

---

[1] See Ref. 3-8 (chap. IV) or Ref. 3-6 (chap. 1, sec. 2a) for a simplified derivation. Note that these writers speak of an "equivalent hard-sphere" model of an atom with a radius which they call σ, so that our cross section Q would be $\pi\sigma^2$ in their notation. However, many writers in this and other fields commonly use σ to mean the cross section itself, i.e., the same as our Q.

[2] There may be several different temperatures describing the atoms in a gas, or particularly in a gas discharge, depending on the various degrees of thermal excitation of the kinetic motion of the atoms, their internal vibrational motion, their rotational motion, and so forth. The kinetic temperature associated with the kinetic motion of atoms as a whole is the relevant parameter in the above expression.

[3] A pressure of 1 torr = 1 mm Hg, or 1 atm = 760 torr.

$$\mathcal{N}_v \text{ (atoms/m}^3) = 9.65 \times 10^{24} \frac{p \text{ (torrs)}}{T \text{ (}^\circ K)} \qquad (5)$$

In a mixture of several different gases the total collision broadening for atoms of any one type must be evaluated by summing the separate collision rates with every other type of atom present, as well as the self-collision rate of that atom with its own species. ■ Collision cross sections Q_{ab} between various types of atoms must usually be determined experimentally.[1] Typical values for many gases[2] fall in the range $Q_{ab} \sim 0.1$ to 1.0×10^{-18} m^2. If we relate these areas to equivalent hard spheres of diameter d, then the equivalent atomic diameters are in the range of a few angstroms. To cite only one specific example of direct importance in the laser field, some of the collision cross sections in CO_2, He, and N_2 have been determined by means of experimental results such as those shown in Fig. 3-10. In these experiments[3] the beam from a 10.6-μ CO_2 laser signal source was passed through an absorption cell containing an adjustable amount of CO_2, together with other added gases, at thermal equilibrium (no electrical discharge or pumping mechanisms in the absorption cell). The attenuation of the 10.6-μ signal due to absorption by the thermal-equilibrium populations on the corresponding CO_2 transition in the absorption cell was measured as a function of gas pressure in the absorption cell.

COLLISION BROADENING IN
GASES: EXPERIMENTAL
RESULTS

The total midband absorption in passing through the cell should be directly proportional to the absorptive part of the susceptibility, i.e., to χ_0'' on the laser transition. This in turn should be directly proportional to the ratio $\Delta\mathcal{N}_v/\Delta f_a$, where $\Delta\mathcal{N}_v$ is the thermal-equilibrium population difference per unit volume on the transition involved and Δf_a is the atomic linewidth of that transition. The population density $\Delta\mathcal{N}_v$ at thermal equilibrium should, moreover, be directly proportional to the CO_2 partial pressure in the absorption cell.

At very low pressures, where the collision rate and collision-broadening effects are small, the linewidth Δf_a should be constant and determined by other mechanisms (doppler broadening in this case), and so the measured absorption should increase directly with the CO_2 pressure because of the increasing number of absorbing atoms $\Delta\mathcal{N}_v$ in the cell. The left-hand portion of Fig. 3-10b shows that this is indeed exactly what is observed. At higher pressures, however, the collision rate among atoms becomes large enough that collision broadening eventually becomes the dominant collision mechanism. Once this occurs, the linewidth Δf_a increases linearly with any further increases in pressure. Hence both of the pressure-dependent factors $\Delta\mathcal{N}_v/\Delta f_a$ increase linearly with further increases in CO_2 pressure, and the midband absorption itself becomes independent of pressure. Figure 3-10b shows clearly this flattening out of the midband absorption at gas pressures above 5 to 8 torrs of CO_2.

Figure 3-10c shows the changeover from doppler broadening at low pressures to collision broadening at high pressures in pure CO_2, as predicted by the absorption data of Fig. 3-10b. The experimental points of Fig. 3-10b fit very closely a smooth theoretical curve based on this assumption. From these results, and others in which N_2 or

---

[1] The collision cross sections relevant to collision broadening are very similar to, although not exactly identical with, collision cross sections used in discussing the viscosity and certain other related physical properties of gases; see Ref. 3-6.

[2] See Ref. 3-8 (chap. IV, table 19) or Ref. 3-6 (table 1.2.2).

[3] Ref. 3-3. Note that the cross section σ_0 used by Gerry and Leonard is the same as our Q_{ab}.

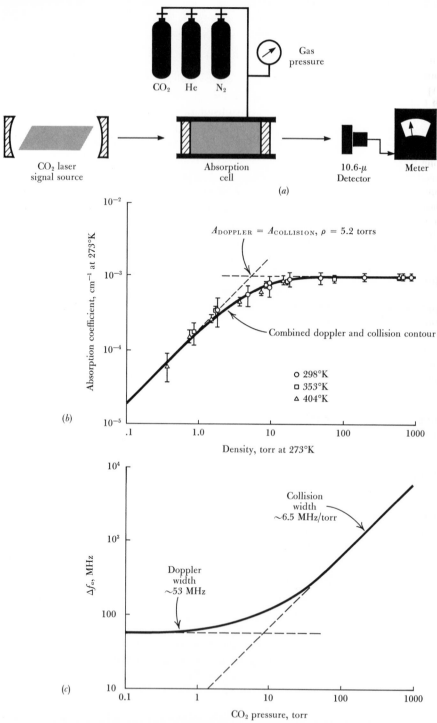

FIG. 3-10 (a) An experiment using a laser signal source to measure the midband absorption on the 10.6-μ CO_2 transition at different pressures and temperatures. (b) Measured midband absorption coefficient versus pressure, including data taken at three different temperatures with appropriate scaling according to the expected population variation with temperature. (c) Linewidth versus pressure as deduced from the data of part (b), showing the changeover from doppler to collision (or pressure) broadening as the CO_2 pressure is increased. Data taken from E. T. Gerry and D. A. Leonard, "Measurement of 10.6 μ CO_2 laser transition probability and optical broadening cross sections," *Appl. Phys. Letters,* **8:**227 (May 1, 1966).

He are also added to the CO_2 cell, it is possible to determine that the relevant collision cross sections are

$$Q_{CO_2\text{-}CO_2} \approx 10^{-18} \text{ m}^2$$
$$Q_{CO_2\text{-}N_2} \approx 10^{-18} \text{ m}^2 \qquad (6)$$
$$Q_{CO_2\text{-}He} \approx 0.3 \times 10^{-18} \text{ m}^2$$

If we use these data, the self-collision broadening in CO_2 is found to be

$$\frac{\Delta f_a}{p_{CO_2}} \approx 6.5 \text{ MHz/torr} \qquad (7)$$

A typical CO_2 laser contains a mixture of CO_2, N_2 and He, and possibly other gases, at a total pressure of $\sim$5 to 20 torrs. Hence the total pressure broadening is in the range of 10 to 100 MHz. By comparison, the purely radiative lifetime of CO_2 on its 10.6-μ laser transition is $\tau_{rad} \sim 5$ sec, giving a purely radiative linewidth contribution of $\sim$0.2 Hz, while the overall lifetime τ due to all nonradiative damping processes is in the millisecond range, giving a total lifetime broadening of only a few kilohertz. Clearly, collision broadening is by far dominant over lifetime broadening in this example (of course, the doppler broadening of $\sim$53 MHz is in turn dominant over the collision broadening, at least at laser pressures of a few torrs).

The collision-broadening values for another laser transition of interest, the 6328-Å transition in the He-Ne laser, are somewhat uncertain, since not all experimental results are in agreement. However, one measurement yields a total pressure broadening of 96 MHz/torr in a 7 : 1 mixture (by pressure) of He[3] and Ne[20]. At normal He-Ne laser operating pressures of a few torrs, the pressure-broadened linewidth is still considerably less than the doppler-broadened linewidth, which is approximately 1500 MHz for this transition.

PROBLEMS

3-1. In the collision-broadening derivation of Sec. 3-2 we assume that collisions between atoms occur entirely independently and at random intervals. If we examine n_0 atoms starting at any particular instant, this assumption leads to an exponential form for the number of atoms $\Delta n(t)$ that had their last previous collision in a small time interval Δt at a time t earlier [see Eq. (12) in Sec. 3-2]. Suppose, as an alternative assumption, that if we examine an atom at any instant, that atom's last previous collision is equally likely to have been at any time between the instant of examination and a time $2T_2$ earlier. Thus, if n_0 atoms are examined, the distribution $\Delta n(t)$ will be a rectangular function with a uniform value from $t = 0$ back to $t = -2T_2$ and will be zero outside that range.

Evaluate $\bar{X}_{av}(\omega)$ and $\bar{\chi}(\omega)$ as defined in the text, but with this new form for $\Delta n(t)$. Discuss the resulting form for the susceptibility. Note particularly the relationship between linewidth and T_2 for this alternate form (note that T_2 in this case still means the average time interval between collisions for an atom). If a computer is available, you might plot the absorption lineshape against frequency for several different amounts of collision broadening relative to lifetime broadening.

3-2. The randomly dephased waveform shown in Fig. 3-1 can equally well represent the oscillatory motion of the atom from a laboratory frame of reference or the applied-signal field from the internal frame of reference of the atom. Following this line of approach, as discussed at the end of Sec. 3-2, apply the techniques of Fourier analysis of random processes to find the power spectral density of the waveform in Fig. 3-1.

Hints: The autocorrelation function of the waveform can be calculated by noting that the correlation after a time interval τ is $\cos \omega_a \tau$ if no collision has occurred during the interval τ and zero if one or more collisions has occurred, and the chance of no collision during an interval of length τ is $e^{-\tau/T_2}$. The power spectral density is then given by the Fourier transform of this autocorrelation function.

3-3. Suppose in Fig. 3-8 that an ac voltage with peak value V_1 and frequency equal to the atomic resonance frequency has been applied across the tuned circuit plus atoms long enough for any transients to have died out and steady-state conditions to have developed. Suppose that the switch is then instantaneously switched from the signal voltage source to the receiver input exactly at the peak of a voltage cycle. Evaluate the resulting transient voltage across the receiver terminals as a function of time in terms of the various experimental parameters (use the lumped-equivalent-circuit model). Assume that the Q_c of the tuned circuit is very much lower than the Q_a of the atomic resonance, and also that the Q_m parameter for this circuit is large.

REFERENCES

3-1.   R. G. Breene, Jr., *The Shift and Shape of Spectral Lines,* Pergamon Press, New York, 1961. This book reviews in exhaustive detail the many variations on the theory of collision broadening, but includes no experimental data.

3-2.   S-Y. Chen and M. Takeo, "Broadening and shifting of spectral lines due to the presence of foreign gases," *Rev. Mod. Phys.,* **29**:20 (January, 1957). This paper reviews the various theories and gives some confirming experimental data, largely on transitions of alkali metal-vapor atoms.

3-3.   E. T. Gerry and D. A. Leonard, "Measurement of 10.6 μ CO_2 laser transition probability and optical broadening cross sections," *Appl. Phys. Letters,* **8**:227 (May 1, 1966). Experimental results showing doppler and collision broadening versus pressure in CO_2.

3-4.   W. Gordy, W. V. Smith, and R. F. Trambarulo, *Microwave Spectroscopy,* Dover Publications, New York, 1966 (originally published 1953). Section 4-2 has a good discussion of lineshapes and line-broadening mechanisms and some experimental data illustrating collision broadening for a microwave transition in a gas.

3-5.   S. R. Hartmann, "Photon echoes," *Scientific American,* April, 1968, p. 32.

3-6.   J. O. Hirshfelder, C. F. Curtiss, and R. B. Bird, *Molecular Theory of Gases and Liquids,* Wiley, New York, 1964. Chapter 1 discusses collision rates and collision cross sections in gases.

3-7.   H. Margenau and W. W. Watson, "Pressure effects on spectral lines," *Rev. Mod. Phys.,* **8**:22 (January, 1936). An early but good review of the semiclassical analysis of collision broadening in real atoms.

3-8.   A. C. G. Mitchell and M. W. Zemansky, *Resonance Radiation and Excited Atoms,* Cambridge University Press, New York, 1961. Chapter 4 provides a good discussion of some of the physics underlying collision broadening (and shifting) of atomic transitions.

MAGNETIC-DIPOLE TRANSITIONS: THE CLASSICAL MAGNETIZED-TOP MODEL

Some atomic transitions respond only to ac electric fields, as illustrated by the classical electron-oscillator model of Chap. 2. However, experiment shows that other atomic transitions respond only to ac magnetic fields. Important examples of such *magnetic-dipole transitions* are the microwave- and radio-frequency transitions observed in electron paramagnetic resonance (EPR) and nuclear magnetic resonance (NMR).[1] This chapter presents a simple classical model for magnetic-dipole transitions and develops some important consequences of this model. Many of the ideas introduced in this chapter will provide valuable insights into both electric-dipole

[1] The electron and nuclear cases are both basically paramagnetic in character; the omission of the *para* prefix in the nuclear cases is merely a matter of custom. Electron paramagnetic resonance is also often referred to as electron spin resonance (ESR).

and magnetic-dipole transitions, and into both low-frequency and optical transitions. However, those readers desiring the quickest possible approach to optical masers, leaving aside microwave solid-state masers and magnetic resonance, may omit this chapter on first reading and proceed directly to Chap. 5. The classical electron oscillator of Chap. 2 involves only the one-dimensional motion of a point mass under an electric force, which is a relatively simple and familiar case. The magnetic-dipole case, by contrast, involves the three-dimensional dynamics of a magnetized gyroscope under the influence of a magnetic torque. These dynamics are both more complex and less familiar than the electron-oscillator case, and so this chapter is considerably longer than Chap. 2.

4-1   MAGNETIC PROPERTIES OF INDIVIDUAL ATOMS: THE CLASSICAL MAGNETIZED-TOP MODEL

Some of the observed properties of magnetic-dipole atomic transitions that we must explain, to some degree of approximation, include the following:

1. Such resonances are usually (though not always) obtained by placing the atoms in a strong dc magnetic field B_0, and the observed resonance frequencies are often (though not always) directly proportional to this dc magnetic field strength.
2. The resonances are excited only if the atoms are subjected to ac magnetic rather than ac electric fields; e.g., the atoms must be placed in the coil of a tuned circuit rather than between the capacitor plates, or in the high-magnetic-field region of a microwave cavity.
3. In many (but not all) instances the atoms respond best to a circularly polarized ac magnetic field with a certain definite sense of circular polarization.
4. Such resonances usually appear together with a static (dc) polarization in the same material.

In this section we will develop a classical magnetized-top or magnetized-gyroscope model for magnetic-dipole transitions which explains these facts and leads to a number of other important conclusions.

BRIEF REVIEW OF ATOMIC MAGNETISM

■ Recall from atomic physics that the electrons and the nucleus of an atom can each possess a net angular momentum and an associated permanent magnetic-dipole moment. The total electronic angular momentum of an atom may come in part from the orbital motion of the electrons circling about the nucleus and in part from the intrinsic spin angular momentum of the electrons. The nucleus by itself may also have an intrinsic angular momentum due to nuclear spin. These angular momenta are generally accompanied by magnetic-dipole moments, since they represent either small current loops (orbits) or spinning electron or nuclear charge distributions. The total angular momentum and the total magnetic-dipole moment of an atom represent the vector sums (in a somewhat complicated quantum-mechanical way) of the orbital, electron-spin, and nuclear-spin contributions from that atom.

Nonzero nuclear-spin values, and hence nuclear magnetic properties, are fairly common throughout the periodic table of the elements. However, the magnetic moment associated with nuclear angular momentum is very much smaller than that associated with electronic angular momentum (in essence, because the nuclear charge distribution is physically much smaller). As a result, nuclear-magnetic-resonance effects are generally fairly weak and occur at much lower frequencies (in the audio-radio range) than electronic magnetic-dipole effects (which are generally in the microwave range). The discussions of this chapter apply equally well to either nuclear- or electronic-magnetic-resonance effects. However, only the electronic-magnetic-resonance case is of much importance for practical maser devices.

Electron paramagnetic resonance is not as widespread in the periodic table as is nuclear magnetic resonance. If the electronic structure of an atom consists entirely of filled shells or orbits, then it turns out that all the electrons in that atom will be paired in such a way as to yield zero total electronic angular momentum, and thus zero electronic magnetic moment, for that atom. Moreover, whenever two or more atoms combine chemically or bond together into a molecule or a solid compound, these atoms generally share their valence electrons in such fashion as to give each atom a filled outer shell. Electronic magnetic resonance is therefore not normally found in solids or chemical compounds, except in the special cases of atoms with partially unfilled inner electron shells. The only atoms normally found with unfilled inner shells are those from the so-called *transition groups,* such as the iron group (Cr, Mn, Fe, Ni, etc.) and the rare-earth group (Ce, Pr, Nd, Gd, Er, etc.). Electronic paramagnetic resonance is generally limited to compounds containing a transition-group, or *magnetic,* element.[1]

■ Figure 4-1 shows an idealized model of a magnetic atom, a single electron of charge $-e$ and mass m orbiting with frequency ω_r in an orbit of radius r about a massive fixed nucleus of charge $+e$. The orbiting frequency ω_r is extremely high, and the orbiting electron may be viewed equally well as a thin uniform ring or loop of charge. The orbital angular momentum l associated with this orbit[2] is given classically by

ELECTRONIC MAGNETIC
MOMENTS

$$l = mr^2\omega_r \tag{1}$$

where ω_r is a vector of magnitude $|\omega_r| = \omega_r$ pointing normal to the plane of the orbit,

---

[1] Numerous other elements can exhibit electronic magnetic behavior when they exist as free atoms in gases, but such atoms have a strong tendency to combine with other atoms or with each other to form nonmagnetic molecules. In any event, the magnetic-resonance response from anything less dense than a solid is too weak to be of practical interest.

[2] In atomic physics l or L is commonly used to indicate the orbital part of electronic angular momentum.

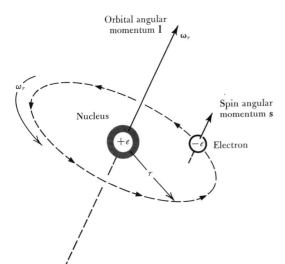

FIG. 4-1 An idealized model of a single-electron atom, showing the orbital angular momentum l and electron-spin angular momentum s. The nuclear angular momentum associated with a possible spin of the nucleus itself is not shown.

in the direction of travel of a right-hand screw rotating in the same sense as the electron. This orbital motion also represents a current loop in which the charge $-e$ traverses the loop once each period, $T_r = 2\pi/\omega_r$. This current loop creates an electronic orbital magnetic-dipole moment $\boldsymbol{\mu}_l$ equal to the loop area times the loop current, or

$$\boldsymbol{\mu}_l = \pi r^2 \frac{-e}{T_r} = -\tfrac{1}{2}er\omega_r \tag{2}$$

The negative sign means that the magnetic dipole points in the opposite direction to the angular momentum, owing to the negative sign of the orbiting charge. Combining the above results (see Fig. 4-1) gives the classical relation between magnetic moment $\boldsymbol{\mu}_l$ and angular momentum $\mathbf{l}$ of a single orbiting electron,

$$\boldsymbol{\mu}_l = -\frac{e}{2m}\mathbf{l} \tag{3}$$

Note that both the orbit size r and the orbiting frequency ω_r drop out of this simple classical expression (which is in fact also the correct quantum expression for a single orbital electron).

The electrons in an atom also possess a spin angular momentum $\mathbf{s}$ and an associated spin magnetic-dipole moment $\boldsymbol{\mu}_s$, and these two quantities turn out to be related, for a single electron spin, by

$$\boldsymbol{\mu}_s = -2\frac{e}{2m}\mathbf{s} \tag{4}$$

The extra factor of 2 appearing in this relation, as compared to the orbital case, is a quantum-mechanical result which has no simple classical interpretation (indeed, the existence of spin itself has no simple classical interpretation).

Finally, when a number of individual electrons, with their orbital and spin momenta, are combined to make up the electronic configuration of a real multiple-electron atom, the individual angular momenta combine vectorially to create a total angular momentum (orbital plus spin) usually labelled $\mathbf{J}$, and the individual magnetic-moment contributions combine to create a total magnetic-dipole moment $\boldsymbol{\mu}_J$ for the complete atom (both these quantities may be equal to zero, as is usually the case in non-transition-group compounds). The total angular momentum and the total magnetic-dipole moment due to the electronic contributions are then connected by the analogous relationship for a complete multiple-electron atom,

$$\boldsymbol{\mu}_J = -g_J\frac{e}{2m}\mathbf{J} \tag{5}$$

The factor g_J is a numerical factor in the range $0 \le g_J \le 2$, the exact value depending on the details of how the orbital and spin contributions combine vectorially to form $\mathbf{J}$ and $\boldsymbol{\mu}_J$ in the atom being considered.

ORDERS OF MAGNITUDE   ■ The angular momentum $\mathbf{J}$ of a real atom is always a multiple or half-multiple of the basic angular-momentum unit $\hbar \equiv h/2\pi$ (where h is Planck's constant), so that

$$|\mathbf{J}| = n\hbar \qquad n = 0, \tfrac{1}{2}, 1, \tfrac{3}{2}, \ldots \tag{6}$$

Therefore the magnetic-dipole moments of real atoms are of magnitude

$$|\boldsymbol{\mu}_J| = ng_J\frac{e}{2m}\hbar = ng_J\beta \tag{7}$$

where

$$\beta \equiv \frac{e\hbar}{2m} = 9.27 \times 10^{-24} \text{ A-m}^2 \qquad (8)$$

The quantity β, which serves as an elementary unit of atomic magnetic-dipole moment, is called the *Bohr magneton* and is equal to the magnetic-dipole moment of a single spinning electron.

■ The angular momentum and magnetic-dipole moment of an atomic nucleus have properties similar to those of the electronic contributions, but with a much smaller value for the magnetic quantities. The total angular momentum of a nucleus due to its nuclear spin is usually denoted by $\mathbf{I}$. The nuclear magnetic-dipole moment associated with this angular momentum is then given by the expression

$$\boldsymbol{\mu}_I = +g_I \frac{e}{2M} \mathbf{I} \qquad (9)$$

which is similar to the electronic expressions above. However, the proton mass M, rather than the electron mass m, appears in the denominator of the ratio. The sign in the expression is now positive because the nucleus has a positive charge, and the quantity g_I is a nuclear g factor, with a value of order unity or a few times unity in typical cases.

Since nuclear angular momenta (and, in fact, all angular momenta in quantum theory) will have magnitudes given by $|\mathbf{I}| = n\hbar$ with $n = 0, \frac{1}{2}, 1, \ldots$, the magnitudes of nuclear magnetic-dipole moments will be of order

$$|\boldsymbol{\mu}_I| = ng_I \frac{e}{2M} \hbar = ng_I \beta_I \qquad (10)$$

where the nuclear analog of the Bohr magneton β is

$$\beta_I \equiv \frac{e\hbar}{2M} = 5.05 \times 10^{-27} \text{ A-m}^2 \qquad (11)$$

This *nuclear magneton*, or basic unit of nuclear magnetic-dipole moment, is 1860 times smaller than the electronic Bohr magneton β. As a result, NMR frequencies and nuclear magnetic effects are smaller than EPR frequencies and electronic magnetic effects by approximately this same ratio.

■ Since real magnetic atoms possess both angular momentum and a permanent or fixed magnetic-dipole moment, the model best suited to represent a magnetic atom would seem to be a classical object also having a net angular momentum and a net magnetic-dipole moment—that is, a spinning magnetized top or gyroscope (perhaps made out of iron or other magnetic material), as shown in Fig. 4-2. This top is assumed to be mounted so that it can rotate freely and orient itself in any direction, and the effects of gravity on it are ignored, since they play no role in the real atomic situation. This model turns out to be, in fact, a very realistic and useful one, even for sophisticated quantum calculations on both magnetic and nonmagnetic atoms.

By analogy with the atomic results above, in this classical model we will also use $\mathbf{J}$ for the total classical angular momentum of the top, and we will suppose that the magnetic-dipole moment $\boldsymbol{\mu}$ of the top is given by

$$\boldsymbol{\mu} = -g \frac{e}{2m} \mathbf{J} \qquad (12)$$

NUCLEAR MAGNETIC MOMENTS

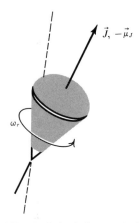

FIG. 4-2 A classical magnetized spinning top.

CLASSICAL MAGNETIZED-TOP MODEL

Here the quantity *g*, called simply the *g factor*, will be a number of order unity used to adjust the model to fit real atomic experiments. Obviously, if we want to fit the model to nuclear-magnetic experiments, we will replace *g* by g_I and $e/2m$ by $e/2M$.

Our next step will be to explore the dynamics of this model when it is placed in a strong dc magnetic field.

4-2 PRECESSIONAL MOTION OF THE MAGNETIZED-TOP MODEL

The natural motion of our classical electron-oscillator model in response to any initial displacement or disturbance is obviously a linear sinusoidal oscillation. In this section we will show that the natural motion of our magnetized-top magnetic-dipole model is a circular oscillation, or precessional motion, of the top's axis in space. Understanding the nature of this motion is vital to understanding the behavior and the dynamics of magnetic-dipole atomic transitions.

EQUATION OF MOTION ■ Let us consider the dynamics of a single magnetized classical top having an angular momentum **J** and a permanent magnetic-dipole moment $\boldsymbol{\mu} = -g(e/2m)\mathbf{J}$, placed in a dc magnetic field B_0. We assume that the axis of the top can rotate freely and without friction through all possible orientations in space.

The basic equation of motion for a system having angular momentum is that the time rate of change of the angular momentum **J** equals the torque exerted on the system. But a magnetic dipole **μ** placed in a magnetic field **b** experiences a vector torque given by the cross product of the dipole moment with the magnetic field. That is, the magnitude of the torque is $|\boldsymbol{\mu} \times \mathbf{b}|$, and the torque is exerted about an axis in the $\boldsymbol{\mu} \times \mathbf{b}$ direction. The equation of motion for the classical top is thus

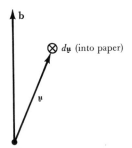

FIG. 4-3 The instantaneous increment *d*μ in μ(*t*) is perpendicular to both **b**(*t*) and μ(*t*), and hence points into the paper. Note that μ(*t*) never changes in length.

$$\frac{d}{dt}\mathbf{J}(t) = \boldsymbol{\mu}(t) \times \mathbf{b}(t) \tag{1}$$

By using the relation between **μ** and **J** and reversing the cross product, we can write this basic equation as

$$\frac{d}{dt}\boldsymbol{\mu}(t) = \frac{ge}{2m}\mathbf{b}(t) \times \boldsymbol{\mu}(t) \tag{2}$$

If we write this in the form

$$d\boldsymbol{\mu} = \frac{ge}{2m}\mathbf{b} \times \boldsymbol{\mu}\, dt \tag{3}$$

it is clear from the properties of cross products that the instantaneous increment *d*μ in μ(*t*) must be perpendicular to both μ(*t*) and **b**(*t*), as illustrated in Fig. 4-3. In fact, as we will see shortly, the above equation of motion implies that the magnetic-dipole vector **μ** rotates or precesses about the instantaneous **b**-field direction in a constant cone angle, with a precession frequency $\omega = (ge/2m)|\mathbf{b}|$ rad/sec.

NATURAL PRECESSION ■ As an illustration, consider the simple case of a dc magnetic field B_0 applied along the *z* axis, $\mathbf{b}(t) = B_0\mathbf{z}$. The equation of motion then becomes

$$\frac{d}{dt}\boldsymbol{\mu}(t) = \frac{ge}{2m}\mathbf{B}_0 \times \boldsymbol{\mu}(t) = \boldsymbol{\omega}_0 \times \boldsymbol{\mu}(t) \qquad \boldsymbol{\omega}_0 = \omega_0\mathbf{z} = \frac{ge}{2m}B_0\mathbf{z} \tag{4}$$

where we define the resonance frequency ω_0 by

$$\omega_0 = |\omega_0| = \frac{ge}{2m} B_0 \tag{5}$$

If the equation of motion is then written out in rectangular coordinates, the three component equations are

$$\frac{d}{dt} \mu_x(t) = -\omega_0 \mu_y(t)$$

$$\frac{d}{dt} \mu_y(t) = +\omega_0 \mu_x(t) \tag{6}$$

$$\frac{d}{dt} \mu_z(t) = 0$$

This set of equations clearly has the steady-state solution

$$\mu_x(t) = \mu_+ \cos(\omega_0 t + \phi_+) = \mathrm{Re}\, \tilde{\mu}_+ e^{j\omega_0 t}$$

$$\mu_y(t) = \mu_+ \sin(\omega_0 t + \phi_+) = \mathrm{Re}\,(-j\tilde{\mu}_+ e^{j\omega_0 t}) \tag{7}$$

$$\mu_z(t) = \mu_{z0} = \text{const}$$

These results say that the longitudinal or z-directed component of $\boldsymbol{\mu}(t)$ is constant, i.e., a constant projection on the dc magnetic field, while the two transverse x and y components of $\boldsymbol{\mu}(t)$ are sinusoidal, varying as $\cos \omega_0 t$ and $\sin \omega_0 t$, respectively.

The phasor amplitude of the transverse x component has been written in the form

$$\tilde{\mu}_+ = \mu_+ e^{j\phi_+} \tag{8}$$

The y component has the same phasor, except for a $90°$ shift in phase angle. A little inspection will show that the transverse or ac component of $\boldsymbol{\mu}(t)$ has constant amplitude; that is,

$$\mu_x{}^2(t) + \mu_y{}^2(t) = |\tilde{\mu}_+|^2 = \text{const} \tag{9}$$

and that this component rotates in the xy plane at frequency ω_0. That is, the vector sum of $\mu_x(t)$ and $\mu_y(t)$ is a vector which has constant length in the xy plane and rotates in this plane with frequency ω_0, as shown in Fig. 4-4. The sense of rotation is from the $+x$ toward the $+y$ direction. We call this form and direction of motion *positive circular polarization* and denote it by the subscript plus sign.

■ The natural oscillation frequency of the classical electron oscillator is fixed in any given case once the mass m and the spring constant K have been specified. In the magnetic case, however, the natural precession frequency is widely tunable by varying the dc magnetic-field value B_0. In fact, the resonance frequency varies linearly with B_0 in our model, and either linearly or reasonably close to it in many real magnetic-dipole atoms. If we write the dc magnetic-field value in the form[1] $B_0 = \mu_0 H_0$ and the frequency in the form $f_0 = \omega_0/2\pi$, the frequency-field relationship becomes

$$f_0 = \frac{1}{2\pi} \frac{ge}{2m} B_0 \quad \text{or} \quad \frac{f_0}{H_0} = \frac{ge\mu_0}{4\pi m} \tag{10}$$

FIG. 4-4 A magnetized top placed in a dc magnetic field B_0 will precess about the direction of the dc magnetic field with a constant precession frequency ω_0 and a constant angle with respect to B_0.

MAGNITUDE OF THE
PRECESSION FREQUENCY

---

[1] By writing $B_0 = \mu_0 H_0$, where μ_0 is the permeability of free space, we are implicitly assuming that the dc magnetic susceptibility of whatever material we are studying is small. This assumption is valid for all paramagnetic materials.

If we use $g = 2$ (since this is the appropriate value for the pure-electron-spin case), and if we express H_0 in the definitely non-mks units of gauss, this expression has the numerical value

$$\frac{f_0}{H_0} \approx 2.8 \text{ MHz/gauss} \tag{11}$$

For a typical laboratory magnetic field of a few thousand gauss, the resonant frequency is in the range of 5 to 10 GHz, or right in the middle of the microwave range. This is the frequency range in which, for example, most microwave solid-state masers operate and in which most laboratory EPR experiments are carried out.

For the case of nuclear magnetic resonance we must replace the electron mass m by the proton mass M or replace β by β_I, thus making NMR frequencies smaller than EPR values by a factor of ~ 2000. For magnetic fields of a few thousand gauss, therefore, typical NMR frequencies are in the radio-frequency range (30 MHz and 60 MHz are common experimental choices). One of the most common NMR examples is the hydrogen nucleus, which is just a single proton, and for which the frequency-field relationship is 4.2 kHz per gauss.

DAMPING MECHANISMS   ■ The alert reader may be wondering why we have not yet introduced any damping terms, either radiative or otherwise, into the magnetic-dipole equations, as we did at a very early stage with the classical electron-oscillator model. Some such decay mechanisms must certainly exist. However, it is simpler for us to disregard damping for the moment and to postpone introducing both damping and the magnetic-dipole analog of collisions until a later section.

We can note, however, that a precessing classical magnetic dipole will certainly radiate electromagnetic energy at its precession frequency, just as does an oscillating classical electric dipole, and we could compute this classical magnetic radiative damping rate if we wished. This rate, however, would turn out to be many orders of magnitude smaller in the magnetic-dipole case than in the electric-dipole case for the same resonance frequency. The reason for this is that a magnetic dipole is simply not a very effective radiating element. Moreover, most magnetic-resonance transitions are at microwave and lower frequencies, where even the electric-dipole radiative transition rates are extremely slow. As a consequence, magnetic-dipole transitions almost invariably are damped and exchange energy with their thermal surroundings chiefly via nonradiative mechanisms (usually through *spin-lattice decay*).

ANALOGY TO QUANTUM   ■ The classical results we have just obtained stand in close analogy to the more correct
ENERGY LEVELS   quantum-mechanical description of magnetic-dipole behavior. According to quantum theory, an atom located in any one of its optical energy levels—which is usually, of course, the ground energy level—may be labeled by a dimensionless total-angular-momentum quantum number J, where $J = 0, \frac{1}{2}, 1, \frac{3}{2}, \ldots$. The total angular momentum of the atom is then given in magnitude by $|\mathbf{J}| = \sqrt{J(J + 1)}\hbar$, although the maximum observable component of $\mathbf{J}$ along any one direction, say the z direction, is only $J_z = J\hbar$. The magnetic-dipole moment of the atom is given by $\boldsymbol{\mu}_J = -g_J\beta\mathbf{J}$, and $\boldsymbol{\mu}_J$ has all the same quantum properties as $\mathbf{J}$.

When such an atom is placed in a dc magnetic field, whose direction we may as well choose to be the z direction, quantum theory says that the optical energy level is split into $2J + 1$ separate energy levels or sublevels. The original energy level was thus *degenerate;* i.e., it really consisted of $2J + 1$ distinct energy levels, all coincident in energy in the absence of a magnetic field. The energies, the z components of angular momentum, and the z components of magnetic-dipole moment of these sublevels are given by

$$
\begin{aligned}
E_M &= M_J g_J \beta B_0 \\
J_{z,M} &= M_J \hbar \qquad\qquad M_J = -J, -J+1, \ldots, +J \qquad (12)\\
\mu_{z,M} &= -M_J g_J \beta
\end{aligned}
$$

where the quantum number M_J runs in integer steps over the $2J + 1$ values from $M_J = -J$ to $M_J = +J$. Note that these energy levels agree with the classical expression for the energy of a magnetic dipole in a magnetic field,

$$
E_M = -\boldsymbol{\mu} \cdot \mathbf{B}_0 = M_J g_J \beta B_0 \qquad (13)
$$

Figure 4-5 illustrates these *Zeeman-split levels* for the case of $J = \frac{3}{2}$.

In this simple type of free-atom angular momentum system, in which we have not included any possible perturbing effects on the magnetic-dipole energy levels, such as the strong dc crystalline electric fields that exist between atoms in solids, the quantum theory says that the only allowed (that is, experimentally observable) magnetic-dipole transitions will be between adjacent levels in an energy-level diagram such as Fig. 4-5. That is, there is a $\Delta M_J = \pm 1$ selection rule for magnetic-dipole transitions. The transition frequencies between adjacent Zeeman levels will all be the same for a particular atom and will be given by

$$
\omega_{M+1,M} = \frac{E_{M+1} - E_M}{\hbar} = \frac{g\beta}{\hbar} B_0 \qquad (14)
$$

or

$$
f_{M+1,M} = \frac{1}{2\pi} \frac{ge}{2m} B_0 \qquad (15)
$$

But this is exactly the same as the classical precession frequency we just calculated for a classical dipole having the same angular-momentum–magnetic-dipole-moment ratio as the quantum atom.

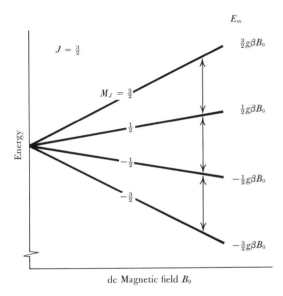

FIG. 4-5   The Zeeman energy levels versus dc magnetic field B_0 for a quantized magnetic-dipole atom having angular-momentum quantum number $J = \frac{3}{2}$. The arrows indicate the allowed $\Delta M_J = \pm 1$ magnetic-dipole transitions in this case.

The analogy between the classical model and the quantum atom is, in fact, deeper than just this agreement between resonance frequencies. A more detailed quantum analysis shows that the ac motion of the atom in the quantum case has exactly the same circularly polarized form as in the classical model. A two-level atomic system ($J = \frac{1}{2}$) is particularly close to the classical model in that the exact Schrödinger quantum equation for this case can be transformed mathematically into identically the same form as the classical equation of motion. In general, our classical model is a very good representation for the quantum-mechanical atomic properties, and we can continue to use it with considerable confidence.

4-3 COLLECTIONS OF MAGNETIC DIPOLES: DC PARAMAGNETIC SUSCEPTIBILITY

The magnetic-dipole "atoms" of this chapter differ from the electric-dipole atoms of Chap. 2 in several important ways:

1. Each individual magnetic dipole has an inherent permanent magnetic-dipole moment μ, whereas an electron oscillator has no permanent electric-dipole moment and acquires an induced ac moment only under the influence of an applied signal.
2. The magnetic dipoles are normally immersed in a large dc magnetic field B_0, whereas no large dc field is normally applied in the electric-dipole case.
3. The frequencies of interest for magnetic resonances are usually (but not invariably) in the microwave range or lower. As a result, the condition $hf/kT \ll 1$ is usually valid for the magnetic case. By contrast, electric-dipole transitions typically fall in the infrared or optical ranges, so that the opposite condition, $hf/kT \gg 1$, often prevails for these transitions.

The first of these statements means that a collection of magnetic dipoles will exhibit a *dc paramagnetic susceptibility* when the dc magnetic field mentioned in the second statement is applied, whereas a collection of electron oscillators will not exhibit any first-order static susceptibility (i.e., there is no "paraelectricity"). We will calculate the dc paramagnetic susceptibility of a collection of magnetic dipoles in this section.

The third statement implies that when we discuss these resonances from a quantum viewpoint, in terms of energy levels and their populations, virtually all the atoms in a typical electric-dipole situation will be in their lowest energy level at thermal equilibrium, because $hf/kT \gg 1$; in a typical magnetic-dipole case at thermal equilibrium there will be significant numbers of atoms (in fact, nearly equal numbers) in both the upper and lower levels of a transition, because $hf/kT \ll 1$. This will be of considerable significance in the following quantum explanation of paramagnetic susceptibility.

MAGNETIC QUANTITIES AND MAGNETIC-DIPOLE COLLECTIONS

■ In electromagnetic theory the three basic magnetic quantities **b**, **h**, and **m** are related in general by

$$\mathbf{b}(t) = \mu_0[\mathbf{h}(t) + \mathbf{m}(t)] \tag{1}$$

where

$$\begin{aligned}\mathbf{b} &= \textit{magnetic flux density or magnetic induction, webers/m}^2\\ \mathbf{h} &= \textit{magnetic field strength or field intensity, A/m}\\ \mathbf{m} &= \textit{magnetic polarization or magnetization, A/m}\end{aligned} \tag{2}$$

and

$$\mu_0 = 4\pi \times 10^{-7} \text{ H/m } (\equiv \text{weber-m/A}) \tag{3}$$

To simplify conversions from the widely used non-mks units of gauss to the mks units of webers per square meter for magnetic flux density **b**, it is worth remembering that 1 weber/m$^2 \equiv 10^4$ gauss.

Relation (1) is quite general. In linear magnetic media (only) the magnetization **m**(*t*) expressed in sinusoidal form may be linearly related to the magnetic field strength **h**(*t*) in the same form by writing

$$\tilde{\mathbf{M}}(\omega) = \tilde{\chi}(\omega)\tilde{\mathbf{H}}(\omega) \tag{4}$$

where $\tilde{\mathbf{M}}(\omega)$ and $\tilde{\mathbf{H}}(\omega)$ are the phasor amplitudes of **m**(*t*) and **h**(*t*) and $\tilde{\chi}(\omega)$ is by definition the *ac magnetic susceptibility*. The relationship between sinusoidal components of **b** and **h** in these media then becomes

$$\tilde{\mathbf{B}}(\omega) = \mu_0[1 + \tilde{\chi}(\omega)]\tilde{\mathbf{H}}(\omega) = \tilde{\mu}(\omega)\tilde{\mathbf{H}}(\omega) \tag{5}$$

where $\tilde{\mu}(\omega)$ is the magnetic permeability of the linear magnetic medium. The linear magnetic susceptibility $\tilde{\chi}(\omega)$ is the magnetic analog of the electric susceptibility $\tilde{\chi}(\omega)$ introduced in Chap. 2. It has many of the same properties and interpretations as the electric susceptibility, is denoted by the same symbol, and appears in the same way in a number of important maser and laser formulas, as we will see later.

The magnetic polarization or magnetization **m** is of particular interest to us here. In close analogy with the electric polarization **p**, the magnetic polarization **m** can be defined as the *total magnetic-dipole moment per unit volume* in a material medium or in a collection of atoms. Consider for example a collection of our classical magnetic dipoles with average density $\mathcal{N}_v$ per unit volume, where the density $\mathcal{N}_v$ is large enough that even if we pick quite small a volume, it will still include many dipoles. Let the instantaneous magnetic-dipole moment of an individual dipole be $\boldsymbol{\mu}_i(t)$. The macroscopic magnetic polarization **m**(*t*) in any small volume *V* will then be just the vector sum of the individual microscopic dipoles per unit volume in that volume; that is,

$$\mathbf{m}(t) = \frac{1}{V} \sum_{\substack{\text{individual} \\ \text{dipoles}}} \boldsymbol{\mu}_i(t) \tag{6}$$

As before, the microscopic atomic dipole moments $\boldsymbol{\mu}_i$ combine to create the macroscopic moment per unit volume **m**. An alternate way of writing this is

$$\mathbf{m}(t) = \mathcal{N}_v\boldsymbol{\mu}_{\text{av}}(t) \tag{7}$$

where $\boldsymbol{\mu}_{\text{av}}(t)$ is an average dipole moment with the averaging process carried out over the dipoles in the small volume considered, so that

$$\boldsymbol{\mu}_{\text{av}}(t) \equiv \frac{1}{\mathcal{N}_vV} \sum_{i=1}^{N_v} \boldsymbol{\mu}_i(t) \tag{8}$$

and $\mathcal{N}_vV$ is the total number of dipoles in the volume *V*.

In any real magnetic-dipole experiment we are, of course, dealing with a collection containing a very large number of individual dipoles. The macroscopic magnetization **m**(*t*) is then the only atomic quantity that is measured or observed by our experimental apparatus. Therefore we must consider not merely the dynamics of individual magnetic dipoles $\boldsymbol{\mu}_i(t)$, but also how these microscopic dipoles add up vectorially to create the macroscopic magnetization **m**(*t*). In this section we will consider the dc aspects of this process, and in the next section we will discuss the relaxation processes that occur in such a collection of magnetic dipoles.

MAGNETIC-DIPOLE ALIGNMENT

■ Consider further our model of a collection of many individual magnetic dipoles contained in some volume with an applied dc magnetic field B_0. The dipoles are assumed to be all identical, but at a given instant the individual dipoles may be oriented in random directions and precessing with random phases, as shown in Fig. 4-6a. In fact, if the individual dipole orientations and precession phases are distributed completely at random, with uniform probability for any direction, then the vector sum of the individual dipole moments will be essentially zero. In this completely random case we will have

$$\mathbf{m}(t) = \mathcal{N}_v \boldsymbol{\mu}_{\mathrm{av}}(t) = 0 \tag{9}$$

In this completely random limit there is no net alignment of the individual dipoles in any direction, and hence no net macroscopic polarization in any direction.

At the opposite extreme, if all the individual dipoles are aligned exactly parallel in the direction of a unit vector **s**, as in Fig. 4-6b, then the macroscopic polarization **m** also points in that direction and has its maximum possible value,

$$\mathbf{m} = \mathbf{m}_{\mathrm{max}} = \mathcal{N}_v \mu \mathbf{s} \tag{10}$$

In this case we speak of *complete alignment* of the collection of dipoles. Complete alignment of all the dipoles is not common in a real collection of atoms, but it can be brought about, at least temporarily, in some cases by applying carefully selected large-amplitude signal pulses.

The most common situation for a collection of real magnetic dipoles is *partial alignment* of the dipoles. In most situations the orientations and precession phases of individual dipoles are largely random, but there may still be some net degree of ordering, or some partial degree of alignment. The result of this partial alignment is then a

FIG. 4-6 (a) A collection of magnetic dipoles, each oriented in some random direction and precessing with random phase, so that no net macroscopic alignment is created. (b) The same dipoles fully aligned and all precessing together to create the maximum macroscope magnetization $\mathbf{m}(t) = N_v \boldsymbol{\mu}(t)$.

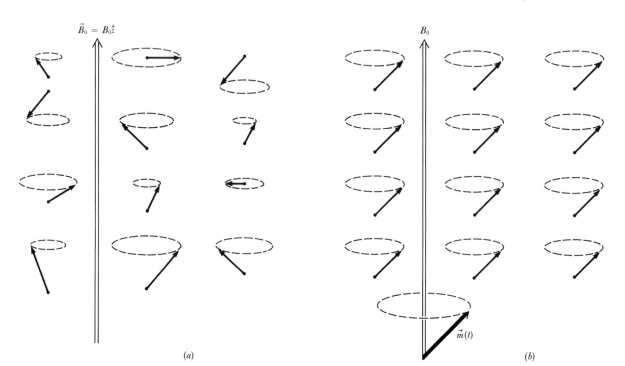

(a) (b)

net macroscopic magnetization $\mathbf{m}(t)$ in the collection that is larger than zero but smaller than the maximum value obtained only for full alignment. Note in particular that for a collection of dipoles $\mathbf{m}(t)$ is obviously not constant in length, whereas the individual dipole moment $\boldsymbol{\mu}(t)$ of a single dipole does have a constant length, with only its direction or orientation varying with t.

■ A situation of particular interest in a collection of magnetic dipoles (Fig. 4-6) is *thermal equilibrium*. Thermal equilibrium is generally thought of as a situation in which the maximum degree of randomization prevails. What alignment, if any, will be present in this situation? In analyzing magnetic-dipole problems we normally choose our coordinate axes such that the dc magnetic field B_0 defines the z axis. Nothing in our model then establishes any preferred choice for the x and y directions or otherwise distinguishes any one transverse direction from any other. The general concept of randomness associated with thermal equilibrium then leads us to believe that at thermal equilibrium the individual dipoles in a collection should have their transverse components distributed with complete uniformity in the transverse xy plane. In other words, we should expect to find no net transverse alignment in a collection of dipoles at thermal equilibrium. The transverse magnetization components at thermal equilibrium should be

$$m_{x0} = \mathcal{N}_v \mu_{x,\mathrm{av}} \sim 0 \qquad m_{y0} = \mathcal{N}_v \mu_{y,\mathrm{av}} \sim 0 \tag{11}$$

We will use the subscript zero to mean the expected values of various quantities at thermal equilibrium.

The situation in the longitudinal or z direction is different. Along this axis there is a preferred direction for an individual dipole—parallel to the dc magnetic field B_0, because the parallel orientation represents a lower-energy situation. Note that this does *not* say that there is any net torque due to B_0 that turns a dipole toward the $+z$ direction. Any individual dipole left to itself in a dc magnetic field will precess steadily at a fixed cone angle, as we saw in Sec. 4-2. Nonetheless, since the orientation energy of a dipole moment $\boldsymbol{\mu}$ in a field $\mathbf{B}_0$ is $W = -\boldsymbol{\mu} \cdot \mathbf{B}_0$, a larger angle θ between the field direction and the cone of precession represents a higher-energy situation. Hence there is a fundamental preference for small-θ dipole orientations. The net result is that a collection of magnetic dipoles in thermal equilibrium will have some net alignment in the longitudinal direction, leading to a finite macroscopic dc polarization m_{z0} in that direction. Calculation of this *paramagnetic dc polarization*, by both classical and quantum methods, will be our next task.

■ The thermal-equilibrium magnetization m_{z0} and the associated dc magnetic susceptibility of a collection of magnetic dipoles can be calculated from either a classical or a quantum approach. The latter is, of course, the only strictly correct method. However, the results of both approaches turn out to be nearly identical, except for a minor numerical factor. In view of the classical emphasis of this book, we will first consider the classical derivation and then briefly discuss the quantum approach for comparison.

Consider a large collection of individual dipoles, such as Fig. 4-6, in thermal equilibrium. At any given instant any individual dipole in this collection will be oriented in some random direction given by the polar angles (θ,ϕ), where θ is the precession cone angle and ϕ is the precession phase, as shown in Fig. 4-7. The orientation energy W of a magnetic-dipole moment $\boldsymbol{\mu}$ in a magnetic field $\mathbf{B}$ is given, as we noted earlier, by

$$W = -\boldsymbol{\mu} \cdot \mathbf{B} \tag{12}$$

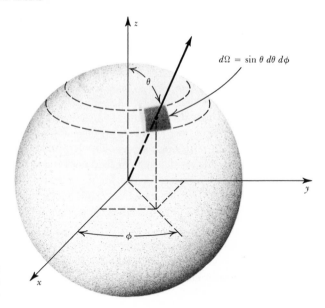

$$d\Omega = \sin\theta \, d\theta \, d\phi$$

FIG. 4-7 Coordinates for discussing the distribution of dipole orientation angles θ and precession phases ϕ in deriving the classical dc paramagnetic susceptibility.

and so a dipole oriented in the direction (θ,ϕ) in the dc field B_0 will have orientation energy

$$W = -\mu B_0 \cos\theta \tag{13}$$

The z component of magnetic-dipole moment associated with this dipole will be

$$\mu_z(\theta) = \mu \cos\theta \tag{14}$$

Obviously, neither W nor μ_z depends on the precession phase angle ϕ.

According to the Boltzmann principle of thermodynamics, if a large number of individual elements, such as these dipoles, are in thermal equilibrium, then owing to thermal agitation, individual elements may be excited to all possible energy levels, but the higher energy levels will be less frequent than the lower ones. Specifically, the relative probability that any individual element will be in a state or condition having energy W is given by

$$\text{Prob }(W) = e^{-W/kT} \tag{15}$$

In our specific problem the relative probability that a dipole will be oriented at the angles (θ,ϕ) is thus given by

$$\text{Prob }(\theta,\phi) = e^{\mu B_0 \cos\theta/kT} \tag{16}$$

Although individual dipole orientations will be distributed all the way from $\theta = 0°$ to $\theta = 180°$, the generally parallel orientations ($\theta < 90°$, or $\cos\theta > 0$) will be more probable than the antiparallel orientations ($\theta > 90°$, or $\cos\theta < 0$).

To calculate the resulting net alignment along the favored $+z$ direction in the collection of dipoles we must average the dipole moment z component $\mu_z(\theta) = \mu \cos\theta$ over all dipoles—that is to say, over all directions (θ,ϕ) weighed by the relative probability or relative number of dipoles pointing in that direction. The necessary averaging process may be written

$$\mu_{z,\mathrm{av}} \equiv \mu_{z0} = \frac{\iint \mu_z(\theta)\ \mathrm{prob}\ (\theta,\phi)\ d(\theta,\phi)}{\iint \mathrm{prob}\ (\theta,\phi)\ d(\theta,\phi)} \tag{17}$$

The integral in the denominator is included to normalize the relative probabilities. The differential $d(\theta,\phi)$ in these integrals means integration over all possible directions indicated by (θ,ϕ), that is, over all possible solid angles $d\Omega = d(\theta,\phi) = \sin\theta\ d\theta\ d\phi$. Figure 4-7 illustrates the geometry for this calculation.

When the integrals in (17) are written out in full, the integration over $d\phi$ becomes trivial and may be simply cancelled off in both numerator and denominator. The remaining integrals over $d\theta$ have the form

$$\mu_{z0} = \mu\ \frac{\displaystyle\int_0^\pi \cos\theta\ \sin\theta\ e^{(\mu B_0/kT)\ \cos\theta}\ d\theta}{\displaystyle\int_0^\pi \sin\theta\ e^{(\mu B_0/kT)\ \cos\theta}\ d\theta} \tag{18}$$

Both these integrals can be evaluated analytically, and the final result for the average dipole component in the z direction is found to be

$$\mu_{z0} = \mu\left[\coth\frac{\mu B_0}{kT} - \left(\frac{\mu B_0}{kT}\right)^{-1}\right] = \mu L\left(\frac{\mu B_0}{kT}\right) \tag{19}$$

The coth notation means the hyperbolic cotangent function, and the function $L(x) \equiv \coth x - 1/x$ is known as the *Langevin function* (after the scientist who derived this result in 1905). Figure 4-8 shows this result in the form of the fractional z-directed alignment μ_{z0}/μ plotted against $\mu B_0/kT$.

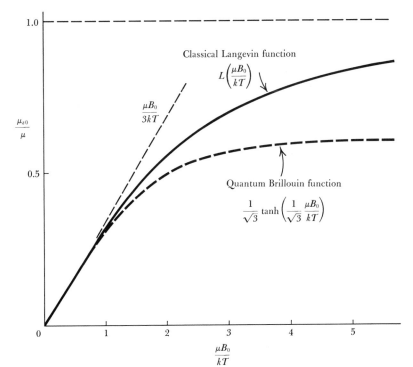

FIG. 4-8 Net longitudinal alignment in a collection of magnetic dipoles at thermal equilibrium as a function of $\mu B_0/kT$, as given by the classical Langevin derivation (solid curve) and by the quantum derivation for $J = \frac{1}{2}$ (dashed curve).

For values of $\mu B_0/kT \ll 1$ the equilibrium alignment increases linearly with the dc magnetic field. Use of the analytic approximation $L(x) \approx x/3$ yields in this region

$$\mu_{z0} \approx \frac{\mu^2 B_0}{3kT} \qquad \mu B_0 \ll kT \tag{20}$$

The equilibrium macroscopic magnetization m_{z0} can then be written as

$$m_{z0} = N_v \mu_{z0} \approx N_v \frac{\mu^2 B_0}{3kT} \qquad \mu B_0 \ll kT \tag{21}$$

The longitudinal magnetization is thus linearly proportional to the applied dc magnetic field in this region. We can therefore define a dc paramagnetic susceptibility χ_{dc} by

$$\chi_{dc} \equiv \frac{m_{z0}}{H_0} = \frac{\mu_0 m_{z0}}{B_0}$$
$$\approx \frac{N_v \mu_0 \mu^2}{3kT} \qquad \mu B_0 \ll kT \tag{22}$$

The susceptibility is directly proportional to the density of dipoles N_v and the dipole magnitude μ^2 and inversely proportional to the temperature T (sometimes referred to as the *Curie temperature dependence*).

The opposite limiting case of $\mu B_0/kT \gg 1$ corresponds to the limit

$$\lim_{x \to \infty} L(x) \approx 1 \tag{23}$$

and thus to the limiting results

$$\begin{aligned} \mu_{z0} &\approx \mu \\ m_{z0} &\approx N_v \mu \end{aligned} \qquad \mu B_0 \gg kT \tag{24}$$

as shown in the right-hand portion of Fig. 4-8. In this region, which occurs only for very strong magnetic fields and/or very low temperatures, essentially all the dipoles are aligned parallel to the magnetic field, and the macroscopic polarization has its maximum possible value along the z direction. Susceptibility has no meaning in this region, since m_{z0} no longer depends linearly on the dc field B_0.

PHYSICAL INTERPRETATION   ■ These results have the following physical interpretation. In the low-field or linear susceptibility region the alignment energy μB_0 of a dipole is small compared to the unit of thermal energy kT. Thermal agitation is then strong enough to disperse the dipole cone angles more or less uniformly over all values of θ, from fully parallel to fully antiparallel. The dc magnetic field is able to impose only a slight preferential tendency toward the slightly lower-energy $+z$ direction. As the dc field is increased, this small net preference increases, and the resulting net alignment also increases, essentially in direct proportion to the ratio of alignment energy μB_0 to thermal energy kT.

For high enough fields and/or low enough temperatures, the alignment energy μB_0 becomes very large compared to the thermal energy. The condition of parallel alignment becomes very strongly favored, and only a vanishingly few dipoles have sufficient thermal agitation to reach precession angles away from $\theta = 0$. The result is essentially complete alignment of all dipoles along B_0, or complete saturation of the system.

The behavior of the angular distribution of the dipoles is very closely analogous to the behavior of the height distribution of, say, the air molecules in a closed room. A molecule of mass M located at a height h above the floor has an excess potential energy MGh compared to its energy at floor level, where G is the gravitational constant. Thus there is a definite energy preference for the air molecules to be closer to the floor than to the ceiling. Now, we know from experience that the air molecules are distributed very nearly uniformly as a result of thermal agitation. The distribution is nearly uniform despite the preference for lower energy levels chiefly because for ordinary air molecules and room heights the change in potential energy is small in relation to the average thermal energy, $MGh \ll kT$. However, there actually are slightly more molecules near the floor than near the ceiling; the atmospheric pressure and density of the air is greater near the floor by a very small, but still finite, amount. We might speak of this as a small but finite *alignment* of the air molecules, in that the average height of the molecules will be slightly less than half the room height, even though the molecules are widely distributed through all possible levels in the room. This behavior is in direct analogy with the orientation behavior of the magnetic dipoles as a result of the conflict between thermal agitation and magnetic field alignment.

The high-field saturated limit also has a simple analog. The most direct analog to increasing the magnetic field strength B_0 is perhaps to increase the gravitational field strength G (which it is not convenient to do). A simple alternative, however, is to increase the mass of individual particles so as to make $MGh \gg kT$. A practical illustration of this would be to place large dust particles in the air; in the absence of turbulent air currents or other nonequilibrium disturbances, these particles will indeed settle out to a "fully aligned" height distribution at the lowest energy position—on the floor or the lowest available surface.

■ Since the magnitude of a typical atomic dipole moment is $\mu = g\beta$, where β is the Bohr magneton, the magnitude of the argument in the Langevin function for atomic dipoles is, for $g = 2$,

HIGH-FIELD SATURATION CONDITION

$$\frac{\mu B_0}{kT} \approx g\beta \frac{B_0}{kT} \approx 1.4 \frac{B_0 \,(\text{webers/m}^2)}{T\,(^\circ\text{K})} \tag{25}$$

The magnetic-field value required to make $\mu B_0 \approx kT$ at room temperature is thus $B_0 \approx 200$ webers/m$^2 \approx 2 \times 10^6$ gauss. Since even advanced superconducting magnets provide fields not larger than $\sim 10^5$ gauss, the linear susceptibility condition $\mu B_0 \ll kT$ prevails for all normal magnetic-resonance situations. The fully aligned regime can be reached experimentally only by combining very low temperatures with abnormally high dc magnetic fields.

■ Because several of the quantum concepts involved may be of use to us later, let us calculate this same thermal-equilibrium paramagnetic-polarization result using a quantum energy-level approach. We now assume that our individual magnetic dipoles are real quantized atoms having the simplest possible quantum properties, total angular momentum $\mathbf{J}$ and associated magnetic-dipole moment $\boldsymbol{\mu}_J = -g\beta\mathbf{J}$ with total-angular-momentum quantum number $J = \frac{1}{2}$. An atom of this type placed in a dc magnetic field B_0 has two allowed energy levels, corresponding to two allowed values of longitudinal

DC PARAMAGNETIC SUSCEPTIBILITY: QUANTUM DERIVATION

angular momentum J_z and longitudinal magnetic moment u_z; that is,

$$E_{1,2} = \mp \frac{g\beta B_0}{2}$$

$$J_{z1,2} = \mp \frac{\hbar}{2}$$ (26)

$$\mu_{z1,2} = \pm \frac{g\beta}{2}$$

Since the magnitude of a quantized angular-momentum vector such as **J** is given by the rather odd expression $|\mathbf{J}| = \sqrt{J(J + 1)}\hbar$, the magnitude of the associated magnetic-dipole moment will be

$$|\mu_J|^2 = J(J + 1)(g\beta)^2 = \tfrac{3}{4}(g\beta)^2 \qquad J = \tfrac{1}{2}$$ (27)

It is one of the peculiarities of the quantum picture that the magnitude of the **J** vector is $\sqrt{J(J + 1)} = \sqrt{\tfrac{3}{4}}$, but the maximum component the vector can have in any single direction (such as the z direction) is $J = \tfrac{1}{2}$.

If a large number of such dipoles form a collection in thermal equilibrium, then N_{10} dipoles will be in the lower energy level E_1 and N_{20} will be in the upper level E_2, where the energy-level populations obey the Boltzmann factor

$$\frac{N_{20}}{N_{10}} = e^{-g\beta B_0/kT}$$ (28)

as shown in Fig. 4-9. Combining this relation with the condition $N_{10} + N_{20} = N$ yields the equilibrium energy-level populations,

$$N_{10} = N\frac{1}{1 + e^{-g\beta B_0/kT}} \approx \frac{N}{2}\left(1 + \frac{g\beta B_0}{kT}\right)$$

$$N_{20} = N\frac{e^{-g\beta B_0/kT}}{1 + e^{-g\beta B_0/kT}} \approx \frac{N}{2}\left(1 - \frac{g\beta B_0}{kT}\right)$$ (29)

where the approximate expressions are valid in the *small-field limit* $g\beta B_0/kT \ll 1$. The N_{10} atoms in level E_1 have a z component of magnetic moment $\mu_z = \mu_{z1} = +g\beta/2$, while the N_{20} upper-level atoms have z component $\mu_z = \mu_{z2} = -g\beta/2$. The average z component of dipole moment in the collection will therefore be the weighted average of these components, or

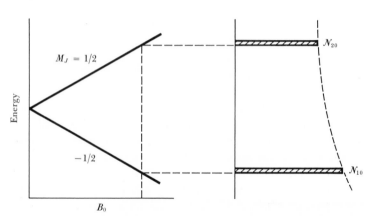

FIG. 4-9 Energy-level diagram and thermal-equilibrium level populations for the quantum case with $J = \frac{1}{2}$.

$$\mu_{z,\text{av}} \equiv \mu_{z0} = \frac{N_{10}}{N}\mu_{z1} + \frac{N_{20}}{N}\mu_{z2} \tag{30}$$

Substitution of the expressions for N_{10} and N_{20} gives, after some minor algebra,

$$\mu_{z0} = \frac{g\beta}{2} \tanh \frac{g\beta B_0}{kT}$$

$$\approx \begin{cases} \dfrac{(g\beta)^2 B_0}{4kT} & g\beta B_0 \ll kT \\[2ex] \dfrac{g\beta}{2} & g\beta B_0 \gg kT \end{cases} \tag{31}$$

Just as in the classical case, the average z component of dipole moment varies linearly with B_0/kT for small values of this parameter and approaches a constant saturated value for large values of the argument.

■ This quantum result is clearly similar, but not exactly identical, to the classical result obtained above. The similarity becomes even more apparent if we identify the quantity $g\beta$ of the quantum calculation with the individual dipole magnitude μ of the classical calculation. There is some uncertainty, however, as to exactly how this identification is best made. We might, for example, identify the classical moment μ with the *maximum projected value* of the quantum moment μ along any axis, by writing $\mu \equiv g\beta/2$. If we do this, we find that the classical and quantum results agree exactly in the saturated limit but differ by a factor of 3 in the small-field or linear region. A preferable alternative is to identify the classical moment μ with the *magnitude* of the quantum moment $\boldsymbol{\mu}$ by writing

$$\mu_{\text{classical}} \equiv |\boldsymbol{\mu}|_{\text{quantum}} = (\tfrac{3}{4})^{1/2} g\beta$$

The classical and quantum derivations then agree exactly in the linear region, as we will see next, and differ by a factor of $3^{1/2} = 1.732$ in the saturated limit.

Using the latter identification, we can write the quantum result as

$$\mu_{z0} = \frac{|\boldsymbol{\mu}|}{\sqrt{3}} \tanh \frac{|\boldsymbol{\mu}|B_0}{\sqrt{3}kT}$$

$$\approx \frac{|\boldsymbol{\mu}|^2 B_0}{3kT} \qquad |\boldsymbol{\mu}|B_0 \ll kT \tag{32}$$

The result in this form is plotted as the dashed line in Fig. 4-8. The dc magnetic susceptibility according to the quantum derivation then becomes

$$\chi_{\text{dc}} = \frac{N_v \mu_{z0}}{H_0} = \frac{N_v \mu_0 |\boldsymbol{\mu}|^2}{3kT} \tag{33}$$

which is exactly the same form as the classical result, with μ^2 replaced by $|\boldsymbol{\mu}|^2$.

Exactly the same type of quantum derivation of the equilibrium magnetization m_{z0} can be carried out for atoms with larger values of angular-momentum quantum number J, and hence larger numbers $(2J + 1)$ of allowed energy levels. As the number of levels increases, the agreement between classical and quantum results becomes steadily better. The classical and quantum results remain the same in the linear region, and the numerical difference at saturation approaches zero as $J \to \infty$.

MEASUREMENT OF DC
SUSCEPTIBILITIES

■ The dc susceptibilities of all available paramagnetic materials are very small compared to unity. Consider a dipole density $N_v = 10^{22}$ cm^{-3} $= 10^{28}$ m^{-3}, which is close to the maximum density of atoms in solids; an electronic dipole moment with $g = 2$; and room temperature, $T = 300°$K. The calculated dc susceptibility for this case is

$$\chi_{dc} \approx \frac{N_v \mu_0 (g\beta)^2}{4kT} \approx 3 \times 10^{-6} \tag{34}$$

Obviously, even increasing the dipole density to the limit and reducing the temperature to the liquid-helium range will still leave the dc susceptibility substantially less than unity.

The dc magnetic susceptibilities of materials can be measured in a number of different ways, although the smallness of the effect makes the measurement difficult. Figure 4-10 shows one possible method, which is perhaps more useful as an illustration of the principles involved than as a practical method. A paramagnetic sample is simply dropped through a multiturn pickup coil, while both the coil and sample are immersed in the steady dc magnetic field of a surrounding solenoid, so that the sample magnetization is constant during its passage through the coil. When the sample is inserted into the coil, the dc magnetization m_{z0} in the sample means that there is an additional magnetic flux density $\Delta B_z = \mu_0 m_{z0}$ temporarily added to the flux density B_0 already linking the coil. As this added flux density first builds up (when the sample enters) and then decays, the time rate of change of flux causes a doublet pulse of induced voltage in the coil, which can be measured with a sufficiently sensitive detector across the terminals of the coil as indicated in Fig. 4-10. The dc magnetization m_{z0} in the sample can then be deduced from the amplitude of this pulse and the geometry of the situation.

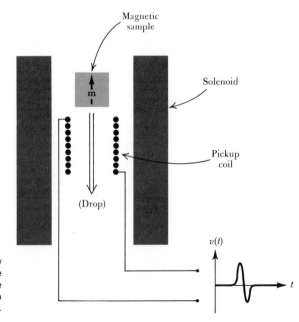

FIG. 4-10   Measurement of the dc magnetization **m** in a sample by dropping it through a pickup coil and sensing the induced voltage $v(t)$ caused by the change in flux linking the coil as the sample passes through. The sample and coil are completely enclosed in a solenoid which provides the uniform dc magnetic field B_0.

4-4   COLLECTIONS OF MAGNETIC DIPOLES: RELAXATION PROCESSES

In a collection of magnetic dipoles at thermal equilibrium the components of the macroscopic magnetization $\mathbf{m}(t)$ should have the thermal-equilibrium values $m_{x0} = m_{y0} = 0$ and $m_{z0} = \chi_{dc}H_0$ (at least in the usual limit $\mu B_0/kT \ll 1$). The next important consideration is the mechanism, or mechanisms, by which a collection of dipoles reaches thermal equilibrium. Consider a collection of dipoles initially set precessing with some distribution of cone angles and precession phases that is very far from thermal equilibrium, such as the fully aligned distribution of Fig. 4-6b. According to our single-dipole analysis in Sec. 4-2, each dipole in the collection should continue precessing indefinitely with the same cone angle and precession phase. If this were the case, the collection would never reach the expected thermal-equilibrium condition. However, there do exist weak interactions, between the dipoles and their surroundings and among the dipoles themselves, that will eventually bring a collection of dipoles to thermal equilibrium from any initial nonequilibrium state. Dipoles in a gas collide with the walls of their containers and with other atoms. Dipoles in solids interact with each other through dipolar interaction and are also jostled and shaken by the thermal vibrations of the surrounding lattice. The blackbody radiation fields which fill all space affect the dipoles, at least weakly.

Without going into great detail about how these thermalizing and equilibrating mechanisms operate, we will describe the important ones and introduce some simple relaxation terms into the equation of motion for $\mathbf{m}(t)$ to account for the various relaxation processes. These relaxation terms will be of great importance in analyzing the complete dynamics of a collection of magnetic dipoles in the following section.

■ We will first discuss the longitudinal relaxation processes, which involve energy exchange between a collection of dipoles and its thermal environment and operate to bring the longitudinal magnetization component $m_z(t)$ to its thermal-equilibrium value. As we have already noted, the orientation energy W_i of a single magnetic dipole $\boldsymbol{\mu}_i$ in a dc magnetic field $B_0\mathbf{z}$ is

LONGITUDINAL RELAXATION

$$W_i = -\boldsymbol{\mu}_i \cdot \mathbf{B}_0 = -\mu_{zi}B_0$$

The average orientation energy per unit volume W_v, in a collection of such dipoles, is then the sum of the individual dipole energies,

$$W_v = \sum_i W_i(t) = -m_z(t)B_0 \tag{1}$$

Thus any change in the value of $m_z(t)$ in the process of coming to thermal equilibrium must entail energy transfer between the dipoles and their thermal surroundings; interactions only among the dipoles themselves are not sufficient to change m_z. Depending on initial conditions, a collection of dipoles may either give energy to or receive energy from the surroundings while coming to equilibrium; that is, the collection of dipoles may be initially hotter or colder than its thermal environment.

The energy-exchange mechanisms that thermalize a collection of magnetic dipoles (or a collection of electric-dipole atoms, for that matter) are, in fact, the same energy-decay or damping mechanisms discussed in earlier chapters. These energy-decay, or damping, or thermalizing effects may have two sources. First, even if no other thermalizing interactions are present, thermal equilibrium of a collection of atoms will always be brought about by purely *radiative interaction,* in which the atoms interact radiatively with the blackbody radiation fields that are present in every enclosure at a finite temperature T. In the absence of any other decay mechanisms, a collection of atoms will always eventually be thermalized by the random effects of these blackbody fields. The classical purely radiative damping of Sec. 2-1 may be viewed as radiation by the atom into these fields. The collection of atoms "learns" the temperature of its surroundings through its interaction with the blackbody radiation fields.

Although purely radiative interaction with the surroundings is the most basic and omnipresent longitudinal thermalizing mechanism, as a practical matter radiative relaxation is very weak for most magnetic-dipole cases, and the strongest longitudinal-relaxation effects for magnetic dipoles in solids come from *nonradiative relaxation mechanisms.* Magnetic dipoles in solids are normally much more strongly coupled to, and much more affected by, the thermal vibrations of their crystalline surroundings than the blackbody electromagnetic surroundings. The dominant thermalization mechanism for $m_z(t)$ is thus the exchange of energy with the thermal vibrations of the surrounding solid.[1]

LONGITUDINAL RELAXATION TIME T_1

■ The details of the physical mechanisms responsible for longitudinal relaxation and thermalization are quite complex. In the absence of such details, the easiest way to account for the longitudinal relaxation of $m_z(t)$ is simply to add to any equation of motion for $m_z(t)$ a *longitudinal-relaxation term* of the form

$$\frac{d}{dt} m_z(t) = -\gamma[m_z(t) - m_{z0}] = -\frac{m_z(t) - m_{z0}}{T_1} \tag{2}$$

With this relaxation term present, any initial nonequilibrium magnetization $m_z(t_0)$ at time t_0 will, in the absence of applied signals, decay toward the thermal-equilibrium value m_{z0} with decay rate γ or time constant T_1 according to

$$m_z(t) = m_{z0} + [m_z(t_0) - m_{z0}]e^{-\gamma(t-t_0)} = m_{z0} + [m_z(t_0) - m_{z0}]e^{-(t-t_0)/T_1} \tag{3}$$

Figure 4-11 illustrates an exponential decay of this type for a typical magnetic-resonance transition.

The damping or thermalizing rate γ introduced here is completely equivalent to the atomic damping or decay rate γ in the electron-oscillator discussions of Chaps. 2 and 3. The decay time or lifetime γ^{-1}, denoted by τ in our discussion of optical-frequency and electric-dipole transitions, is denoted here by T_1, which is more commonly used in analyzing magnetic-resonance transitions. This time constant T_1 is called the *longitudinal relaxation time,* since it applies to the longitudinal component m_z, or the *spin-lattice relaxation time,* since in many cases it represents relaxation between a collection of magnetic dipoles, or spins, and a surrounding crystal lattice. The time constant T_1 also corresponds in quantum analysis to the decay time or lifetime for the on-diagonal elements of the quantum density matrix.

---

[1] Recall that the nonradiative interactions are "nonradiative" only in that they do not involve *electromagnetic* radiation. The fundamental character of both radiative and nonradiative relaxation processes is really very similar. Radiative relaxation involves the exchange of thermal *photons* with the blackbody *electromagnetic* energy density present in every enclosure, while nonradiative relaxation involves an exactly analogous exchange of thermal *phonons* with the blackbody *acoustic* energy density (thermal vibrations) present in every crystal lattice.

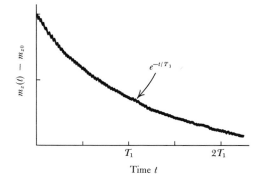

FIG. 4-11 Exponential decay of $m_z(t)$, with time constant T_1.

The relaxation term in the equation of motion ensures the decay of $m_z(t)$ to thermal equilibrium in the absence of any applied signals. These relaxation processes are presumably attempting to drive $m_z(t)$ toward thermal equilibrium, however, even when there are applied signals which may be attempting to drive $m_z(t)$ toward some other value. The best way to include both relaxation and signal terms in a complete equation of motion for $m_z(t)$ is thus to add the relaxation term to the signal terms. We will do exactly this in the following section.

■ The magnetization components $m_x(t)$ and $m_y(t)$ in a collection of dipoles relax toward their thermal-equilibrium values of zero as a result of somewhat different mechanisms, the *transverse relaxation processes*. The x component of magnetization $m_x(t)$ in a collection of precessing dipoles is given by the expression

TRANSVERSE RELAXATION

$$m_x(t) = m_+ \cos (\omega_0 t + \phi) = \sum_i \mu_{xi}(t) = \sum_i \mu_{+i} \cos (\omega_0 t + \phi_i) \qquad (4)$$

with a similar expression for the y component. The existence of macroscopic transverse components m_x and m_y implies that there must be at least some net alignment of dipoles in the transverse direction, and hence at least some alignment of the precession phases ϕ_i of the individual dipoles. The distribution of individual precession phases ϕ_i cannot be completely uniform over all possible phase angles (although it may be largely random, there must still be at least some weak ordering and alignment of the phases). Any mechanism that then rephases individual dipoles, or causes individual dipole precession phases ϕ_i to become randomized, will contribute to the gradual decay and elimination of the macroscopic moments $m_x(t)$ and $m_y(t)$.

A portion—in many cases the major portion—of the decay of $m_x(t)$ and $m_y(t)$ will be caused by *purely transverse* relaxation processes. By this we mean any mechanism that tends to randomize or scramble the transverse precession phases without changing the precession cone angles or altering the total orientation energy of the dipole collection. Such purely transverse relaxation mechanisms may include elastic collisions and dipolar interactions among the dipoles themselves and purely elastic interactions between the dipoles and their immediate surroundings.

Dipolar interactions are especially important as a purely transverse decay mechanism for magnetic dipoles in solids. Any one magnetic dipole in a solid has a number of other nearby dipoles as neighbors. Since each neighboring dipole is really a small

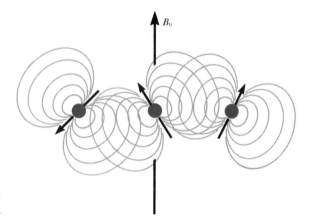

FIG. 4-12 The dipolar fields from one magnetic atom may overlap nearby atoms, leading to dipolar coupling effects whose strength depends on the spacings between atoms.

permanent magnet, the one dipole experiences a total magnetic field consisting of not only the applied dc field B_0, but also time-varying magnetic fields due to the neighboring dipoles. Figure 4-12 illustrates these overlapping dipole fields for adjacent atoms. In practical cases (such as microwave solid-state maser crystals) neighboring dipoles can be near enough and strong enough to cause significant average fields (a few gauss to a few tens of gauss) at each other's locations.

Each individual dipole then has a time-varying natural precession frequency determined by the total instantaneous field (and its direction) at that dipole's location. The precession frequency changes slightly with time as neighboring dipoles precess or vary their orientations. The net results are that the dipoles are all weakly inter-coupled, and a certain randomness or random variability with time is introduced into the precessional motion of each dipole. If a number of dipoles are started precessing together, all with the same transverse phase, as in Fig. 4-6b, they will all precess at slightly different and variable rates and after some characteristic time will become spread out and randomized in their transverse phases, thus destroying the macroscopic transverse magnetization.

TRANSVERSE RELAXATION TIME T_2 ■ Whatever the purely transverse mechanisms involved, the simplest way to account for their effects on $m_x(t)$ and $m_y(t)$ is to add to the equations of motion for these quantities linear decay terms with a decay time T_2 or a decay rate T_2^{-1}; thus for purely transverse relaxation

$$\frac{d}{dt} m_x(t) = -\frac{1}{T_2} m_x(t)$$

$$\frac{d}{dt} m_y(t) = -\frac{1}{T_2} m_y(t)$$

(5)

These terms will obviously cause m_x and m_y to decay to zero in the absence of applied signals. Moreover, following the same line of argument as for longitudinal relaxation, these relaxation processes will be operative even with signals present, and we can obtain reasonable equations of motion for m_x and m_y by simply adding these relaxation terms to the signal terms for $(d/dt)m_x(t)$ and $(d/dt)m_y(t)$.

Before doing this, however, we must also take into account possible transverse relaxation that may be caused by the *longitudinal* decay mechanisms, in addition to the purely transverse relaxation represented by T_2. That is, longitudinal decay mechanisms such as inelastic collisions and interactions with the thermal surroundings may, in addition to causing a damping of $m_z(t)$, also have damping effects on $m_x(t)$ and $m_y(t)$. The longitudinal damping rate, at least for $m_z(t)$, is $\gamma \equiv 1/T_1$. Following the rule that relaxation rates due to different mechanisms are additive, we might propose to add this longitudinal decay rate $1/T_1$ to the purely transverse relaxation rate $1/T_2$ to obtain a total relaxation rate $1/T_2 + 1/T_1$ for $m_x(t)$ and $m_y(t)$. However, it is not obvious, nor is it true, that the longitudinal decay mechanisms will have exactly the same effect on m_x and m_y as they do on m_z. This matter is complicated, and we cannot go into a fully satisfactory discussion here. However, if we look back at the results of Sec. 3-2, where we considered both dephasing (or collisional) T_2 effects and energy-decay $(\gamma = 1/\tau = 1/T_1)$ effects for the electric-dipole case, we see that the combination appearing in the final results there was not simply the sum $1/T_2 + 1/T_1$, but rather

$$\gamma + \frac{2}{T_2} = 2\left(\frac{1}{T_2} + \frac{1}{2T_1}\right) \tag{6}$$

This earlier result may be taken as a strong, and correct, hint that both the purely transverse relaxation and the *transverse effects of longitudinal relaxation* will be properly accounted for by writing the total transverse relaxation as

$$\frac{d}{dt} m_x(t) = -\left(\frac{1}{T_2} + \frac{1}{2T_1}\right) m_x(t) = -\frac{1}{T_2'} m_x(t)$$

$$\frac{d}{dt} m_y(t) = -\left(\frac{1}{T_2} + \frac{1}{2T_1}\right) m_y(t) = -\frac{1}{T_2'} m_y(t) \tag{7}$$

That is, the total transverse decay time T_2' is correctly given by

$$\frac{1}{T_2'} = \frac{1}{T_2} + \frac{1}{2T_1} \tag{8}$$

The rather odd fact that $1/2T_1$ rather than $1/T_1$ appears in this combination is confirmed by more rigorous quantum calculations. Only this combination will give the same lineshape for the magnetic-dipole case that we obtained for the electric-dipole case. Note that if the amplitudes m_x and m_y have a decay rate $1/2T_1$ due to the longitudinal mechanisms, then the transverse amplitudes squared, $m_x^2(t)$ and $m_y^2(t)$, which represent a kind of precessional energy, will have decay rates of $1/T_1$, and this is in accord with the idea of $1/T_1$ as basically an *energy decay* rate. This last argument is not to be taken as a proof, but only as another way of making the use of $1/2T_1$ seem more reasonable.

As a final complication, now that we have taken the trouble to introduce and explain the $1/2T_1$ term, the prime on T_2' is ignored in most magnetic-resonance literature, and the transverse relaxation rate $1/T_2 + 1/2T_1$ is written simply as $1/T_2$. In many (but not all) magnetic-resonance experiments purely transverse relaxation takes place at a much more rapid rate than longitudinal relaxation; the dipoles are in most cases dephased much more rapidly than their longitudinal energies are equilibrated, so that $T_2 \ll T_1$. In these cases the $1/2T_1$ term is unimportant and can be ignored with negligible error. In most of our subsequent analyses, for simplicity we will also ignore the $1/2T_1$ term in transverse relaxation; that is, we will simply write T_2 instead of T_2', so that the transverse decay terms for $m_x(t)$ and $m_y(t)$ become

$$\frac{d}{dt}\,m_x(t) = -\,\frac{m_x(t)}{T_2}$$

$$\frac{d}{dt}\,m_y(t) = -\,\frac{m_y(t)}{T_2} \tag{9}$$

We will then understand that a $(2T_1)^{-1}$ factor is implicitly contained in the T_2^{-1} terms, and that this factor may have to be written out explicitly in special situations.

TRANSVERSE BROADENING
AND COLLISION BROADENING

■ It will become more evident after Sec. 4-5 that the dipolar and other transverse dephasing effects we are discussing here play exactly the same basic role in the magnetic-dipole case as do the collisional and related dephasing effects of Chap. 3 in the electric-dipole case. The meaning of the dephasing time T_2 in terms of the dephasing of individual atomic motions is the same in both cases. The effects of this parameter in terms of additional line broadening and in terms of the decay of any initial coherent polarization or magnetization are also the same in both cases. Moreover, the strength of at least the collisional and dipolar effects increases linearly with the density or concentration of atoms N_v in both cases.

In subsequent discussions we will rather casually interchange the concepts and terminology of these two approaches. In gases there are collisions and in magnetic-dipole solids there are dipolar interactions, but the net effect in either case is dephasing of the oscillation or precession behavior with a time constant T_2. We might use the general term *transverse decay* to designate this behavior—although even this term obviously derives from the transverse nature of the precessional motion in the magnetic-dipole rather than the electric-dipole case.

DIPOLAR BROADENING

■ The broadening of an atomic resonance line by dipolar interactions has a simple electric-circuit analogy. When two sharply resonant electric (or mechanical) circuits with the same resonance are weakly coupled together, their overall resonant response will gradually broaden with increased coupling. In fact, for just two coupled circuits the response may eventually split into a double-humped resonance. As a generalization of this, if many identical resonant circuits (or resonant atoms) are weakly intercoupled, there will again be a steady broadening of the overall response with increasing degree of coupling (but usually no splitting of the response with many resonant circuits). *Dipolar broadening* is the atomic analog of this broadening, caused by weak coupling among many identical resonant systems.

Some progress has been made on rigorous analyses of dipolar broadening, particularly in the field of magnetic resonance. The general problem is extremely complex and is still unsolved, but the analyses predict that dipolar interactions should usually lead to a resonance lineshape that is more or less (but not exactly) lorentzian, with a linewidth that increases directly with atomic density in most cases. The lineshape is invariably taken to be exactly lorentzian for any practical computations. We will consider experimental data on dipolar broadening in a common EPR material in the next section.

4-5   COLLECTIONS OF MAGNETIC DIPOLES: THE BLOCH EQUATIONS AND THEIR SOLUTIONS

We have now developed enough background to write down an equation, or rather a set of equations, that describes with good accuracy the complete dynamics of the magnetization in a collection of magnetic-dipole atoms. In this section we will first develop these *Bloch equations* and then find solutions to them which describe the linearized small-signal behavior of the dipole collection caused by an applied ac signal at or near resonance.

■ In Sec. 4-2 we found that the equation of motion for a single magnetic dipole $\boldsymbol{\mu}_i$ in the presence of a time-varying magnetic field $\mathbf{b}(t)$ is

DERIVATION OF THE BLOCH EQUATIONS

$$\frac{d}{dt}\boldsymbol{\mu}_i(t) = \frac{ge}{2m}\mathbf{b}(t) \times \boldsymbol{\mu}_i(t) \tag{1}$$

Then in Sec. 4-3 we noted that the macroscopic magnetization $\mathbf{m}(t)$ in a collection of dipoles is

$$\mathbf{m}(t) = \frac{1}{V}\sum_i \boldsymbol{\mu}_i(t) \tag{2}$$

Hence, if we simply apply the summation process of Eq. (2) to both sides of Eq. (1), we obtain exactly the same equation of motion for $\mathbf{m}(t)$ as for $\boldsymbol{\mu}_i(t)$,

$$\frac{d}{dt}\mathbf{m}(t) = \frac{ge}{2m}\mathbf{b}(t) \times \mathbf{m}(t) \tag{3}$$

or, written out in cartesian coordinates,

$$\frac{d}{dt}m_x(t) = \frac{ge}{2m}[b_y(t)m_z(t) - b_z(t)m_y(t)]$$

$$\frac{d}{dt}m_y(t) = \frac{ge}{2m}[b_z(t)m_x(t) - b_x(t)m_z(t)] \tag{4}$$

$$\frac{d}{dt}m_z(t) = \frac{ge}{2m}[b_x(t)m_y(t) - b_y(t)m_x(t)]$$

These equations, however, do not take into account any damping or relaxation effects, interactions among the dipoles, or interactions between the dipoles and the thermal surroundings. To take all these effects into account, we must include in the equations of motion the relaxation terms discussed in Sec. 4-4. We assume that relaxation proceeds independently of the effects of the applied magnetic fields $\mathbf{b}(t)$, and hence we simply add the relaxation terms directly to the signal-induced terms to obtain the complete equations of motion for $\mathbf{m}(t)$. The extended equations of motion for $\mathbf{m}(t)$ thus take the form

$$\frac{d}{dt}m_x(t) = \frac{ge}{2m}[b_y(t)m_z(t) - b_z(t)m_y(t)] - \frac{m_x(t)}{T_2}$$

$$\frac{d}{dt}m_y(t) = \frac{ge}{2m}[b_z(t)m_x(t) - b_x(t)m_z(t)] - \frac{m_y(t)}{T_2} \tag{5}$$

$$\frac{d}{dt}m_z(t) = \frac{ge}{2m}[b_x(t)m_y(t) - b_y(t)m_x(t)] - \frac{m_z(t) - m_{z0}}{T_1}$$

where, as we discussed in Sec. 4-4, the $1/T_2$ terms appearing in the transverse, or xy, equations represent transverse relaxation or dephasing caused by collisions, dipolar interactions, and any other purely transverse mechanisms, as well as a longitudinal $1/2T_1$ contribution that is understood to be contained in the $1/T_2$ terms. The $1/T_1$ term in the longitudinal equation represents the exchange of energy between the dipole collection and its thermal surroundings which causes $m_z(t)$ to move toward its thermal-equilibrium value m_{z0}.

These extended equations, called the *Bloch equations*,[1] give a very accurate description of the dynamics of the magnetization $\mathbf{m}(t)$ in NMR and EPR experiments, and with appropriate interpretation, in many other atomic-resonance experiments as well. By solving these rather complex equations in greater or lesser detail for different experimental situations, we can predict and verify experimentally a great variety of atomic-resonance phenomena, some of which exhibit very complex dynamical behavior.[2] As we noted previously, the exact quantum-mechanical equations of motion for any two-energy-level system can be transformed into exactly the same mathematical form as the Bloch equations. Thus the terminology and concepts of the Bloch equations are useful not only for magnetic resonance, but for any two-level quantum system subjected to applied signals.

LINEARIZED SOLUTIONS TO THE BLOCH EQUATIONS

■ Our next step is to seek linearized steady-state ac solutions to the Bloch equations, assuming that a sinusoidal ac magnetic field is applied to the dipoles in addition to the usual dc magnetic field. It is understood in all these discussions that the dipoles are subjected to a strong dc magnetic field B_0, whose direction we take to be the z direction. The natural motion of the dipoles, and hence of $\mathbf{m}(t)$ if we neglect damping for the moment, is then a precession at a fixed cone angle, so that m_z has a constant value and m_x and m_y are sinusoidal with a positive circularly polarized motion at frequency ω_a, where

$$\omega_a = \frac{ge}{2m} B_0 \tag{6}$$

For consistency, from now on we will use ω_a rather than ω_0 for the resonance frequency of the magnetic-dipole atoms.

Now, the instantaneous rate of energy exchange between a magnetization vector $\mathbf{m}(t)$ and an applied magnetic field $\mathbf{b}(t)$ is given by $dW(t)/dt = -\mathbf{b}(t) \cdot d\mathbf{m}(t)/dt$. Hence we would expect that ac magnetic fields $\mathbf{b}(t)$ applied in the xy plane, especially positive circularly polarized fields, would be most likely to have strong cumulative interactions with the dipoles. With this in mind, we assume that the applied dc and ac magnetic fields have the form[3]

$$b_x(t) = \tfrac{1}{2}[\tilde{B}_x(\omega)e^{j\omega t} + cc]$$
$$b_y(t) = \tfrac{1}{2}[\tilde{B}_y(\omega)e^{j\omega t} + cc] \tag{7}$$
$$b_z(t) = B_0$$

[1] First introduced by Felix Bloch in analyzing his nuclear-magnetic-resonance experiments at Stanford University in 1944–1946. Simultaneous demonstrations of nuclear magnetic resonance were carried out independently by E. M. Purcell at Harvard University and they shared the Nobel Prize in Physics in 1952. See Refs. 4-4 and 4-9.

[2] The richness and complexity of these phenomena can be attributed to the fact that the Bloch equations are nonlinear. Nonlinear equations have a much greater variety of solutions than do linear equations. Some of the more complicated magnetic-resonance phenomena which we will not attempt to analyze in this section include spin echoes, adiabatic rapid passage, and 90° and 180° pulses. See Ref. 4-8 for an introduction to some of these effects.

[3] It may not be completely apparent at this point that an ac magnetic field applied in the z direction, in addition to the dc field B_0, will cause no first-order sinusoidal response. However, a more extended analysis including such a signal component shows that the first-order or linearized response along the z axis is indeed zero. A strong enough ac signal in the z direction can cause nonlinear effects, such as harmonic generation, but first-order linear effects come only from the transverse ac signal components.

where $\tilde{B}_x(\omega)$ and $\tilde{B}_y(\omega)$ are the phasor amplitudes of the ac signal components in the x and y directions. Then, using the free-precession no-signal behavior of $m(t)$ as a guide, we assume that the magnetization solutions will also be of the form

$$m_x(t) \approx \tfrac{1}{2}[\tilde{M}_x(\omega)e^{j\omega t} + cc]$$
$$m_y(t) \approx \tfrac{1}{2}[\tilde{M}_y(\omega)e^{j\omega t} + cc] \tag{8}$$
$$m_z(t) \approx M_z$$

We assume, that is, that the transverse magnetization components will be sinusoidal at the applied-signal frequency $\omega \approx \omega_a$, while the longitudinal magnetization m_z will be quasi-dc; that is, m_z will be, if not absolutely constant, at least very slowly changing compared to the signal frequency.

■ Substitution of the applied fields (7) and the assumed solutions (8) into the first two Bloch equations now leads to the pair of ac steady-state relationships

TRANSVERSE AC SOLUTIONS

$$\left(j\omega + \frac{1}{T_2}\right)\tilde{M}_x + \omega_a\tilde{M}_y = \frac{ge}{2m}m_z\tilde{B}_y$$
$$\tag{9}$$
$$-\omega_a\tilde{M}_x + \left(j\omega + \frac{1}{T_2}\right)\tilde{M}_y = -\frac{ge}{2m}m_z\tilde{B}_x$$

These can be solved to obtain the steady-state ac magnetization $\tilde{M}_x(\omega)$ in terms of the applied ac fields $\tilde{B}_x(\omega)$ and $\tilde{B}_y(\omega)$ in the form

$$\tilde{M}_x = \frac{ge}{2m}\frac{T_2\omega_a\tilde{B}_x + (1 + jT_2\omega)\tilde{B}_y}{[1 + jT_2(\omega + \omega_a)][1 + jT_2(\omega - \omega_a)]}T_2m_z \tag{10}$$

with a similar equation for $\tilde{M}_y$.

It turns out that in these solutions, just as in the electric-dipole solutions, the transverse decay time T_2 is related to the full atomic linewidth $\Delta\omega_a$ by $T_2 = 2/\Delta\omega_a$, and since we are interested only in reasonably narrow lines, we may use the approximation $T_2\omega_a = 2\omega_a/\Delta\omega_a \gg 1$. Also, we may assume that $\omega \approx \omega_a$; in fact we can treat ω and ω_a interchangeably everywhere except in the resonance denominator term $1 + jT_2(\omega - \omega_a) = 1 + 2j(\omega - \omega_a)/\Delta\omega_a$. Then the first bracketed factor in the denominator of (10) can be approximated by

$$1 + jT_2(\omega + \omega_a) \approx 1 + 2jT_2\omega_a \approx 2jT_2\omega_a \tag{11}$$

since $T_2\omega_a \gg 1$, with a similar approximation for the bracketed factor before $\tilde{B}_y$ in the numerator. With these approximations, the transverse ac solutions take the form

$$\tilde{M}_x(\omega) = -j\frac{ge}{4m}\frac{T_2m_z}{1 + jT_2(\omega - \omega_a)}[\tilde{B}_x(\omega) + j\tilde{B}_y(\omega)]$$
$$\tag{12}$$
$$\tilde{M}_y(\omega) = -j\frac{ge}{4m}\frac{T_2m_z}{1 + jT_2(\omega - \omega_a)}[-j\tilde{B}_x(\omega) + j\tilde{B}_y(\omega)]$$

We see that the transverse ac solutions have a lorentzian frequency response whose full linewidth between half-power points is given by

$$\Delta\omega_a = \frac{2}{T_2} \quad \left(+\frac{1}{T_1} \text{ understood}\right) \tag{13}$$

exactly as in the collision-broadened electric-dipole case. Also, it will be important later to note that the magnitude of the transverse responses is directly proportional to the quasi-dc longitudinal magnetization m_z.

■ If we include for completeness a longitudinal ac signal field $\tilde{B}_z(\omega)$ which will excite no first-order sinusoidal response and a longitudinal ac magnetization $\tilde{M}_z(\omega)$ which is always zero in the first order of approximation, we can express the above results in the tensor form

$$
\begin{bmatrix} \tilde{M}_x(\omega) \\ \tilde{M}_y(\omega) \\ \tilde{M}_z(\omega) \end{bmatrix} = -j\frac{ge}{2m}\frac{1}{\Delta\omega_a}\frac{m_z}{1 + 2j(\omega - \omega_a)/\Delta\omega_a} \begin{bmatrix} 1 & +j & 0 \\ -j & 1 & 0 \\ 0 & 0 & 0 \end{bmatrix} \begin{bmatrix} \tilde{B}_x(\omega) \\ \tilde{B}_y(\omega) \\ \tilde{B}_z(\omega) \end{bmatrix} \tag{14}
$$

This can be written in more compact form with $\tilde{\mathbf{B}}(\omega)$ replaced by $\mu_0\tilde{\mathbf{H}}(\omega)$, as

$$
\tilde{\mathbf{M}}(\omega) = \bar{\mathbf{\chi}}(\omega)\tilde{\mathbf{H}}(\omega) \tag{15}
$$

where the *ac magnetic susceptibility tensor* $\bar{\mathbf{\chi}}(\omega)$ is given by

$$
\bar{\mathbf{\chi}}(\omega) = -j\left(\frac{ge\mu_0}{2m}\right)\frac{m_z}{\Delta\omega_a}\frac{1}{1 + 2j(\omega - \omega_a)/\Delta\omega_a} \begin{bmatrix} 1 & j & 0 \\ -j & 1 & 0 \\ 0 & 0 & 0 \end{bmatrix} \tag{16}
$$

Let us take a few paragraphs to examine briefly the meaning of this matrix or tensor form for the response. We found for the electric-dipole case in Chap. 2 that the induced polarization $\tilde{P}_x$ was directly proportional only to the applied-field component $\tilde{E}_x$, and for a simple symmetric atomic model such as Fig. 2-1*b*, we would obtain exactly the same form of response for $\tilde{P}_y$ in terms of $\tilde{E}_y$ and $\tilde{P}_z$ in terms of $\tilde{E}_z$. The induced polarization for this simple model could then be written as

$$
\begin{bmatrix} \tilde{P}_x(\omega) \\ \tilde{P}_y(\omega) \\ \tilde{P}_z(\omega) \end{bmatrix} = -j\frac{N_v e^2}{m\,\Delta\omega_a}\frac{1}{1 + 2j(\omega - \omega_a)/\Delta\omega_a} \begin{bmatrix} 1 & 0 & 0 \\ 0 & 1 & 0 \\ 0 & 0 & 1 \end{bmatrix} \begin{bmatrix} \tilde{E}_x(\omega) \\ \tilde{E}_y(\omega) \\ \tilde{E}_z(\omega) \end{bmatrix} \tag{17}
$$

or, in short form,

$$
\tilde{\mathbf{P}}(\omega) = \bar{\mathbf{\chi}}_e(\omega)\epsilon_0\tilde{\mathbf{E}}(\omega) \tag{18}
$$

where in this case

$$
\bar{\mathbf{\chi}}_e(\omega) = -j\frac{N_v e^2}{m\epsilon_0\,\Delta\omega_a}\frac{1}{1 + 2j(\omega - \omega_a)/\Delta\omega_a} \begin{bmatrix} 1 & 0 & 0 \\ 0 & 1 & 0 \\ 0 & 0 & 1 \end{bmatrix} \tag{19}
$$

The electric susceptibility tensor has equal diagonal elements and zero off-diagonal elements, implying that the response is *isotropic*, i.e., the same in every direction.[1] By contrast, the magnetic susceptibility tensor (16) has nonequal diagonal elements, which means that the response is *anisotropic*; it also has some imaginary off-diagonal elements, which implies that the dipoles respond best to some form of circular or elliptical polarization of the ac fields. The simple tensor form (16) responds best, in fact, to positive circular polarization in the *xy* plane. This simple type of circu-

---

[1] The response is isotropic for our simple classical model; however, the response of a real electric-dipole atomic transition is in general *not* isotropic.

lar anisotropic response is sometimes called a *gyrotropic response,* obviously because of the gyrolike natural behavior of the dipoles. (Note that it is also a *nonreciprocal* response; e.g., it is not reciprocal so far as opposite senses of circular polarization are concerned. Nonreciprocal devices can be built from materials with gyrotropic responses.)

If m_z remains at its thermal-equilibrium value $m_z = m_{z0} = \chi_{dc}H_0$ (which does not hold for higher signal powers, as we will see shortly), the ac susceptibility for a collection of dipoles in thermal equilibrium can be related to the dc susceptibility by

$$\frac{|\tilde{\chi}(\omega_a)|}{\chi_{dc}} = \frac{\omega_a}{\Delta\omega_a} \tag{20}$$

The peak ac susceptibility at resonance is larger than the dc susceptibility by the resonance factor $\omega_a/\Delta\omega_a \gg 1$, although $|\tilde{\chi}(\omega)|$ is still much smaller than unity in almost all cases. The ac susceptibility, like the dc susceptibility, has the same direct dependence on atomic density $\mathcal{N}_v$ [or on the atomic population-difference density $(\mathcal{N}_m - \mathcal{N}_n)_v$ for real atomic transitions] and inverse dependence on temperature T.

■ To demonstrate the circular-polarization properties of the transverse ac response more explicitly it is worth the trouble to make a change of variables. Suppose that we define two new phasor quantities, $\tilde{M}_+(\omega)$ and $\tilde{M}_-(\omega)$, by

CIRCULAR-POLARIZATION VARIABLES

$$\begin{aligned}\tilde{M}_+(\omega) &= \tfrac{1}{2}[\tilde{M}_x(\omega) + j\tilde{M}_y(\omega)] = M_+(\omega)e^{j\phi_+(\omega)}\\ \tilde{M}_-(\omega) &= \tfrac{1}{2}[\tilde{M}_x(\omega) - j\tilde{M}_y(\omega)] = M_-(\omega)e^{j\phi_-(\omega)}\end{aligned} \tag{21}$$

Inverting these definitions gives the inverse relations

$$\begin{aligned}\tilde{M}_x(\omega) &= \tilde{M}_+(\omega) + \tilde{M}_-(\omega)\\ \tilde{M}_y(\omega) &= -j\tilde{M}_+(\omega) + j\tilde{M}_-(\omega)\end{aligned} \tag{22}$$

The real transverse magnetization components can then be written as

$$\begin{aligned}m_x(t) &= \text{Re } \tilde{M}_x(\omega)e^{j\omega t}\\ &= M_+ \cos(\omega t + \phi_+) + M_- \cos(\omega t + \phi_-)\\ m_y(t) &= \text{Re } \tilde{M}_y(\omega)e^{j\omega t}\\ &= M_+ \sin(\omega t + \phi_+) - M_- \sin(\omega t + \phi_-)\end{aligned} \tag{23}$$

Examination of these expressions shows that $\tilde{M}_+$ represents the positive circularly polarized part of the transverse magnetization and $\tilde{M}_-$ represents the negative circularly polarized part. That is, if the component $\tilde{M}_- \equiv 0$ and only the $\tilde{M}_+$ component is present, then the motion is purely circular polarization in the positive sense, while if $\tilde{M}_+ \equiv 0$ and only $\tilde{M}_-$ is present, the opposite sense of circular polarization prevails. If both components are present in some mixture, then in general some elliptical or linear state of polarization prevails.

The transverse ac B fields can be expressed in the same terms as

$$\begin{aligned}\tilde{B}_+(\omega) &= \tfrac{1}{2}[\tilde{B}_x(\omega) + j\tilde{B}_y(\omega)]\\ \tilde{B}_-(\omega) &= \tfrac{1}{2}[\tilde{B}_x(\omega) - j\tilde{B}_y(\omega)]\end{aligned} \tag{24}$$

and hence

$$\begin{aligned}\tilde{B}_x(\omega) &= \tilde{B}_+(\omega) + \tilde{B}_-(\omega)\\ \tilde{B}_y(\omega) &= -j\tilde{B}_+(\omega) + j\tilde{B}_-(\omega)\end{aligned} \tag{25}$$

If the steady-state equations (9) or (12) are rewritten in terms of these new variables, the results are

$$\tilde{M}_+(\omega) = -j\frac{ge}{2m}\frac{T_2 m_z}{1 + 2j(\omega - \omega_a)/\Delta\omega_a}\tilde{B}_+(\omega)$$

$$\tilde{M}_-(\omega) = +j\frac{ge}{2m}\frac{T_2 m_z}{1 + 2j(\omega + \omega_a)/\Delta\omega_a}\tilde{B}_-(\omega)$$

(26)

The advantages of using the slightly more abstract circular-polarization notation now become apparent. In rectangular coordinates, the linearly polarized component $\tilde{M}_x(\omega)$ is excited by *both* $\tilde{B}_x(\omega)$ and $\tilde{B}_y(\omega)$, with a similar effect on $\tilde{M}_y(\omega)$. But in the circular-polarization notation the positive circularly polarized component $\tilde{M}_+(\omega)$ is driven by only the positive circularly polarized component $\tilde{B}_+(\omega)$, and the negative component $M_-(\omega)$ is driven by only the negative component $\tilde{B}_-(\omega)$. The circularly polarized components are clearly the "normal modes" of the problem, since the positive and negative components are uncoupled from each other, while the x and y components are not.

Let us again use $\tilde{\mathbf{B}}(\omega) = \mu_0\tilde{\mathbf{H}}(\omega)$ and write these responses in the form

$$\tilde{M}_+(\omega) = \tilde{\chi}_+(\omega)\tilde{H}_+(\omega)$$

$$\tilde{M}_-(\omega) = \tilde{\chi}_-(\omega)\tilde{H}_-(\omega)$$

(27)

where $\tilde{\chi}_+(\omega)$ and $\tilde{\chi}_-(\omega)$ are the susceptibilities for the two senses of circular polarization, as implicitly defined by Eqs. (26) and (27). Then the ratio of these two responses is

$$\frac{|\tilde{\chi}_-(\omega)|}{|\tilde{\chi}_+(\omega)|} = \left|\frac{1 + 2j(\omega - \omega_a)/\Delta\omega_a}{1 + 2j(\omega + \omega_a)/\Delta\omega_a}\right|$$

$$\approx \frac{\Delta\omega_a}{2\omega_a} = \frac{1}{2Q_a}\qquad \omega = \omega_a$$

(28)

That is, the negative circularly polarized response is weaker than the positive one by a ratio of order $1/2Q_a \ll 1$. For resonances of medium or large atomic Q_a the negative circularly polarized response $\tilde{\chi}_-$ will be so much smaller than the positive response $\tilde{\chi}_+$ that the usual procedure is to neglect $\tilde{\chi}_-(\omega)$ entirely. That is, given any applied ac fields $\tilde{B}_x$ and $\tilde{B}_y$, we first compute only the positive component $\tilde{B}_+$, ignoring the negative component $\tilde{B}_-$. Then we compute the resulting positive circularly polarized response $\tilde{M}_+$ from

$$\tilde{M}_+ = \tilde{\chi}_+\tilde{B}_+$$

(29)

and finally convert back to $\tilde{M}_x$ and $\tilde{M}_y$, if desired, using only the positive component $\tilde{M}_+$ and ignoring the negligible component $\tilde{M}_-$.

Note that no matter what the form of polarization of $\tilde{\mathbf{B}}(\omega)$ is, as long as it contains some component of positive circular polarization, the resulting magnetization will have completely positive circular polarization. The approximation of dropping the $\tilde{M}_-$ component in Eq. (29) is, in fact, exactly the same as the approximations we made earlier in going from Eq. (10) to Eqs. (12).

LONGITUDINAL DC SOLUTIONS ■ Having used the two transverse Bloch equations and the assumption $m_z \approx$ constant to find the linearized small-signal ac response, we can now feed these transverse results back into the third, longitudinal Bloch equation to find the actual time variation of $m_z(t)$. The third Bloch equation is

$$\frac{d}{dt} m_z(t) = \frac{ge}{2m} [b_x(t)m_y(t) - b_y(t)m_x(t)] - \frac{m_z(t) - m_{z0}}{T_1} \tag{30}$$

The expression in square brackets contains products of sinusoidal terms $m(t)$ and $b(t)$ varying as $e^{\pm j\omega t}$. These products will contain difference-frequency terms at $\omega - \omega = 0$, or dc, and sum-frequency terms at the second-harmonic frequency $\pm 2\omega$. Writing out the bracketed terms as sinusoidal components gives, in fact,

$$b_x m_y - b_y m_x = \frac{j}{2}(\tilde{B}_+ \tilde{M}_+^* - \tilde{B}_+^* \tilde{M}_+) - \frac{j}{2}(\tilde{B}_- \tilde{M}_+ e^{2j\omega t} - \tilde{B}_-^* \tilde{M}_+^* e^{-2j\omega t}) \tag{31}$$

where the dc terms are shown first and the 2ω terms second. If the applied signal is entirely positively circularly polarized ($\tilde{B}_- = 0$), then the second-harmonic component is entirely zero. Even if this is not the case, the 2ω terms can still be ignored, and the second-harmonic variation in $m_z(t)$ will still be negligible for all reasonable applied-signal levels. One way of justifying this assertion is to note that the dc and 2ω terms appear on the right-hand side of an equation in which $(d/dt)m_z(t)$ is the left-hand side. If we integrate both sides of the equation with respect to time over a cycle or so of ω, the dc term will give a cumulative contribution and the 2ω term will integrate out to zero over a cycle. To put this in another way, the integration of $e^{\pm 2j\omega t}$ puts a factor of 2ω in the denominator, and this large number makes the second-harmonic variation or ripple in $m_z(t)$ small.

We therefore retain only the quasi-dc terms in the longitudinal Bloch equation (31). If $\tilde{M}_+$ is then related to $\tilde{B}_+$ by means of Eq. (26), Eq. (31) becomes

$$[b_x(t)m_y(t) - b_y(t)m_x(t)] = -\frac{ge}{m\,\Delta\omega_a} \frac{|\tilde{B}_+|^2 m_z}{1 + [2(\omega - \omega_a)/\Delta\omega_a]^2} \tag{32}$$

Hence the longitudinal Bloch equation becomes

$$\frac{d}{dt} m_z(t) = -2\left[\left(\frac{ge}{4m}\right)^2 \frac{2T_2}{1 + T_2^2(\omega - \omega_a)^2} |\tilde{B}_+|^2\right] m_z(t)$$
$$- \frac{m_z(t) - m_{z0}}{T_1} \tag{33}$$

For reasons that will become more apparent shortly, we define an applied-signal quantity W_{12}, which we will call the *stimulated transition probability*, by

$$W_{12} = \left(\frac{ge}{4m}\right)^2 \frac{2T_2}{1 + T_2^2(\omega - \omega_a)^2} |\tilde{B}_+|^2$$
$$= \left(\frac{ge}{2m}\right)^2 \frac{1}{\Delta\omega_a} \frac{1}{1 + [2(\omega - \omega_a)/\Delta\omega_a]^2} |\tilde{B}_+|^2 \tag{34}$$

In terms of this quantity our final form for the longitudinal Bloch equation is

$$\frac{d}{dt} m_z(t) = -2W_{12}m_z(t) - \frac{m_z(t) - m_{z0}}{T_1} \tag{35}$$

■ The W_{12} term defined above represents the influence on m_z of the applied ac signal. This quantity is, first of all, directly proportional to the power density or energy density of the applied signal. The time-averaged energy density in the ac magnetic signal fields is

LONGITUDINAL SOLUTIONS: SATURATION OF m_z

$$W_s = \frac{1}{2\mu_0}[\overline{b_x^2(t)} + \overline{b_y^2(t)}] = \frac{1}{2\mu_0}[|B_+(\omega)|^2 + |\tilde{B}_-(\omega)|^2] \tag{36}$$

Obviously, the $|\tilde{B}_+|^2$ factor in W_{12} represents that part of the signal field that is effective in inducing response from the magnetic dipoles. The quantity W_{12} is also inversely proportional to $\Delta\omega_a$—i.e., the narrower the resonance line, the stronger it is—and it has the frequency variation of a lorentzian lineshape with linewidth $\Delta\omega_a$—i.e., for a given signal strength W_{12} decreases as the signal frequency ω is tuned away from resonance ω_a.

We have already seen that in the absence of an applied signal the T_1 relaxation term in (35) will cause the longitudinal magnetization m_z to relax toward its thermal-equilibrium value m_{z0} with time constant T_1; that is,

$$m_z(t) = m_{z0} + [m_z(t = 0) - m_{z0}]e^{-t/T_1} \qquad W_{12} \equiv 0 \tag{37}$$

Figure 4-13 illustrates this exponential recovery for initial magnetizations both above and below m_{z0}. By contrast, the effect of the W_{12} term in (35) by itself will clearly be to drive m_z toward a steady-state value of zero at a rate $2W_{12}$, or with a time constant $(2W_{12})^{-1}$. We can then guess that the combined effect of signal plus relaxation terms will be to drive m_z toward some steady-state value intermediate between thermal equilibrium and zero, with a time constant that is some combination of the two time constants involved.

To verify this, assume an initial magnetization $m_z(t = 0)$ at time $t = 0$. If we turn on the applied signal W_{12} at that instant and solve (35) for $m_z(t)$, the result is

$$m_z(t) = m_{z,\text{st}} + [m_z(t = 0) - m_{z,\text{st}}]e^{-(2W_{12}+1/T_1)t} \tag{38}$$

where $m_{z,\text{st}}$, the steady-state magnetization, is given by

$$m_{z,\text{st}} = \frac{1}{1 + 2W_{12}T_1}m_{z0} = \frac{1}{1 + (ge/2m)^2|\tilde{B}_+|^2T_1T_2}m_{z0} \tag{39}$$

The second equality includes the assumption, for simplicity, of a signal exactly on resonance, $\omega = \omega_a$. The general nature of the transient solution (38) is illustrated in

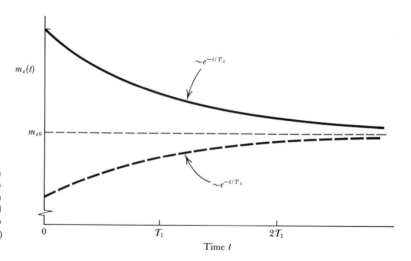

FIG. 4-13 Relaxation of $m_z(t)$ from a non-thermal-equilibrium initial value to the thermal-equilibrium value m_{z0}, with relaxation-time constant T_1. The solid and dashed lines correspond to two different initial conditions with $m_z(t=0)$ either greater or less than m_{z0}.

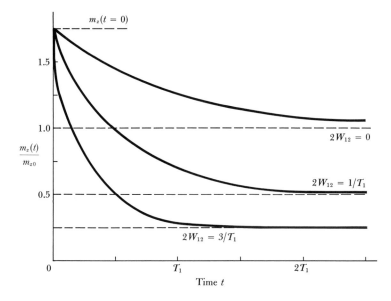

FIG. 4-14 Transient response of $m_z(t)$ from an initial value $m_z(t=0) = 1.8m_{z0}$ to the final values $m_{z,\mathrm{st}}$ at three different applied-signal strengths. Note the faster response and the reduced steady-state values for larger applied-signal strengths.

Fig. 4-14, which shows one initial condition $m_z(t=0) = 1.8m_{z0}$ and three different applied-signal strengths W_{12}, including no signal, $W_{12} = 0$.

The most important aspect of these solutions is that under an applied signal W_{12} the longitudinal magnetization m_z is driven toward a steady-state value $m_{z,\mathrm{st}}$ which is in general less than the thermal-equilibrium value m_{z0} but greater than zero, and which approaches zero as the applied-signal level is increased. Figure 4-15 shows this *saturation*, or reduction toward zero, of the steady-state longitudinal magnetization at large signal levels. For weak applied signals the relaxation processes predominate over the signal-induced effects, and the steady-state magnetization remains essentially at the thermal-equilibrium value; that is,

$$m_{z,\mathrm{st}} \approx m_{z0} \qquad \text{if } 2W_{12} \ll \frac{1}{T_1} \tag{40}$$

However, for strong enough applied-signal fields the signal effects will predominate over the relaxation effects, and the steady-state magnetization will be pushed essentially to zero; that is,

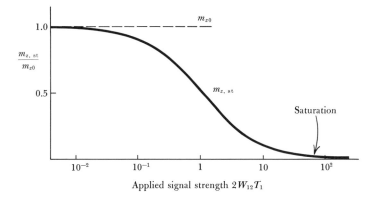

FIG. 4-15 As the applied-signal strength parameter $2W_{12}T_1$ increases, the steady-state longitudinal magnetization $m_{z,\mathrm{st}}$ becomes increasingly saturated (is forced closer to zero).

$$m_{z,\text{st}} \to 0 \qquad \text{if } 2W_{12} \gg \frac{1}{T_1} \tag{41}$$

The time constant required to reach the steady-state value from an arbitrary initial value also decreases as the applied-signal strength increases; thus the transient time constant takes the form

$$\left(2W_{12} + \frac{1}{T_1}\right)^{-1} \leq T_1 \tag{42}$$

The response is obviously faster the stronger the applied signal, as illustrated by the curves of Fig. 4-14.

This type of saturation behavior is, in fact, a general and very important characteristic of atomic transitions, both magnetic-dipole and electric-dipole, in both absorptive and emissive (maser) conditions. Note especially from Eqs. (14), (16), or (26) that the ac response and the ac susceptibility $\tilde{\chi}(\omega)$ vary directly as m_z. Hence saturation of m_z implies that the ac response and the ac susceptibility will also be reduced or saturated toward zero in the same way as the applied-signal level is increased. As a general rule for almost any atomic transition, the response at larger signal levels will saturate with increasing signal level in the form of Fig. 4-15,

$$[\tilde{\chi}(\omega)]_{\text{large-sig}} = [\tilde{\chi}(\omega)]_{\text{small-sig}} \times \frac{1}{1 + \text{const} \times W_s} \tag{43}$$

where W_s is the signal energy density applied to the atomic transition. It is this saturation behavior that reduces the large-signal gain of maser amplifiers, limits the maximum power output from maser systems, and determines the oscillation power level of laser oscillators.

APPROXIMATIONS AND
RELATIVE TIME CONSTANTS

■ We now have a complete and consistent set of linearized approximate solutions to the Bloch equations. The steps shown here are typical of many atomic analyses, both classical and quantum-mechanical. In brief, the two transverse Bloch equations are first solved as linear ac or sinusoidal equations, with the approximation that m_z is a quasi-dc quantity. The ac sinusoidal solutions from these transverse equations are then substituted into the longitudinal Bloch equation to obtain a quasi-dc equation for the slow time variation of m_z.

It may not seem consistent to analyze the transient time dependence of $m_z(t)$ due to the signal parameter W_{12}, as in Eqs. (35) and (38), when the transverse sinusoidal results that lie behind the definition of W_{12} in Eq. (34) are based on the assumption that m_z is a constant that does *not* vary with time. However, as long as the longitudinal magnetization $m_z(t)$ varies sufficiently slowly, it is a mathematically valid approximation to treat m_z as constant in solving the transverse equations of motion, and then to feed these transverse ac results back into the longitudinal equation to find the actual (very slow) variation of m_z. To understand this it is necessary to consider the relative magnitudes of the time scales involved. In a typical microwave EPR transition, for example, the resonance frequency may be $f_a = \omega_a/2\pi \sim 10^{10}$ Hz, and so the sinusoidal solutions will have a period of $\sim 10^{-10}$ sec. Such a transition may have an atomic linewidth Δf_a of several tens or hundreds of megahertz, so that the transverse relaxation time T_2 is in the range of 10^{-7} to 10^{-8} sec. From Eq. (5) or Eq. (9), the transient response of the transverse equations to an applied signal occurs with a time constant on the order of the transverse relaxation time T_2, that is, $\sim 10^{-7}$ to 10^{-8} sec. However, in materials of interest for microwave masers the longitudinal relaxation time T_1 may be $\sim 10^{-3}$ to 10^{-5} sec. Therefore, even for saturating signals for which W_{12} is several times $1/T_1$, the time variations of m_z are indeed very slow in relation not only to the period of the sinusoidal solutions, but even to the transient response time T_2 of the sinusoidal equations. Essentially the same situation prevails in most materials of interest for masers or lasers.

It is also necessary to be careful in speaking of small-signal and large-signal behavior in connection with these solutions, since two quite different conditions are involved. One of these is the condition for *linearization* of the Bloch equations, i.e., the condition that m_z is quasi-dc. One way of expressing this condition is to require that the signal-induced time rate of change $(d/dt)m_z$ in Eq. (33) must remain small compared to the transient response rate $1/T_2$ in the transverse equation. That is, the condition for linearization of the Bloch equation implies

$$\left(\frac{ge}{2m}\right)^2 |\tilde{B}_+|^2 \ll \left(\frac{1}{T_2}\right)^2 \tag{44}$$

Signals satisfying this condition are small-signal in the sense that they do not cause such phenomena as spin echoes or $180°$ pulse effects.

The other condition is that for *saturation* of the ac response by reduction of m_z to near zero. From Eq. (39), this condition is $2W_{12} \gg 1/T_1$; that is,

$$\left(\frac{ge}{2m}\right)^2 |\tilde{B}_+|^2 \gg \frac{1}{T_1 T_2} \tag{45}$$

Now, is it possible for a signal to be small-signal in the sense that linearization of the Bloch equations still remains valid, and at the same time be large-signal in that the signal is strong enough to saturate the transition? The joint condition for this is evidently

$$\frac{1}{T_1 T_2} \ll \left(\frac{ge}{2m}\right)^2 |\tilde{B}_+|^2 \ll \left(\frac{1}{T_2}\right)^2 \tag{46}$$

which can be true only if the relaxation times satisfy the condition

$$T_2 \ll T_1 \qquad \text{where} \qquad T_2 \equiv \frac{2}{\Delta\omega_a} \tag{47}$$

Most useful laser and magnetic-resonance transitions do indeed meet this requirement, and hence we can have large-signal saturation of the response while still staying well within the range of validity for the linearization of the atomic equations.

■ To summarize the linearized Bloch equation solutions, let us first define a normalized signal-strength, or saturation, parameter S, by

SUMMARY OF TRANSVERSE AND LONGITUDINAL SOLUTIONS

$$S^2 = \left(\frac{ge}{2m}\right)^2 \frac{1}{1 + T_2^2(\omega - \omega_a)^2} T_1 T_2 |\tilde{B}_+|^2$$

$$= \frac{T_1}{T_2} \frac{1}{1 + [2(\omega - \omega_a)/\Delta\omega_a]^2} \frac{(ge/2m)^2}{(\Delta\omega_a/2)^2} |\tilde{B}_+|^2 \tag{48}$$

The steady-state results may then be written as

$$m_{z,\text{st}} = m_{z0} \frac{1}{1 + S^2}$$

$$
\begin{aligned}
\tilde{M}_+(\omega) &= -j\frac{ge}{2m}\frac{2m_{z,\text{st}}}{\Delta\omega_a}\frac{1}{1 + 2j(\omega - \omega_a)/\Delta\omega_a}\tilde{B}_+(\omega) \\
&= -j\frac{1}{1 + S^2}\frac{ge}{2m}\frac{2m_{z0}}{\Delta\omega_a}\frac{1}{1 + 2j(\omega - \omega_a)/\Delta\omega_a}\tilde{B}_+(\omega) \\
&= \mu_0^{-1}\tilde{\chi}_+(\omega)\tilde{B}_+(\omega)
\end{aligned}
\tag{49}
$$

The magnitude of the transverse ac response may also be written in the form

$$|\tilde{M}_+| = \left(\frac{T_2}{T_1}\right)^{1/2}\frac{S}{1 + S^2} \tag{50}$$

If the magnetization vector $\mathbf{m}(t)$ is visualized as precessing in a cone about the z axis at frequency ω, then the cone angle of this precessional motion is given by

$$
\begin{aligned}
\theta &= \tan^{-1}\frac{|\tilde{M}_+|}{m_z} = \tan^{-1}\left[\left(\frac{T_2}{T_1}\right)^{1/2}S\right] \\
&\approx \left(\frac{T_2}{T_1}\right)^{1/2}S \qquad S \gtrsim \left(\frac{T_1}{T_2}\right)^{1/2}
\end{aligned}
\tag{51}
$$

as illustrated in Fig. 4-16a.

These expressions make it evident that for weak or nonsaturating applied signals, $S \ll 1$, the transverse ac magnetization $\tilde{M}_+(\omega)$ and the precession cone angle θ are directly proportional to the applied-signal strength $\tilde{B}_+(\omega)$, while the longitudinal magnetization remains essentially undisturbed from its thermal-equilibrium value m_{z0}.

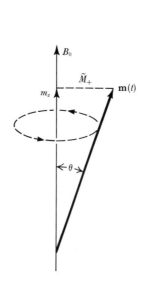

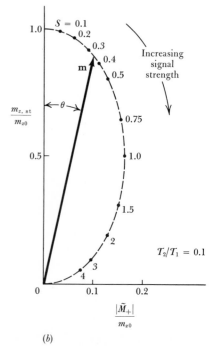

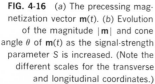

FIG. 4-16 (a) The precessing magnetization vector $\mathbf{m}(t)$. (b) Evolution of the magnitude $|\mathbf{m}|$ and cone angle θ of $\mathbf{m}(t)$ as the signal-strength parameter S is increased. (Note the different scales for the transverse and longitudinal coordinates.)

(a)

(b)

In this region the applied ac signal imposes a small amount of ordering or transverse alignment on the random precession phases of individual atomic dipoles so as to create the macroscopic transverse $\tilde{M}_+(\omega)$. This transverse ordering is opposed by the relatively strong dephasing effects of the transverse relaxation process $1/T_2$. Hence the extent of transverse alignment, although it increases linearly with the signal strength, is not great.

As the applied-signal strength increases, so that $S \geq 1$, the longitudinal magnetization m_z begins to decrease because of saturation effects. Since the transverse ac response is proportional to m_z as well as to the applied signal, the reduction in m_z also causes a reduction in the transverse response. In fact, Eq. (50) and Fig. 4-16b show that at very large signal levels the magnitude of $\tilde{M}_+(\omega)$ actually reaches a maximum value and then decreases in proportion to S^{-1} for further increases in signal strength. In physical terms, the applied signal attempts to rotate the cone angles of individual dipoles over toward $90°$. This rotation of all of the dipoles over into the transverse plane is opposed by the longitudinal relaxation processes $1/T_1$, which attempt to restore a thermal-equilibrium distribution of cone angles. Since this restoring effect is comparatively weak if $T_1 \gg T_2$, the longitudinal magnetization component becomes saturated at relatively low signal levels, before any very large amount of transverse ordering can be accomplished and before $\tilde{M}_+(\omega)$ can become very large. The saturation of m_z then blocks further expansion of $\tilde{M}_+(\omega)$ and in fact eventually pulls it down to zero.

This large-signal or saturation behavior of $\mathbf{m}(t)$ is illustrated graphically in Fig. 4-16b by the plot of the longitudinal and transverse components of $\mathbf{m}(t)$ on a kind of polar diagram, with S as a parameter. The exact shape of this plot depends on the relaxation-time ratio T_1/T_2, which is chosen equal to 10 here for ease of display (an expanded x scale has also been used in order to broaden out the pattern). In more realistic cases the T_1/T_2 ratio may be even larger, with the result that the $\mathbf{m}(t)$ vectors in Fig. 4-16b would be confined to an even narrower lobe along the z axis.

A final point of interest is that for signals exactly on resonance, $\omega = \omega_a$, the transverse component of magnetization $\tilde{M}_+(\omega)$ lags the signal field $\tilde{B}_+(\omega)$ by $90°$ because of the $-j$ factor in the expression for $\tilde{M}_+$. This has the physical significance that when an ac magnetic field $\mathbf{b}(t)$ and an ac magnetization $\mathbf{m}(t)$ are present in a medium, the instantaneous work done per unit time and per unit volume by the field on the magnetization is given by

$$\frac{dW}{dt} = \mathbf{b}(t) \cdot \frac{d}{dt}\mathbf{m}(t) \tag{52}$$

Now, if $\mathbf{m}(t)$ and $\mathbf{b}(t)$ are sinusoidal and $\mathbf{m}(t)$ lags $\mathbf{b}(t)$ by $90°$, then its time derivative $(d/dt)\mathbf{m}(t)$ will be exactly in phase with $\mathbf{b}(t)$. Hence the applied signal $\mathbf{b}(t)$ does work on the dipoles; that is, the signal continuously supplies energy to them. The dipoles in turn pass this energy along to the thermal surroundings via the longitudinal relaxation processes $1/T_1$. In thermodynamic terms, the signal tends to heat up the dipoles, but the dipoles are also simultaneously cooled by their thermal connections to the surroundings through the longitudinal relaxation process.

■ One particularly direct demonstration of magnetic-dipole precession effects can be performed with the apparatus shown[1] in Fig. 4-17. The dipoles in this case are the

DEMONSTRATION OF DIPOLAR PRECESSION

---

[1] For a more complete description of this demonstration see Ref. 4-11.

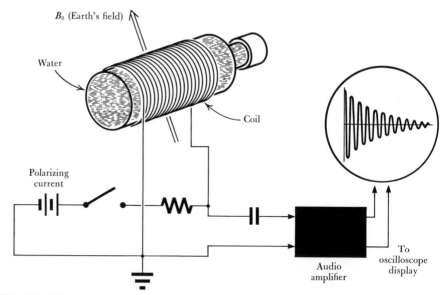

FIG. 4-17 A demonstration experiment using the nuclear dipole moments of hydrogen nuclei in water to demonstrate the free precession of the magnetization **m**(t) and its decay with the transverse decay time T_2.

nuclear spins of the hydrogen-atom nuclei in a small bottle of distilled water, which is wrapped with a coil having many turns of fine wire. The dc magnetic field for the experiment is provided conveniently by the earth's magnetic field. Since the frequency-field ratio for protons is 4.26 kHz/gauss, their resonance frequency in the earth's approximately half-gauss field is $f_a \approx 2000$ Hz.

A temporary dc current large enough to produce a dc field of several tens of gauss—the larger the better, within limits—is first sent through the coil of wire. This current produces a large temporary dc field B_{x0} inside the coil along the direction of the coil axis, which we will call the x axis. This axis should be at right angles to the earth's field direction, which we will call the z axis. If the field B_{x0} is applied long enough for the system to come to equilibrium (several times T_1), there will be a comparatively large initial magnetization in the x direction, given by

$$m_x(t_0) = \chi_{dc}\mu_0 B_{x0} \tag{53}$$

At time t_0 the coil current is rapidly switched off, leaving only the earth's dc field in the z direction, but also leaving the large initial magnetization $m_x(t_0)$ in the x direction. This magnetization will then precess in the xy plane about the earth's field, at the precession frequency $f_a \approx 2$ kHz. The sinusoidally varying component $m_x(t)$, since it represents a sinusoidally varying flux linking the coil, will induce a small ac voltage at the precession frequency across the terminals. This voltage can be amplified by a sensitive amplifier and displayed directly on an oscilloscope.

The amplitude of this sinusoidal voltage will decay exponentially as the initial transverse magnetization is destroyed by dephasing effects, and the envelope of the decaying voltage will thus give a more or less direct measure of the transverse decay time T_2. This experiment is possible, in fact, only because the relaxation times T_1 and T_2 can be extremely long (on the order of seconds) for proton spins in pure water.[1]

---

[1] There are also some other complexities in this case, particularly in that the approximation $T_2 \ll T_1$

Although this experiment is simple in concept, it requires some care. The initial polarizing current must be switched off rapidly compared to a period of the final resonance frequency, but this creates a large inductive voltage against which the sensitive amplifier must be protected. The induced voltage itself is very small, and so a sensitive low-noise preamplifier is required. In principle the tunability of f_a with the final field value B_0 can also be demonstrated by using a Helmholtz coil to replace or supplement the earth's magnetic field. Note, however, that if the dc field strength is spatially inhomogeneous, that is, if it differs from point to point inside the sample, the nuclei in different regions of the sample will precess at different rates. The contributions from different nuclei will then get out of phase after a certain number of cycles and begin to interfere, and the observed signal voltage will decay much more rapidly than the true T_2 value.[1]

■ The stimulated response of a collection of magnetic dipoles to an applied signal can be demonstrated with a simple NMR or EPR spectrometer of the type shown in Fig. 1-10. Inexpensive radio-frequency NMR/EPR demonstration spectrometers are available commercially from manufacturers of physics teaching apparatus or can be built from published descriptions.[2] However, the circularly polarized behavior and other features of magnetic-dipole responses are perhaps best illustrated by the nuclear-induction type of spectrometer introduced by Bloch in his first NMR experiments.[3]

BLOCH NUCLEAR-INDUCTION EXPERIMENT

As shown in Fig. 4-18, the induction type of spectrometer uses two sets of rf coils oriented with their axes perpendicular to each other and to the dc magnetic field B_0.

---

[1] For additional information relevant to the construction of this fascinating and elegant demonstration see Refs. 4-7 and 4-11.

[2] See Ref. 4-2 for some older vacuum-tube circuits, or Refs. 4-5 and 4-11 for an introduction to some simple transistorized NMR circuits.

[3] See Ref. 4-4.

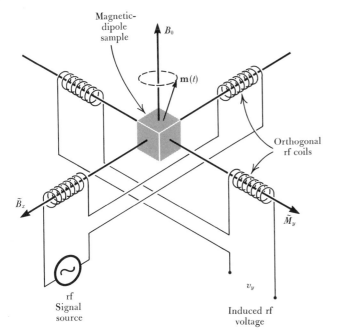

FIG. 4-18 The nuclear-induction experimental arrangement used by Bloch.

An rf signal is applied to one coil to produce a signal field B_x along, say, the x axis. Since the axes of the two coils are perpendicular, this field will not directly induce any voltage in the y-axis coil. However, according to the Bloch equations, an applied ac field $\tilde{B}_x$ along the x axis will produce a rotating transverse magnetization with ac components $\tilde{M}_x$ and $\tilde{M}_y$ of equal magnitude along the x and y axes. The sinusoidally varying magnetization $m_y(t)$ will then induce an output voltage $v_y(t) \propto (d/dt)m_y(t)$ in the y-axis coil. The magnitude of this voltage will be maximum, and the phase relative to the applied x field will have a known value, when the signal frequency and/or the dc magnetic field are tuned to resonance.

This experiment is, in general, more difficult to carry out than the conventional single-coil type of magnetic-resonance experiment. The induced voltage is very weak, and it has proved difficult to reduce stray capacitive and inductive coupling between the coils to a level where the voltages in the y coil caused by stray coupling do not mask the desired induced voltage. Nonetheless, this experiment does provide a more convincing illustration of the circularly polarized or tensor properties of the magnetic dipoles than the more conventional type of NMR or EPR spectrometer.

As a side note, in the absence of such an induction demonstration, the X-band dark-ruby EPR demonstration outlined in Fig. 2-9 provides a strong and easily observed demonstration of magnetic resonance with relatively simple experimental apparatus.

EXPERIMENTAL VERIFICATION
OF DIPOLAR BROADENING

■ Solution of the transverse Bloch equations including the $1/T_2$ transverse-relaxation terms has led to a lorentzian magnetic-resonance lineshape with a linewidth $\Delta f_a = 1/\pi T_2$, exactly as in the case of collision broadening with a collision time T_2. For most EPR magnetic-resonance transitions in solids, dipolar interactions provide the dominant mechanism responsible for the T_2 decay. Moreover, when the density of atoms in a solid is increased, the resulting closer interatomic spacings generally cause the dipolar broadening to increase linearly with concentration, exactly like the concentration or pressure dependence of the collision broadening in gases.

As a typical example,[1] Fig. 4-19 shows plots of the measured atomic linewidth for a particular EPR transition of the Cr^{3+} ion in ruby, at a magnetic field value $B_0 = 4000$ gauss and a resonance frequency $f_0 = 9300$ MHz, for six different ruby samples, with Cr^{3+} ion concentrations ranging from $\sim 10^{18}$ to 10^{19} ions/cm³. The linear increase in linewidth from 60 MHz ($T_2 \approx 5.3 \times 10^{-9}$ sec) to 250 MHz

[1] Data are from Ref. 4-3.

FIG. 4-19 An experimental plot of linewidth versus concentration for a typical microwave EPR transition in ruby, showing the linear increase of linewidth with concentration due to dipolar interactions. The residual linewidth at zero concentration results from random inhomogeneities or strains. The figure of merit $N_v/\Delta f_a \propto 1/Q_m$ is also plotted to show that this quantity becomes nearly independent of N_v at larger concentration. Experimental conditions: $f_a = 9300$ MHz, $B_0 = 4000$ gauss, $T = 77°$K). (E. O. Ammann, doctoral dissertation, Stanford University, 1963.)

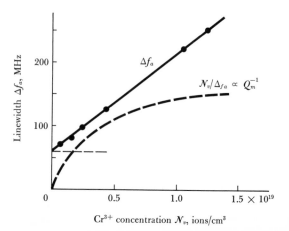

$(T_2 \approx 1.27 \times 10^{-9}$ sec) represents the effect of increased dipolar broadening at increased atomic density.

The residual linewidth observed at zero concentration in this example is also typical. Different ions in the ruby crystal generally have slightly different local surroundings owing to crystalline imperfections and inhomogeneities, strains, and other local variations in the crystal. As a result, the resonance frequencies of different ions are slightly shifted, and the overall response of the collection is smeared out over a frequency range approximately equal to the zero-concentration intercept. At low concentrations the dipolar broadening of any individual atom becomes small, but the overall response of the entire collection of atoms still spreads over a finite frequency range because of the random shifting of individual resonance frequencies. This type of random residual line broadening is also common for optical transitions of atoms in solids, and we will encounter it again for some optical examples in Chap. 9.

The maximum effect of a maser transition such as this when it is placed in, say, a resonant cavity is determined by a molecular or maser Q_m parameter essentially the same as that defined in Chap. 2. The inverse of this parameter, which is the figure of merit for atomic response, is directly proportional to the ratio of atomic density to atomic linewidth, $N_v/\Delta f_a$, as discussed in Sec. 3-3. The dashed line in Fig. 4-19 illustrates the fact that at high enough concentrations the figure of merit becomes essentially independent of atomic concentration, because the linewidth Δf_a increases in direct proportion to the atomic concentration N_v (there are other important practical reasons, to be discussed in Chap. 7, that make fairly low atomic densities optimum for solid-state maser and laser materials).

4-6   REACTION BACK ON THE ELECTROMAGNETIC FIELD: EQUIVALENT CIRCUIT

In any real magnetic-dipole problem some electromagnetic structure, cavity, or circuit produces the ac magnetic field distribution into which the magnetic dipoles are placed. The ac magnetic fields then induce a response in the collection of dipoles, as we saw in Sec. 4-5. The induced response or magnetization in the atoms then reacts back on the electromagnetic structure or circuit, providing the magnetic counterpart of the electric-dipole back reaction discussed in Sec. 2-3. In this section we will develop a simple equivalent circuit for the magnetic-dipole back reaction.

In principle this problem is already solved once we know the ac magnetic susceptibility $\bar{\chi}(\omega)$, whose tensor form for a collection of magnetic dipoles was derived in the previous section. The electromagnetic field patterns, voltages, and currents in any structure containing this magnetic medium can, in principle, be calculated. Any differences between corresponding results with and without the dipolar $\bar{\chi}(\omega)$ then represent the reaction of the dipoles back on the circuitry.

When an electromagnetic structure is filled (or, more often, partly filled) with dipoles, exact evaluation of the change in electromagnetic field patterns is usually prohibitively difficult—all the more so because of the tensor nature of $\bar{\chi}(\omega)$. Fortunately, for $|\bar{\chi}(\omega)| \ll 1$, which is almost always the case, the changes in field patterns are very small and need not be known exactly. The changes in such important parameters as circuit impedance, cavity Q, cavity frequency, and propagation constant can be calculated with the assumption that the field patterns are unchanged by the dipoles.

We will pursue this type of "electromagnetic" approach to atomic effects, using wave-propagation theory, in the following chapter. However, since high-frequency and even optical circuits can be represented with high accuracy by simple lumped circuits, let us consider a simple lumped-circuit model for magnetic-dipole back reactions.

LUMPED EQUIVALENT CIRCUIT   ■ The lumped-circuit element of interest for magnetic field interactions is obviously a coil or inductance. Consider an inductance more or less embedded in a collection of magnetic dipoles, as in Fig. 4-20. The magnetic field $h(t)$ at any point in or near the coil, produced by the current $i(t)$ flowing through the coil, may be written as

$$h(t) = Ki(t) \tag{1}$$

The constant K is a function of the coil geometry and the position at which we determine the field $h(t)$. However, we do not need to know this function explicitly for our purposes. The magnetic field $h(t)$ is, of course, a vector quantity, but we may also ignore the vectorial aspects here.

The instantaneous voltage drop $v(t)$ across a coil or inductance is directly proportional to the instantaneous rate of change of the total magnetic flux linking the inductance; that is,

$$v(t) = \frac{d}{dt}\Phi(t) \tag{2}$$

where we suppose that the number of turns in the coil is included in the definition of $\Phi(t)$. But the total flux $\Phi(t)$ linking the coil and the magnetic flux density $b(t)$ at any point near the coil are linearly related; that is,

$$\Phi(t) = K'b(t) \tag{3}$$

where K' is another function which depends only on coil geometry and on the choice of observation point. Finally, $b(t)$ and $h(t)$ are, of course, related by

$$b(t) = \mu_0[h(t) + m(t)] \tag{4}$$

where $m(t)$ is the macroscopic magnetization in the medium surrounding the coil. In the present case this magnetization results from the induced resonant response in the magnetic dipoles. Combining all the above relations gives the result

$$v(t) = \mu_0 K' \frac{d}{dt}[h(t) + m(t)] = \mu_0 K K' \frac{d}{dt}i(t) + \mu_0 K' \frac{d}{dt}m(t)$$

$$= L\frac{d}{dt}i(t) + \mu_0 K' \frac{d}{dt}m(t) \tag{5}$$

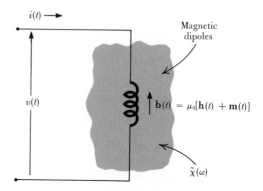

$i(t) \longrightarrow$

$v(t)$

Magnetic dipoles

$\mathbf{b}(t) = \mu_0[\mathbf{h}(t) + \mathbf{m}(t)]$

$\tilde{\chi}(\omega)$

FIG. 4-20 A lumped inductance or coil embedded in a magnetic medium (dipole collection) having an ac magnetic susceptibility $\tilde{\chi}(\omega)$.

The combination of parameters $\mu_0 K K'$ must obviously be just the basic inductance L of the coil itself, without the magnetic dipoles. The additional $(d/dt)m(t)$ term gives the additional voltage, or atomic back emf, induced by the magnetic dipoles in the coil.

Writing these expressions with all quantities in sinusoidal form gives

$$\tilde{H}(\omega) = K\tilde{I}(\omega) \qquad \tilde{B}(\omega) = \mu_0[\tilde{H}(\omega) + \tilde{M}(\omega)] \tag{6}$$

and

$$\tilde{V}(\omega) = j\omega K'\tilde{B}(\omega) = j\omega\mu_0 K'[\tilde{H}(\omega) + \tilde{M}(\omega)] \tag{7}$$

However, inclusion of the relationship $\tilde{M}(\omega) = \tilde{\chi}(\omega)\tilde{H}(\omega)$ gives

$$\begin{aligned}\tilde{V}(\omega) &= j\omega\mu_0 K K'[1 + \tilde{\chi}(\omega)]\tilde{H}(\omega) \\ &= j\omega L[1 + \tilde{\chi}(\omega)]\tilde{I}(\omega)\end{aligned} \tag{8}$$

It is apparent that with magnetic dipoles present, the input impedance as viewed into the coil terminals is

$$\tilde{Z}(\omega) \equiv \frac{\tilde{V}(\omega)}{\tilde{I}(\omega)} = j\omega L + j\omega L\tilde{\chi}(\omega) = j\omega L + \tilde{Z}_a(\omega) \tag{9}$$

This impedance consists of the basic inductance $j\omega L$ of the empty coil in series with a complex atomic impedance $\tilde{Z}_a(\omega)$, given by

$$\tilde{Z}_a(\omega) = j\omega L\tilde{\chi}(\omega) \tag{10}$$

This is indicated schematically at the left of Fig. 4-21. The atomic impedance $\tilde{Z}_a(\omega)$ represents the back-reaction effects of the magnetic medium on the collection of magnetic dipoles. It is the magnetic equivalent of the atomic admittance that appeared in the electric-dipole case in Chap. 2. However, as will be explained in more detail below, the magnetic-dipole $\tilde{Z}_a(\omega)$ and the electric-dipole $\tilde{Y}_a(\omega)$ are *not* related by $\tilde{Z}_a(\omega) = \tilde{Y}_a^{-1}(\omega)$.

■ This derivation of $\tilde{Z}_a(\omega)$ is oversimplified in two ways. First, there will probably not be magnetic dipoles everywhere around the coil. Instead of being totally embedded in the magnetic medium, the coil will simply contain some larger or smaller sample of the magnetic material somewhere inside the coil. Reducing the volume occupied by dipoles will certainly reduce the total contribution of the dipoles to the voltage $v(t)$. Second, the susceptibility is really a tensor quantity. The strongest response will be obtained only if the ac magnetic field $h(t)$ has the optimum polarization for exciting the magnetic dipoles at every point in the coil where there are magnetic dipoles. Otherwise the effective value of $\tilde{\chi}(\omega)$ to be used in determining $\tilde{Z}_a(\omega)$ will be reduced.

FILLING FACTOR

To take into account these two reduction factors it is customary to multiply $\tilde{\chi}(\omega)$ by a dimensionless factor commonly called the *filling factor* η, where $\eta \leq 1$ in general. The filling factor has its maximum value of unity only if there are magnetic dipoles everywhere there is ac magnetic field and if the ac magnetic field everywhere has the optimum polarization for inducing magnetic-dipole response. Although we did not introduce such a filling factor in Chap. 2, an analogous quantity is applicable in the electric-dipole case.

Radio-frequency coils or microwave-frequency cavities normally produce linearly polarized ac magnetic fields. The appropriate susceptibility $\tilde{\chi}(\omega)$ for a linearly polarized H-field component in the transverse plane is given by the susceptibility expression, Eq. (16) of Sec. 4-5, if the final tensor portion is simply ignored. The polarization factor in the filling factor η will then be simply $\cos^2 \gamma$, where γ is the angle between the linear H field and the plane transverse to B_0.

ATOMIC IMPEDANCE   ■ Using the filling factor η and our magnetic-dipole susceptibility results from Sec. 4-4, we can write the series atomic impedance $\tilde{Z}_a(\omega)$ for a lorentzian magnetic-dipole response as

$$\tilde{Z}_a(\omega) = j\eta\omega L\tilde{\chi}(\omega) = \eta\omega L\chi_0'' \frac{1}{1 + 2j(\omega - \omega_a)/\Delta\omega_a} \tag{11}$$

where χ_0'' is the midband value defined by $\tilde{\chi}(\omega_a) = -j\chi_0''$. From Eq. (16) of Sec. 4-5, χ_0'' is given by

$$\chi_0'' = \frac{ge\mu_0}{2m} \frac{m_z}{\Delta\omega_a} \tag{12}$$

The collection of parameters $\eta\omega L\chi_0''$ has the dimensions of impedance or resistance, and so we define an *atomic resistance* R_a as

$$R_a = \eta\omega L\chi_0'' = \eta \frac{ge\mu_0}{2m} \frac{m_z}{\Delta\omega_a} \omega L \tag{13}$$

In terms of this quantity the total atomic impedance becomes

$$\tilde{Z}_a(\omega) = R_a \frac{1}{1 + 2j(\omega - \omega_a)/\Delta\omega_a} \tag{14}$$

But this is essentially the same[1] as the series impedance of the parallel resonant circuit $R_a L_a C_a$ shown on the right-hand side of Fig. 4-21. That is, the impedance of the parallel resonant circuit is

---

[1] There are two valid approximations involved in this derivation. First, R_a has a slow frequency dependence since it contains a factor ω, but the small variation due to this will be negligible compared to the resonance denominators, and we can justifiably replace ω by ω_a in the expression for R_a. Second, we use the familiar approximation in which the factor $\omega/\omega_a - \omega_a/\omega$ is replaced by $2(\omega - \omega_a)/\omega_a$ in the resonance denominator. As noted before, this is valid provided merely that $(\omega - \omega_a) \ll \omega_a$, which is entirely valid over the range of signal frequencies of interest.

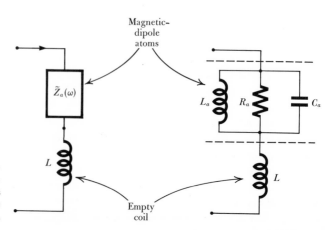

FIG. 4-21 The inductance and the surrounding magnetic-dipole medium shown in Fig. 4-20 can be accurately represented by connecting the atomic impedance $\tilde{Z}_a(\omega)$, which is essentially a parallel resonant tuned circuit in series with the basic inductance L.

$$\tilde{Z}_a(\omega) = R_a \frac{1}{1 + 2j(\omega - \omega_a)/\Delta\omega_a} \approx \frac{1}{1/R_a + j(\omega C_a - 1/\omega L_a)} \tag{15}$$

provided that we identify the atomic frequency ω_a and the atomic linewidth $\Delta\omega_a$ as

$$\omega_a = (L_a C_a)^{-1/2} \qquad \Delta\omega_a = \frac{\omega_a{}^2 L_a}{R_a} = (R_a C_a)^{-1} \tag{16}$$

As an alternative expression of the linewidth requirement, we can say that the equivalent impedance $\tilde{Z}_a(\omega)$ and the magnetic-resonance transition should have the same atomic or linewidth $Q = Q_a$; in other words,

$$Q_a = \frac{\omega_a}{\Delta\omega_a} = \omega_a R_a C_a \tag{17}$$

The back reaction of the magnetic dipoles contained in the circuit inductance L is then represented to a very high degree of accuracy by the lumped-equivalent-circuit elements shown in Fig. 4-21. The equivalent-circuit elements are given in terms of the magnetic-dipole parameters by

$$R_a = \frac{ge\mu_0}{2m} \frac{\omega_a L m_z}{\Delta\omega_a} = \eta\omega L \chi''_0$$

$$L_a = \frac{R_a}{Q_a \omega_a} \tag{18}$$

$$\frac{1}{C_a} = \frac{\omega_a R_a}{Q_a}$$

In particular, all three circuit elements are directly proportional to the longitudinal magnetization m_z. If m_z saturates, so do R_a, L_a, and $C_a{}^{-1}$; and if m_z changes sign, then all three circuit parameters also change sign.

■ Magnetic-dipole interactions always involve a lumped inductance L, or the equivalent of such an inductance in higher-frequency electromagnetic structures, because these interactions require ac magnetic fields, and ac magnetic fields mean stored magnetic energy, or inductive reactance. In practical experiments maximum ac current flow, and hence maximum magnetic field interaction, can be obtained most easily if this inductive reactance is balanced or resonated with an equal and opposite capacitive reactance. In the lumped-circuit model this means making the inductance L one element in a resonant circuit or cavity by adding a circuit or cavity capacitance C and a circuit or cavity resistance R in series, as shown in Fig. 4-22, so that the cavity resonance frequency ω_c and cavity quality factor Q_c are

RESONANT-CAVITY EQUIVALENT CIRCUIT

$$\omega_c = (LC)^{-1/2} \qquad Q_c = \frac{\omega_c L}{R} = \frac{\omega_c}{\Delta\omega_c} \tag{19}$$

where $\Delta\omega_c$ is then the linewidth of the cold-cavity response, ignoring the magnetic-dipole effects. The atoms then form a parallel resonant circuit connected in series with these series resonant-cavity elements, as in Fig. 4-22.

■ To complete the magnetic problem, just as in the electric-dipole case, we must define a parameter that indicates how heavily the magnetic dipoles load the cavity circuit (or vice versa). This parameter is the molecular, or in this case the magnetic, quality factor Q_m. Since in the circuit of Fig. 4-22 the magnetic-dipole resistance R_a is in series with the cavity series elements L and C, we define Q_m as

MOLECULAR OR MAGNETIC Q_m

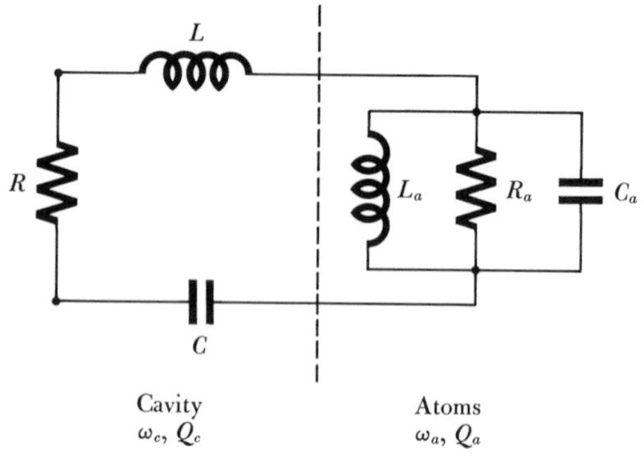

FIG. 4-22 The inductance L of Figs. 4-20 and 4-21 is often resonated with a capacitance C and resistance R to form a cavity resonant circuit with resonant frequency ω_c and quality factor Q_c. The atomic resonant circuit is then in series with this cavity resonant circuit. (Compare this magnetic-dipole result with the dual but essentially equivalent electric-dipole circuit of Fig. 2-7.)

$$Q_m = \frac{\omega L}{R_a} \tag{20}$$

The form of this definition is the dual or inverse of its form in the electric-dipole case, but the physical significance is exactly the same. The inverse molecular Q_m can also be identified as

$$\frac{1}{Q_m} = \frac{R_a}{\omega L} = \eta \chi_0'' = \eta |\bar{\chi}(\omega_a)| \tag{21}$$

Just as in Sec. 2-4, the inverse Q_m is found to be simply the peak atomic susceptibility (magnetic susceptibility in this case) at resonance, except that now we have increased the generality of this result by including the filling factor η.

Note in particular that, except for the secondary factor η, the parameter Q_m depends primarily on the properties of the atomic material (i.e., the magnetic dipoles) and almost not at all on the construction or properties of the electromagnetic circuit. Consider a collection of real magnetic dipoles with no saturation, so that $m_z \approx m_{z0}$. Using the linear quantum or classical dc susceptibility for m_{z0}, with $\mu B_0/kT \ll 1$, we can write the molecular Q_m as

$$\frac{1}{Q_m} = \eta \frac{\omega_a}{\Delta\omega_a} \frac{\mu_0 N_v |\mu|^2}{3kT} \tag{22}$$

This emphasizes the fact that the strength of the atomic reaction back on the cavity, as measured by $1/Q_m$, varies directly as the filling factor, the frequency, the atomic density N_v, and the atomic moment μ squared and varies inversely as the temperature T (which enters through the Boltzmann factor) and the atomic linewidth $\Delta\omega_a$. Alternatively, if we use the quantum expression for m_{z0} in a two-level system, we can write this as

$$\frac{1}{Q_m} = \eta \frac{\mu_0 (N_1 - N_2)_v (g\beta)^2}{8\hbar \, \Delta\omega_a} \tag{23}$$

This emphasizes very directly the vital fact that Q_m^{-1} depends, in both magnitude and sign, on the *population difference* on the two-level transition.

The overall circuit of Fig. 4-22 is now fully characterized by the two resonant frequencies ω_a and ω_c and the three quality factors Q_a, Q_c, and Q_m, which describe the magnetic-dipole atoms, the cavity, and the coupling between them, respectively. Figure 4-23 shows how these three different Q parameters are defined.

■ Comparison of these magnetic-dipole equivalent-circuit results with the corresponding electric-dipole results in Sec. 2-3 (especially Figs. 2-7 and 2-8) shows that the electric-dipole case led to a *series resonant atomic circuit* connected in *parallel* with a parallel resonant cavity circuit, while the magnetic-dipole case led to a *parallel resonant atomic circuit* connected in *series* with a series resonant cavity circuit. Despite the differences in form, we should now emphasize that these electric-dipole and magnetic-dipole results are really identical in character. The equivalent circuits are, in fact, exactly the duals of each other, and any calculations based on them (such as calculations of maser gain-bandwidth product) will lead to exactly the same results, regardless of which form is employed. Either form, series-parallel or parallel-series, will serve equally well for analyzing the basic problem of a resonant electromagnetic circuit (cavity) containing a resonant atomic circuit (atomic transition).

  Note that the symbols R, L, and C and R_a, L_a, and C_a do not refer to the same quantities, but to essentially dual quantities. For example, the cavity Q in the magnetic-dipole model is $Q_c = \omega_c L/R$, whereas in the electric-dipole model it must be written $Q_c = R/\omega_c L$. As another example, R_a in the magnetic case varies directly as the number of atoms and inversely as the atomic linewidth, whereas in the electric-dipole case it is the dual quantity $G_a \equiv R_a^{-1}$ that varies in this fashion. The inherent problem is that the electric-dipole analysis leads most naturally to the series-parallel equivalent circuit, whereas the magnetic-dipole analysis leads most naturally to exactly the dual of this. Thus we are confronted with the dilemma of either introducing different nota-

COMPARISON WITH ELECTRIC-DIPOLE RESULTS

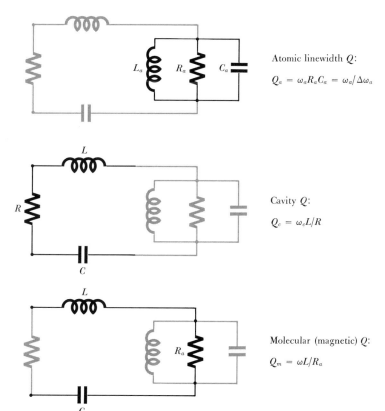

Atomic linewidth Q:

$$Q_a = \omega_a R_a C_a = \omega_a/\Delta\omega_a$$

Cavity Q:

$$Q_c = \omega_c L/R$$

Molecular (magnetic) Q:

$$Q_m = \omega L/R_a$$

FIG. 4-23 The shaded elements define the three different Q parameters necessary to characterize fully the coupled cavity and atomic resonant circuits.

tion for each case, which would double the amount of notation to be learned, or using the same notation with two meanings and risking the possibility of some confusion. Nevertheless, the fundamental quantities in either form are the frequencies ω_a and ω_c and the quality factors Q_a, Q_c, and Q_m, and the fundamental properties of these systems are exactly the same regardless of which equivalent-circuit model is employed.

4-7 POPULATION DIFFERENCES AND RATE EQUATIONS

The magnetic-dipole results obtained in this chapter offer an excellent opportunity for an advance look at two important topics we will later be discussing in more detail: population differences and rate equations.

POPULATION DIFFERENCES ■ In all our results thus far, the ac responses, such as the ac susceptibility $\tilde{\chi}(\omega)$ and the ac magnetization $\tilde{M}_+(\omega)$, have contained the factor m_z, so that

$$\tilde{\chi}(\omega) \propto m_z \qquad \text{and} \qquad \tilde{M}_+(\omega) \propto m_z \tag{1}$$

However, in the quantum description of a magnetic-dipole system with just two energy levels ($J = \frac{1}{2}$) the longitudinal magnetization m_z is given by

$$m_z = \frac{g\beta}{2}(N_1 - N_2)_v \tag{2}$$

Therefore the longitudinal magnetization m_z, and hence the ac response of the magnetic dipoles, are directly proportional, in sign and in magnitude, to the population-difference density on the transition being excited; that is,

$$\tilde{\chi}(\omega) \propto (N_1 - N_2)_v \qquad \text{and} \qquad \tilde{M}_+(\omega) \propto (N_1 - N_2)_v \tag{3}$$

It was stressed earlier that this dependence is a characteristic of all atomic transitions, magnetic-dipole, electric-dipole, or whatever. However, the direct proportionality between ac response and *population difference* is obtained in a particularly direct fashion with the magnetic-dipole approach. The essence of maser action is that if and when the population difference $(N_1 - N_2)_v$ becomes negative, the ac response also changes sign, so that the equivalent atomic resistance R_a in Figs. 4-21 and 4-22 becomes a negative resistance. This leads, as we will see very shortly, to useful maser amplification and oscillation.

The equivalent atomic reactances L_a and C_a in Figs. 4-21 and 4-22 then also become negative. This appearance of negative L and C is a somewhat strange, but still correct, consequence of our analysis. It does not lead to any notable difficulties, as we will see later.

RATE EQUATIONS ■ We also obtained the longitudinal Bloch equation for $m_z(t)$,

$$\frac{d}{dt} m_z(t) = -2W_{12}m_z(t) - \frac{m_z(t) - m_{z0}}{T_1} \tag{4}$$

where the stimulated transition probability W_{12} is given by

$$W_{12} = \left(\frac{ge}{2m}\right)^2 \frac{1}{\Delta\omega_a} \frac{1}{1 + [2(\omega - \omega_a)/\Delta\omega_a]^2} |\tilde{B}_+|^2 \tag{5}$$

If we examine in particular the quantum-mechanical two-energy-level case in which $m_z \propto N_1 - N_2$, then this longitudinal Bloch equation can equally well be written as

$$\frac{d}{dt}(N_1 - N_2) = -2W_{12}(N_1 - N_2) - \frac{(N_1 - N_2) - (N_{10} - N_{20})}{T_1} \tag{6}$$

where we have dropped the subscript v on $(N_1 - N_2)_v$ for simplicity (since it makes no real difference in the following discussion whether we speak of N_v atoms per unit volume or N total atoms in some specified total volume). Since the total number of atoms $N_1 + N_2 = N$ is constant, we may write $(d/dt)(N_1 + N_2) = 0$, or $(d_2/dt)N_2 = -(d/dt)N_1$. We calculated in Sec. 4-3 that the thermal-equilibrium-level populations are

$$N_{10} = \frac{e^{hf/kT}}{e^{hf/kT} + 1} N = \frac{e^{hf/kT}}{e^{hf/kT} + 1}(N_1 + N_2)$$

$$N_{20} = \frac{1}{e^{hf/kT} + 1} N = \frac{1}{e^{hf/kT} + 1}(N_1 + N_2) \tag{7}$$

If we introduce these results into the longitudinal equation, then after some manipulation we can put this equation into the form

$$\frac{d}{dt} 2N_1 = -2W_{12}(N_1 - N_2) - \frac{2}{T_1}\left(\frac{1}{e^{hf/kT} + 1} N_1 - \frac{e^{hf/kT}}{e^{hf/kT} + 1} N_2\right)$$

$$= -\frac{d}{dt} 2N_2 \tag{8}$$

Let us define an *upward* longitudinal-relaxation transition probability w_{12} by

$$w_{12} \equiv \frac{1}{T_1} \frac{1}{e^{hf/kT} + 1} \tag{9}$$

and a *downward* relaxation transition probability w_{21} by

$$w_{21} \equiv \frac{1}{T_1} \frac{e^{hf/kT}}{e^{hf/kT} + 1} \tag{10}$$

Then we can write the longitudinal equation in the final form

$$\frac{d}{dt} N_1 = -W_{12}N_1 + W_{21}N_2 - w_{12}N_1 + w_{21}N_2 = -\frac{d}{dt} N_2 \tag{11}$$

In this form the longitudinal equation can now be interpreted as a *rate equation*.

Consider the energy-level-population diagram of Fig. 4-24. Examining the first two terms in the above rate equation, we can interpret the stimulated transition probability W_{12}, which is proportional to the applied-signal strength, as the probability per unit time that an atom in either level will jump, or make a transition, to the other level under the influence of the applied signal. Thus, as shown in the rate equation and in Fig. 4-24, there is the *upward* signal-stimulated transition rate $W_{12}N_1$ atoms/sec and the *downward* signal-stimulated transition rate $W_{12}N_2$ atoms/sec. The upward and the downward signal-stimulated transition *probabilities* W_{12}, the probability per second that any one atom in either level will jump to the other level, are the same. The transition *rates*, the total number of transitions per second in either direction, are the per-atom transition probabilities times the number of atoms available in the starting state for the transition.

The rate equation and Fig. 4-24 also indicate that there are *relaxation* transitions,

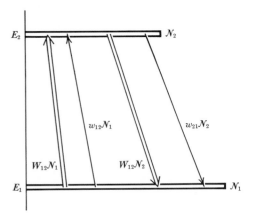

FIG. 4-24 Each arrow corresponds to one of the terms in the rate equation derived from the longitudinal Bloch equation.

which are in reality stimulated transitions stimulated by the thermal surroundings of the atom rather than by an applied signal. Owing to the thermal surroundings, there are upward and downward relaxation transition probabilities w_{12} and w_{21}, with corresponding relaxation transition rates $w_{12}N_1$ and $w_{21}N_2$. The upward and downward relaxation probabilities w_{12} and w_{21} are *not* equal like the stimulated probabilities, $W_{12} = W_{21}$, but instead stand in the Boltzmann ratio,

$$\frac{w_{21}}{w_{12}} = e^{(E_2 - E_1)/kT} \tag{12}$$

This guarantees the necessary condition of no net flow of atoms upward or downward at thermal equilibrium; that is, for relaxation only

$$w_{12}N_{10} \equiv w_{21}N_{20} \tag{13}$$

The downward relaxation transition probability must always be larger, since the thermal-equilibrium population of the upper level is always smaller. Thus in this modified rate-equation interpretation of the longitudinal Bloch equation an applied signal at or near a transition frequency causes atoms to transfer from level E_1 to level E_2, or vice versa, at the respective rates $W_{12}N_1$ and $W_{21}N_2 = W_{12}N_2$. In addition, there are simultaneous relaxation transitions in the two directions at the rates $w_{12}N_1$ and $w_{21}N_2$, owing to the thermal surroundings of the atoms.

While we have derived these results from the two-level magnetic-dipole approach, they are in fact very general and apply equally well to any two-level transition, magnetic or electric-dipole, as we will see in Chap. 6. Rate equations of this type can be very useful in laser and maser analyses, as we will see in later chapters. It is important to remember, however, that the rate equation represents only the longitudinal part of the Bloch equations. The rate equation by itself does not contain any of the important information about the ac polarization or alignment or susceptibility of the dipoles, or about the reactive effects in the atomic response, or about the phases of the signal and the response. These can be obtained only by considering the transverse Bloch equations as well.

In a correct quantum picture individual atoms are not in just one or the other of a pair of energy levels, but are in a mixed quantum state which contains a mixture of the two energy levels. Similarly, in a rigorous quantum picture individual atoms do not actually make discrete transitions or jumps from one level to the other. In the presence of an applied signal the mixed quantum state of each individual atom undergoes a continuous smooth evolution; i.e., the state mixture changes with time under the influence of the applied signal. The numbers N_1 and N_2 are not really integers, but represent continuous averages evaluated on a probabilistic basis over the entire collection of mixed-state atoms. The rate equations really describe the average result over the entire collection of the small continuous changes in the state mixture for each atom. It is often convenient to speak in terms of discrete jumps of individual atoms rather than a gradual evolution of every individual atom in its state mixture. However, it can be misleading to carry the description in terms of discrete jumps too far without keeping in mind the real meaning behind this simplification. This point is discussed in detail in Appendix A.

PROBLEMS

4-1. Suppose an electron travels in a circular orbit at a typical optical frequency, say, 5×10^{14} Hz. What radius must this orbit have for the associated magnetic-dipole moment to equal one Bohr magneton?

4-2. The nucleus of a hydrogen atom (which is just a single proton) has nuclear spin $I = \frac{1}{2}$ and nuclear g value $g_I = 5.58$. Calculate the resonance frequency f_a of the proton's NMR response as a function of dc magnetic field B_0, expressed in kilohertz per gauss. *Note:* The mks unit for B_0 is webers per square meter, now officially known as the *tesla*; 1 tesla $\equiv$ 1 weber/m$^2 \equiv 10^4$ gauss.

4-3. Use the data from Prob. 4-2 to calculate the dc paramagnetic susceptibility χ_{dc} in water at $300°$K due to the nuclear spins (the nuclear spins of the two H atoms in each H_2O molecule act independently).

4-4. A sample of water comes to complete thermal equilibrium at room temperature in a dc magnetic field of 10,000 gauss. The dc magnetic field is then reduced to 100 gauss in a time much shorter than the longitudinal relaxation time T_1. Just after the field reduction the upper and lower proton energy levels, and hence m_z, will still have populations appropriate to the larger dc field value, and it will take several relaxation times T_1 before the populations and m_z relax to their thermal-equilibrium values in the new dc field.

(a) How much energy per unit volume of water will the proton spins need to take from (or give to) the water in the process of coming to the new equilibrium?

(b) If the water is insulated from its surroundings during this process (no heat transfer to the container walls), approximately how much will the water itself be heated (or cooled) during this demagnetization process?

4-5. A two-energy-level magnetic-dipole collection with $g = 2$ comes to thermal equilibrium in a liquid-helium bath at $T = 4.2°$K in a magnetic field $B_0 = 40,000$ gauss. The sample is then thermally isolated and the magnetic field quickly (in a time $\ll T_1$) reduced to $B_0 = 500$ gauss. Evaluate the temperature which will be appropriate to the magnetic dipoles just after B_0 is reduced, i.e., before any T_1 relaxation occurs. If the dipole collection has $N_v = 10^{20}$ dipoles/cm^3, evaluate the specific heat of the dipole collection at that particular temperature.

4-6. If a magnetic-dipole moment μ is located at the origin of an xyz coordinate system and is pointing in the z direction, the z-directed magnetic field B produced by this dipole in the xy plane at a distance r from the dipole is $B_z = \mu_0|\mu|/4\pi r^3$. Assuming that $|\mu|$ equals two Bohr magnetons, plot the resonance-frequency shift, in hertz, that this field will cause for a neighboring dipole of the same type versus the distance, in angstroms, between the two dipoles. Use logarithmic graph paper and dipole separations from 2 to 20 Å.

4-7. Does a nuclear spin precess with positive or negative circular polarization in a dc field B_0?

4-8. The maximum magnetic-dipole ac susceptibility $\bar{\chi}(\omega)$ at resonance is very much larger than the dc magnetic susceptibility χ_{dc}—in fact, by the ratio $|\bar{\chi}(\omega_a)|/\chi_{dc} = f_a/\Delta f_a \gg 1$. Show, however, that the maximum ac *magnetization* $|\bar{M}_+(\omega_a)|$ will always be less than or at most equal to the dc magnetization m_{z0}, and that it will be considerably less if $T_2 \ll T_1$. Show also what ac magnetic field strength $|\bar{B}_+(\omega_a)|$ is required to produce the maximum ac magnetization.

4-9. Let us define the complex but time-varying quantity $\tilde{m}(t) = m_x(t) + jm_y(t)$, where $m_x(t)$ and $m_y(t)$ are the x and y components of the real moment $\mathbf{m}(t)$ as a function of time. *Note:* $\tilde{m}(t)$ defined in this way is *not* a phasor, as used in the text, but simply a complex quantity whose real and imaginary parts give the real time-varying vector components $m_x(t)$ and $m_y(t)$ directly.

(a) Show that with this notation, and with $\mathbf{b}(t)$ expressed in the same form, the two separate transverse dipole equations of motion (or the two transverse equations of the Bloch equations) can be combined into a single simple equation for $\bar{m}(t)$.

(b) Show that if this quantity has the form $\bar{m}(t) = \tilde{A}e^{+j\omega t} + \tilde{B}e^{-j\omega t}$, then the $\tilde{A}$ and $\tilde{B}$ terms represent positive and negative circularly polarized components of the vector $\mathbf{m}(t)$, respectively.

(c) Noting that $m_x(t) = \frac{1}{2}[\bar{m}(t) + \bar{m}^*(t)]$, with a similar expression for $m_y(t)$, express the right-hand side of the longitudinal or z equation in terms of $\bar{m}(t)$ and $\bar{b}(t)$.

4-10. Analyze Bloch's nuclear-magnetic-resonance induction technique as described in the text and in Fig. 4-18. In particular, assume that the driving or x-axis coil is resonated by a series capacitance and resistance, and that this series resonant circuit is then driven by an rf voltage source $\tilde{V}_x$. Calculate the resulting induced voltage $\tilde{V}_y$ across the terminals of the pickup or y-axis coil, and plot the magnitude and phase of $\tilde{V}_y$ (relative to $\tilde{V}_x$) versus B_0, assuming a fixed signal frequency ω and a variable dc field B_0 (as would be used in practice). Estimate the peak voltage-transfer ratio $|\tilde{V}_y/\tilde{V}_x|$ that might be obtained in a practical case, using protons in H_2O as the sample.

4-11. To verify the essential duality of the electric-dipole and magnetic-dipole equivalent-circuit models, assume that an external transmission line of characteristic impedance $\tilde{Z}_0$ is connected into the magnetic-dipole circuit of Fig. 4-22 in *series* with the cavity circuit elements. Calculate the input impedance $\tilde{Z}(\omega)$ as viewed into the circuit from the end of this transmission line and the reflection coefficient $\tilde{\rho}(\omega)$ in the transmission line due to the terminating input impedance $\tilde{Z}(\omega)$. Compare these results with analogous results for an external transmission line of characteristic admittance $\tilde{Y}_0$ connected in *shunt* across the electric-dipole circuit of Fig. 2-7. Show that these results are the duals of each other and that they have exactly the same functional form when expressed in terms of the parameters ω_a, ω_c, Q_a, Q_c, and Q_m.

4-12. *Special computer project:* Because of the nonlinearity of the Bloch equations, the available analytical solutions can be very profitably supplemented by computer evaluations. We can assume, for example, that the transverse quantities in the Bloch equations are essentially sinusoidal, as in Sec. 4-5, but with some slow variation in the phasor amplitudes; that is, $\bar{M}_+ = \bar{M}_+(t)$ and $\bar{B}_+ = \bar{B}_+(t)$. Computer integration of the resulting transient equations for the time variation of $\bar{M}_+(t)$, $\bar{B}_+(t)$, and $m_z(t)$ can then be used to explore the transient build-ups toward the steady-state solutions given in Sec. 4-5 (for example, in the case when an applied signal is suddenly turned on). Develop the necessary transient equations from the Bloch equations by allowing the phasor amplitudes M_+ and $\bar{B}_+$ themselves to have slow time variations in addition to the $e^{j\omega t}$ variation, and then use numerical integration of the resulting differential equations on a computer to explore the transient behavior for various values of T_1 and T_2 and for various initial conditions. *Note:* This is a fairly difficult undertaking, requiring appropriate scaling and normalization of the equations, and the handling of complex quantities such as $\bar{M}_+$ and $\bar{B}_+$.

REFERENCES

4-1. A. Abragam, *The Principles of Nuclear Magnetic Resonance*, Oxford University Press, New York, 1961. The classic general reference book on NMR, highly recommended for its clarity, extensive coverage, excellent illustrations, and even for the witty quotations at the start of each chapter.

4-2. American Association of Physics Teachers, Committee on Resource Letters, *NMR and EPR: Selected Reprints*, American Institute of Physics, Department BN, New York (paperback). A good collection of reprints of both basic research papers and tutorial papers. Unfortunately, the papers on experimental apparatus all cover pretransistor vacuum-tube circuits that are now largely obsolete.

4-3. E. O. Ammann, "A broadbanded solid-state microwave maser operating at 77.4°K," *IEEE Trans.*, **MIT-13**:186 (March, 1965). Data on ruby EPR.

4-4. F. Bloch, "Nuclear induction," *Phys. Rev.*, **70**:460 (1946). Bloch's original paper on NMR by the induction method, still good reading (see also the following paper in the same journal).

4-5. E. A. Faulkner and A. Holman, "An improved circuit for nuclear magnetic resonance detection," *J. Scientif. Instruments*, **44**:391 (May, 1967). Typical transistorized NMR apparatus.

4-6. R. P. Feynman, F. L. Vernon, Jr., and R. W. Hellwarth, "Geometrical representation of the Schrödinger equation for solving maser problems," *J. Appl. Phys.*, **28**:49 (January, 1957). Shows how the Schrödinger equation for any two-level system can be transformed into the Bloch equations.

4-7. P. A. Grivet and L. Malner, "Measurement of weak magnetic fields by magnetic resonance," in L. Marton (ed.), *Advances in Electronics and Electron Physics*, vol. 23, p. 40, Academic Press, New York, 1967. Descriptions of some fascinating demonstrations of nuclear free precession and NMR maser oscillators. [For additional information see also P. Grivet, A. Blaquiere, and G. Bonnet, "Magnétomètres à maser et à oscillateurs de spin," in P. Grivet and N. Bloembergen (eds.), *Quantum Electronics III*, p. 231, Columbia University Press, New York, 1964.]

4-8. S. R. Hartmann, "Photon echoes," *Scientific American*, April, 1968, p. 32. A simple description of some interesting nonlinear effects possible with the Bloch equations at large enough applied-signal levels.

4-9. E. M. Purcell, H. C. Torrey, and R. V. Pound, "Resonance absorption by nuclear magnetic moments in a solid," *Phys. Rev.*, **69**:37 (1946). A basic paper on NMR by the absorption method, still good reading.

4-10. C. P. Slichter, *Principles of Magnetic Resonance*, Harper and Row, New York, 1963. Another good book for general coverage of EPR and NMR, with a good selected bibliography.

4-11. C. L. Stong, "The amateur scientist: Building a sensitive magnetometer . . . ," *Scientific American*, February, 1968, p. 124. A "how-to-do-it" article on a simple nuclear magnetometer of the type described in Ref. 4-7.

4-12. Y-T Yang and Y-C Chen, "Simplification of transistorized NMR fluxmeter," *Rev. Scientif. Instruments*, **37**:1274 (September, 1966). Another simple transistorized NMR circuit.

CHAPTER FIVE

THE FUNDAMENTALS
OF
MASER AMPLIFICATION

We have now developed sufficient background information to begin studying the maser amplification process itself—that is, how the atomic responses can be combined with appropriate electromagnetic circuit elements (cavities, transmission lines, mirrors, etc.) to obtain useful maser amplification or oscillation. Practical maser devices usually have one of three basic forms: resonant or cavity-type devices, single-pass traveling-wave devices, and regenerative traveling-wave devices (which are really resonant-cavity devices in another form). We will discuss each of these in turn in this chapter.

5-1   POPULATION INVERSION, NEGATIVE RESISTANCE, AND NEGATIVE TEMPERATURE

Before we discuss the interaction of maser materials with electromagnetic circuits, it may be useful to review the most important basic principle involved in maser action— the principle that the response of a collection of atoms on any of its atomic transitions depends directly, in magnitude and in sign, on the population *difference* between the upper and lower quantum energy levels responsible for that transition. A rigorous proof of this basic principle requires a quantum-theoretical analysis, which we are not prepared to carry out here. We can, however, consider a somewhat more detailed explanation of this principle and introduce some useful new concepts.

■ Recall that each type of atom (ion, molecule) has a set of discrete quantum energy states, with a specific energy value E_n associated with each such energy state (called *eigenstates* and *eigenvalues* in quantum literature). The transition between a pair of levels E_n and E_m, $E_m > E_n$, leads to a transition with resonance frequency $f_{mn} = (E_m - E_n)/h$.

ATOMIC RESPONSE: QUANTUM DESCRIPTION

The quantum theory does not encourage us to say that at any specific instant an atom will be in just one of its allowed energy states; rather, the overall quantum state of an atom at any instant is generally a weighted mixture of its various quantum energy states. This mixture varies from atom to atom, and will vary with time for each individual atom in the presence of an applied signal. This quantum-state mixture has a probabilistic interpretation. Suppose we make repeated measurements of the energy of a single atom, starting each measurement with the same premeasurement state mixture. Then the outcome of the measurement each time will be one of the allowed energy values E_n, but the particular value recorded will vary randomly from measurement to measurement, much as if the atom chose to appear in a different energy level on each measurement. Quantum theory cannot predict the exact outcome each time in such a series of measurements. It can say only that the *relative probability* of recording each possible answer E_n—that is, the relative number of times that particular answer will appear in the series of measurements—is equal to the square of the amount of the E_n quantum state contained in the atom's premeasurement state mixture. That is, the atom does not generally appear *in* any one energy level; rather, it has a set of relative probabilities of being in the various available energy levels.

Of course, there can be special situations when an atom, or even a whole group of atoms, are indeed all in one single energy level. For example, in a collection of atoms at thermal equilibrium, with $hf/kT \gg 1$ for all transitions, essentially all the atoms will be in the ground energy level only. In this case all the relative probabilities mentioned above have the value zero, except for the ground-state probability, which has the value unity (very nearly).

Returning to the general case, we can, at least in principle, record for each individual atom the instantaneous probabilities for that atom to be in each level E_n and then sum the probability, or the fractional occupancy, of each level E_n over all the $\mathcal{N}$ atoms in a collection. The resulting number $\mathcal{N}_n \leq \mathcal{N}$ is the probable number of atoms that would be found in level E_n if all the atoms in the collection were measured at that particular instant. The relative probabilities for each atom must sum to unity, and hence the level populations $\mathcal{N}_n$ of all the energy levels must sum to the total number of atoms $\mathcal{N}$. For many purposes we can then speak loosely of the collection of atoms as having $\mathcal{N}_1$ atoms in level E_1, $\mathcal{N}_2$ atoms in level E_2, and so forth, as illustrated by the energy-

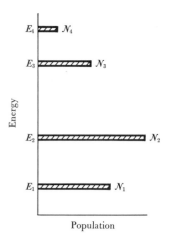

FIG. 5-1   A typical energy-level-population diagram. The $1 \rightarrow 2$ transition is shown inverted.

level diagram of Fig. 5-1. It must be kept in mind, however, that underlying this simple description is the more complex description in which each atom is in a mixed state, and in which the populations N_n really represent the sums of probabilities that individual measurements will find individual atoms in these energy levels.[1]

EFFECT OF AN APPLIED SIGNAL   ■ When a signal at or near one of the atomic transition frequencies f_{mn} is applied to such a collection of atoms, according to quantum theory, the quantum-state mixture of each atom will begin to change, so as to change in particular the relative probabilities associated with the E_n and E_m levels directly involved in the transition. This signal-induced response has two important aspects. First, there is the signal-induced ac electric or magnetic polarization produced in the collection of atoms, and the resulting ac reaction back on the electromagnetic circuitry. The net result, when we take into account both the signal-induced effects and the relaxation processes present in every collection of atoms, is that the average or macroscopic response in the collection of atoms is directly proportional to the applied signal field and to the population difference $N_n - N_m$ on the transition being excited. The dependence on population difference or on state-mixture difference comes from the quantum theory. Aside from this, the form of the atomic response and its dependence on relaxation effects and other parameters is predicted very well by the classical analyses given in the preceding chapters. The other aspect of the response is the signal-induced change or evolution in the quantum-state mixture of each individual atom. When averaged over all atoms in the collections, these changes are described by the rate equations, which give expressions for $(d/dt)N_n(t)$ and $(d/dt)N_m(t)$ due to an applied signal, as will be discussed in the following chapter.

Quantum theory shows that the dependence of the ac response on population difference on a transition is a very general result and applies equally to any transition between any pair of levels in any kind of atomic system. The essential feature of the quantum result is that wherever the total number (or number density) of atoms appears in the ac results of Chaps. 2 or 4 it should be replaced by the population difference on the particular transition being stimulated.

POPULATION INVERSION   ■ For any collection of atoms in thermal equilibrium at a positive temperature T, there are always more atoms in a lower energy level than in a higher energy level. If popula-

[1] For a full discussion of this point see Appendix A.

tion difference is calculated as lower-level population minus upper-level population, then the population differences are all positive. The ac response under these circumstances will always be absorptive; i.e., there will be net absorption of energy by the collection of atoms from any applied signal.

The essential feature of maser action is that, under proper circumstances, by pumping or exciting a collection of atoms in appropriate fashion we can cause a temporary *population inversion,* in which the collection of atoms will have more atoms in some upper energy level E_m than in some lower energy level E_n (as shown by the E_1 and E_2 levels in Fig. 5-1). In this inverted condition—in which the population difference $\mathcal{N}_n - \mathcal{N}_m$ changes sign and becomes negative, since $\mathcal{N}_m > \mathcal{N}_n$—a signal applied to the $m \to n$ transition will cause an emissive rather than an absorptive response. That is, the response will represent a net emission of energy by the atoms and a net transfer of energy from the atoms to the signal. Because this response is definitely induced or stimulated by the applied signal, there is complete phase coherence between the applied signal and the induced response; hence this process of *stimulated emission* leads to coherent, linear, phase-preserving *amplification* of the applied signal. This amplification process is the common feature of all forms of maser devices in all frequency ranges.

■ The dependence of atomic response on population difference extends to the lumped equivalent circuits for atomic response developed in Chaps. 2 and 4 for the electric- and magnetic-dipole cases. When the pumping process is turned on in a maser and the population is inverted, the resistance R_a, the inductance L_a, and the capacitance C_a in the atomic equivalent circuit all change sign and become negative. Maser action can then be analyzed in terms of the circuit properties of a complete circuit containing these negative circuit elements to represent the inverted atomic response.

NEGATIVE RESISTANCE AND NEGATIVE REACTANCE IN MASER CIRCUITS

The appearance of negative resistance in the equivalent circuit for an inverted atomic system may seem a reasonable concept, since negative resistance is familiar in other amplifying devices, such as tunnel-diode equivalent circuits. The concept of *negative reactance,* however, in the form of negative inductance and capacitance values, may be more difficult to understand. These are, nonetheless, genuine and observable effects. When the population difference on a transition changes sign, both the absorptive and the reactive, or phase-shift, parts of the atomic response change sign, since both the real and reactive parts of the susceptibility $\chi'(\omega)$ and $\chi''(\omega)$ are proportional to the population difference, and hence both must change sign. Note that an inverted atomic transition is a situation of higher-than-normal stored atomic energy, and it is not too surprising that it leads to some unusual results.

■ The successful operation of any maser device can be regarded as experimental confirmation of the ideas discussed in this section. Detailed confirmation for one specific case, however, the microwave maser transition in a ruby crystal, is also provided by the experimental results shown in Fig. 5-2. With the ruby crystal placed in a tunable microwave cavity and cooled to $4.2°\text{K}$, and with a dc magnetic field $B_0 \approx 2500$ gauss applied at $90°$ to the symmetry axis, the real and reactive susceptibility components, $\chi'(\omega)$ and $\chi''(\omega)$, were measured against ω on a maser transition in the ruby crystal at frequencies $f_a \approx 2.85$ GHz. This was done both before and after the maser pumping process was turned on to invert the signal population. The pumping process was the Bloembergen three-level microwave maser scheme described in Sec. 1-4, with a pumping frequency $f_p \approx 13.65$ GHz.

EXPERIMENTAL CONFIRMATION

Figure 5-2a shows exactly how the midband susceptibility $\chi''(\omega_a)$ inverts, going

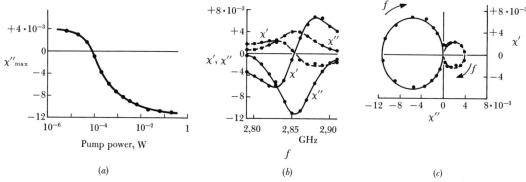

FIG. 5-2 Experimental results confirming that the values of both $\chi'(\omega)$ and $\chi''(\omega)$ do change sign when an atomic transition (in this case a microwave maser transition in ruby) is inverted from its normal absorptive condition (pump off) to an inverted maser condition (pump on). The plots show (a) the change of the midband susceptibility $\chi'(\omega_a)$ from absorptive to amplifying as the pump power is applied, (b) the frequency variation of $\chi'(\omega)$ and $\chi''(\omega)$ in both normal and inverted states plotted against ω, and (c) the normal and inverted loci in the $\chi' - \chi''$ plane as f is varied. [Taken from H. Kiemle, "Die komplexe magnetische Suszeptibilitat von Rubin fur Mikrowellenmaser," *Zeit. Angewandte Physik*, **18**:260 (1964).]

from positive to negative[1] as the pump power is increased, while Fig. 5-2*b* shows $\chi'(\omega)$ and $\chi''(\omega)$ versus ω with the pump both full on and full off. The curves of $\chi'(\omega)$ and $\chi''(\omega)$ in Fig. 5-2*b* clearly have the expected shapes for a lorentzian response, and the change in sign of both $\chi'(\omega)$ and $\chi''(\omega)$, without any change in shape, as a result of the pumping process is clearly verified by these results. The inverted susceptibility components with the pumping process applied are approximately three times as large as the normal components with the pump off. This indicates that the inverted population difference obtained by pumping the atomic system is about three times as large as the normal thermal-equilibrium population difference with the pump off, which means that this is a rather good microwave maser operating point. Figure 5-2*c* shows the same data plotted in the $\chi'\chi''$ plane.

NEGATIVE TEMPERATURE   ■ For a collection of two-level atoms in thermal equilibrium at temperature T_a, the population of the two levels E_1 and $E_2 > E_1$ are related by the Boltzmann ratio

$$\frac{\mathcal{N}_2}{\mathcal{N}_1} = e^{-(E_2 - E_1)/kT_a} = e^{-hf_a/kT_a} \tag{1}$$

where the subscript a on T_a indicates that this is the *atomic temperature* associated with the internal motions of this collection of two-level atoms. If the total number of atoms is $\mathcal{N}_1 + \mathcal{N}_2 = \mathcal{N}$, the thermal-equilibrium populations as functions of T_a are given by

$$\mathcal{N}_1 = \frac{1}{1 + e^{-hf_a/kT_a}} \mathcal{N} \qquad \mathcal{N}_2 = \frac{1}{1 + e^{+hf_a/kT_a}} \mathcal{N} \tag{2}$$

and the population difference on the transition is given by

$$\Delta \mathcal{N}_{12} \equiv \mathcal{N}_1 - \mathcal{N}_2 = \mathcal{N} \tanh \frac{hf_a}{2kT_a} \tag{3}$$

---

[1] An opposite sign convention for χ'' was used in this work, so that an absorptive χ'' is positive in these figures.

We normally think of temperature as a parameter having only positive values. However, we can describe a possible inverted maser population in our atomic system, while still making use of the Boltzmann expression, if we are willing to allow T_a also to take on negative values. That is,

$$N_2 > N_1 \quad \text{and} \quad \Delta N_{12} < 0 \quad \text{if } T_a < 0 \tag{4}$$

An atomic transition will have a population inversion, and will thus lead to a negative-resistance atomic equivalent circuit, provided that the populations can be described by a negative value of the temperature T_a in the Boltzmann relation. To appreciate more clearly the significance of a negative atomic temperature, suppose that the arbitrary zero level of energy for the energy levels is chosen midway between the two atomic energy levels,[1] so that $E_1 = -hf_a/2$ and $E_2 = +hf_a/2$. The internal energy W of the collection of atoms as a function of temperature is then given by

$$W_a(t) = N_1 E_1 + N_2 E_2 = -\frac{Nhf_a}{2} \tanh \frac{hf_a}{2kT_a} \tag{5}$$

Figure 5-3 shows this energy and the population difference ΔN_{12} plotted as a function of the inverse-temperature parameter hf_a/kT_a for both positive and negative values of this quantity.

[1] This choice is indeed completely arbitrary, since the zero level of energy in any closed system can always be chosen anywhere we like; it is only *changes* in energy that are ever experimentally important.

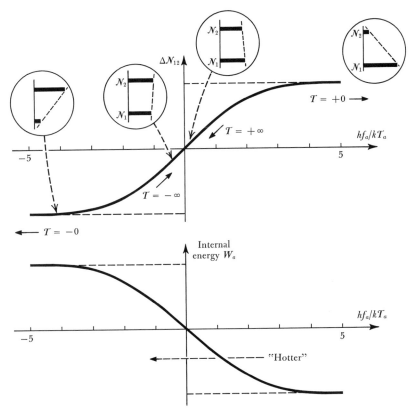

FIG. 5-3 Variation of the internal atomic energy W_a and the population difference ΔN_{12} in a two-level quantum system as a function of the parameter hf_a/kT_a, for both positive and negative values of temperature T_a.

This figure should be studied carefully. At the right-hand end of the scale the temperature approaches absolute zero, $T_a \to +0°\text{K}$, and hence all the atoms are frozen into the lower energy level. The population difference has its largest possible value, $\Delta N_{12} \approx N_1 \approx N$, and the atomic energy has the lowest possible value, $W_a = -Nhf_a/2$. As the temperature is increased above absolute zero (to the left along the scale), more and more atoms can acquire sufficient thermal energy to reach the upper energy level. In fact, as $T_a \to +\infty$ the level populations become nearly equal, $N_2 \approx N_1$ (but with $N_2 < N_1$), and the population difference ΔN_{12} approaches zero from above. The energy increases from its value at absolute zero, but there is only a finite increase even as $T_a \to +\infty$, since even then only half the atoms have been lifted up across the finite energy gap between levels.

Moving further to the left in Fig. 5-3, past the origin, we see that the energy can be increased still further simply by lifting still more atoms into the upper energy level. In terms of temperature this evidently means a discontinuous jump from $T_a = +\infty$ to $T_a = -\infty$, or a smooth transition through zero in the variable[1] hf_a/kT_a. As the temperature variation continues on from $T_a = -\infty$ toward finite negative temperatures, the upper-level population and the atomic energy W_a continue to increase. It thus becomes evident that negative temperatures are, in a very real sense, *hotter* than positive temperatures. In fact, the hottest possible temperature (highest possible thermal energy) is $T_a = -0°\text{K}$, at which limit all the atoms are in the upper energy level. The population difference then has the largest possible inverted value, $\Delta N_{12} = -N_2 = -N$, corresponding to the strongest possible maser action.

For most familiar types of motion, such as the kinetic motions of gas atoms or the lattice vibrations in a solid, calculations of the thermal energy as a function of temperature show that the energy varies directly as the absolute temperature at large enough temperature (energy kT per degree of freedom). Hence for these cases an infinite (positive) temperature always implies infinite energy, and the energy-temperature expressions diverge or are meaningless for negative values of T. In sharp contrast, the total heat energy $W_a(t)$ associated with the internal atomic motion in a collection of two-level atoms does not diverge as $T_a \to +\infty$, or even as T_a becomes negative. As shown in Fig. 5-3, the internal energy varies as minus the population difference ΔN_{12}, and both these quantities have the hyperbolic tangent dependence on $hf_a/2kT_a$.

For a two-level atomic system the negative temperatures described here are fully as real, meaningful, and sensible as the more usual positive ones. Indeed, as shown in Appendix B, negative temperatures are an unavoidable consequence of a consistent application of the basic definitions of thermodynamics to a two-level atomic system (or to any system having a bounded set of possible energy values).[2] The particular temperature T_a in these expressions must be interpreted, however, as giving only the temperature associated with the *internal* motions of the atoms. These same two-level atoms generally also have external motions and associated thermal energies (e.g., their kinetic motions as moving particles in a gas). These external motions have a separate (and always positive) external temperature. The internal motion of the atoms really forms a separate and essentially isolated thermal system, particularly since the equilibrium time

---

[1] It has often been noted that thermodynamic expressions can be more neatly and sensibly expressed with the inverse-temperature parameter $\beta \equiv 1/kT$. The jump from $T = +\infty$ to $T = -\infty$ is then a smooth transition from $\beta = 0+$ to $\beta = 0-$.

[2] For additional discussions of negative temperature see chap. 5 of Ref. 5-11, and also Ref. 5-7.

between the internal motion and the thermal surroundings ($\sim T_1$) can be very much longer than the time required for the internal atomic motion to come to equilibrium within its own system ($\sim T_2$).

In full thermal equilibrium the temperature associated with the internal and the external motions of the atoms will be the same, and equal to the temperature of the other thermal surroundings. Under other circumstances, however, the internal atomic temperature T_a can be quite different from the surrounding temperature T, and in maser situations it becomes negative. It is no more surprising in thermodynamics to have a hotter atomic energy-level system located inside a colder crystal or gas than it is to have, say, a hot furnace located inside a colder room.[1]

Negative temperatures are most easily explained in the simple two-level case. The case of a multiple-energy-level system having a population inversion on, say, one pair of levels but not on others is somewhat more complex. Such a system must be described as having different apparent temperatures associated with each transition. Suppose we make measurements on the system (or in effect make contact with the system) only through applied signals at or near one transition frequency f_{mn}. Then we really see only the populations N_n and N_m ($E_m > E_n$) of the atomic system, and as far as these measurements are concerned, the system is indistinguishable (noisewise and in every other way) from a simple two-level system with $N_1 \equiv N_n$ and $N_2 \equiv N_m$. Hence for all these measurements the system has an effective temperature T_{mn} given by

$$T_{mn} = -\frac{hf_{mn}}{k} \ln \frac{N_m}{N_n} \qquad (6)$$

and this T_{mn} must be negative if the transition is inverted, $N_m > N_n$. The concept of negative temperature is thus altogether meaningful and thermodynamically valid. Calorimetry experiments have even been carried out entirely at negative temperatures by mixing and equilibrating two different two-level atomic systems, starting at two different negative temperatures and finishing at a third, intermediate negative temperature.[2] Negative resistance and negative temperature always go hand in hand in any maser system, as we will see particularly in the noise discussions of Chap. 11.

■ In the pulsed large-signal effect on magnetic-dipole transitions called *adiabatic rapid passage,* a very strong ac signal is applied to the dipoles at a frequency well above (or below) the resonance frequency, and the signal frequency is then rapidly scanned or swept into the center of the resonance line and on out the other side. As a result of this rapid passage of the signal frequency f through the transition frequency f_a, the populations of the upper and lower energy levels become exactly reversed; that is, $N_{1,\text{after}} = N_{2,\text{before}}$ and $N_{2,\text{after}} = N_{1,\text{before}}$. Hence this effect is one way of obtaining a population inversion for maser purposes—but of course only on a temporary or pulsed basis. This very-large-signal effect can be analyzed by means of the Bloch equations of Chap. 4, but only for applied-signal fields substantially stronger than those assumed in the linearized analysis given in Sec. 4-5.

MORE EXPERIMENTAL CONFIRMATION

Because NMR transitions in particular often have very long relaxation times

---

[1] There has been some objection to describing an inverted atomic system by a negative but still real temperature because the inverted system is "not in equilibrium with its surroundings." However, most people find nothing objectionable in measuring widely different temperatures for, say, a hot oven, the freezer section of a refrigerator, and the open air of the kitchen, despite the fact that this is also a highly nonequilibrium set of situations.

[2] See Ref. 5-1 for a particularly outstanding example of this type of experiment.

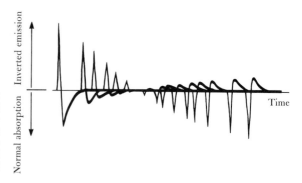

FIG. 5-4   Recovery of a two-level atomic transition back to thermal equilibrium with time constant T_1 following an initial inversion of the transition by adiabatic rapid passage. The experiment was performed using a nuclear magnetic resonance at $f_0 = 60$ MHz in D_2O. [J. A. Glasel, "A simple device for T_1 measurements on a nuclear magnetic resonance spectrometer by adiabatic rapid passage," J. Scientif. Instruments, **1**:963 (1968).]

(both T_1 and T_2), the large-signal conditions necessary to produce adiabatic rapid passage, and other similar large-signal effects, can be achieved in some NMR materials with rather small-signal power levels. Figure 5-4 shows the results of an experiment in which a two-level NMR transition is inverted by adiabatic rapid passage from a thermal-equilibrium absorptive condition to an inverted or amplifying condition and then, after a variable time delay, is probed by a weak signal pulse. The delayed signal pulse measures the net absorption or emission of the atoms after the variable time delay, and thus measures the population difference on the transition at variable times after the initial inversion.

The multiple pulses in Fig. 5-4 are multiple oscilloscope traces representing repeated performances of the experiment with successively larger time delays between the initial inversion and measurement pulse. Clearly, the observed pulse is fully inverted for very short times and gradually recovers up through zero and back to a normal positive thermal-equilibrium absorptive condition for long enough time delays. Thus this one experimental result rather graphically demonstrates several vital points: (1) the genuine inversion, or change in sign, of the atomic response when the population difference on the transition is inverted; (2) the accurately exponential recovery of the population difference from a nonequilibrium initial condition just after inversion to a final thermal equilibrium, with the longitudinal relaxation time T_1; and (3) the smooth, continuous exponential nature of this recovery even when the initial population is inverted, showing the continuous transition from an initial negative atomic temperature, on through $T_a = -\infty$ to $T_a = +\infty$, and then to a final positive equilibrium temperature.

5-2   CAVITY MASER AMPLIFIERS: EQUIVALENT CIRCUIT

In Chap. 1 we discussed a number of practical methods for obtaining a population inversion on a selected transition in a collection of atoms. It may be helpful to review some of those pumping methods at this point; we will also discuss some of them in more detail in later chapters. For the present, however, let us consider only the question of how we can employ such an inverted maser medium to obtain useful maser amplification. In this section and the next we will discuss the case of *resonant-cavity maser amplifiers,* in which the inverted maser material is placed inside a resonant cavity or tuned circuit. The lumped-equivalent-circuit models we have already developed accurately represent low-frequency masers, microwave-frequency resonant-cavity-type masers, and even, to a very good approximation, optical cavity masers.

■ Let us begin with one of the lumped cavity-atom equivalent circuits (series-parallel or parallel-series) from Chap. 2 (Fig. 2-7) and Chap. 4 (Fig. 4-22). As we have already seen, either form will lead to identical final results (cf. Prob. 4-11). For no particularly important reasons, we will choose the electric-dipole model of Chap. 2, in which the atomic resonance appears as a series resonant circuit in parallel with the circuit capacitance. Because the atomic system is now to be a maser material with an inverted population, the atomic circuit elements must all change sign. To emphasize this, we will change the subscripts on these elements from a for *atomic* to m for *maser*, as shown in Fig. 5-5. Also, from now on we will use the following notation:

$$R_a \equiv -R_m \quad \text{and} \quad G_m \equiv 1/R_m$$
$$L_a \equiv -L_m \tag{1}$$
$$C_a \equiv -C_m$$

where R_m, L_m, and C_m are positive numbers for an inverted transition. The atomic Q_a, that is, the Q associated with the atomic linewidth, then becomes

$$Q_a = \frac{\omega_a L_m}{R_m} = \frac{\omega_a}{\Delta\omega_a}$$

For best maser performance we want operation at frequencies at or near the atomic resonance frequency, and we therefore want to resonate the circuit capacitance (in the electric-dipole case) or the circuit inductance (in the magnetic-dipole case) by adding additional circuit reactance of the opposite sign, so that the cavity itself is resonant at or near the atomic resonance frequency. The resulting equivalent circuit for the atoms-plus-cavity model is shown in Fig. 5-5.

This calls for several comments. First, the simplest form of resonant circuit is a *single-tuned* resonant circuit, by which we mean a simple LC resonant circuit, or a single-mode cavity resonator, as in Fig. 5-5. We will consider only this single-tuned type of circuit, although we will find shortly that such a single-tuned resonant circuit has a rather limited gain-bandwidth product. The gain-bandwidth performance can be improved by using more complex multiple-element multiple-tuned resonant circuits. Nonetheless, the simple single-tuned circuit is widely used because multiple resonant

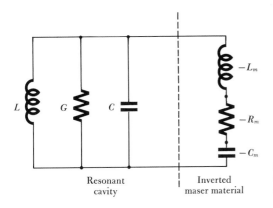

Resonant cavity | Inverted maser material

FIG. 5-5 Equivalent circuit for a cavity-maser amplifier, not including any external coupling. The equivalent-circuit elements for the maser material all become negative when the maser transition is inverted.

circuits are fairly difficult to design and even more difficult to construct and adjust properly. Second, the very best maser amplification is generally obtained when the cavity and the atomic resonance are tuned to slightly different frequencies, that is, ω_a for the atoms and $\omega_c \neq \omega_a$ for the cavity. The improvement in performance due to this stagger tuning, as compared to the synchronous case $\omega_c = \omega_a$, is generally quite small, however; and so to keep the analysis as simple as possible we will make the assumption in all of the following analysis that $\omega_c = \omega_a = \omega_0$.

MASER Q_m ■ Whether we use a lumped equivalent circuit or a full-fledged field approach, the negative maser resistance is always accompanied by a circuit reactance (the capacitance C in the electric-dipole model or the inductance L in the magnetic-dipole model). To elicit an atomic response there must always be some volume containing the atoms and the driving electromagnetic E or H fields. These electromagnetic fields represent a certain amount of electromagnetic stored energy, i.e., a certain amount of reactance, that cannot be gotten rid of. In Chaps. 2 and 4 we defined a *molecular* Q_m as the amount of loading introduced into a circuit by the presence of an atomic transition. We are now going to change the sign of this parameter (because the atomic resistance has changed sign) and rename it the *maser* Q_m. If in the electric-dipole version the circuit reactance is C and the atomic resistance is $-R_m$, then the maser Q_m is

$$Q_m = \frac{\omega_0 C}{G_m} = \frac{R_m}{\omega_0 L} \tag{2}$$

(in the magnetic-dipole version this would be $Q_m = \omega_0 L / R_m$). This maser Q_m is essentially the ratio of the unavoidable circuit reactance to the atomic negative resistance.

The Q value of any circuit element can be defined in the most basic way as

$$Q = \frac{\text{angular frequency} \times \text{energy stored}}{\text{power dissipated}} \tag{3}$$

For a given volume containing maser material (atoms), we may thus define the maser Q_m as

$$Q_m = \frac{\text{angular frequency} \times \text{electromagnetic energy stored}}{\text{power emitted by the maser material}} \tag{4}$$

For an electric-dipole case with an atomic susceptibility $\tilde{\chi} = \chi' + j\chi''$ we have from electromagnetic theory that

$$\text{electromagnetic energy stored per unit volume} = \tfrac{1}{2}\epsilon_0 |\tilde{E}|^2 \tag{5}$$

where E is the ac electromagnetic field phasor. Similarly, the power emitted by the inverted atoms (given a signal at $\omega = \omega_0$) is

$$\text{Power emitted by atoms per unit volume} = \tfrac{1}{2}\omega_0 \chi''(\omega_0)\epsilon_0 |\tilde{E}|^2 \tag{6}$$

We must integrate these two expressions over the volume of the electromagnetic circuit and of the atoms. The result is then

$$\frac{1}{Q_m} = \frac{\tfrac{1}{2}\omega_0 \epsilon_0 \iiint_{\text{atoms}} \chi''(\omega_0) |\tilde{E}|^2 \, dV}{\tfrac{1}{2}\omega_0 \epsilon_0 \iiint_{\text{circuit}} |\tilde{E}|^2 \, dV} = \eta \chi''(\omega_0) \tag{7}$$

The *filling factor* η in this expression is clearly given by

$$\eta = \frac{\iiint_{\text{atoms}} |\bar{E}|^2 \, dV}{\iiint_{\text{circuit}} |\bar{E}|^2 \, dV} \leq 1 \tag{8}$$

By computing the volume integrals of (5) and (6) over the electromagnetic field patterns, we can, at least in principle, calculate η and Q_m for any real electromagnetic structure, such as a microwave cavity or an optical cavity. A lumped equivalent circuit such as Fig. 5-5 will then provide an accurate model for the real cavity if we simply make the lumped circuit have the same frequency ω_c and the same maser Q_m value as does the real maser-cavity structure.

Be sure to keep clear the distinction between the maser Q_m, which means the *strength* of the atomic response in the circuit, and the atomic or linewidth Q_a, which measures the frequency *linewidth* of the atomic transition, quite independently of its strength.

■ To return now to our amplifier circuit, we included in Fig. 5-5 a shunt circuit conductance G to represent ohmic or other internal losses in the resonant circuit. In fact, however, practical masers are, in so far as possible, constructed so that their internal cavity losses will be small compared to external coupling and atomic effects. Moreover, including such internal losses in the analysis complicates the analytic expressions without adding much to the fundamental understanding. Therefore from now on we will neglect any internal losses in our cavity analysis.[1] This is the same as saying that the empty unloaded Q of the cavity is assumed to be considerably higher than either the maser Q_m or the loaded Q of the cavity due to external coupling.

EXTERNAL COUPLING

We must, however, include the effects of external coupling or loading in the equivalent circuit. That is, the maser amplifier must be connected to the outside world by an external signal coupling or transmission line of some sort. In the microwave case the external coupling line may be a waveguide or a coaxial line and in the optical case it may be a partially transmitting end mirror; it may be coupled to the amplifier cavity in a variety of ways, employing capacitive probes, inductive loops, or coupling through holes in the cavity wall. Furthermore, in order to control the amplification the strength of this coupling is usually made adjustable. Figure 5-6 shows a number of typical inductive and capacitive coupling methods for microwave cavities and lumped resonant circuits. The strength of the coupling in these examples can be changed by varying the probe lengths, altering the size or orientation of the coupling loops, or changing the size and position of the coupling holes.

As long as this external coupling is not so strong as to seriously distort the resonant behavior of the amplifier circuit, and as long as we consider frequencies in the vicinity of the cavity resonance frequency, all these various coupling schemes can be represented with good accuracy by the general coupling scheme of Fig. 5-7a. In lumped-equivalent-circuit terms,[2] the external coupling is represented by an external transmission line of characteristic impedance Z_0 or characteristic admittance $Y_0 =$

---

[1] Including such losses in the analysis makes the maser's performance poorer; see Prob. 5-5.

[2] A classic work on equivalent circuits for microwave cavities and other microwave elements is Ref. 5-8; see especially chap. 7, Resonant Cavities as Microwave Circuit Elements, by Robert Beringer. For a modern text covering this material see Ref. 5-9, chap. II.

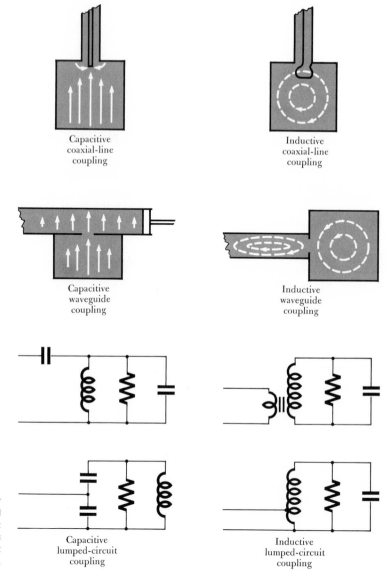

FIG. 5-6 Some typical examples of how external transmission lines can be coupled to microwave cavities or to lumped resonant circuits. The solid arrows represent electric field lines and the dashed loops represent magnetic field lines.

Z_0^{-1}, connected to the amplifier circuit through an ideal transformer of turns ratio n. The turns ratio is assumed to be variable, to represent the variable or adjustable strength of the external coupling.

Now, any admittance $\tilde{Y}$ seen through an ideal transformer appears to have the value $n^2\tilde{Y}$, or $\tilde{Y}/n^2$, depending on which way the transformer is connected. Hence the amplifier-circuit admittances as seen from the external line may all be varied in magnitude by varying the transformer turns ratio; or, conversely, the apparent characteristic admittance of the external line as seen from the resonant circuit is equally variable. To simplify our circuits and discussions, we can, in fact, drop the ideal transformer and simply assume that the characteristic admittance of the external line, as seen from the amplifier, is freely variable, as shown in Fig. 5-7b. We will denote this variable

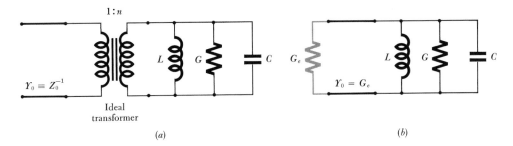

(a)   (b)

characteristic admittance by G_e, where the subscript e stands for *external*. We can then define an external Q_e for the amplifier equivalent circuit by

$$Q_e = \frac{\omega_0 C}{G_e} = \frac{R_e}{\omega_0 L} \tag{9}$$

This Q_e is a measure of the degree to which the external coupling loads down the resonant circuit. In practice, the external Q_e of a real circuit can be varied from $Q_e = \infty$ (zero coupling) down to some low value (maximum coupling).

■ There are two basic modes of operation for a cavity amplifier. One mode uses two separate external transmission lines for the signal input and signal output, forming a *two-port*, or *transmission*, type of maser amplifier, as shown in Fig. 5-8a. However, significantly better performance is obtained with only a single input-output line, forming a *one-port*, or *reflection*, type of maser amplifier, as shown in Fig. 5-8b. The reflection-type cavity maser amplifier is the only one we will discuss here. Analysis of the transmission type follows by an easy extension (see Prob. 5-6).

The reflection type of amplifier is often referred to as a *circulator* type, since it has a nonreciprocal device called a circulator to separate the input and output signals in the single external coupling line. A circulator, a transmission-line device having three (or more) ports or terminals, has the nonreciprocal property that a signal coming from a transmission line into one of its ports, say port 1, will emerge from port 2, but a signal fed back into port 2 will go to port 3 instead of returning to port 1, and so on in cyclic progression around however many ports the circulator has. Circulators generally employ internal ferrite elements to give them their nonreciprocal properties. Good circulator devices are available through the uhf and microwave-frequency bands, as well as in the optical range. Both three-port and four-port circulators are common.

In a circulator maser amplifier, the source of the signal to be amplified, such as a receiving antenna, is connected to, say, port 1 of the circulator, so that the signal from the antenna goes into port 1, out of port 2, and down the coupling line to the maser amplifier. The signal is amplified by the cavity and then comes back from the maser on the same coupling line, so that it reenters the circulator at port 2. This amplified signal then emerges at port 3 and proceeds on to further amplifier stages, or to some subsequent receiving apparatus.

It is apparent from this description that the signal amplification consists essentially of the amplified reflection of the incoming signal back from the resonant amplifier circuit. In fact, the voltage gain of the amplifier in the circulator case is just the voltage-reflection coefficient in the coupling line caused by the presence of the amplifier circuit on the end of the coupling line—hence the designation reflection type. Because the maser circuit contains negative resistance, this reflection coefficient has the unusual

FIG. 5-7 (a) A general equivalent circuit which can represent any of the coupling schemes shown in Fig. 5-6. (b) A simpler (but equally general) form in which the ideal transformer is eliminated by transforming all admittances to one side of the transformer.

TRANSMISSION-TYPE VERSUS REFLECTION-TYPE AMPLIFIERS

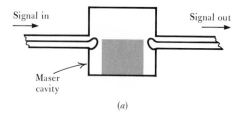

(a)

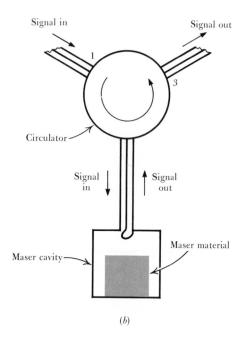

(b)

FIG. 5-8 Two ways of operating a cavity-maser amplifier: (a) a two-port, or transmission-type, amplifier and (b) a one-port, or reflection-type, amplifier, using a circulator. The reflection type has better gain-bandwidth performance.

property that its magnitude is greater than unity. The task of the next section will be to analyze this greater-than-unity reflection coefficient by applying simple transmission-line theory to the equivalent circuit we have just developed.

5-3 RESONANT NEGATIVE-RESISTANCE AMPLIFICATION: GAIN AND GAIN-BANDWIDTH PRODUCT

The voltage gain of a reflection-type cavity maser amplifier is simply the reflection coefficient as viewed in the cavity circuit from the external coupling line. We will now calculate this gain, using the complete equivalent-circuit model summarized in Fig. 5-9.

REFLECTION-COEFFICIENT
EXPRESSION

■ According to a standard formula from transmission-line theory, when a load admittance $\tilde{Y}_{\text{load}}$ is connected to the end of a transmission line with characteristic impedance $\tilde{Y}_0$, the resulting voltage-reflection coefficient $\tilde{\rho}$ is given by

$$\tilde{\rho} = \frac{\text{complex amplitude of reflected wave}}{\text{complex amplitude of incident wave}} = \frac{\tilde{Y}_0 - \tilde{Y}_{\text{load}}}{\tilde{Y}_0 + \tilde{Y}_{\text{load}}} \tag{1}$$

In the cavity-maser case the magnitude of the reflection coefficient is greater than unity

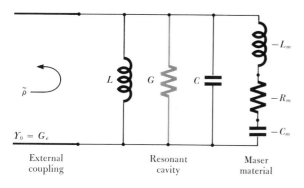

FIG. 5-9 Complete equivalent-circuit model for the analysis of a reflection-type cavity maser. The cavity-loss conductance G is shown shaded because for simplicity any such cavity losses have been neglected in this analysis.

External coupling | Resonant cavity | Maser material

and is essentially the voltage gain of the amplifier; that is, the maser voltage gain $\tilde{g}(\omega)$ is defined by

$$\tilde{g}(\omega) = \tilde{\rho}(\omega) \tag{2}$$

The maser power gain is then

$$G(\omega) = |\tilde{g}(\omega)|^2 = |\tilde{\rho}(\omega)|^2 \tag{3}$$

Note that in this notation the voltage gain, or voltage-reflection coefficient, is in general a complex number, with a magnitude and a phase angle.

Expression (1) is quite general and remains valid even if the load admittance contains a negative resistance or conductance. Equations (1) to (3) will be the basic equations for our analysis. In this case the characteristic admittance of the external line is $\tilde{Y}_0 \equiv G_e$, and from Fig. 5-9, the load admittance created by the maser-cavity equivalent circuit is

$$\tilde{Y}_{\text{load}}(\omega) = j\left(\omega C - \frac{1}{\omega L}\right) - \frac{1}{R_m + j(\omega L_m - 1/\omega C_m)} \tag{4}$$

If we use the usual resonant-circuit approximation and the quality factors already defined, this can be rewritten as

$$\tilde{Y}_{\text{load}}(\omega) = 2jG_e Q_e \frac{\omega - \omega_0}{\omega_0} - \frac{G_m}{1 + 2jQ_a(\omega - \omega_0)/\omega_0} \tag{5}$$

At midband, $\omega = \omega_0$, the susceptance terms become zero, and the net load admittance becomes simply the negative conductance, $\tilde{Y}_{\text{load}}(\omega_0) = -G_m$.

■ To gain some preliminary insight into negative-resistance amplification let us first consider the simple case of a transmission line of characteristic admittance $\tilde{Y}_0 = G_e$ terminated in an arbitrary pure conductance $\tilde{Y}_{\text{load}} = G_{\text{load}}$, where G_{load} may be variable over positive or negative values. This corresponds to the midband case, where the load susceptance terms are all zero. The reflection coefficient then becomes

NEGATIVE-RESISTANCE AMPLIFICATION

$$\rho = \frac{G_e - G_{\text{load}}}{G_e + G_{\text{load}}} = \frac{1 - G_{\text{load}}/G_e}{1 + G_{\text{load}}/G_e} \tag{6}$$

Figure 5-10 is a plot of this reflection coefficient as a function of the ratio G_{load}/G_e for both positive and negative values of G_{load}. This plot illustrates several very important points. First, we see that on the positive G_{load} side the reflection coefficient becomes identically zero when the load admittance exactly equals the characteristic

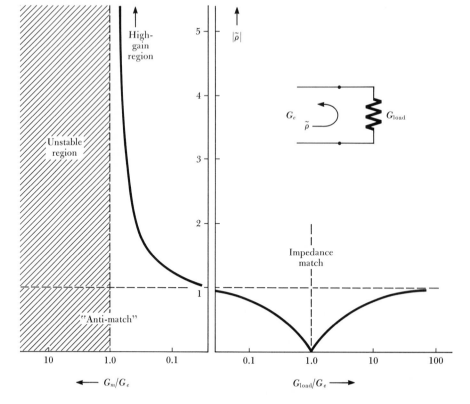

FIG. 5-10 Variation of the reflection coefficient from a purely resistive load as a function of the load conductance G_{load}, for both positive and negative ($G_{\text{load}} = -G_m$) values of the load conductance.

admittance of the line, $G_{\text{load}} = G_e$. This is the *impedance-matched case*, for which there is no reflected power. Moving away from this value in either direction causes the reflection coefficient to increase, approaching 100 percent, $|\rho| = 1$, either for very large positive G_{load} (short-circuit case) or for very small positive G_{load} (open-circuit case).

If we next continue the variation of G_{load} to small negative values, it is apparent that the reflection coefficient becomes greater than unity, $|\rho| > 1$, as asserted earlier. If we write $G_{\text{load}} = -G_m$, and use $g_0 = |\rho|$ for the reflection gain, we then have

$$g_0 \equiv |\rho| = \frac{G_e + G_m}{G_e - G_m} \geq 1 \tag{7}$$

Furthermore, as G_m approaches what we might call the *anti-matched value*, $G_{\text{load}} \equiv -G_m = -G_e$, the voltage gain diverges; that is,

$$g_0 \to \infty \qquad \text{as} \qquad G_m \to G_e \qquad \text{or} \qquad G_{\text{load}} \to -G_e \tag{8}$$

In order to have fairly high gain we must approach quite close to this unstable point by carefully adjusting the value of either G_e or G_m. Neither of these values can then fluctuate or drift by much if there is to be a stable value of gain.

If we consider still larger values of negative conductance, to the left of the anti-match line in Fig. 5-10, so that $G_m > G_e$, or $G_{\text{load}} < -G_e$, then the analytical expression (7) again gives a finite value for the reflection coefficient. However, examination of Fig. 5-9 shows that this situation implies that the *total*, or *net* conductance connected across the tuned circuit has become negative. Such a circuit is unstable; its transient response consists of an exponentially growing sinusoidal oscillation. Any initial noise or disturbance present in the circuit will grow indefinitely, or at least until some sort of saturation sets in. In short, the circuit will oscillate. Hence the region in which the negative conductance is greater than the positive loading, $G_m > G_e$, is not of interest for stable amplifiers.

In the stable negative-conductance regime the expression above gives the midband voltage gain for a resonant maser amplifier (or for a tunnel-diode amplifier, or parametric amplifier, or any negative-resistance amplifier having a similar equivalent circuit). If we now divide both the conductances in (7) by $\omega_0 L$, we may also write this midband gain as

$$g_0 = \frac{1/Q_e + 1/Q_m}{1/Q_e - 1/Q_m} = \frac{Q_m + Q_e}{Q_m - Q_e} \tag{9}$$

This shows the very important feature that the absolute impedance levels of the lumped equivalent circuit and the external coupling line drop out, so that the gain expression contains only the two dimensionless quality factors Q_e and Q_m. It is always possible either to compute or to measure experimentally these Q values for any real maser amplifier, at radio, microwave, or optical frequencies. The midband gain can then be calculated from just these two Q values.

■ A real microwave cavity maser amplifier usually has a fixed value of maser Q_m, determined by the maser material, the pumping method, and so on. We calculated earlier that $Q_m^{-1} = \eta \chi''(\omega_0)$, where $j\chi''(\omega_0)$ is the midband inverted susceptibility of the atoms. Thus the maser Q_m depends almost entirely on purely atomic parameters, such as atomic linewidth and density of atoms. Cavity or circuit parameters enter Q_m only through the filling factor, η, which is a rather minor parameter, since it is likely to lie between $\eta = 0.5$ and $\eta = 1.0$ for almost any reasonable cavity design.

To control the maser's midband gain, the external Q_e of a microwave maser cavity must then be varied by adjusting the degree of external coupling to the cavity. Depending on the type of coupling, as in Fig. 5-6, this may entail varying the length of a capacitive probe wire, changing the size or orientation of a coupling loop, or varying the size or position of a coupling hole. For stability, the positive external coupling must load the cavity more heavily than does the negative atomic or maser conductance. High gain is then obtained by decreasing the positive coupling until it just barely exceeds the negative loading. In other words, high gain is obtained by adjusting the circuit precariously close to the border of instability.

To illustrate this operation at the border of instability, suppose that the fractional difference between Q_e and Q_m is δ, so that $Q_m = (1 + \delta)Q_e$. The midband gain then becomes

$$g_0 = \frac{2 + \delta}{\delta} \approx \frac{2}{\delta} \qquad \delta \ll 1 \tag{10}$$

To obtain a midband power gain of, say, $g_0^2 = 30$ dB $= 10^3$, or $g_0 = 31.6$, requires that $\delta \sim 0.06$, or only a 6 percent margin in Q_e between 30-dB gain and complete instability. This operation at the margin of instability is one major defect of all resonant negative-resistance amplifiers.

Cavity maser amplifiers are not commonly employed in the optical range, for

PRACTICAL CONSIDERATIONS

various practical reasons. When optical-cavity-maser experiments are done, however, the more usual situation is to have a fixed external coupling Q_e and to vary the maser Q_m, so as to obtain controlled high gain, by varying the strength of the pumping process. The same difficulties in operating on the margin of instability are present in either case, whether it is Q_e or Q_m that is varied.

■ We now calculate the frequency variation of the maser gain away from midband by returning to the complete form for $\tilde{Y}_{load}(\omega)$, including the susceptance terms. The complete gain expression becomes

$$\tilde{g}(\omega) = \frac{G_e - \tilde{Y}_{load}(\omega)}{G_e + \tilde{Y}_{load}(\omega)} \tag{11}$$

where

$$\tilde{Y}_{load}(\omega) = -G_m \frac{1}{1 + 2jQ_a(\omega - \omega_0)/\omega_0} + 2jG_eQ_e \frac{\omega - \omega_0}{\omega_0} \tag{12}$$

With a little rearrangement this becomes

$$\tilde{g}(\omega) = \frac{Q_m + Q_e \dfrac{1}{1 + 2jQ_a(\omega - \omega_0)/\omega_0} - 2jQ_mQ_e \dfrac{\omega - \omega_0}{\omega_0}}{Q_m - Q_e \dfrac{1}{1 + 2jQ_a(\omega - \omega_0)/\omega_0} + 2jQ_mQ_e \dfrac{\omega - \omega_0}{\omega_0}} \tag{13}$$

There is a tilde over $\tilde{g}(\omega)$ because in general this is a complex gain, expressing both a gain magnitude and a phase shift. Note that this entire gain expression is expressed only in terms of the three quality factors, Q_e, Q_m, and Q_a, and that all the specific admittance values have dropped out.

■ The exact gain-vs.-frequency expression (13) can be considerably simplified by making some well-justified approximations. In realistic cases the useful amplification bandwidth of a cavity maser amplifier will be much narrower than either the atomic linewidth or the cold-cavity bandwidth (with external loading, but without maser action). Any signal that is within the high-gain region of the amplifier passband will be well inside the atomic linewidth. As a consequence, for all frequencies ω within the amplifier passband, we are justified in assuming that $|\omega - \omega_0| \ll \omega_0/Q_a$, which then leads to the approximation

$$\frac{1}{1 + 2jQ_a(\omega - \omega_0)/\omega_0} \approx 1 - 2jQ_a \frac{\omega - \omega_0}{\omega_0} \tag{14}$$

With this approximation, the admittance as viewed into the maser cavity takes on the approximate form

$$\tilde{Y}_{load}(\omega) \approx -G_m + 2j(G_eQ_e + G_mQ_a)\frac{\omega - \omega_0}{\omega_0} \tag{15}$$

If we go back to the exact equivalent-circuit expression (4) and make this same approximation, the admittance of the cavity-plus-atoms expression may also be written as

$$\begin{aligned} \tilde{Y}_{load}(\omega) &= j\left(\omega C - \frac{1}{\omega L}\right) - \frac{1}{1/G_m + j(\omega L_m - 1/\omega C_m)} \\ &\approx j\left(\omega C - \frac{1}{\omega L}\right) - G_m\left[1 + jG_m\left(\omega L_m - \frac{1}{\omega C_m}\right)\right] \\ &= -G_m + j\left(\omega C^* - \frac{1}{\omega L^*}\right) \end{aligned} \tag{16}$$

where

$$C^* \equiv C + G_m{}^2 L_m \qquad \frac{1}{L^*} = \frac{1}{L} + \frac{G_m{}^2}{C_m} \tag{17}$$

These values may also be written as

$$C^* = \frac{Q_m + Q_a}{Q_m} C \qquad L^* = \frac{Q_m}{Q_m + Q_a} L \tag{18}$$

Writing the approximation in this form makes it clear that, at least for frequencies near the center of the atomic linewidth, the negative atomic reactances $-L_m$ and $-C_m$ connected in series across the cavity give admittance contributions that are essentially the same as positive susceptances $G_m{}^2 L_m$ and $G_m{}^2/C_m$ connected in parallel across the cavity. Thus, within the narrowband approximation, the cavity elements L and C are converted to the modified elements L^* and C^*, as given by (17) and (18), and the maser-amplifier circuit of Fig. 5-9 is converted to the simpler parallel resonant circuit of Fig. 5-11. This simplification is valid for all high-gain narrow-bandwidth situations.

With this approximation, the voltage gain of the maser amplifier now becomes

$$\begin{aligned}
\tilde{g}(\omega) &= \frac{(G_e + G_m) - 2j(Q_e G_e + Q_a G_m)(\omega - \omega_0)/\omega_0}{(G_e - G_m) + 2j(Q_e G_e + Q_a G_m)(\omega - \omega_0)/\omega_0} \\
&= \frac{(Q_m + Q_e) - 2j(Q_m + Q_a)Q_e(\omega - \omega_0)/\omega_0}{(Q_m - Q_e) + 2j(Q_m + Q_a)Q_e(\omega - \omega_0)/\omega_0}
\end{aligned} \tag{19}$$

When the signal frequency ω is tuned off resonance, $\omega \neq \omega_0$, the same reactive $(\omega - \omega_0)/\omega_0$ term appears in both the numerator and denominator of the gain expression. However, this reactive term has much more importance when it is added to the small difference term $G_e - G_m$ in the denominator, since $G_e - G_m \approx 0$ for high gain, than when it is added to the large sum term $G_e + G_m$ in the numerator. In fact, the power gain is cut essentially in half (3 dB points) when the reactive term becomes equal to $G_e - G_m$, and at this point the reactive term is still very small compared to the $G_e + G_m$ term. Hence it is another valid approximation to drop $\omega - \omega_0$ entirely in the numerator, thus simplifying the gain expression to

$$\begin{aligned}
\tilde{g}(\omega) &= \frac{Q_m + Q_e}{(Q_m - Q_e) + 2j(Q_m + Q_a)Q_e(\omega - \omega_0)/\omega_0} \\
&= \frac{Q_m + Q_e}{Q_m - Q_e} \frac{1}{1 + 2j[Q_e(Q_m + Q_a)/(Q_m - Q_e)](\omega - \omega_0)/\omega_0}
\end{aligned} \tag{20}$$

This may be written in compact form as

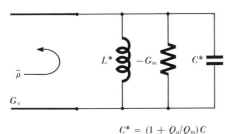

$$C^* = (1 + Q_a/Q_m)\,C$$

$$L^* = (1 + Q_a/Q_m)^{-1}L$$

FIG. 5-11 Simplified form of the maser equivalent circuit of Fig. 5-9, valid for high-gain narrow-bandwidth situations.

$$\tilde{g}(\omega) = g_0 \frac{1}{1 + 2jQ_{\text{total}}(\omega - \omega_0)/\omega_0} \tag{21}$$

which shows that the cavity gain expression has exactly the same form (at least within the approximations we have made) as a simple tuned-circuit response, with a midband gain value

$$g_0 = \frac{Q_m + Q_e}{Q_m - Q_e} \tag{22}$$

However, this tuned-circuit response has an overall or total Q given by

$$Q_{\text{total}} = \frac{Q_e(Q_m + Q_a)}{Q_m - Q_e} \tag{23}$$

With the aid of (22), we may also write this as

$$Q_{\text{total}} = \frac{g_0 - 1}{2}(Q_m + Q_a) \tag{24}$$

It is apparent that as the midband gain g_0 increases, Q_{total} also increases. For high gain, $g_0 \gg 1$, the effective Q_{total} of the amplifier will be very much higher than either the atomic linewidth Q_a or the external $Q_e \approx Q_m$ of the circuit. Therefore any signals falling within, say, the 3-dB bandwidth of the amplifier will certainly be well inside both the cavity and atomic linewidths; hence the narrowband assumptions we made above are well justified.

AMPLIFIER BANDWIDTH AND GAIN-BANDWIDTH PRODUCT

■ It is instructive to rewrite the total amplifier Q in the form

$$\frac{1}{Q_{\text{total}}} = \frac{Q_m}{Q_m + Q_a}\left(\frac{1}{Q_e} - \frac{1}{Q_m}\right) \tag{25}$$

In combining various Q values to get a total Q, we must in general add *inverse* Q values. In this case it is clear that Q_{total} becomes very large, or $1/Q_{\text{total}}$ becomes very small, because the negative maser loading $1/Q_m$ very nearly cancels the positive external loading $1/Q_e$, leaving the overall circuit with very small loading and hence a very high Q_{total}. The $Q_m/(Q_m + Q_a)$ factor is a slight additional complexity which enters because the complete maser circuit consists, not of just a single tuned circuit, but of two shunt-parallel tuned circuits, the cavity and the atoms. Note that this same factor appears in reducing the full equivalent circuit of Fig. 5-9 to the simplified equivalent circuit of Fig. 5-11.

The gain-vs.-frequency curves of a cavity amplifier for different values of midband gain g_0 have the general form illustrated in Fig. 5-12, which also includes two cavity absorption curves (atomic population not inverted) for comparison. Note that the gain curves become sharper as the midband gain becomes higher. In fact, since the amplifier voltage-gain expression (21) has just the form of a tuned-circuit response with $Q = Q_{\text{total}}$, the full bandwidth of the amplifier between its 3-dB points ($|g| = 0.707$) is given by

$$\Delta f_{\text{3dB}} = \frac{f_0}{Q_{\text{total}}} = \frac{1}{g_0 - 1}\frac{2f_0}{Q_m + Q_a} \tag{26}$$

Clearly, as the midband gain g_0 increases, the bandwidth decreases as $1/(g_0 - 1)$. In fact, for high gain, where the distinction between g_0 and $g_0 - 1$ is negligible, the am-

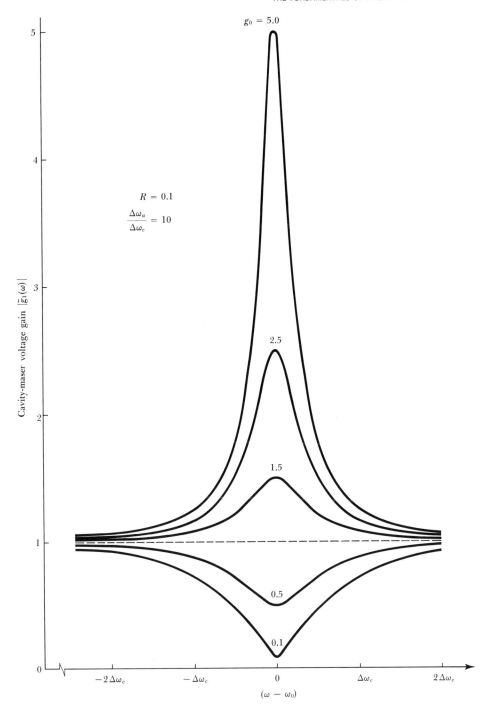

FIG. 5-12 Voltage gain versus frequency in a typical cavity-maser amplifier for three different values of midband gain g_0, showing the increasing values of Q_{total} as the amplifier is adjusted increasingly closer to oscillation. Two typical cavity absorption curves (maser-amplification process turned off) are also shown for comparison.

plifier has a fixed *voltage-gain–bandwidth product* given by

$$g_0 \, \Delta f_{3dB} \approx (g_0 - 1) \, \Delta f_{3dB} = \frac{2 f_0}{Q_m + Q_a} \tag{27}$$

Given a fixed center frequency f_0 and fixed values of the atomic maser parameters Q_a and Q_m, we can obtain any desired midband gain g_0 by operating arbitrarily close to instability. But increasingly higher values of gain require a tradeoff in the form of increasingly smaller values of bandwidth, as illustrated in Fig. 5-12, and also in Fig. 5-13. This fixed gain-bandwidth product is, in fact, characteristic of all singly resonant negative-resistance amplifier devices, including tunnel-diode and parametric amplifiers as well as maser amplifiers.

DEMONSTRATION OF AN AUDIO-FREQUENCY CAVITY MASER

■ With an equivalent circuit as simple as Fig. 5-11, it is particularly tempting to try to obtain gain-vs.-frequency curves like those of Fig. 5-12 with audio-frequency lumped-circuit elements plus some sort of electronically simulated variable negative-resistance element. Figure 5-14 shows a practical circuit design that will accomplish just this.

A small-signal ac negative resistance can be obtained in a variety of ways with transistors or integrated circuits. The circuit of Fig. 5-14a, with a high-gain operational amplifier, seems to provide in practice a particularly simple, stable, and easily variable negative resistance, with no dc offset and with a sizable dynamic range. For sufficiently high gain in the operational amplifier, the negative input conductance is given by

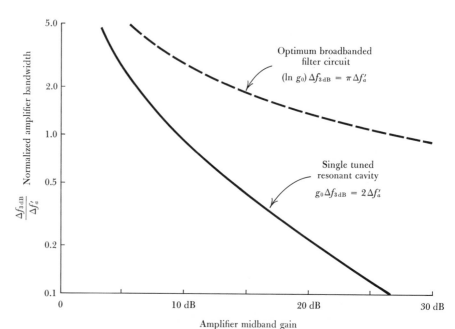

FIG. 5-13 Amplifier 3-dB bandwidth versus midband decibel gain for a reflection-type cavity-maser amplifier. The solid line is for a simple single-tuned cavity amplifier which has a fixed voltage-gain–bandwidth product. The dashed line shows the theoretically achievable bandwidth for the same cavity maser with an optimum (and ideally lossless) broadbanding network added. The normalizing factor for the amplifier bandwidth is $\Delta f'_a \equiv f_0/(Q_m + Q_a)$.

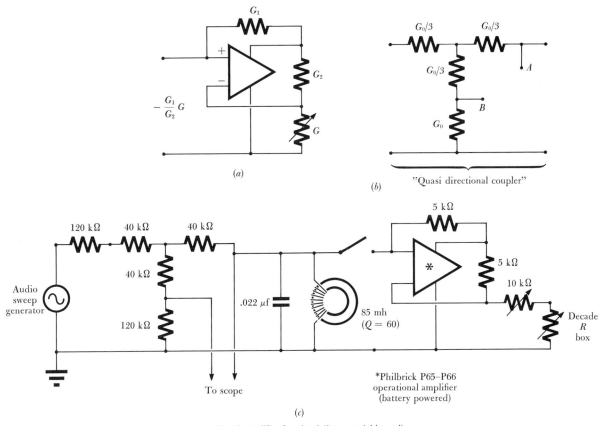

FIG. 5-14 (a) A simple circuit containing an operational amplifier for simulating a variable audio-frequency negative resistance. (b) A "quasi directional coupler" for measuring reflection coefficient at low frequencies. (c) A complete low-frequency circuit for simulating negative-resistance cavity-maser amplification at $f_0 \approx 3500$ Hz.

$$G_n = -\frac{G_1}{G_2} G \tag{28}$$

Making G_n variable by varying G seems to work well in practice.

Direct measurement of the reflection coefficient $\tilde{\rho}(\omega)$ or reflection gain $\tilde{g}(\omega)$ requires either a circulator or a directional coupler, neither of which is readily obtainable at audio frequencies. However, a simple but effective substitute is illustrated in Fig. 5-14b. In the circuit shown, the signal source, with characteristic admittance G_0, is connected through a matched "tee pad," or attenuator, having the same characteristic admittance, to the load admittance $\tilde{Y}_{load}$. A simple circuit analysis shows that the voltage difference between the two test points A and B on the diagram is given by

$$v_B - v_A = \frac{1}{8} \frac{G_0 - \tilde{Y}_{load}}{G_0 + \tilde{Y}_{load}} v_0 = \frac{\tilde{\rho} v_0}{8} \tag{29}$$

If a meter or oscilloscope with a differential input is connected between points A and B, this circuit acts as a quasi-differential coupler, the output voltage being, except for a scale factor, exactly the reflected voltage we wish to measure.

A typical complete circuit is shown in Fig. 5-14c, and some typical experimental

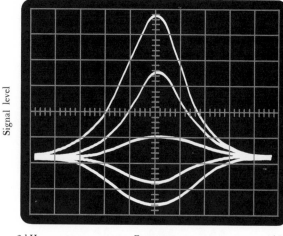

FIG. 5-15 Reflection gain versus frequency from the demonstration circuit of Fig. 5-14c.

2 kHz   Frequency   4 kHz

results are shown in Fig. 5-15. The design of this circuit began with the largest- and highest-Q inductance that was conveniently available (a ferrite toroid in this case). The characteristic admittance was then chosen to provide a near impedance match to the tuned circuit, including coil losses, so as to have a strong cavity dip with the negative resistance removed. The resonance frequency, and hence the capacitance value, is a compromise between high Q for the inductor and the usable frequency range of the particular operational amplifier (which was used simply because it was on hand). Note that the ac voltmeter or oscilloscope used to detect the output must have a differential input, and also an input impedance at least several times the characteristic impedance level of the coupler if it is not to load down the coupler and thus distort the signal. The typical results shown in Fig. 5-15 display the characteristic features predicted by Fig. 5-12. The minor distortions evident in some of the curves are presumably due to the fact that none of the circuit elements really approach ideal lumped-circuit elements with great accuracy.

THE RUBY MICROWAVE MASER ■ As a more realistic example, we can consider a cavity-type microwave solid-state maser amplifier using ruby as the maser material and operating at $f_0 \approx 3000$ MHz. Figure 5-16 is a plot of bandwidth versus gain for one such amplifier in which the relevant parameters were:

Material: Pink ruby (Cr^{3+} in Al_2O_3)
Operating point: $B_0 = 2650$ gauss at $23.5°$ to ruby c axis
Signal frequency: $f_0 = 2970$ MHz
Pump frequency: $f_p = 10,300$ MHz
Pump power: ~ 5 mW
Cavity Q: $Q_c = 2600$ at $4.2°$K
Filling factor: $\eta \lesssim 0.5$
Maser Q: $Q_m \approx 800$

The resulting gain-bandwidth product (taking into account the rather poor cavity Q_c of the cavity employed) is $g_0 \Delta f \approx 4.7$ MHz, as shown by the experiment results of Fig. 5-16. The gain and bandwidth were varied in these experiments by mechanically

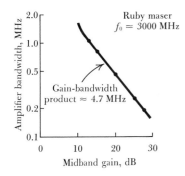

FIG. 5-16 Experimental results from a ruby microwave solid-state maser operating at $f_0 = 3000$ MHz. [From W. S. C. Chang, J. Cromack, and A. E. Siegman, *J. Electron. Control* (June, 1959).]

changing the penetration of a coaxial signal-coupling probe into the maser cavity (which was shown in Fig. 1-24).

Considerably better results, probably approaching the best possible with ruby in this frequency range, were obtained with this same cavity by using a larger ruby sample and shifting to a better operating point, where the relevant parameters were:

Operating point: $\beta_0 \approx 2800$ gauss at $90°$ to ruby c axis
Signal frequency: $f_0 = 2750$ MHz
Pump frequency: $f_p = 13,600$ MHz
Atomic linewidth: $\Delta f_a \approx 55$ MHz
Linewidth Q: $Q_a = 2750/55 = 50$
Filling factor: $\eta \approx 0.8$–0.9
Maser Q: $Q_m \approx 50$

The resulting gain-bandwidth product is

$$(g_0 - 1)\, \Delta f_{3dB} \approx \frac{2 \times 2750 \,(\text{MHz})}{50 + 50} \approx 55 \text{ MHz} \tag{30}$$

For a midband power gain $g_0{}^2 = 500 = 27$ dB, the resulting voltage gain and bandwidth are

$$g_0 \approx 23 \quad \text{and} \quad \Delta f_{3dB} \approx 2.5 \text{ MHz} \tag{31}$$

This is a narrow bandwidth for a microwave amplifier, representing a fractional bandwidth $\Delta f_{3dB}/f_0$ of only 0.1 percent. However, it may still be large enough to be useful in some applications, such as radar or radio astronomy. The bandwidth could be increased to, say, $\Delta f_{3dB} \approx 6$ MHz by lowering the midband gain to $g_0{}^2 = 10^2 = 20$ dB.

In general this type of microwave solid-state cavity maser will have a larger gain-bandwidth product at higher signal frequencies, both because of the factor of f_0 in the gain-bandwidth expression and because Q_m generally gets better (smaller) at higher frequencies. The best way to broaden the bandwidth of a microwave solid-state maser, however, is to dispense with the cavity and use a traveling-wave type of maser such as that discussed in Chap. 7.

■ There are two final points to be made in this section. First, the final answers we obtained for amplifier gain and amplifier bandwidth depended only on the dimensionless quality factors of the maser amplifier, and not on the specific impedance (or admittance) levels in the lumped equivalent circuit. This is, in fact, a general characteristic. To state this result more broadly, let us suppose that the cavity and atomic resonance fre-

EQUIVALENT CIRCUITS AND
GAIN-BANDWIDTH PRODUCT

quencies are not necessarily the same ($\omega_c \neq \omega_a$), and let us also now suppose that there may be some internal loss (such as ohmic wall loss) in the cavity or resonant circuit. This loss can be represented in the lumped equivalent circuit by a conductance G_0 connected across the tuned circuit. The internal or unloaded ohmic $Q = Q_c$ of the circuit is then

$$Q_c = \frac{\omega_0 C}{G_0} = \frac{R_0}{\omega_0 L} \tag{32}$$

The lumped equivalent circuit representing a single-tuned resonant-cavity amplifier thus has seven lumped-circuit elements,

$$R_m \quad L_m \quad C_m \quad L \quad C \quad G_0 \quad G_e \tag{33}$$

However, any real cavity maser amplifier has six physical amplifier parameters,

$$\omega_a \quad \omega_c \quad Q_c \quad Q_e \quad Q_a \quad Q_m \tag{34}$$

These parameters can be measured or determined for any real resonant maser amplifier, microwave or otherwise, regardless of the type of resonant-cavity structure or the coupling method employed.

Given the six parameter values for the real structure, we can obtain from formulas given earlier the values for all seven of the circuit elements of the lumped equivalent circuit, except for an arbitrary scale factor or arbitrary choice of absolute impedance level. To put this another way, we can express any six of the circuit elements in terms of the seventh. The important point, then, is that every measurable amplifier property, such as gain or bandwidth, depends only on *ratios of circuit elements,* and is independent of the arbitrary scale factor. A lumped equivalent circuit will give the correct answer for every measurable attribute of any real maser amplifier, provided only that the lumped equivalent circuit and the real maser amplifier both have the same values of atomic frequency ω_a, cavity frequency ω_c, atomic linewidth Q_a, unloaded cavity Q_c, cavity external Q_e, and maser Q_m. These six parameters can be determined for any real maser structure, either by calculation or by appropriate measurements.

The other point is that the limited gain-bandwidth product derived here for a resonant negative-resistance amplifier is primarily a limitation of the simple single-tuned resonant circuit itself, rather than a fundamental limitation on the maser amplification process or on negative-resistance amplification generally. The gain decreases away from midband because the susceptance term in the denominator of the gain expression increases linearly as the frequency is detuned on either side. It is possible to add to the cavity-maser circuit additional lossless susceptance or reactance elements that will more or less completely cancel the undesirable susceptance term in the gain expression, thereby increasing the amplifier bandwidth, at least over a limited frequency range. In essence, the amplifier is designed as a multiple-tuned filter, with filter theory used to shape and broaden the amplifier passband into a "maximally flat" or an "equal-ripple" type of response.[1]

In principle, this technique enables us to reach a new gain-bandwidth limit given, more or less, by

$$\ln g_0 \times \Delta f_{3dB} \approx \frac{\pi f_0}{Q_m + Q_a} \tag{35}$$

[1] Techniques for accomplishing this are described in sec. 6-4 of Ref. 5-10.

and shown by the dashed line in Fig. 5-13. This technique obviously gives a substantially larger bandwidth, at least in theory, and particularly at higher gain values. In practice, however, the design of such filter networks is complex, and the tuning and adjustment of the additional circuit elements is very critical and difficult. Also, the small but inevitable losses in the added elements have serious effects and very rapidly reduce the available bandwidth improvement. The traveling-wave type of maser, which we will discuss in the following sections, is a much better approach for obtaining broader bandwidths.

5-4 TRAVELING-WAVE MASER AMPLIFICATION: THE PLANE-WAVE CASE

Low-frequency and microwave-frequency cavity masers, and even optical-frequency cavity masers, can be accurately described by the lumped circuits of Sec. 5-3, and maser amplification in a tuned circuit is a very basic process. However, the electromagnetic signals in optical maser devices, as well as in microwave traveling-wave masers, are basically *traveling* waves, and maser amplification of a traveling wave is an equally basic process. In this section we will attempt to gain additional understanding of maser interactions by considering the maser amplification (and phase shift) of a traveling plane wave propagating through a maser medium.

■ We will consider at this point only the maser amplification of elementary extended plane waves, or waves that are reasonably close to this, as in Fig. 5-17. Real microwave traveling-wave masers use microwave slow-wave circuits, which propagate in wave patterns that are considerably more complex, and we will reserve them for a later chapter. The plane-wave analysis, however, is almost always a very good model for optical maser devices. Most optical maser devices are many optical wavelengths long, and the optical signals inside them consist of light waves traveling essentially in the axial direction, which we will label the z direction. The beams in laser devices also usually extend a fairly large number of optical wavelengths in the transverse direction, which is to say that the lowest-order modes in such laser structures usually have a very slow rate of transverse variation. As a result, if we use $u(x, y, z, t)$ to refer to the optical field strength of one of these modes, where u may refer to either the E or the H field of the optical wave, then, as a good first approximation,

PLANE-WAVE APPROXIMATION

$$\frac{\partial}{\partial x} u \approx \frac{\partial}{\partial y} u \approx 0 \tag{1}$$

Therefore, to first order, the waves in laser devices are uniform axially directed plane waves, with no x or y variations. We will discuss the modes of typical real laser struc-

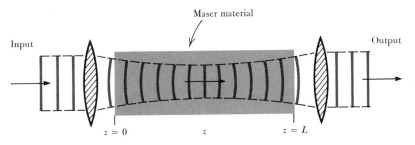

FIG. 5-17 Maser amplification of traveling waves passing through an inverted maser material.

tures in more detail later; for our present purposes a plane-wave analysis will be entirely sufficient.

■ The basic equations for any electromagnetic signal are, of course, *Maxwell's equations*. For sinusoidal time variation, these equations are

$$\boldsymbol{\nabla} \times \tilde{\mathbf{E}} = j\omega\tilde{\mathbf{B}} \qquad \boldsymbol{\nabla} \times \tilde{\mathbf{H}} = \tilde{\mathbf{J}} + j\omega\tilde{\mathbf{D}} \tag{2}$$

where $\tilde{\mathbf{B}}, \tilde{\mathbf{H}}, \tilde{\mathbf{E}}, \tilde{\mathbf{D}}$, and $\tilde{\mathbf{J}}$ are the complex *phasor-vector amplitudes* of the appropriate vector field components. Writing out the curl expressions term by term in rectangular coordinates and then applying the plane-wave assumption that $\partial/\partial x = \partial/\partial y = 0$ immediately shows that the z components of $\tilde{\mathbf{B}}$ and of $\tilde{\mathbf{J}} + j\omega\tilde{\mathbf{D}}$ must be identically zero; i.e., these field quantities are entirely *transverse*. If these fields exist in an extended medium with conductivity σ, magnetic permeability μ, and dielectric constant ϵ, then the field components are related by

$$\tilde{\mathbf{B}} = \mu\tilde{\mathbf{H}} \qquad \tilde{\mathbf{J}} = \sigma\tilde{\mathbf{E}} \qquad \tilde{\mathbf{D}} = \epsilon\tilde{\mathbf{E}} \tag{3}$$

and so Maxwell's equations become

$$\boldsymbol{\nabla} \times \tilde{\mathbf{E}} = -j\omega\mu\tilde{\mathbf{H}}$$

$$\boldsymbol{\nabla} \times \tilde{\mathbf{H}} = (j\omega\epsilon + \sigma)\tilde{\mathbf{E}} = j\omega\epsilon\left(1 - \frac{j\sigma}{\omega\epsilon}\right)\tilde{\mathbf{E}} \tag{4}$$

To be rigorous we should take into account that the permeabilities μ and ϵ, and even the conductivity σ, are in general anisotropic tensor quantities. However, since this would only complicate the mathematical derivation without changing the essential results, we will ignore this complexity and treat μ, ϵ, and σ as isotropic scalar quantities.

Note that the conductivity σ can be absorbed into an expanded dielectric constant ϵ if we write

$$\boldsymbol{\nabla} \times \tilde{\mathbf{H}} = j\omega\,\tilde{\epsilon}\,\tilde{\mathbf{E}}$$

where

$$\tilde{\epsilon} = \epsilon\left(1 - \frac{j\sigma}{\omega\epsilon}\right) \tag{5}$$

Thus the conductivity—which is certainly a dissipative, or loss, mechanism—appears as an *imaginary* part of a complex dielectric constant ϵ; moreover, this positive loss is represented by a *negative* value for the imaginary part of ϵ.

■ By applying the curl operator to both sides of either one of Maxwell's equations and then making use of the other equation, the two equations can be combined into the single wave equation

$$\boldsymbol{\nabla} \times \boldsymbol{\nabla} \times \tilde{\mathbf{U}} = \omega^2\mu\,\tilde{\epsilon}\,\tilde{\mathbf{U}} \tag{6}$$

where the neutral symbol $\tilde{\mathbf{U}}$ may represent the phasor amplitude of either of the field vectors $\tilde{\mathbf{E}}$ and $\tilde{\mathbf{H}}$. From now on we will simply use $\tilde{\mathbf{U}}$ to signify the electromagnetic field amplitude, without worrying about which specific field vector, $\tilde{\mathbf{E}}$ or $\tilde{\mathbf{H}}$, it represents. With the use of a standard vector identity, the wave equation then becomes

$$\boldsymbol{\nabla}(\boldsymbol{\nabla} \cdot \tilde{\mathbf{U}}) - \nabla^2\tilde{\mathbf{U}} = \omega^2\mu\,\tilde{\epsilon}\,\tilde{\mathbf{U}} \tag{7}$$

In the case at hand, since $\partial/\partial x$, $\partial/\partial y$, and U_z are all zero, the $\boldsymbol{\nabla} \cdot \tilde{\mathbf{U}}$ term is certainly zero, and so we have, finally,

$$(\nabla^2 + \omega^2\mu\tilde{\epsilon})\tilde{\mathbf{U}} = 0 \tag{8}$$

However, since ∇^2 is simply $\partial^2/\partial z^2$ in this case, we may as well drop the boldface vector notation for $\tilde{\mathbf{U}}$ and simply use the scalar $\tilde{U}(z)$ for the transverse component of $\tilde{\mathbf{U}}$. The final result is then

$$\left(\frac{\partial^2}{\partial z^2} + \omega^2\mu\tilde{\epsilon}\right)\tilde{U}(z) = 0 \tag{9}$$

This is the standard elementary one-dimensional form for the wave equation, identical to the wave equation on a one-dimensional uniform transmission line.

■ We have already assumed an $e^{j\omega t}$ time variation for $u(z,t)$. At this point we may also assume an $e^{-\Gamma z}$ space dependence; that is,

WAVE PROPAGATION

$$u(z,t) = \tilde{U}(z)e^{j\omega t} = \tilde{U}_0 e^{j\omega t}e^{-\Gamma z} \tag{10}$$

where Γ is the axial-propagation factor. Substitution into the wave equation then gives

$$(\Gamma^2 + \omega^2\mu\tilde{\epsilon})\tilde{U}(z) = 0 \tag{11}$$

If $U(z)$ is not to be identically zero, the propagation factor Γ must be given by

$$\Gamma = \sqrt{-\omega^2\mu\tilde{\epsilon}} = \pm j\omega\sqrt{\mu\tilde{\epsilon}} = \pm j\omega\sqrt{\mu\epsilon\left(1 - \frac{j\sigma}{\omega\epsilon}\right)} \tag{12}$$

The choice of signs corresponds to the fact that a wave can propagate in either the $+z$ or $-z$ directions. We will not carry along both signs, but will merely keep in mind the fact that propagation is possible in both directions.

If μ and ϵ are both purely real (no loss, $\sigma = 0$, $\tilde{\epsilon} = \epsilon$), then clearly Γ is purely imaginary; that is, for this lossless case

$$\Gamma = j\beta_0 = j\omega(\mu\epsilon)^{1/2} \qquad \sigma = 0 \tag{13}$$

where we will call β_0 the *propagation constant*.[1] In this case the field amplitude varies with time and space in the form

$$u(z,t) = \tilde{U}_{01} e^{j(\omega t - \beta_0 z)} + \tilde{U}_{02} e^{j(\omega t + \beta_0 z)} \tag{14}$$

These terms represent lossless or freely propagating traveling waves, with propagation factor $\Gamma = j\beta_0 = j\omega(\mu\epsilon)^{1/2}$, traveling in the $+z$ and $-z$ directions.

In lossy cases, however, ϵ also has an imaginary part, $\tilde{\epsilon} = \epsilon(1 - j\sigma/\omega\epsilon)$ as described above. The propagation factor Γ then becomes complex rather than purely imaginary. We must take this into account by writing

$$\Gamma = \alpha_0 + j\beta_0 = j\omega(\mu\epsilon)^{1/2}\left(1 - \frac{j\sigma}{\omega\epsilon}\right)^{1/2} \qquad \sigma \neq 0 \tag{15}$$

The wave in either direction then becomes a lossy, or attenuating, wave,

$$u(z,t) = \tilde{U}_0 e^{-\alpha_0 z} e^{j(\omega t - \beta_0 z)} \tag{16}$$

As a practical matter we are interested only in low-loss situations, those situations in

[1] The notation $\Gamma = jk$ or jk_0 instead of $j\beta$ or $j\beta_0$ is also very commonly used, especially in optical analyses, and β or k is also often called the *wave vector* or *wave number*.

which $\alpha_0 \ll \beta_0$, which implies $\sigma/\omega\epsilon \ll 1$. Within this assumption the propagation factor can be approximated by

$$\Gamma = \alpha_0 + j\beta_0 = j\omega(\mu\epsilon)^{1/2}\left(1 - \frac{j\sigma}{\omega\epsilon}\right)^{1/2}$$

$$\approx j\omega(\mu\epsilon)^{1/2}\left[1 - \frac{j\sigma}{2\omega\epsilon}\right] = \left[(\mu\epsilon)^{1/2}\frac{\sigma}{2\epsilon}\right] + j\omega(\mu\epsilon)^{1/2} \qquad (17)$$

Thus, to first order, the propagation constant β_0 is unaffected by the loss term, while the attenuation factor α_0 is given by

$$\alpha_0 = \frac{(\mu\epsilon)^{1/2}\sigma}{2\epsilon} = \frac{\sigma}{2}\sqrt{\frac{\mu}{\epsilon}} \qquad \frac{\sigma}{\omega\epsilon} \ll 1 \qquad (18)$$

This loss term is often called the *ohmic-loss term,* since it arises from ohmic conductivity in the medium being considered. The ratio $(\mu/\epsilon)^{1/2}$ has the dimensions of ohms and is often called the *characteristic impedance of the medium for plane waves,* by analogy with the characteristic impedance of transmission lines. It can be shown that this characteristic impedance gives the ratio of the transverse E field strength to transverse H field strength for a plane wave in the medium. For free space this has the numerical value $(\mu_0/\epsilon_0)^{1/2} = 377\ \Omega$.

PROPERTIES OF TRAVELING WAVES

■ Let us review some elementary traveling-wave properties, just to be sure all our definitions and concepts are in order. When a propagating signal wave is written as

$$u(z,t) = \tilde{U}_0 e^{j(\omega t - \beta z)} \qquad (19)$$

we understand that the fixed amplitude at any point z and instant t is given by the real part of the complex expression on the right-hand side. If we could somehow take a snapshot of the real field amplitude $u(z,t)$ at one particular instant $t = t_1$, we would see a sinusoidal wave pattern in space like the solid line in Fig. 5-18. Since this spatial pattern varies as a sinusoidal function of βz, the wavelength λ of the wave is given by

$$\lambda = \frac{2\pi}{\beta} \qquad (20)$$

A similar snapshot taken at a later time $t = t_2$ would show that the wave pattern had moved some distance to the right, as illustrated by the dashed line in Fig. 5-18. An observer (or an atom) sitting at a fixed point in space, say, $z = z_1$, would thus see a sinusoidal field amplitude as a function of time, $u(t) \sim e^{j\omega t}$, as the wave moves past, with a relative phase given by the $e^{-j\beta z_1}$ factor (and by any initial phase angle contained in $\tilde{U}_0$).

The speed at which the observer would have to move to stay at a fixed point

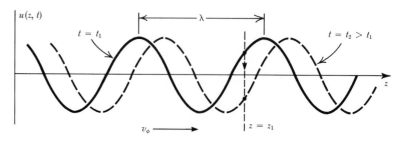

FIG. 5-18 Some of the elementary properties of a traveling wave.

on the traveling sinusoidal wave is called the *phase velocity* v_ϕ of the wave. Clearly, if the observer is to see a constant value of the phase factor $\omega t - \beta z$ in the exponent as time goes on, he must travel at a velocity given by

$$v_\phi = \frac{z}{t} = \frac{\omega}{\beta} \tag{21}$$

Thus the propagation constant β can also be written in the forms

$$\beta = \omega(\mu\epsilon)^{1/2} = \frac{\omega}{v_\phi} = \frac{2\pi}{\lambda} \tag{22}$$

where $v_\phi = \omega/\beta = (\mu\epsilon)^{-1/2}$ and $\lambda = 2\pi/\beta$ are the phase velocity and wavelength in the medium described by the magnetic and electric permeabilities μ and ϵ. The total phase shift $\phi = \beta L$ which the wave undergoes in passing through a total distance L in the medium is sometimes called the *electrical length* of the medium.

If the medium is *free space,* the wave travels at the velocity of light in free space, c, and the propagation constant becomes

$$\beta = \omega(\mu_0\epsilon_0)^{1/2} = \frac{\omega}{c} \tag{23}$$

If, however, the wave is propagating through some solid (or liquid) *medium,* such as a ruby or glass laser rod, the phase velocity v_ϕ will be slower, and we must write

$$\beta = \omega(\mu\epsilon)^{1/2} = \frac{\omega}{v_\phi} = \frac{n_0\omega}{c} \tag{24}$$

where the dimensionless factor $n_0 = c/v_\phi \geq 1$ is the index of refraction of the medium. Most materials of interest to us have $\mu \approx \mu_0$, especially at optical frequencies, but many, if not all, solid materials have dielectric constants $\epsilon > \epsilon_0$. Hence the relation

$$n_0 = \frac{c}{v_\phi} = \sqrt{\frac{\epsilon}{\epsilon_0}} \tag{25}$$

is the usual relationship between the index of refraction and dielectric constant.

■ Our elementary traveling-wave analysis can now be easily extended to include interaction with a maser (or, for that matter, a nonmaser) atomic transition. The approach is simple, and is essentially the same for either electric-dipole or magnetic-dipole transitions. Let us consider first the slightly simpler magnetic-dipole case.

TRAVELING-WAVE MASER AMPLIFICATION

As noted above, virtually all maser materials of interest, even solids, have essentially the same magnetic permeability as free space, $\mu \approx \mu_0$, in the absence of maser action. When atoms with a magnetic-dipole transition are present, however, the material acquires a small (but important) magnetic susceptibility $\tilde{\chi}(\omega)$ at frequencies near the atomic transition frequency, so that the magnetic permeability acquires the slightly complex value

$$\tilde{\mu}(\omega) = \mu_0[1 + \tilde{\chi}(\omega)] = \mu_0[1 + \chi'(\omega) + j\chi''(\omega)] \tag{26}$$

If ohmic losses are present, we may also write the dielectric permeability in the complex form

$$\tilde{\epsilon}(\omega) = \epsilon\left(1 - \frac{j\sigma}{\omega\epsilon}\right) \tag{27}$$

The propagation factor for a wave propagating through this maser medium then becomes

$$\Gamma(\omega) = j\omega \sqrt{\tilde{\mu}(\omega)\tilde{\epsilon}(\omega)} = j\omega(\mu_0\epsilon)^{1/2} \sqrt{[1 + \tilde{\chi}(\omega)](1 - j\sigma/\omega\epsilon)} \tag{28}$$

With the usual assumptions that both the maser susceptibility and the ohmic losses are small, this can be approximated to first order by

$$\Gamma(\omega) \approx j\omega(\mu_0\epsilon)^{1/2}\left[1 + \tfrac{1}{2}\tilde{\chi}(\omega) - \frac{j\sigma}{2\omega\epsilon}\right]$$

$$= j\omega(\mu_0\epsilon)^{1/2}\left[1 + \tfrac{1}{2}\chi'(\omega) + \tfrac{1}{2}j\chi''(\omega) - \frac{j\sigma}{2\omega\epsilon}\right] = \alpha(\omega) + j\beta(\omega) \tag{29}$$

Let us denote the propagation constant without maser action by

$$\beta_0 = \omega(\mu_0\epsilon)^{1/2} = \frac{\omega}{v_\phi} \tag{30}$$

and the attenuation due to ohmic loss alone by

$$\alpha_0 = \frac{\sigma}{2}\left(\frac{\mu_0}{\epsilon}\right)^{1/2} \tag{31}$$

The propagation constant and attenuation with the maser action included then become

$$\beta(\omega) = \beta_0 + \frac{\omega}{2v_\phi}\chi'(\omega) = \beta_0 + \tfrac{1}{2}\beta_0\chi'(\omega) \tag{32}$$

$$\alpha(\omega) = \alpha_0 - \frac{\omega}{2v_\phi}\chi''(\omega) = \alpha_0 - \tfrac{1}{2}\beta_0\chi''(\omega) \tag{33}$$

Before we discuss these very basic and important results, let us also consider the electric-dipole case, which leads to exactly the same results, but with a few slight additional complexities. Because most solid maser materials have an electric permeability ϵ that is significantly larger than the free-space value ϵ_0 even without maser action, we must write in general for the electric quantities in such media

$$\tilde{D} = \epsilon_0\tilde{E} + \tilde{P}_{\text{medium}} + \tilde{P}_{\text{maser}} = \epsilon\tilde{E} + \tilde{P}_{\text{maser}} \tag{34}$$

Here the $\tilde{P}_{\text{medium}}$ term and the basic dielectric constant ϵ represent the dielectric polarization contributions due to the host crystal or solid by itself, without any maser action, while the $\tilde{P}_{\text{maser}}$ term gives the additional small contribution due to the maser atomic transition. For example, in a ruby maser crystal $\tilde{P}_{\text{medium}}$ represents the relatively large dielectric polarization of the host sapphire (Al_2O_3) lattice, while $\tilde{P}_{\text{maser}}$ represents the small additional effects of the maser (laser) transition in the Cr^{3+} maser ions diffused throughout the sapphire host lattice. A gaseous maser medium will have $\tilde{P}_{\text{medium}} \approx 0$ and $\epsilon \approx \epsilon_0$, disregarding the maser transition.

The host polarization $\tilde{P}_{\text{medium}}$ is also basically an atomic polarization, caused by other atomic and molecular responses in the host material. We treat these as phenomena separate from the maser atomic transition, however, because we wish to distinguish the weak but sharply resonant effects of the maser transition ($\tilde{P}_{\text{maser}}$) from the generally very broad but strong effects due to the host dielectric polarization ($\tilde{P}_{\text{medium}}$), which is present and essentially unchanged whether or not the maser atoms are present or the maser pumping process is turned on.

In the general case, if we define the maser susceptibility $\tilde{\chi}(\omega)$ by

$$\tilde{P}_{\text{maser}} = \tilde{\chi}(\omega)\epsilon\tilde{E} \tag{35}$$

then we can write

$$\tilde{D} = \epsilon\tilde{E} + \tilde{P}_{\text{maser}} = \epsilon[1 + \tilde{\chi}(\omega)]\tilde{E} \tag{36}$$

This definition of the maser $\tilde{\chi}(\omega)$ is not quite proper; we should use ϵ_0 instead of ϵ in the basic expression. However, defining it this way here will make our expressions simpler without changing the final results.

If we also include a conductivity or ohmic-loss term, the total complex dielectric constant may be written

$$\tilde{\epsilon}(\omega) = \epsilon\left[1 + \tilde{\chi}(\omega) - \frac{j\sigma}{\omega\epsilon}\right] = \epsilon\left[1 + \chi'(\omega) + j\chi''(\omega) - \frac{j\sigma}{\omega\epsilon}\right] \tag{37}$$

The propagation factor for the electric-dipole case then becomes

$$\Gamma(\omega) = j\omega\sqrt{\mu_0\tilde{\epsilon}(\omega)} = j\omega(\mu_0\epsilon)^{1/2}\sqrt{1 + \tilde{\chi}(\omega) - \frac{j\sigma}{\omega\epsilon}} \tag{38}$$

This result is similar, but not quite identical, to the corresponding magnetic-dipole result. Expanded to first order in the small maser and loss terms, however, it becomes

$$\Gamma(\omega) \simeq j\omega(\mu_0\epsilon)^{1/2}\left[1 + \tfrac{1}{2}\tilde{\chi}(\omega) - \frac{j\sigma}{2\omega\epsilon}\right]$$

$$= j\omega(\mu_0\epsilon)^{1/2}\left[1 + \tfrac{1}{2}\chi'(\omega) + \tfrac{1}{2}j\chi''(\omega) - \frac{j\sigma}{2\omega\epsilon}\right] \tag{39}$$

which is exactly the same as the magnetic-dipole result. Thus in either case the final results with maser action present are

$$\beta(\omega) = \beta_0(\omega) + \Delta\beta_m(\omega) \tag{40a}$$

where

$$\Delta\beta_m(\omega) = \frac{\omega}{2v_\phi}\chi'(\omega) = \tfrac{1}{2}\beta_0\chi'(\omega) \tag{40b}$$

and

$$\alpha(\omega) = \alpha_0 - \alpha_m(\omega) \tag{40c}$$

where

$$\alpha_m(\omega) = \frac{\omega}{2v_\phi}\chi''(\omega) = \tfrac{1}{2}\beta_0\chi''(\omega) \tag{40d}$$

where $\chi'(\omega)$ and $\chi''(\omega)$ may represent either the magnetic susceptibility of a magnetic-dipole maser transition or the electric susceptibility of an electric-dipole maser transition (defined as $\chi = P_{\text{maser}}/\epsilon E$).

■ The maser action or atomic susceptibility obviously produces two important and distinct effects. First, there is an additional *positive or negative attenuation factor* for the traveling waves, given by the $-\tfrac{1}{2}\beta_0\chi''(\omega)$ term. This attenuation, or amplification, adds directly to the usual attenuation factor α_0 caused by ohmic losses, scattering, and

LOSS AND PHASE-SHIFT EFFECTS

other effects. If the maser transition is not inverted, then $\chi''(\omega)$ will invariably be a negative number, and so the atomic transition will cause an additional loss or absorption of the wave in propagating through the maser medium, over and above the ohmic-loss term. This additional loss due to absorption on the atomic transition will have a maximum value at the atomic resonance frequency, dropping off in accordance with the atomic lineshape at other frequencies.

Besides the additional loss (or gain) term, the negative susceptibility term $\frac{1}{2}\beta_0\chi'(\omega)$ also causes an additional *frequency-dependent phase shift,* or a small change in the phase velocity and the electrical length through the medium. With the usual frequency dependence of $\chi'(\omega)$, this added phase shift is zero exactly at atomic resonance, with two peaks of opposite sign for frequencies just above and just below the exact resonance frequency.

If the population difference on the atomic transition is now inverted, so that the absorptive condition is changed to a condition of maser action, then *both* $\chi'(\omega)$ and $\chi''(\omega)$ change sign. The loss term $-\frac{1}{2}\beta_0\chi''(\omega)$ then becomes an exponential *gain* or growth term. If this maser-gain factor $|\frac{1}{2}\beta_0\chi''(\omega)|$ exceeds the ohmic-loss factor α_0, a wave propagating through the medium experiences a net exponential growth in amplitude and a net increase in energy or power with distance. This exponential growth is traveling-wave maser amplification.

The added-phase-shift term $\frac{1}{2}\beta_0\chi'(\omega)$ is still present in the inverted, or maser case. However, its sign is reversed, both above and below resonance, because of the change in sign of $\chi'(\omega)$ when the atomic population difference changes sign.

TRAVELING-WAVE MASER GAIN   ■ The simplest and most straightforward method of traveling-wave amplification is simply to allow the signal that is to be amplified to propagate for a distance L through an appropriately inverted maser medium. If we take the input plane to be $z = 0$, the output wave amplitude in this case is

$$\tilde{U}(L) = \tilde{U}_0 \exp\left[\tfrac{1}{2}\beta_0\chi''(\omega)L - \alpha_0 L\right] \exp\left[-j\beta_0 L - j\tfrac{1}{2}\beta_0\chi'(\omega)L\right] \qquad (41)$$

The complex voltage gain[1] $\tilde{g}(\omega)$ of the amplifier is then

$$\tilde{g}(\omega) \equiv \frac{\tilde{U}(L)}{\tilde{U}(0)} = \exp\left[\tfrac{1}{2}\beta_0\chi''(\omega)L - \alpha_0 L\right] \exp\left[-j\beta_0 L - j\tfrac{1}{2}\beta_0\chi'(\omega)L\right] \qquad (42)$$

where the first exponential factor gives the increase in magnitude and the second gives the total phase shift or electrical length of the wave in passing through the amplifier.

Let us now suppose that the maser susceptibility has the complex lorentzian form

$$\tilde{\chi}(\omega) = j\chi_0'' \frac{1}{1 + 2j(\omega - \omega_a)/\Delta\omega_a} \qquad (43)$$

where $\Delta\omega_a$ is the atomic linewidth and $\chi_0'' \equiv \chi''(\omega = \omega_a)$ is the midband or peak value of $\chi''(\omega)$. For an inverted maser transition χ_0'' is a positive number. If we neglect the ohmic loss factor α_0 (which is in fact often quite small), the voltage-gain magnitude becomes

---

[1] Although "voltages" in the lumped-circuit sense are not directly involved in this wave analysis, we will use the term *voltage gain* as convenient shorthand for gain in signal-wave amplitude. The power gain is then the magnitude of the voltage gain squared.

$$g(\omega) \equiv |\tilde{g}(\omega)| = \exp\left[\frac{\omega\chi_0''L}{2v_\phi} \frac{1}{1 + [2(\omega - \omega_a)/\Delta\omega_a]^2}\right] \tag{44}$$

with peak or midband voltage gain

$$g_0 \equiv g(\omega = \omega_a) = \exp\frac{\omega_a\chi_0''L}{2v_\phi} \tag{45}$$

The total phase shift of the wave in passing through the amplifier becomes

$$\phi(L) - \phi(0) = \beta_0 L + \frac{\omega\chi_0''L}{2v_\phi} \frac{2(\omega - \omega_a)/\Delta\omega_a}{1 + [2(\omega - \omega_a)/\Delta\omega_a]^2}$$

$$= \beta_0 L + \ln g_0 \frac{2(\omega - \omega_a)/\Delta\omega_a}{1 + [2(\omega - \omega_a)/\Delta\omega_a]^2} \tag{46}$$

Figure 5-19 shows $\chi''(\omega)$ and $\chi'(\omega)$ and the resulting gain and phase shift plotted against frequency. The added-phase-shift contribution due to $\chi'(\omega)$ is considerably exaggerated to emphasize its form.

FIG. 5-19 The frequency variation of $\chi''(\omega)$ and $\chi'(\omega)$, and of the associated traveling-wave maser gain and phase-shift curves $g(\omega)$ and $\phi(\omega)$. The size of the added-phase-shift contribution due to maser action is exaggerated for emphasis.

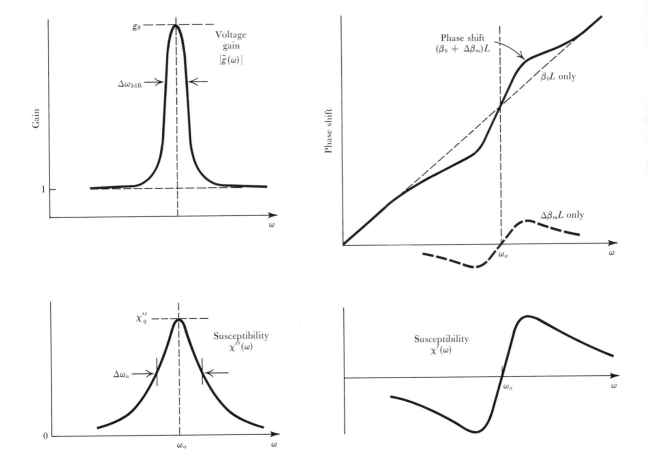

(a)   (b)

■ For a lorentzian atomic lineshape the voltage gain versus frequency may also be written in the form

$$g(\omega) = \exp\left[\frac{\omega L}{2v_\phi}\chi''(\omega)\right] = \exp\left\{\frac{\ln g_0}{1 + [2(\omega - \omega_a)/\Delta\omega_a]^2}\right\} \tag{47}$$

The linewidth of the exponent in this expression is just the atomic linewidth $\Delta\omega_a$. However, the voltage gain itself, the complete exponential function, has a narrower bandwidth, because the exponential function decreases more rapidly than the exponent (see Fig. 5-19a).

To calculate the 3-dB bandwidth of a traveling-wave maser amplifier we must evaluate the frequency shift $\delta\omega = \omega - \omega_a$, for which the gain is reduced to $g(\omega) = 0.707g_0 = g_0/\sqrt{2}$, by solving for $\delta\omega$ in the expression

$$\exp\left\{\frac{\ln g_0}{1 + [2\delta\omega/\Delta\omega_a]^2}\right\} = 2^{-1/2}\exp(\ln g_0) = \exp(\ln g_0 - \tfrac{1}{2}\ln 2) \tag{48}$$

with the result

$$\delta\omega = \pm\frac{\Delta\omega_a}{2}\sqrt{\frac{\ln 2}{2\ln g_0 - \ln 2}} \tag{49}$$

The full 3-dB bandwidth of the amplifier is twice this, or

$$\Delta\omega_{3\mathrm{dB}} = 2|\delta\omega| = \sqrt{\frac{\ln 2}{2\ln g_0 - \ln 2}}\,\Delta\omega_a \tag{50}$$

The amplifier bandwidth decreases with increasing midband gain, but not nearly so rapidly as in the cavity-maser case.

This same result can be derived more easily and expressed more clearly if we convert the voltage gain $g(\omega)$ into power gain $G(\omega) = g^2(\omega)$, and then express this in decibels; that is,

$$G_{\mathrm{dB}}(\omega) = 10\log G(\omega) = 20\log g(\omega) \tag{51}$$

With a little algebra we obtain

$$G_{\mathrm{dB}}(\omega) = G_{\mathrm{dB}}(\omega_a)\frac{1}{1 + [2(\omega - \omega_a)/\Delta\omega_a]^2} \tag{52}$$

That is, the power gain expressed in decibels has exactly the same lorentzian lineshape as the atomic transition. The half-power or 3-dB points are then obtained by solving for the frequency shifts that produce

$$G_{\mathrm{dB}}(\omega_a + \delta\omega) = G_{\mathrm{dB}}(\omega_a) - 3 \tag{53}$$

The result is, of course, exactly the same as above, but expressed in the more convenient form

$$\Delta\omega_{3\mathrm{dB}} = \sqrt{\frac{3}{G_{\mathrm{dB}}(\omega_a) - 3}}\,\Delta\omega_a \tag{54}$$

The bandwidth of a single-pass traveling-wave maser is less than the atomic linewidth $\Delta\omega_a$ for gains greater than 6 dB. But, as shown in Fig. 5-20, the bandwidth decreases only to ∼30 or 40 percent of the atomic linewidth even for fairly large gain values. It is not possible to compare traveling-wave-maser and cavity-maser bandwidths directly

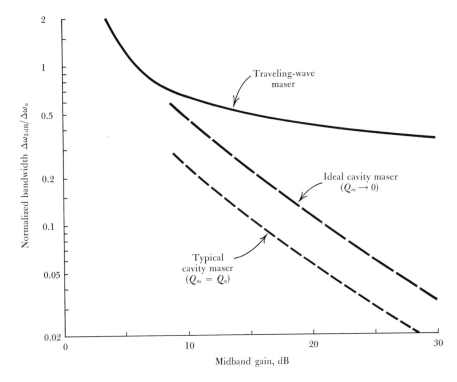

FIG. 5-20 Maser-amplifier 3-dB bandwidth relative to atomic linewidth, as a function of midband power gain in decibels. The substantial superiority of the traveling-wave maser over the cavity maser is evident, particularly at higher gain values.

because the cavity bandwidth depends on both Q_m and Q_a, while the traveling-wave bandwidth depends only on Q_a. Figure 5-20 does show, however, the much smaller bandwidths obtained at high gain both for an optimum cavity maser, in which $Q_m \to 0$, and for a typical cavity, in which $Q_m = Q_a$ (about the best that is usually achieved in practice).

■ As noted earlier, the most general way of defining the quality factor Q of any element is   MASER Q_m

$$Q = \frac{\omega \times \text{average signal energy stored in the element}}{\text{average signal power dissipated (or generated) in the element}} \qquad (55)$$

In a traveling-wave maser we may consider as an *element* any small increment of length dz along the propagation direction in the maser medium. Now, if a traveling wave grows in amplitude with distance in the form $|\tilde{U}(z)| \propto e^{+\alpha_m z}$, then the power associated with that wave grows with distance as $P(z) \propto |\tilde{U}(z)|^2 \propto e^{+2\alpha_m z}$. Therefore the net power $dP(z)$ added to the wave within the small increment of length dz must be

$$dP(z) = 2\alpha_m P(z)\, dz \qquad (56)$$

At the same time, the stored energy $W(z)$ per unit length associated with any propagating wave is given by the power in the wave divided by the group velocity for that wave (see Appendix D). For plane waves in simple dielectric media the group and phase velocities are equal, and so the net signal energy $dW(z)$ stored in the length increment dz is

$$dW(z) = \frac{P(z)}{v_\phi}\, dz \qquad (57)$$

The maser Q_m of this incremental length of maser material can then be written as

$$Q_m = \frac{\omega \times \text{signal energy stored in length } dz}{\text{signal-energy gain in length } dz \text{ due to maser action}}$$

$$= \frac{\omega \, dW(z)}{dP(z)} = \frac{\omega}{2\alpha_m v_\phi} \tag{58}$$

or

$$\alpha_m = \frac{\omega}{2Q_m v_\phi} \tag{59}$$

Comparison with our earlier result $\alpha_m = (\omega'/2v_\phi)\chi''$ then leads to the identification

$$Q_m = \frac{1}{\chi''} \tag{60}$$

This is the same result derived several times in earlier chapters. Its physical interpretation is that power absorption, or maser emission, on an atomic transition requires a certain amount of stored energy in the signal fields that produce the absorption or emission. The maser Q_m measures essentially the ratio of the reactive signal energy stored to the signal power dissipated, or the amplification per cycle in each little increment dz of the wave-propagating system.

The χ'' value to use in determining Q_m should presumably be the peak or midband value χ_0'', so that a lorentzian susceptibility can equally well be written as

$$\tilde{\chi}(\omega) = j \frac{1}{Q_m} \frac{1}{1 + 2j(\omega - \omega_a)/\Delta\omega_a} \tag{61}$$

The midband voltage gain of a traveling-wave maser (of the plane-wave type) may then be written as

$$g_0 = \exp\left(\frac{\omega_a L}{2Q_m v_\phi}\right) \tag{62}$$

or, in decibels,

$$G_{\text{dB}}(\omega_a) = 8.68 \ln g_0 = \frac{4.34\omega_a L}{Q_m v_\phi} \tag{63}$$

We will see this form, or a modification of it, again in the discussion of microwave solid-state masers in Chap. 7.

5-5 TRAVELING-WAVE MASER AMPLIFICATION: REGENERATIVE TRAVELING-WAVE AMPLIFIERS

Some strong optical maser transitions have sufficiently high gain per unit length to provide useful single-pass amplification within a practical and convenient length. For example, a strongly pumped ruby rod can provide as much as several decibels of amplification per centimeter of length at the ruby laser wavelength of 6943 Å. The 5145-Å laser transition in a pulsed mercury (Hg^+) discharge, and the 3.39-μ and 3.51-μ cw laser transitions in He-Ne and He-Xe discharges, are also noted for their extremely high gains per unit length (≥ 100 dB/m in some cases).

Many other laser transitions, however, provide only very small gains per unit length; for example, only ~20 percent power gain (~2 dB) per meter in the 6328-Å He-Ne visible laser transition. For useful laser amplification to be obtained on such transitions within a practical length, the net gain must be increased by the use of positive feedback or regeneration. We will analyze in this section the gain and bandwidth characteristics that result when regenerative feedback is applied to a traveling-wave maser amplifier. As we will see, when the gain of a traveling-wave amplifier is strongly enhanced by regenerative feedback, the resulting amplifier acquires essentially the same gain-bandwidth characteristics and limitations as a cavity maser amplifier. In fact, a traveling-wave amplifier provided with strong regeneration or positive feedback essentially *becomes* a cavity type of amplifier.

■ Figure 5-21a shows the type of physical system we are discussing: an extended maser medium (such as a solid-state laser rod or a gas laser tube) placed between two partially reflecting mirrors, with a quasi-plane wave propagating through the system and reflecting back and forth between the mirrors. This can be simplified to the form of Fig. 5-21b if we assume that essentially all the space between the mirrors is filled with maser material. The mirrors themselves may be metal films (silver, aluminum, gold) evaporated on glass or directly on the laser rod, or they may be multilayer dielectric films that can have higher reflectivities and much lower absorption losses than metal films.

We will analyze this system as a transmission-type maser amplifier, in which the signal to be amplified is directed into one end of the system and the amplified output emerges from the opposite end. It is equally possible to operate this system as a reflection-type amplifier, using the reflected and amplified signal from the input end in the manner of Sec. 5-3. Appropriate circulator devices (Faraday rotators) to separate the input and reflected output signals are available at optical frequencies. However, for convenience and simplicity most optical amplifiers are operated as transmission-type, or two-port, devices rather than as reflection-type, or one-port, devices. The basic properties of reflection and transmission operation are very similar in any event.

PHYSICAL CONFIGURATION AND BASIC RELATIONS

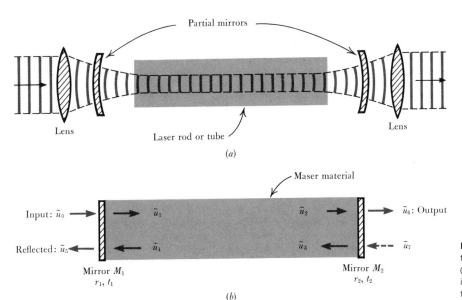

FIG. 5-21 (a) A regenerative traveling-wave amplifier, and (b) diagram of the various waves in a simplified analytical model of the amplifier.

Using the notation of Fig. 5-21b, suppose that an incident wave $\tilde{u}_0$ at the amplifier input causes a series of transmitted and reflected waves $\tilde{u}_1, \tilde{u}_2, \ldots, \tilde{u}_6$ at each end of the laser, as shown. In particular, the net reflected wave at the input is $\tilde{u}_5$, and the net transmitted wave at the output is $\tilde{u}_6$. We assume that there is no input wave $\tilde{u}_7$ at the output end of the amplifier. The basic problem is to calculate the net gain from the input wave $\tilde{u}_0$ to the output wave $\tilde{u}_6$.

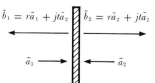

$$\tilde{b}_1 = r\tilde{a}_1 + jt\tilde{a}_2 \qquad \tilde{b}_2 = r\tilde{a}_2 + jt\tilde{a}_2$$

$$\tilde{a}_1 \longrightarrow \qquad \longleftarrow \tilde{a}_2$$

FIG. 5-22 Reflection and transmission coefficients for a lossless partially transmitting mirror. (From S. Ramo, J. R. Whinnery and T. Van Duzer, *Fields and Waves in Communication Electronics*, pp. 604–609, Wiley, New York, 1965.)

For simplicity let us suppose that the mirrors are lossless partially transmitting mirrors, and that we can neglect any ohmic or scattering losses α_0 in the maser medium itself (this is analogous to neglecting internal cavity losses in Sec. 5-3). Each end mirror then has an amplitude-reflection (or voltage-reflection) coefficient r_1 or r_2 and a transmission coefficient jt_1 or jt_2, as shown in Fig. 5-22. For lossless mirrors these satisfy the relationships $|r_1|^2 + |t_1|^2 = |r_2|^2 + |t_2|^2 = 1$. Although in general r and t are complex quantities, it is always possible to choose a reference plane in the mirror such that both r and t are purely real. The factor of j before the transmission coefficient then represents an additional $90°$ phase shift relative to the reflection coefficient.[1]

The mirrors thus impose the following relationships between the various waves in Fig. 5-21b:

$$\tilde{u}_1 = jt_1\tilde{u}_0 + r_1\tilde{u}_4$$
$$\tilde{u}_3 = r_2\tilde{u}_2$$
$$\tilde{u}_5 = r_1\tilde{u}_0 + jt_1\tilde{u}_4 \tag{1}$$
$$\tilde{u}_6 = jt_2\tilde{u}_2$$

The wave amplitudes $\tilde{u}_2$ and $\tilde{u}_4$ are simply the wave amplitudes $\tilde{u}_1$ and $\tilde{u}_3$ amplified by a single pass of traveling-wave amplification through the maser medium, so that

$$\frac{\tilde{u}_4}{\tilde{u}_3} = \frac{\tilde{u}_2}{\tilde{u}_1} = \tilde{g}_1(\omega) \tag{2}$$

where $\tilde{g}_1(\omega)$ is the complex single-pass traveling-wave voltage gain

$$\tilde{g}_1(\omega) = \exp\left[-j\,\frac{n_0\omega L}{c} - j\,\frac{n_0\omega L}{2c}\,\tilde{\chi}(\omega) \right] \tag{3}$$

as derived in the preceding section. We have used the form $\beta_0 = \omega/v_\phi = n_0\omega/c$ where n_0 is the index of refraction of the maser medium.

MASER-GAIN EXPRESSION ■ The overall transmission gain $\tilde{g}(\omega)$ of this amplifier is, by definition,

$$\tilde{g}(\omega) \equiv \frac{\text{output-signal wave}}{\text{input-signal wave}} = \frac{\tilde{u}_6}{\tilde{u}_0} \tag{4}$$

We have given above a total of six relations among seven unknown wave amplitudes. It is a matter of straightforward algebra to eliminate unwanted amplitudes and obtain the desired result,

$$\tilde{g}(\omega) = \frac{\tilde{u}_6}{\tilde{u}_0} = \frac{-t_1 t_2 \tilde{g}_1(\omega)}{1 - r_1 r_2 \tilde{g}_1{}^2(\omega)} \tag{5}$$

This important result expresses the overall, or regenerative, transmission gain $\tilde{g}(\omega)$ of

---

[1] A proof that this additional phase shift is unavoidable in a lossless mirror is given in Appendix C.

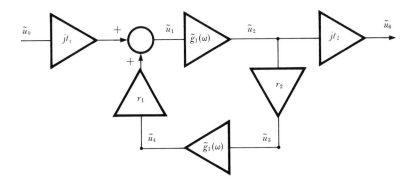

FIG. 5-23 A block diagram of the signals in the regenerative traveling-wave amplifier of Fig. 5-21b, showing the direct correspondence to a regenerative feedback loop.

the amplifier in terms of the mirror coefficients and the single-pass, or nonregenerative, traveling-wave gain $\tilde{g}_1(\omega)$ of the maser medium.

This overall gain expression has a straightforward but important interpretation in feedback-amplifier terms. If the reflected wave $\tilde{u}_3$ at the output mirror is temporarily blocked, the net forward amplifier gain due to the signal transmission through the two mirrors plus one pass through the maser medium is $jt_1jt_2\tilde{g}_1(\omega) = -t_1t_2\tilde{g}_1(\omega)$. But the reflection r_2 at the output mirror, followed by traveling-wave gain $\tilde{g}_1(\omega)$ in the reverse direction and reflection r_1 back again from the input mirror, has exactly the same effect as providing a positive feedback path with net reverse gain $\beta = r_1r_2\tilde{g}_1(\omega)$. Figure 5-23 shows this equivalent feedback system in block-diagram form, making it clear that only the forward gain $A = \tilde{g}_1(\omega)$ is inside the feedback loop, while the two mirror transmission factors jt_1 and jt_2 are outside the loop on either end.

For a feedback system with forward gain A and positive feedback β, the well-known overall gain expression is $\tilde{g} = A/(1 - A\beta)$. If we use the values given above in this expression and add on the mirror transmission factors at each end, we can immediately write down the general gain expression (5) from inspection of the equivalent feedback system in Fig. 5-23. Note that the open-loop gain of the system is $A\beta = r_1r_2\tilde{g}_1{}^2(\omega)$, where the single-pass gain $\tilde{g}_1(\omega)$ appears squared because a wave is amplified by $\tilde{g}_1(\omega)$ twice in going completely around the loop.

Let us now examine the typical behavior of the overall regenerative amplifier gain. Figure 5-24 shows a typical plot of the overall gain versus frequency within the atomic linewidth for a case in which the single-pass midband voltage gain is chosen to be $|\tilde{g}_1(\omega a)| = 1.4$ and the end-mirror reflectivities are increased in steps from zero to successively larger values. Two points are immediately apparent: first, the overall regenerative gain $\tilde{g}(\omega)$ at certain frequencies within the atomic linewidth can become very much larger than the single-pass $\tilde{g}_1(\omega)$ of the maser medium itself; second, these high-gain frequencies seem to occur in narrow but regularly spaced frequency bands within the atomic linewidth.

To readers familiar with feedback systems, the causes of this behavior may be fairly obvious. The first major point is that even though the single-pass forward gain $\tilde{g}_1(\omega)$ by itself may be small, large net gain $\tilde{g}(\omega)$ can still be obtained in a positive feedback system such as that in Fig. 5-23 if the amount of feedback is adjusted so that the loop gain is nearly unity—that is, if the mirror reflections and the single-pass gain are adjusted so that $r_1r_2\tilde{g}_1{}^2(\omega) \sim 1$, but still less than unity for stability. In other words, for high gain the system must be operated with positive feedback sufficient to place it close to the boundary of instability and oscillation, but still in the stable regime. (Of

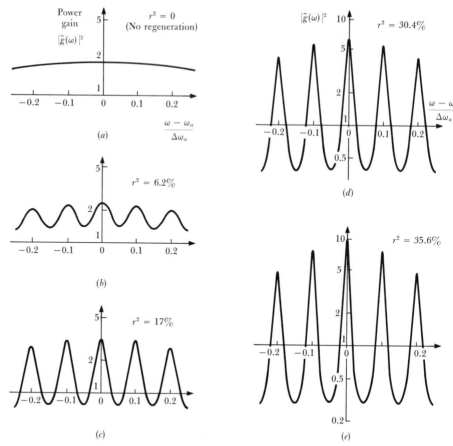

FIG. 5-24 Examples of gain $G(\omega)$ versus frequency in a regenerative traveling-wave amplifier for a fixed value of single-pass amplifier gain $g_1(\omega)$ and increasing values of the mirror reflectivity r.

course, if the single-pass gain by itself were already large, $|\tilde{g}_1(\omega)| \gg 1$, there would be no need for the mirrors or the resulting feedback effects; in fact, feedback would probably be undesirable.)

A second crucial property of this system is that the single-pass gain $\tilde{g}_1(\omega)$ is a complex number, with a strongly frequency-dependent phase angle. The largest part of this phase variation comes from the free-space-propagation factor, that is, $\tilde{g}_1(\omega) \sim e^{-jn_0\omega L/c}$, so that the phase angle increases approximately linearly with frequency, through many complete cycles of 2π variation in most cases. As a result, the overall phase shift around the feedback loop varies periodically between *regenerative* or *positive* feedback, in which $r_1 r_2 \tilde{g}_1{}^2(\omega) \approx 1$, leading to strong gain enhancement, and *degenerative* or *negative* feedback, in which $r_1 r_2 \tilde{g}_1{}^2(\omega) \approx -1$, leading to gain reduction. Hence there will be only certain periodically spaced frequencies at which the feedback is regenerative and the overall gain is high, exactly as we see in Fig. 5-24.

AXIAL-MODE FREQUENCIES   ■ Let us now examine these high-gain regions in more detail. As noted above, the main contribution to the overall phase shift of $\tilde{g}_1(\omega)$ comes from the $n_0\omega L/c$ term, which is doubled for one complete pass around the loop (round-trip gain = $\tilde{g}_1{}^2$). The feedback will be regenerative and the overall gain high only for frequencies at which this phase factor is (nearly) an integer multiple of 2π, that is, those frequencies $\omega \approx \omega_q$, where we define the equally spaced frequencies ω_q, for q an integer, by

$$\frac{2n_0\omega_q L}{c} = q2\pi \tag{6}$$

or

$$f_q = \frac{\omega_q}{2\pi} = q\frac{c}{2n_0 L} \tag{7}$$

These frequencies are commonly called the *axial-mode frequencies* or *axial-mode resonances* of the laser structure. The qth axial mode occurs at the frequency for which the spacing between mirrors is exactly q half-wavelengths. If $\lambda_q \equiv c/f_q$ is the free-space wavelength corresponding to frequency f_q, the associated axial-mode integer q is

$$q = \frac{2n_0 L}{\lambda_q} \tag{8}$$

Since the cavity length L in real devices may range from a few centimeters to a few meters, while λ_q for an optical frequency is in the range of $\sim 1\mu = 10^{-4}$ cm $= 10^{-6}$ m, typical q values for laser resonators are

$$q \sim 10^4 \text{ to } 10^6 \tag{9}$$

There are this many half-wavelengths in the standing wave between the mirrors at an axial-mode resonance.

Another axial-mode gain peak occurs each time the axial-mode number q increases by one. The frequency spacing between two adjacent axial modes is given by

$$\Delta f_{\text{axial}} \equiv f_{q+1} - f_q = \frac{c}{2n_0 L} \tag{10}$$

Note that this spacing is independent of the center frequency at which the laser operates but varies inversely with resonator length. Typical values for the axial-mode spacing are

$$\Delta f_{\text{axial}} \approx \begin{cases} 150 \text{ MHz} & \text{for } L = 1 \text{ m, } n_0 = 1 \\ 2000 \text{ MHz} & \text{for } L = 5 \text{ cm, } n_0 = 1.67 \end{cases} \tag{11}$$

In many, if not most, practical lasers there are several of these axial-mode frequencies (anywhere from three to several hundred) lying within the atomic linewidth of the laser transition. Thus in regenerative laser operation these lasers will exhibit a series of high-gain resonance peaks at or very close to each axial-mode frequency. If the regeneration is increased to the point of oscillation, the laser will generally be able to oscillate simultaneously in several of these axial modes. The general behavior of the axial-mode resonances is summarized in Fig. 5-25. Note that the centermost axial mode need not be located right at the center of the atomic line, and that the regenerative-gain enhancement is largest for this central mode.

■ The numerator $t_1 t_2 \tilde{g}_1(\omega)$ of the traveling-wave gain expression, although its phase angle may rotate rapidly, still has only a slow magnitude variation with frequency, particularly if the single-pass gain $\tilde{g}_1(\omega)$ is not too large or narrow. However, the denominator $1 - r_1 r_2 \tilde{g}_1^2(\omega)$ is the difference between the constant 1 and the rapidly rotating factor $r_1 r_2 \tilde{g}_1^2(\omega)$, whose magnitude may be nearly unity. Figure 5-26a illus-

GEOMETRIC INTERPRETATION OF REGENERATION

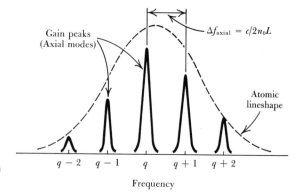

FIG. 5-25 Further illustration of the multiple gain peaks when there are several axial modes lying within the atomic linewidth.

trates this denominator expression in the complex plane. The vector representing $-r_1 r_2 \tilde{g}_1^2(\omega)$ is pivoted at the point $(1,0)$ and rotates rapidly about it because of the $e^{-jn_0\omega L/c}$ factor. The vector shown dashed then represents $1 - r_1 r_2 \tilde{g}_1^2(\omega)$, so that its length is inversely proportional to the overall gain magnitude. Each time the tip of the $r_1 r_2 \tilde{g}_1^2(\omega)$ sweeps close to the origin, the gain becomes very high, and another axial-mode resonance is generated.

The vector $-r_1 r_2 \tilde{g}_1^2(\omega)$ sweeps through many cycles because of the $e^{-jn_0\omega L/c}$ dependence. At the same time it decreases more slowly in length as ω goes away from line center because of the $e^{2\alpha_m(\omega)L}$ dependence. Figure 5-26b shows geometrically how the successive axial-mode resonances are generated, and how the gain shrinks with increasing q indices (away from line center) because the crossings are successively farther from the origin.

FREQUENCY PULLING OF THE AXIAL MODES ■ The centers of the axial-mode gain peaks will actually not be located exactly at the unperturbed axial-mode frequencies, because of pulling effects caused by the phase-

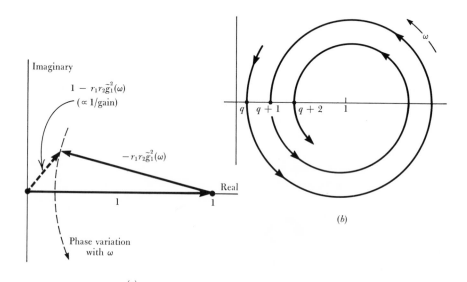

FIG. 5-26 Geometrical interpretation of the gain expression for axial-mode resonances (a) near one resonance and (b) for several successive resonances.

shift contribution of the laser transition itself. To see this, let us now assume that that atomic lineshape is lorentzian, so that

$$\tilde{\chi}(\omega) = j\frac{1}{Q_m}\frac{1}{1 + 2j(\omega - \omega_a)/\Delta\omega_a} \tag{12}$$

The single-pass maser gain will then take the form

$$\tilde{g}_1(\omega) = \exp\left[\alpha_m(\omega)L\right]\exp\left[-j\frac{n_0\omega L}{c} - j\,\Delta\beta_m(\omega)L\right] \tag{13}$$

where the single-pass gain and added-phase-shift coefficients are given by

$$\alpha_m(\omega) = \frac{n_0\omega}{2Q_mc}\frac{1}{1 + [2(\omega - \omega_a)/\Delta\omega_a]^2} \tag{14}$$

and

$$\Delta\beta_m(\omega) = \frac{n_0\omega}{2Q_mc}\frac{2(\omega - \omega_a)/\Delta\omega_a}{1 + [2(\omega - \omega_a)/\Delta\omega_a]^2} = \alpha_m(\omega)\frac{2(\omega - \omega_a)}{\Delta\omega_a} \tag{15}$$

We will also manipulate the $n_0\omega L/c$ term in (13) into the form

$$\frac{n_0\omega L}{c} = \frac{n_0\omega_q L}{c}\left(1 + \frac{\omega - \omega_q}{\omega_q}\right) = q\pi\left(1 + \frac{\omega - \omega_q}{\omega_q}\right) \tag{16}$$

where ω_q is any one of the axial-mode frequencies.

The loop gain $r_1r_2\tilde{g}_1{}^2(\omega)$ of the overall system can now be written

$$r_1r_2\tilde{g}_1{}^2(\omega) = r_1r_2\exp\left[2\alpha_m(\omega)L\right]\cdot$$

$$\exp\left\{-j\left[q2\pi + \frac{2n_0L}{c}(\omega - \omega_q) + \frac{4\alpha_m(\omega)L}{\Delta\omega_a}(\omega - \omega_q)\right]\right\} \tag{17}$$

The $q2\pi$ factor in the second exponent is immaterial, and with some minor algebraic manipulations this loop gain can be put into the form

$$r_1r_2\tilde{g}_1{}^2(\omega) = r_1r_2\exp\left[2\alpha_m(\omega)L\right]\exp\left\{-2j\left[\frac{n_0L}{c} + \frac{2\alpha_m(\omega)L}{\Delta\omega_a}\right](\omega - \omega_q')\right\} \tag{18}$$

This result makes it clear that the phase of the loop gain becomes a multiple of 2π, and hence the regenerative gain becomes maximum, not at ω_q, but at a slightly shifted or *pulled axial-mode frequency* ω_q', given by

$$\omega_q' = \frac{(n_0L/c)\omega_q + [2\alpha_m(\omega)L/\Delta\omega_a]\omega_a}{n_0L/c + 2\alpha_m(\omega)L/\Delta\omega_a} \tag{19}$$

With some minor manipulation this takes the form

$$\omega_q' = \frac{Q_m\omega_q + Q_a\omega_a}{Q_m + Q_a} \tag{20}$$

as we will see in more detail in Chap. 10. Thus in general the gain resonance located close to the axial-mode frequency ω_q in Fig. 5-25 will be pulled slightly away from ω_q toward the atomic line center ω_a, ending up at the shifted value ω_q' given by (20). This slight pulling of the axial-mode frequency is basically a result of the added phase shift $\Delta\beta_m L$ caused by the reactive $\chi'(\omega)$ portion of the atomic susceptibility.

■ The case of particular interest is the highly regenerative traveling-wave amplifier, in which the single-pass gain is very little greater than unity and the regenerative feedback plays a dominant role. In this case the useful amplifier bandwidth, i.e., the bandwidth of any single gain peak in Fig. 5-24 or 5-25, turns out to be much narrower than the atomic linewidth. In fact, the behavior of each separate axial-mode resonance becomes exactly like the behavior of a resonant-cavity maser amplifier, and the gain expression also becomes, to a very good approximation, the same as the gain expression for a cavity maser. To all intents and purposes, the highly regenerative traveling-wave maser *becomes* a cavity maser, as we will now explore in more detail.

We will find that in the highly regenerative case the amplification bandwidth of each of the resonances is determined much more by the frequency variation of the feedback phase angle than by the frequency variation of the single-pass gain magnitude. The single-pass gain coefficient $\alpha_m(\omega)$ is a rather slowly varying function of frequency, with a linewidth $\Delta\omega_a$ which is usually large compared to the axial-mode widths. Thus in the highly regenerative case it is permissible in evaluating the gain, the bandwidth, and the frequency-pulling factor for each individual ω_q axial mode to assume that within that mode resonance $\alpha_m(\omega)$ has the constant value

$$\alpha_m(\omega) \approx \alpha_m(\omega_q) \equiv \alpha_{mq} \qquad \omega \approx \omega_q \tag{21}$$

The small variation in $\alpha_m(\omega)$ across the narrow gain peak is not significant.

If the single-pass gain is very little greater than unity, so that $\alpha_{mq}L \ll 1$, and the width of the axial-mode gain peak is narrow compared to the axial-mode spacing $c/2n_0L$, then the single-pass gain may be expanded in the following fashion:

$$\tilde{g}_1(\omega) = \exp\left[\alpha_m(\omega)L - j\left(\frac{n_0L}{c} + \frac{2\alpha_mL}{\Delta\omega_a}\right)(\omega - \omega_q')\right]$$

$$\approx 1 + \alpha_{mq}L - j\left(\frac{n_0L}{c} + \frac{2\alpha_{mq}L}{\Delta\omega_a}\right)(\omega - \omega_q') \tag{22}$$

and also

$$\tilde{g}_1^2 \approx 1 + 2\alpha_{mq}L - 2j\left(\frac{n_0L}{c} + \frac{2\alpha_{mq}L}{\Delta\omega_a}\right)(\omega - \omega_q') \qquad \omega \approx \omega_q \approx \omega_q' \tag{23}$$

If we use this approximation in the denominator of the expression for overall amplifier gain, and if we also note that the $\tilde{g}_1(\omega)$ in the numerator may as well be approximated by unity, then the overall gain becomes

$$\tilde{g}(\omega) = \frac{-t_1t_2}{1 - r_1r_2[1 + 2\alpha_{mq}L - 2j(n_0L/c + 2\alpha_{mq}L/\Delta\omega_a)](\omega - \omega_q')} \tag{24}$$

■ To convert the overall-gain expression into a more convenient form we need some Q parameters and loss parameters for the highly regenerative case. In this case the reflectivities of the two end mirrors must be close to unity to provide nearly unity feedback, since the single-pass forward gain is assumed to be only slightly greater than unity. It has become customary to write the mirror reflectivities in the form

$$r_1^2 \equiv 1 - \delta_1 \qquad r_2^2 \equiv 1 - \delta_2 \qquad \delta_1, \delta_2 \ll 1 \tag{25}$$

Since r_1^2 and r_2^2 are the power reflectivities of the mirrors, the quantities δ_1 and δ_2 give the fractional power losses per reflection off the mirrors. The mirror reflection and transmission coefficients may then be written

$$r_1 = \sqrt{1 - \delta_1} \approx 1 - \tfrac{1}{2}\delta_1 \qquad t_1 = \sqrt{1 - r_1^2} = \delta_1^{1/2}$$
$$r_2 = \sqrt{1 - \delta_2} \approx 1 - \tfrac{1}{2}\delta_2 \qquad t_2 = \sqrt{1 - r_2^2} = \delta_2^{1/2} \qquad (26)$$

The fractional power losses δ_1 and δ_2 may be on the order of a few percent per bounce, perhaps 10 to 20 percent per bounce at most, in practical laser devices. The losses δ_1 and δ_2 represent primarily external coupling out of the laser via the mirror transmission.[1] Therefore we can define an external coupling Q_e for this case, exactly as in the earlier resonant-cavity case. To find an expression for the external Q_e, consider a pair of highly reflective mirrors facing each other so as to form an optical resonator or cavity of length L, as in Fig. 5-21. Suppose that the waves traveling back and forth between the two mirrors have a total energy density or stored energy W_s' per unit length between the mirrors, so that the total stored energy between the two mirrors is $W_s'L$. Now, half of this stored energy may be associated with the wave in each direction and may be viewed as moving in that direction with velocity c/n_0. Since the power flow in a traveling wave is given by the stored energy density times the velocity of propagation, the average power striking each end mirror is $(W_s'/2)(c/n_0)$. Of this, a fraction r_i^2 is reflected and a fraction $\delta_i = 1 - r_i^2$ is transmitted through to the outside and lost from the resonator. Combining the power losses from both ends, we are led to define an external Q_e for this optical resonator system as

$$Q_e = \frac{\omega \times \text{total stored energy in the resonator}}{\text{average power loss due to external coupling}}$$

$$= \frac{\omega \times W_s'L}{(\delta_1 + \delta_2)(W_s'/2)(c/n_0)} = \frac{n_0\omega L}{c}\frac{1}{\tfrac{1}{2}(\delta_1 + \delta_2)} \qquad (27)$$

This total external Q_e due to both end mirrors can be divided into separate external Q_e factors for the two ends individually by writing

$$Q_{e1} = \frac{2n_0\omega L}{c}\frac{1}{\delta_1} \qquad Q_{e2} = \frac{2n_0\omega L}{c}\frac{1}{\delta_2} \qquad (28)$$

These Q terms then combine according to the usual rule for combining Q values,

$$\frac{1}{Q_e} = \frac{1}{Q_{e1}} + \frac{1}{Q_{e2}} \qquad (29)$$

The external Q_e terms defined in this fashion have exactly the same significance for the optical resonator as do the external Q_e terms defined for more conventional resonant circuits in Sec. 5-2. The small fractional transmission through the end mirror provides the external coupling to the optical cavity.[2]

Now, the midband single-pass gain coefficient $\alpha_m(\omega_a)$ and the midband maser Q_m (at the center of the atomic line) are related by

[1] If the mirrors are not perfectly lossless, then δ_1 and δ_2 will also include some power absorption in the mirrors themselves.

[2] In other cases it is also possible to use small holes in the end mirrors, partially reflecting or scattering elements located between the mirrors, and various other practical techniques to couple to an optical cavity. The above expressions will still apply so long as the power coupled out per bounce is represented by the symbol δ. Note that if partially transmitting end mirrors are used, there is no simple way of adjusting the cavity external coupling during operation other than by replacing the mirrors with others of different value.

$$\alpha_m(\omega_a) = \frac{n_0\omega_a}{2Q_mc} \tag{30}$$

The gain coefficient α_{mq} for any axial mode located away from the atomic line center is reduced by the lorentzian lineshape factor. It seems reasonable to define an *effective maser Q_m*, call it Q_{mq}, for the qth axial mode or gain peak by writing

$$Q_{mq} = \frac{n_0\omega_a}{2\alpha_{mq}c} = Q_m(\omega_a)\left\{1 + \left[\frac{2(\omega_q' - \omega_a)}{\Delta\omega_a}\right]^2\right\} \tag{31}$$

In other words, the effective maser Q_m is optimum (lowest) for an axial mode located exactly at line center, $\omega_q = \omega_a$, and deteriorates (becomes larger) for axial modes farther out from line center, in accordance with the above expression.

CAVITY BEHAVIOR OF
REGENERATIVE
TRAVELING-WAVE AMPLIFIERS

■ Using the Q parameters we have just defined, we can write the overall gain expression for the highly regenerative traveling-wave amplifier near one axial mode resonance in the form

$$\tilde{g}(\omega) = \frac{-2(\delta_1\delta_2)^{1/2}}{(\delta_1 + \delta_2 - 4\alpha_{mq}L) + j(4n_0L/c)(1 + 2\alpha_{mq}c/n_0\,\Delta\omega_a)(\omega - \omega_q')}$$

$$= -\frac{(Q_{e1}Q_{e2})^{1/2}}{Q_{e1} + Q_{e2}} \frac{2Q_{mq}}{(Q_{mq} - Q_e) + 2j[Q_e(Q_{mq} + Q_a)](\omega - \omega_q')/\omega_q'} \tag{32}$$

This begins to look very much like a simple resonant-circuit type of response—in fact very much like the gain expression for the simple lumped-resonant-circuit case of Eq. (20) in Sec. 5-3. This expression can be written in the form

$$\tilde{g}(\omega) = g_{0q}\frac{1}{1 + 2jQ_{\text{total}}(\omega - \omega_q')/\omega_q'} \tag{33}$$

where the midband gain for the qth axial-mode resonance is

$$g_{0q} = -\frac{(Q_{e1}Q_{e2})^{1/2}}{Q_{e1} + Q_{e2}} \frac{2Q_{mq}}{Q_{mq} - Q_e} \tag{34}$$

and the total Q for the same gain peak is given by

$$\frac{1}{Q_{\text{total}}} = \frac{Q_{mq}}{Q_{mq} + Q_a}\left(\frac{1}{Q_e} - \frac{1}{Q_{mq}}\right) \tag{35}$$

These results are also very much like the resonant-cavity expressions (21), (22), and (25) in Sec. 5-3.

The minus sign in the definition of g_0 merely represents a constant added phase shift of one-half cycle, or an added distance of $\lambda/2$ in the equivalent overall length of the amplifier. It arises from the particular choice of mirror reference planes used in our analysis, has no practical significance, and can be ignored. The overall gain obviously becomes unstable, $g_0 \to \infty$, as $Q_e \to Q_{mq}$. To keep the amplifier from oscillating there must be a certain minimum total external loading Q_e due to the two end mirrors combined, so that $Q_e < Q_{mq}$. At the same time, high gain requires that $Q_e \approx Q_{mq}$, the usual operation on the margin of instability.

The first term in the definition of g_0, Eq. (34), depends on how the required total external loading Q_e is distributed between the input and output mirrors. It has the range

$$\frac{(Q_{e1}Q_{e2})^{1/2}}{Q_{e1} + Q_{e2}} = \frac{(\delta_1\delta_2)^{1/2}}{\delta_1 + \delta_2} \leq \frac{1}{2} \tag{36}$$

The optimum value of $\frac{1}{2}$ for this factor is obtained when the required total loading is distributed equally between the input and output mirrors, i.e., when there are identical mirrors at both ends.

■ If we assume for simplicity equal coupling at each end, the total amplifier Q can be written in terms of the midband gain as

GAIN-BANDWIDTH PRODUCT

$$Q_{\text{total}} = (g_{0q} - 1)(Q_{mq} + Q_a) \tag{37}$$

Just as in the lumped-circuit case, when the midband gain becomes very large, the total amplifier Q becomes correspondingly large and the amplifier bandwidth correspondingly narrow. The amplifier bandwidth is then

$$\Delta f_{3dB} = \frac{f_q}{Q_{\text{total}}} = \frac{1}{g_0 - 1}\frac{f_q}{Q_{mq} + Q_a} \tag{38}$$

and the axial-mode gain peak obviously has a fixed voltage-gain–bandwidth product given by

$$g_{0q}\,\Delta f_{3dB} \approx (g_{0q} - 1)\,\Delta f_{3dB} = \frac{f_q}{Q_{mq} + Q_a} \tag{39}$$

It is easily verified that any distribution of input-output coupling other than the balanced distribution $\delta_1 = \delta_2$ makes the gain-bandwidth product worse.

■ The gain and bandwidth expressions we have just obtained for the regenerative traveling-wave amplifier have very nearly the same forms as the corresponding expressions for a simple resonant-cavity type of amplifier derived in Sec. 5-3. The differences between the two are, in fact, due entirely to the fact that we are considering here a *two-port*, or *transmission-type*, *amplifier*, whereas in Sec. 5-3 we considered a *one-port*, or *reflection-type*, *amplifier*. A lumped-circuit two-port cavity amplifier would, in fact, lead to exactly the same gain expressions as obtained here (see Prob. 5-6).

CAVITY PROPERTIES

To put this another way, the strongly regenerative traveling-wave amplifier is in essence a cavity maser—or rather, each axial-mode gain peak of the traveling-wave amplifier is a separate cavity amplifier, with resonance frequency ω_q', maser $Q_m = Q_{mq}$, and external couplings Q_{e1} and Q_{e2}. In exact correspondence to the cavity case, the regenerative traveling-wave amplifier achieves high gain only by operating on the verge of oscillation. The resulting amplification passbands have the same limited bandwidth and fixed gain-bandwidth product as in the cavity case. The one practical difference is that in the optical traveling wave case, there may be several such amplification passbands or axial-mode gain peaks within a single atomic linewidth. (Investigation will show, however, that in general, if the centermost axial mode is set to have a reasonable peak gain, then the adjacent axial modes will all have substantially lower peak gains. Hence only the centermost axial mode is likely to be useful.)

Since a regenerative traveling-wave amplifier has exactly the same form of frequency response near any of its resonant modes as does a simple lumped resonant circuit, we may simply replace the traveling-wave system by the lumped equivalent resonant circuit for purposes of analysis, taking care to make appropriate identification of the system parameters. That is, an optical-frequency axial mode plus the inverted atomic system in a laser may be replaced, for purposes of analysis, by a simple lumped equivalent circuit such as Fig. 5-9 or 5-11, provided only that the lumped circuit has the same values of Q_{mq}, Q_e, Q_a, ω_a, and ω_q' as does the real laser mode. This justifies our many earlier statements concerning the wide applicability of simple lumped-circuit models, as well as the numerous uses we will make of these models in later chapters.

The expressions for Q_{total} and for the gain-bandwidth product in this section differ by a factor of 2 from the corresponding expression in Sec. 5-3. This has nothing to do with traveling-wave versus lumped models, but simply represents the general result that the gain-bandwidth performance of a transmission-type amplifier, even with optimum input-output coupling, is only half as good as that of a reflection-type amplifier. In essence, this is because the transmission-type amplifier provides not only transmission gain from input to output, but also a simultaneous reflection gain at the input end, which represents wasted energy in transmission operation.

MORE ON Q DEFINITIONS ■ If a resonant traveling-wave system is essentially a cavity, then the various Q values associated with this cavity are of considerable interest. The different Q expressions for an optical cavity can all be expressed in a similar way, as follows. Let δ, with appropriate subscripts, indicate either an average fractional power loss per bounce due to any loss mechanism in the cavity or, alternatively, the fractional power gain per one-way pass down the laser cavity due to the maser-gain mechanism. Then the external and maser Q terms defined in this section can all be cast into a common form. Thus with finite mirror reflectivities there is a fractional loss δ_1 on one pass and a fractional loss δ_2 on the other, or an average fractional loss per pass (half a round trip) of $\delta_e = (\delta_1 + \delta_2)/2$. For a small single-pass maser gain we may write

$$|g_1|^2 = e^{2\alpha_m L} \approx 1 + 2\alpha_m L = 1 + \delta_m$$

where $\delta_m = 2\alpha_m L$ may be interpreted as the average fractional power gain per pass. Both the Q definitions given earlier (Q_e and Q_m) are then equivalent to the general optical cavity Q

$$Q = \frac{n_0 \omega L}{c}\frac{1}{\delta} = \frac{2\pi n_0 L}{\lambda}\frac{1}{\delta} = \frac{q\pi}{\delta} \qquad \delta = \delta_e, \delta_m, \ldots \tag{40}$$

The second and third forms of Q above are particularly interesting. A common intuitive impression seems to be that if a system has, say, $\delta = 0.1$, or 10 percent loss per pass, then the corresponding Q value of that system must be on the order of $Q \approx 1/\delta \approx 10$. This is not the case, however. The Q value is instead approximately π/δ multiplied by the number of half-wavelengths between the mirrors, or q, which is typically a very large number. As a result, a cavity with 10 percent loss per bounce may still have a Q value in the range of 10^5 to 10^7 for optical frequencies. There is indeed 10 percent loss per bounce, but since the cavity is a great many wavelengths long, a bounce requires a great many cycles of the resonant frequency to complete.

PHYSICAL INTERPRETATION OF REGENERATIVE GAIN ■ It is interesting to consider the physical interpretation of the traveling-wave gain results above. For example, the input mirror to a regenerative amplifier may have, say, 98 percent reflectivity (from either side). It may then appear that 98 percent of an incident signal is immediately reflected back from the laser input and wasted, with only 2 percent entering the amplifier to be amplified. However, the high-reflectivity mirrors really permit the energy entering the amplifier to recirculate or reverberate inside the cavity many times, being further amplified on each additional bounce. On each re-verberation this energy also transmits another incremental unit of wave amplitude through both the input and output mirrors. These increments of wave amplitude must then be summed, and it is this coherent reinforcement that constitutes the large gain (in both transmission and reflection) that occurs at resonance. Moreover, the amplifier gain decreases off resonance because after many bounces these increments of wave amplitude no longer add exactly in phase, so that the total wave output decreases in amplitude.

Some practical comments may also be useful. First, as we have already noted, the optical cavity formed by two mirrors has another axial-mode resonance each time q increases by one, or f_q increases by $c/2n_0L$. This frequency spacing is small enough ($c/2L \approx 3$ GHz for $L = 5$ cm, or 150 MHz for $L = 1$ m) that there may often be several axial-mode frequencies within a single atomic linewidth. In this case, each axial mode will operate as essentially a separate cavity resonance, giving the separate resonant-amplification bands shown in Fig. 5-25. But, since the peak overall gain of a single mode depends critically on the magnitude of the single-pass gain $\tilde{g}(\omega)$, which falls off away from the atomic line center, the axial mode at or nearest to the atomic line center will show considerably higher gain than the axial mode farther out on the sides of the atomic line. Hence only this one axial mode is really useful.

As a practical matter, regenerative amplification is not yet extensively used at optical frequencies, in part because of a lack of important applications so far, but also to a large extent because of the difficult tolerances required for the limited performance available. The laser mirrors must be carefully aligned facing each other and the input optical beam carefully matched in direction and curvature to the mirrors for optimum performance. In the absence of continuously variable mirror reflectivities, we must make the critical gain adjustments required for high but stable overall gain by means of careful control of the laser pumping level, often a difficult task. The bandwidths that are then obtained are not large. Consider, for example, an He-Ne 6328-Å laser amplifier 1 m long. The single-pass gain for this length may correspond at most to $2\alpha_m L \approx 0.25$, so that

$$Q_m = \frac{2\pi L}{\lambda}\frac{1}{2\alpha_m L} \sim 4 \times 10^7 \tag{41}$$

The atomic linewidth Q_a is much smaller than this and may be ignored in the gain-bandwidth expression (for this line $\Delta f_a \approx 1.5 \times 10^9$ Hz and $Q_a \approx 2 \times 10^5$). If we ask for 20 dB of overall gain ($g_0 = 10$), the predicted amplifier bandwidth is

$$\Delta f_{3dB} \approx \frac{f_a}{(g_0 - 1)Q_m} \sim 14 \text{ MHz} \tag{42}$$

This is hardly better in absolute terms than a microwave solid-state maser and represents a fractional bandwidth of only five parts in 10^7. Moreover, note that if the optical cavity changes length by an amount δL due to thermal expansion or vibrations, then the center frequency of each axial mode will shift by an amount

$$\frac{\delta f_q'}{f_q'} \approx -\frac{\delta L}{L} \tag{43}$$

If the center frequency of a mode is not to shift by more than the amplifier bandwidth, the mirror spacing must not fluctuate by more than

$$\delta L \approx \frac{L}{f_a} \Delta f_{3\text{dB}} \approx \frac{L}{(g_0 - 1)Q_m} \approx 40 \text{ Å} \tag{44}$$

for $L = 1$ m, $Q_m = 4 \times 10^7$, and $g_0 = 10$.

This is a required mechanical stability of less than one-hundredth of a wavelength of visible light. The thermal-expansion coefficients of most materials give $\delta L/L \approx 10^{-5} \delta T (°\text{C})$. Hence the necessary thermal stability of the laser structure to keep the thermal drift below this value will be

$$\delta T \approx 10^5 \left(\frac{\delta L}{L} \right) \lesssim 4 \times 10^{-4} \text{ °C} \tag{45}$$

These values should indicate some of the practical problems in constructing and using an optical regenerative maser amplifier.

Most of these difficulties arise chiefly from the fact that we must use a very-high-order axial mode (large value of q). If the atomic gain per unit length can be sufficiently high to permit simple straight-through, nonregenerative amplification, the situation becomes much more favorable, and such amplifiers are in fact employed in practical laser applications (such as pulsed ruby laser power amplifiers).

EXPERIMENTAL RESULTS ■ Because of the experimental difficulties in obtaining and measuring stable regenerative gain at optical frequencies, experimental data showing the axial-mode gain resonances are not readily available. However, when a laser is pumped sufficiently far above its oscillation threshold, it tends to oscillate simultaneously at several axial-mode frequencies, and these simultaneous axial-mode outputs can be rather observed by a variety of methods. One particularly convenient indirect method is to observe the axial-mode beats at multiples of the basic frequency interval $c/2n_0 L$ by letting the laser oscillation fall on a photodetector and examining the photodetector output with an rf-spectrum analyzer or receiver. We will not take the time to explore this method, but it provides a simple class demonstration or experiment.

Another way of observing the axial-mode outputs is to use a photodetector preceded by a type of narrowband-scanning optical filter called a *scanning Fabry-Perot interferometer*. Figure 5-27 shows some typical results from this type of experiment. In

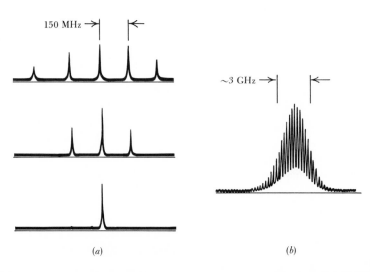

150 MHz →| |←

~3 GHz →| |←

FIG. 5-27 Examples of multiple-axial-mode oscillations in lasers: (a) an He-Ne 6328-Å laser at different levels of excitation and (b) a mode-locked Nd-YAG laser at $\lambda = 1.06$ μ.

(a)

(b)

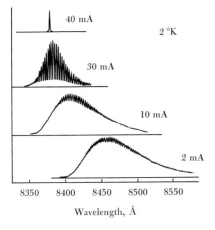

FIG. 5-28 Emission spectrum of a cooled cw GaAs injection laser at various injection current levels, showing the development of the axial-mode structure in the spontaneous emission below threshold and the emergence of one dominant axial mode at oscillation threshold (top curve). The photodetector gain is reduced as the injection current is increased.

Fig. 5-27a the output of a 1-m-long He-Ne laser at 6328 Å is shown as the pump excitation is increased so that the laser oscillates first in one, then in three, and finally in five axial modes spaced by $c/2L = 150$ MHz. Figure 5-27b shows the multiple-axial-mode output of a Nd-YAG laser at $\lambda = 1.06$ μ. The wider atomic linewidth in this laser permits many axial modes within the atomic linewidth.[1]

The semiconductor-diode or injection type of laser has such a short optical cavity (a few thousandths of an inch in typical cases) that the axial-mode separation is very large. The frequency spacing is on the order of 1000 GHz, or a wavelength spacing of several angstroms between modes, which can readily be resolved by an ordinary optical-grating spectrometer. At the same time, the atomic linewidth of this laser is also very large. Figure 5-28 shows the output spectra of a cooled cw GaAs injection laser ($\sim 2°$ K) at different values of the injected dc current. The strong buildup of the axial-mode structure is evident and can be compared directly with Fig. 5-24. In this case, for the currents below 40 mA the output is essentially amplified spontaneous emission or noise rather than coherent oscillation, so that the curves give a roughly accurate picture of the amplifier gain profile. At the highest current value (for which the photodetector gain is very greatly reduced) the laser breaks into oscillation at the centermost axial mode, so that this one mode is then greatly dominant over all the others.

Despite the experimental difficulties described earlier, the gain-bandwidth properties of a highly regenerative traveling-wave laser amplifier have also been verified at least in one careful experiment. In the experiments to be summarized here[2] the problems of mechanical vibration and thermal expansion were minimized by building the tunable laser oscillator and the laser amplifier to be measured side by side in the same rigid mechanical structure, as well as by employing careful construction, shock mounting, and vibration isolation. The He-Ne 6328-Å laser oscillator, which served as the signal source, could be scanned in frequency by changing the cavity length, since one of the mirrors was mounted on a piezoelectric crystal whose thickness could be changed by applying a variable voltage. The He-Ne laser amplifier was approximately

---

[1] The Nd-YAG laser in this case was mode-locked by an intracavity modulator at the axial-mode spacing frequency, which makes the usually rather random array of modes appear particularly clean and orderly in this photograph.

[2] From Ref. 5-2.

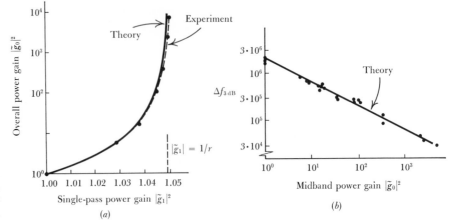

FIG. 5-29 Experimental results from a regenerative traveling-wave He-Ne laser amplifier at 6328 Å: (a) overall regenerative power gain $|g_0|^2$ versus single-pass power gain $|g_1|^2$ and (b) experimental verification of $g_0 \Delta f_{3dB}$ = const.

2 m long and had mirrors of sufficiently high reflectivity ($\sim$95 percent) that a single-pass power gain of $\sim$5 percent was sufficient to bring the amplifier to the verge of threshold. Gain-vs.-frequency curves for the laser amplifier were measured directly at various laser excitation levels by scanning the frequency of the laser oscillator and recording the power output versus frequency from the laser amplifier on an oscilloscope.

A laser amplifier with single-pass power gain $|\tilde{g}_1|^2 = G_1 \approx 1$ and with equal mirror reflectivities $r_1^2 = r_2^2 = R$ at each end should, according to our analysis, have an overall midband power gain $|g_0|^2 = G_0$ given by

$$G_0 = \frac{T^2 G_1}{(1 - RG_1)^2} \approx \frac{(1 - R)^2}{(1 - RG_1)^2} \tag{46}$$

Figure 5-29a is a plot of measured overall regenerative gain G_0 versus single-pass gain G_1 (measured by removing the mirrors from the laser amplifier). At low signal intensities agreement with the theoretical result is excellent. At higher signal intensities the gain is reduced by saturation effects, which have not been included in our analysis thus far. Of course, a major prediction of the analysis is that the regenerative amplifier should have a fixed voltage-gain–bandwidth product given by

$$g_0 \, \Delta f_{3dB} = G_0^{1/2} \, \Delta f_{3dB} \approx \frac{f_a}{Q_e} \qquad Q_a \ll Q_m \tag{47}$$

Figure 5-29b shows an experimental test of this relationship, again demonstrating excellent agreement between theory and experiment. Note that with a length $L \approx 2$ m and a fractional power loss $\delta = 5$ percent per pass, the predicted external Q_e at a wavelength of 0.6 μ (6328 Å) is $Q_e \approx 2 \times 10^8$. The predicted gain-bandwidth product is then $g_0 f_{3dB} = f_0/Q_e \approx 2.5 \times 10^6$, in excellent agreement with the measured value of $\sim$2 MHz shown in Fig. 5-29b.

PROBLEMS

5-1. The plots in Fig. 5-2 of $\chi'(\omega)$ versus $\chi''(\omega)$, with ω as a parameter, appear to be nearly perfect circles. Show that these curves should indeed be circles if the atomic lineshape is exactly lorentzian, and develop expressions for the center and radius of the circle in the $\chi'\chi''$ plane.

5-2. If the signal transition shown in the curves of Fig. 5-2 is treated as a simple two-level transition, what value of negative temperature should be associated with the inverted population of this transition when the pump is on?

5-3. Consider an atomic system with three equally spaced energy levels. Develop expressions for the energy-level populations of the three levels and for the total internal energy of the system as a function of the internal temperature T of the system. Plot the three population differences on the three pairs of energy levels as a function of T (or of the inverse temperature $\beta = 1/kT$) for both positive and negative values of temperature.

5-4. Suppose that you wish to determine experimentally both the cavity quality factor Q_c and the external-coupling quality factor Q_e for a real microwave or optical reflection-type cavity having nonzero internal losses, in the absence of any atomic absorption or maser action. This can be done by measuring the power-reflection coefficient $|\bar{\rho}(\omega)|^2$ in the vicinity of the cavity resonance, i.e., the cavity dip with the atoms removed. Derive expressions that will give Q_e and Q_c in terms of directly measurable parameters of the cavity dip in $|\bar{\rho}(\omega)|^2$.

5-5. Calculate the midband gain, the gain versus frequency, the 3-dB bandwidth, and the gain-bandwidth product for a lumped-circuit reflection-type cavity maser amplifier, taking into account an internal loss conductance G_0 (a finite cavity Q_c) in the cavity equivalent circuit. Use the same general approach and approximations as in the derivation of Sec. 5-3.

5-6. Evaluate the gain, bandwidth, and gain-bandwidth product of a lumped-circuit two-port (transmission-type) cavity maser amplifier. Assume a lossless cavity and represent the input and output coupling lines by transmission lines of characteristic admittance G_{e1} and G_{e2} both connected across the cavity equivalent circuit. Discuss the overall stability criterion, the optimum balance of input and output coupling, and the overall performance of the transmission-type compared to the reflection-type cavity maser. Compare your results with those for the traveling-wave transmission-type system in Sec. 5-5.

5-7. Develop an expression for the voltage gain versus frequency of a lumped-circuit reflection-type cavity maser in which the cavity frequency ω_c and the atomic frequency ω_a are not equal. Evaluate the possibilities of improving maser performance (improving the bandwidth at a given gain) through this type of stagger tuning. Use either analytical manipulations of the gain-vs.-frequency expression or computer evaluation of the resulting gain profiles.

5-8. Program a computer routine to compute the exact voltage gain and phase shift of a reflection-type cavity maser, without making any of the high-gain or narrow-bandwidth approximations, as well as a routine to compute the gain and phase shift versus frequency, using the approximate forms derived in Sec. 5-3. Tabulate (or plot) both the exact and approximate expressions for some typical choices of parameters, including some relatively low gain values, and evaluate how satisfactory our analytical approximations are for various choices of parameters.

5-9. Repeat Prob. 5-8, considering instead a regenerative traveling-wave amplifier, and explore the exact gain-vs.-frequency curves for various choices of axial-mode spacing compared to linewidth, single-pass gain and mirror reflectivity, and other parameters. Consider particularly the behavior as the system goes from highly regenerative (single-pass gain nearly unity and high mirror reflectivity) to nonregenerative (single-pass gain equals total gain, no mirrors at all), keeping a constant midband total gain with some large value such as 20 or 30 dB.

5-10. Approximate values for α_m and β_m for a wave propagating through a medium with ohmic conductivity σ are derived in Sec. 5-4 by a first-order Taylor series expansion of Γ. Extend this expansion to whatever higher-order terms are necessary to get the next-order correction factors to both α_m and β_m. How large must the loss per wavelength be (in the first-order approximation) before these next-order corrections to α_m and β_m amount to as much as 10 percent correction?

5-11. In a certain laser the axial-mode spacing $c/2L$ is exactly one-fifth the atomic linewidth Δf_a, and one axial mode (the qth axial mode, say) is located exactly at the atomic line center. The mirror reflectivity is 5 percent at each end, and the atomic line has a lorentzian shape. Plot the peak power gains for the three closest axial modes (the $q + 1$, $q + 2$, and $q + 3$ modes) as a function of peak power gain of the centermost axial mode. What limiting gain values in decibels do the off-center modes approach as the gain of the central mode approaches infinity?

5-12. If the inverted population difference on a maser transition changes by a small fractional amount, owing to fluctuations in the pumping rate or some other cause, there will be an equal fractional change $\delta G_m/G_m$ in the cavity-circuit element or $\delta\alpha_m/\alpha_m$ in the traveling-wave gain coefficient. The resulting fractional change in midband power gain, $\delta G_0/G_0$, divided by the fractional change in the inverted population, is called the *gain sensitivity* of the maser. Calculate and plot the gain sensitivity of the reflection-type cavity maser and of the single-pass traveling-wave maser, each as a function of the midband power gain G_0.

5-13. In some applications it is important to know not only the 3-dB bandwidth of an amplifier, but also how fast the amplifier gain falls off outside this bandwidth (to determine how much a strong interfering signal outside the amplifier passband will be suppressed, for example). Compare the performance of cavity and single-pass traveling-wave maser amplifiers in this particular respect, taking as specifications a midband gain of 30 dB and the same 3-dB bandwidth in each case, and find the frequency shifts in each case necessary to reduce the gain by 15, 20, and 25 dB below the peak value.

REFERENCES

5-1. A. Abragam and W. G. Procter, "Spin temperature," *Phys. Rev.*, **109**:1441 (1958). Gives a lengthy and full discussion of the spin-temperature concept and of calorimetric experiments carried out entirely at negative temperatures.

5-2. H. Boersch and G. Herziger, "Theoretical and experimental investigation of regenerative laser amplifiers and their applications," *IEEE J. Quantum Electron.*, **QE-2**:549 (September, 1966).

5-3. W. S. C. Chang, J. Cromack, and A. E. Siegman, "Cavity maser experiments using ruby at S-band," *J. Electron. Control*, **6**:508 (June, 1959).

5-4. W. P. Dumke, "Fundamentals of injection lasers," *Microwaves* (Laser Technology Section), September, 1968, p. 64.

5-5. J. A. Glasel, "A simple device for T_1 measurements on a nuclear magnetic resonance spectrometer by adiabatic rapid passage," *J. Scientific Instruments*, **1**:963 (1968).

5-6. H. Kiemle, "Die komplexe magnetische suszeptibilitat von rubin fur mikrowellen-maser," *Zeit. angewandte Physik*, **18**:260 (1965).

5-7. C. Kittel, *Elementary Statistical Physics*, Wiley, New York, 1968; esp. sec. 24, p. 113, "Negative Temperatures."

5-8. C. G. Montgomery, R. H. Dicke, and E. M. Purcell (eds.), *Principles of Microwave Circuits*, Radiation Laboratory Series, vol. 8, McGraw-Hill, New York, 1948.

5-9. S. Ramo, J. R. Whinnery, and T. Van Duzer, *Fields and Waves in Communication Electronics*, Wiley, New York, 1965.

5-10. A. E. Siegman, *Microwave Solid-state Masers*, McGraw-Hill, New York, 1964. See especially chaps. 6 and 7, and references therein.

5-11. M. W. Zemansky, *Temperatures Very Low and Very High*, Van Nostrand, Princeton, N. J., 1964 (paperback). See especially chap. 5, "Beyond Infinity to Negative Temperatures," p. 112.

RATE EQUATIONS
FOR
ATOMIC TRANSITIONS

When an ac signal is applied to an atomic transition, two very deeply interrelated but separately describable effects take place in the atoms. First, the applied signal causes an induced ac response in the form of an *induced electric or magnetic polarization* in the collection of atoms. In previous chapters we used simple semiclassical models to calculate this induced polarization for both electric-dipole and magnetic-dipole atoms. From quantum theory, the magnitude and sign of this induced response varies directly as the population difference on the particular transition involved. Second, under the influence of the applied signal *the quantum-state mixtures and the energy-level populations of the atoms begin to change* under the influence of the applied signal. In very rough terms, the applied signal causes atoms to jump, or make transitions, between the two energy levels responsible for the transition, so that the energy-level populations begin to change. These changes in energy-level populations are governed by *rate equations,* which we will describe in detail in this chapter.

In previous chapters we used analytical approaches that keep track of both the amplitude and the phase of the atomic response, and the importance of both the resistive and reactive parts (χ' and χ'') of the ac response was emphasized. These detailed approaches are important in a complete description of the induced atomic response or ac polarization, particularly in evaluating the reactive or phase-shift effects caused by an atomic transition. However, our simple classical models have at least two serious disadvantages: they apply directly only to a single two-level atomic transition at a time, and these approaches require the solution of either a second-order differential equation for the atomic response [the equation of motion for $x(t)$ in the electric-dipole model] or of two coupled first-order differential equations (the two transverse Bloch equations in the magnetic-dipole model).

By contrast, the rate-equation approach we will develop in this chapter condenses these double equations into a single first-order differential equation which describes the flow of atoms between the two atomic energy levels involved in a given transition. Furthermore, the rate-equation approach can immediately be extended to handle the total flow of atoms among energy levels in multiple-energy-level atoms subjected to multiple signals on multiple transitions simultaneously.

The rate equations are thus very valuable, first, because they are mathematically simpler, and second, because they are immediately adaptable to multiple-energy-level systems—and essentially every useful maser device involves the dynamics of multiple energy levels rather than just two energy levels. One limitation of the rate equations is that they do not in themselves provide any direct information about the ac susceptibility or the reactive or phase effects of the atomic response. However, with what we already have learned, we do not need to have the rate equations provide this information. We can deduce the ac polarization response from what we already know and then use the rate equations to predict how the atomic populations will vary in response to applied signals. Since knowledge of the atomic populations is essential to determine the population differences and hence the induced ac responses, the rate equations play a very important role.

In this chapter we will first derive and then discuss the rate equations for a simple two-level system and then extend these equations to the multiple-energy-level case. We will also review the important concept of the saturation of a transition by a strong applied signal. These results will be of great importance for analyzing practical maser systems in succeeding chapters.

6-1   RATE EQUATION FOR A TWO-LEVEL SYSTEM

The rate equation describing the change in energy-level populations in a two-level, or even a multiple-level, atomic system has exactly the same form whether the system is electric-dipole, magnetic-dipole, or any other type. The form of this rate equation is perhaps most easily derived from a magnetic-dipole model, but the resulting equation has very general validity. In this section we will first review the magnetic-dipole derivation (presented in Chap. 4) and then give a similar heuristic derivation in terms of an electric-dipole model.

MAGNETIC-DIPOLE DERIVATION   ■ In the magnetic-dipole analysis of Chap. 4 we found that the Bloch equations of motion separated naturally into two *transverse,* or ac, equations of motion, and one *longitudinal,* or quasi-dc, equation of motion. The ac magnetization and the ac magnetic susceptibility $\tilde{\chi}$ are obtainable entirely from the two transverse ac equations, and the longitudinal equation in essence provides the rate equation for this system.

When the ac solutions of the transverse Bloch equations are substituted into the longitudinal equation for the quasi-dc magnetization component $m_z(t)$, the longitudinal equation takes the form

$$\frac{d}{dt} m_z(t) = -2W_{12}m_z(t) - \frac{m_z(t) - m_{z0}}{T_1} \tag{1}$$

where the stimulated transition probability W_{12} for the magnetic-dipole case is given by

$$W_{12} = \left(\frac{ge}{2m}\right)^2 \frac{1}{\Delta\omega_a} \frac{1}{1 + [2(\omega - \omega_a)/\Delta\omega_a]^2} |\tilde{B}_+|^2 \tag{2}$$

Note again that this expression contains the atomic lineshape, i.e., the frequency-dependence characteristic of $\chi''(\omega)$, and that it is directly proportional to the ac field strength squared, i.e., to the applied-signal energy density. This longitudinal equation is essentially the desired two-level rate equation, as we will now see.

In the quantum description of a collection of two-level paramagnetic atoms the longitudinal magnetization is directly proportional to the atomic population difference; that is,

$$m_z = (N_1 - N_2)\mu \tag{3}$$

where N_1 and N_2 are the populations per unit volume of the two energy levels and μ is the maximum projection of a single magnetic-dipole atom along the z axis. The m_z equation can therefore equally well be written as

$$\frac{d}{dt}(N_1 - N_2) = -2W_{12}(N_1 - N_2) - \frac{(N_1 - N_2) - (N_{10} - N_{20})}{T_1} \tag{4a}$$

or

$$\frac{d}{dt}\Delta N_{12}(t) = -2W_{12}\,\Delta N_{12}(t) - \frac{\Delta N_{12}(t) - \Delta N_0}{T_1} \tag{4b}$$

But from the Boltzmann rule, the thermal-equilibrium level populations N_{10} and N_{20} can be written as

$$\Delta N_0 = N_{10} - N_{20} = \frac{e^{hf_a/kT} - 1}{e^{hf_a/kT} + 1}(N_1 + N_2) \tag{5}$$

By substituting this result into the equation of motion and making use of the fact that $N_1 + N_2 = N$, and hence $(d/dt)N_2 = -(d/dt)N_1$, we can further modify the m_z equation to

$$\frac{d}{dt}N_1 = \underbrace{-W_{12}N_1 + W_{12}N_2}_{\text{stimulated terms}} \underbrace{- w_{12}N_1 + w_{21}N_2}_{\text{relaxation terms}} = -\frac{d}{dt}N_2 \tag{6}$$

where the two *relaxation transition probabilities* w_{12} and w_{21} are given by

$$w_{12} = \frac{1}{e^{hf_a/kT} + 1}\frac{1}{T_1} \qquad w_{21} = \frac{e^{hf_a/kT}}{e^{hf_a/kT} + 1}\frac{1}{T_1} \tag{7}$$

The simple differential equation (6), or alternatively, (4), is the rate equation for a two-energy-level system. Given the applied-signal strength W_{12} and the longitudinal-relaxation time T_1 (or the relaxation rates w_{12} and w_{21}), we can solve for the variation with time of the energy-level populations $N_1(t)$ and $N_2(t)$, starting from any specified initial conditions $N_1(0)$ and $N_2(0)$.

INTERPRETATION OF
RATE-EQUATION TERMS

■ Examination of the terms in this rate equation leads to the following physical interpretations. The quantities N_1 and N_2, as we have noted several times, are proportional to the averaged probabilities that atoms are likely to be found (by some appropriate measurement method) to be in level 1 or level 2. In rough terms, N_1 and N_2 are the number of atoms in levels 1 and 2, respectively. The rate equations evidently give the rates at which these numbers or energy-level populations change with time.

The first two terms in Eq. (6) may be interpreted as meaning that a signal W_{12} applied to a two-level transition causes a flow of atoms out of level 1 and into level 2 at a rate given by $W_{12}N_1$ atoms per unit time, and a simultaneous counterflow from level 2 into level 1 given by $W_{12}N_2$ atoms per unit time. These flows are indicated by the double arrows in Fig. 6-1. The flow in each direction is given by the transition probability per atom per unit time, W_{12}, times the number of atoms N_1 or N_2 available in the starting level to make transitions. Since these transitions are apparently caused or stimulated by the applied signal, we call W_{12} the *stimulated transition probability* (per atom per unit time). This transition probability per atom is the same in either direction, upward or downward. It is maximized for signals tuned exactly to the atomic resonance frequency and decreases according to the transition lineshape as the signal frequency is tuned away from resonance in either direction.

It must be clearly understood that there is no way of experimentally isolating the "separate" flows $W_{12}N_1$ and $W_{12}N_2$ in the upward and downward directions, since they occur simultaneously and cannot be excited separately. Measurements of $N_1(t)$ and $N_2(t)$ as a function of time can only reveal the total changes due to the net or combined effect of the two flows. The net flow rate is, of course, proportional to the population difference, that is, $W_{12}(N_1 - N_2)$, just as is the ac polarization response. The separation into two flows in opposite directions is really only a conceptual fiction that we find convenient for purposes of analysis and discussion.

The second pair of terms in Eq. (6) shows that there are also relaxation flow rates of atoms between the levels, in addition to the stimulated transition rates. Again with

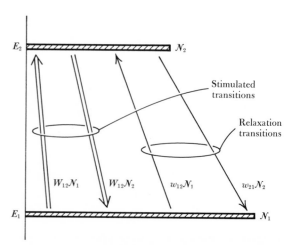

FIG. 6-1 Stimulated transitions (double arrows) and relaxation transitions (single arrows) in a two-level atomic system.

the fictional separation into upward and downward transitions, the upward relaxation flow rate is $w_{12}N_1$ atoms per unit time from 1 to 2, and the downward rate is $w_{21}N_2$ atoms per unit time from 2 to 1. These transitions are indicated by single arrows in Fig. 6-1.

A major difference between the signal-stimulated and the relaxation transition probabilities is that the two relaxation transition probabilities per atom per unit time are not the same in either direction. Rather, the upward relaxation probability w_{12} and the downward relaxation probability w_{21} stand in the Boltzmann ratio for the transition in question; that is,

$$\frac{w_{21}}{w_{12}} = e^{(E_2 - E_1)/kT} \tag{8}$$

Since at thermal equilibrium the level populations also stand in the Boltzmann ratio, this condition ensures that the net flow of atoms between the levels under thermal-equilibrium conditions will be zero; that is,

$$\frac{d}{dt}N_1(t) = -w_{12}N_{10} + w_{21}N_{20} \equiv 0 \tag{9}$$

This is certainly what we would expect for a system in thermal equilibrium. The downward relaxation probability w_{21} is always larger than the upward probability w_{12}, but the upper-level population N_{20} at equilibrium is corresponding smaller than the lower-level population N_{10}, so that the net flow at equilibrium is identically zero.

The per-atom relaxation rates in these equations are of order $w_{12} \sim w_{21} \sim 1/T_1$, where T_1 is the longitudinal relaxation time that we attributed in Chap. 4 to interactions of the atoms with their thermal surroundings. The relaxation transitions are, in fact, essentially stimulated transitions, but caused by the action of the random thermal surroundings on the atoms rather than any applied signal.[1]

There are no simple formulas for the magnitudes of the relaxation times in atomic systems (although complicated quantum calculations are sometimes attempted), and the relaxation time T_1 is generally a parameter that is determined experimentally. As a very rough indication of typical values, radio-frequency NMR transitions can have T_1 values ranging from many to $\sim 10^{-3}$ sec, microwave EPR transitions have values ranging from $\sim 10^{-3}$ to 10^{-7} sec, and optical-frequency transitions can have a wide range of values, all the way from $\sim 10^{-3}$ down to $\sim 10^{-12}$ sec.

■ Although the rate equation above was derived from a magnetic-dipole analysis, the rate equation in the form (4) or (6), together with all of the subsequent discussion, applies equally well to the stimulated response of any two-level system, whether the transition is magnetic-dipole, electric-dipole, or any other type. Because of the nature of the classical electron-oscillator model used to represent electric-dipole transitions in Chap. 2, the derivation of the rate equation from the electric-dipole model is not so straightforward as in the magnetic-dipole case. However, it can also be derived, at least in a rough way, as follows. The total internal energy W_a, kinetic plus potential, asso-

ELECTRIC-DIPOLE DERIVATION

---

[1] It is obviously significant that the signal-stimulated transition probability W_{12} is the same in either direction, but the thermal-stimulated, or relaxation, transition probabilities w_{12} and w_{21} are not. The reason the thermal-stimulated or relaxation probability is larger in the downward direction is that w_{21} also includes a certain amount of spontaneous emission or spontaneous relaxation, which is entirely in the downward direction. However, this is a matter that we will not take up in detail until Chap. 11.

ciated with the internal motions of a collection of N classical electron oscillators may be written as

$$W_a(t) = \tfrac{1}{2}Nm[\dot{x}^2(t) + \omega_0{}^2x^2(t)] \tag{10}$$

where $x(t)$ really means the average motion, averaged over all the atoms, as discussed in Chap. 3. Since the basic equation of motion for each oscillator is

$$\ddot{x}(t) + \gamma\dot{x}(t) + \omega_0{}^2x(t) = -\frac{e}{m}\,e_x(t) \tag{11}$$

the time derivative of the internal energy can be written as

$$\frac{d}{dt}\,W_a(t) = Nm\dot{x}(t)[\ddot{x}(t) + \omega_0{}^2x(t)]$$

$$= -Ne[e_x(t)\dot{x}(t)] - Nm\gamma\dot{x}^2(t) \tag{12}$$

For an oscillating system such as this the kinetic and potential energies are essentially equal,

$$\tfrac{1}{2}m\dot{x}^2 \approx \tfrac{1}{2}m\omega_0{}^2x^2 \approx \tfrac{1}{2}W_a \tag{13}$$

so that the second term on the right-hand side in (12) is simply $-\gamma W_a(t) = -W_a(t)/T_1$, the energy-decay or damping term. The first term, $-Ne[e_x(t)x(t)]$, represents the energy transfer between the atoms and the applied signal.

If we write both $e_x(t)$ and $x(t)$ in sinusoidal form and then use the solutions from Chaps. 2 and 3 for the forced sinusoidal motion $\tilde{X}(\omega)$ in terms of $\tilde{E}_x(\omega)$, the energy-transfer term becomes

$$-Ne[e_x(t)x(t)] = \frac{Ne^2}{2m\,\Delta\omega_a}\frac{1}{1 + [2(\omega - \omega_a)/\Delta\omega_a]^2}\,|\tilde{E}_x|^2 \tag{14}$$

In writing this we have left out a small second-harmonic 2ω component, since the 2ω component represents only reactive energy which sloshes back and forth between the atoms and the field, without any average energy transfer. The energy equation then becomes

$$\frac{d}{dt}\,W_a(t) = \frac{Ne^2}{2m\,\Delta\omega_a}\frac{1}{1 + [2(\omega - \omega_a)/\Delta\omega_a]^2}\,|\tilde{E}_x|^2 - \gamma W_a(t) \tag{15}$$

This equation is close to being an electric-dipole rate equation, and we will now convert it into one. This conversion to a quantum-mechanical rate equation requires three changes:

1. If the electric-dipole transition is between two energy levels $E_1 = -\hbar\omega_a/2$ and $E_2 = +\hbar\omega_a/2$, then the total energy of a collection of atoms distributed between the two levels is

$$W_a(t) = N_1(t)E_1 + N_2(t)E_2 = (N_2 - N_1)\frac{\hbar\omega_a}{2} = -\Delta N_{12}\frac{\hbar\omega_a}{2} \tag{16}$$

and this can be substituted for W_a in the equation.

2. While the response of a collection of classical oscillators is proportional to the total number of atoms N, the quantum response is proportional instead to the popula-

tion difference $N_1 - N_2$. Therefore N should be replaced by $N_1 - N_2$ in the energy-transfer term.

3. The energy of the classical oscillator damps out to $W_a = 0$, but the energy of a real collection of atoms in contact with thermal surroundings damps out to a thermal-equilibrium value W_{a0}, given by

$$W_{a0} = (N_{20} - N_{10})\frac{\hbar\omega_a}{2} = -\Delta N_0 \frac{\hbar\omega_a}{2} \tag{17}$$

where N_{10} and N_{20} are the thermal-equilibrium level populations. Therefore the final, or damping, term must be changed from $-\gamma W_a$ to $-\gamma(W_a - W_{a0})$.

These changes convert the energy equation into exactly the desired rate-equation form,

$$\frac{d}{dt}\Delta N_{12} = -2W_{12}\,\Delta N_{12} - \frac{\Delta N_{12} - \Delta N_0}{T_1} \tag{18}$$

where

$$W_{12} = \frac{e^2}{2m\hbar\omega_a}\frac{1}{\Delta\omega_a}\frac{1}{1 + [2(\omega - \omega_a)/\Delta\omega_a]^2}\,|\tilde{E}_x|^2 \tag{19}$$

is the stimulated transition probability for the electric-dipole case. The rate equation has exactly the same form as in the magnetic-dipole derivation, provided that we identify the damping rate γ with the longitudinal relaxation time T_1 by $\gamma \equiv T_1^{-1}$, as we did earlier. Just as in the magnetic-dipole case, the stimulated transition probability is proportional to the ac signal strength squared and has the same frequency response as the absorptive part of the atomic lineshape.

■ Under the influence of an applied ac signal at or near the resonant frequency, the dynamics of the level populations in any two-level quantum system can be described by a rate equation having the simple form (4), or (6), or (18). The stimulated-transition-probability factor in the rate equation will always contain the ac signal strength squared, and will also contain the atomic lineshape, i.e., the lineshape of the absorptive part of the atomic susceptibility.   SUMMARY OF TWO-LEVEL RATE EQUATIONS

The transition probabilities for magnetic- or electric-dipole transitions in real atoms have the values derived from the semiclassical arguments of this section, except that the magnitude or strength of the transition probability is multiplied by the oscillator-strength parameter introduced in Sec. 2-4. The oscillator strength is a dimensionless measure of how strongly allowed a particular transition is, as determined by a quantum-mechanical parameter called the *matrix element* of the transition in question. Oscillator strengths are of order unity for strongly allowed transitions, in which case our semiclassical results give not only the correct form, but even the correct magnitude for the transition probabilities. Many atomic transitions, however, are substantially weaker than this, with oscillator strengths substantially smaller than unity. Oscillator strengths for various transitions can be computed by quantum-mechanical calculations, at least in simple atoms, but in many cases they can be determined only experimentally.

A quantum-mechanically correct form for the stimulated transition probability on any electric-dipole transition can be obtained by using the classical radiative-damping formula to write (19) in the form

$$W_{12} = \frac{3}{8\pi^2} \frac{\omega_a}{\Delta\omega_a} \frac{\epsilon_0 |\tilde{E}|^2 \lambda^3}{\hbar\omega_a} \left(\frac{1}{\tau_{\mathrm{rad}}}\right) \frac{1}{1 + [2(\omega - \omega_a)/\Delta\omega_a]^2} \tag{20}$$

This form is equally valid in the quantum case, provided only that the true atomic linewidth $\Delta\omega_a$ and the true radiative damping time τ_{rad} for the particular transition are used in calculating W_{12}. This rather interesting result says that the stimulated transition rate is essentially the inverse of the radiative damping time $1/\tau_{\mathrm{rad}}$ multiplied by the atomic-linewidth quality factor $Q_a \equiv \omega_a/\Delta\omega_a$, and further multiplied by the number of applied-signal photons per wavelength cubed.

As a final point, we may note that magnetic-dipole stimulated transition probabilities are generally very much weaker than their electric-dipole counterparts. For electromagnetic signals in free space, the signal energy density may be given in terms of either the electric or magnetic field strengths by

$$W = \tfrac{1}{2}\epsilon_0 |\tilde{E}|^2 \quad \text{or} \quad W = \tfrac{1}{2}\mu_0 |\tilde{H}|^2 \tag{21}$$

Therefore equal amounts of energy in the E and H fields means that the ac field strengths stand in the ratio

$$\left| \frac{\tilde{E}}{\tilde{H}} \right| = \left(\frac{\mu_0}{\epsilon_0} \right)^{1/2} = 377 \; \Omega \tag{22}$$

If we compare the magnetic-dipole and electric-dipole stimulated transition probabilities W_{12}, assuming the same signal energy density and the same atomic linewidth in each case, the result, after cancelling all common factors, is

$$\frac{W_{12,\mathrm{mag}}}{W_{12,\mathrm{elec}}} = \frac{g^2}{2} \frac{\hbar\omega_a}{mc^2} \tag{23}$$

The denominator of this ratio is the so-called *self-energy* of an electron, $mc^2 \approx 0.5 \times 10^6$ eV and the numerator is the *photon energy* of the transition, which even for an optical-frequency transition is only $\hbar\omega_a \approx 1$ eV. Hence magnetic-dipole transition rates are typically $\sim 10^{-6}$ times smaller than electric-dipole transition rates, unless the electric-dipole oscillator strength happens to be extremely small.

6-2   SATURATION OF A TWO-LEVEL TRANSITION

We will next consider the very important phenomenon of saturation of the population difference on a two-level transition by a strong applied signal.

RATE EQUATION AND
TRANSIENT SOLUTION

■ The rate equation we obtained for a two-level system was written finally in the form

$$\frac{d}{dt}\mathcal{N}_1 = -W_{12}\mathcal{N}_1 + W_{21}\mathcal{N}_2 - w_{12}\mathcal{N}_1 + w_{21}\mathcal{N}_2 = -\frac{d}{dt}\mathcal{N}_2 \tag{1}$$

This particular form for the rate equation, with the upward and downward transition terms written separately, provides the starting point from which to generalize the rate equations for multilevel systems, which we will do in the next section. For the simple two-level case, however, it is more convenient to go back to the form of the rate equation involving the population difference $\mathcal{N}_1 - \mathcal{N}_2$. The equation is then easier to solve, and $\Delta\mathcal{N}_{12}$ is the quantity most often of interest in calculations or experiments.

If we define the population difference as $\Delta\mathcal{N}(t) = \mathcal{N}_1(t) - \mathcal{N}_2(t)$, omitting the subscripts on $\Delta\mathcal{N}_{12}$ for simplicity, the general rate equation for a two-level system may also be written as

$$\frac{d}{dt} \Delta \mathcal{N}(t) = -2W_{12} \Delta \mathcal{N}(t) - \frac{\Delta \mathcal{N}(t) - \Delta \mathcal{N}_0}{T_1} \tag{2}$$

where $\Delta \mathcal{N}_0$ is the thermal-equilibrium value. With no applied signal present, $W_{12} = 0$, the population difference $\Delta \mathcal{N}(t)$ obviously relaxes toward the thermal-equilibrium value $\Delta \mathcal{N}_0$ with time constant T_1; that is,

$$\Delta \mathcal{N}(t) = \Delta \mathcal{N}_0 + [\Delta \mathcal{N}(0) - \Delta \mathcal{N}_0]e^{-t/T_1} \qquad W_{12} = 0 \tag{3}$$

where $\Delta \mathcal{N}(0)$ is the initial value of $\Delta \mathcal{N}(t)$ at $t = 0$. But if a constant applied signal W_{12} is present (or is turned on at $t = 0$), then for the same initial condition the population difference varies with time in the form

$$\Delta \mathcal{N}(t) = \Delta \mathcal{N}_{st} + [\Delta \mathcal{N}(0) - \Delta \mathcal{N}_{st}]e^{-(2W_{12}+1/T_1)t} \tag{4}$$

The transient response now approaches, not the thermal-equilibrium value $\Delta \mathcal{N}_0$, but rather a steady-state value $\Delta \mathcal{N}_{st}$, given by

$$\Delta \mathcal{N}_{st} = \Delta \mathcal{N}_0 \frac{1}{1 + 2W_{12}T_1} \tag{5}$$

This steady-state value is clearly always less than the thermal-equilibrium value. The time constant with which this value is approached is also shorter, being given by

$$\left(2W_{12} + \frac{1}{T_1}\right)^{-1} = T_1 \frac{1}{1 + 2W_{12}T_1} \tag{6}$$

The stronger the applied signal, the more rapid the transient approach to the final steady-state value.

■ By way of example, Fig. 6-2 shows the transient response of the population difference to steady state, with the same initial condition in each case, but for three different applied-signal strengths (including no signal, $W_{12} = 0$). It is clear from these curves as   SATURATION BEHAVIOR

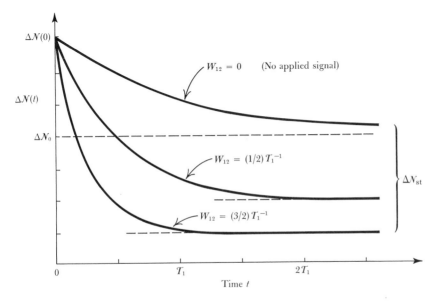

FIG. 6-2   Transient response of the population difference $\Delta N(t)$ in a two-level system for three different applied-signal levels (including zero applied signal). The same arbitrarily chosen initial value is used in each case. Note the faster time constant of the response, and the reduced steady-state value, as the signal strength is increased.

well as from the expression for $\Delta \mathcal{N}_{st}$ that when an applied signal W_{12} is present, the steady-state value $\Delta \mathcal{N}_{st}$ is reduced below the thermal-equilibrium value $\Delta \mathcal{N}_0$. In fact, $\Delta \mathcal{N}_{st}$ is driven toward zero if the signal strength becomes large enough; that is,

$$\Delta \mathcal{N}_{st} \to 0 \qquad W_{12} \gg \frac{1}{T_1} \tag{7}$$

Figure 6-3a plots this *saturation* behavior of $\Delta \mathcal{N}_{st}$, showing how the level populations are forced to become nearly equal under the influence of a sufficiently strong applied signal. The saturation of an atomic transition caused by a strong applied signal is a very important process in many maser and laser situations we will meet later.

As an experimental illustration of saturation behavior, Fig. 6-3b shows the saturation of the power absorption in a short test section of a traveling-wave maser device (see Chap. 7) as the signal-power input to the device is increased. The absorption in

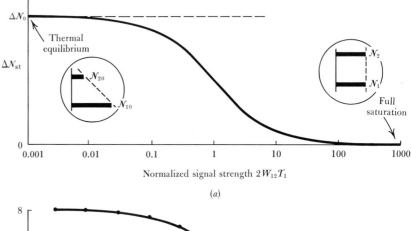

Normalized signal strength $2W_{12}T_1$

(a)

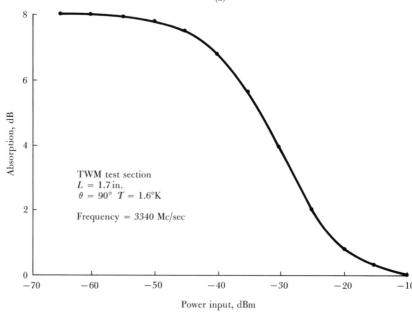

FIG. 6-3 Saturation behavior of a two-level system, showing how the steady-state population difference $\Delta \mathcal{N}_{st}$ decreases as the applied-signal strength increases: (a) theoretical prediction and (b) an experimental example.

Power input, dBm

(b)

this case is caused by a transition between two levels in a multiple-level microwave maser material (in which the pumping process is not turned on, so that the transition is still absorptive rather than providing maser amplification). Even though this is a multi-level system, the saturation of the absorption on a particular transition behaves in essentially the same way as the saturation of a simple two-level system. Another complication is that this is a traveling-wave system which has considerable absorption, at least at low power levels. Therefore the signal power level at low power inputs is 8 dB higher at the input end than at the output end of the test section. Obviously, saturation of the atomic population difference begins to occur first at the input end of the line and then gradually spreads along the line toward the output end at higher power inputs. Even with these complications, however, the experimental result of Fig. 6-3b is obviously very close to the theoretical prediction of Fig. 6-3a.

The form of the two-level rate equation makes it clear that the T_1 relaxation process always strives to relax $\Delta \mathcal{N}(t)$ toward the thermal-equilibrium value $\Delta \mathcal{N}_0$ at a rate $1/T_1$, while the stimulated transition processes, by contrast, attempt to drive $\Delta \mathcal{N}(t)$ toward zero at a rate $2W_{12}$. The steady-state value $\Delta \mathcal{N}_{st}$ then represents a balance between these two competing processes. Basically, either $\Delta \mathcal{N}_{st} \approx \Delta \mathcal{N}_0$ if the low-level condition $2W_{12} \ll 1/T_1$ prevails or $\Delta \mathcal{N}_{st} \approx 0$ if the saturation condition $2W_{12} \gg 1/T_1$ prevails.

■ The saturation process in a two-level system has an instructive thermodynamic interpretation in terms of the steady-state atomic temperature appropriate to the level populations of the two-level atoms, as discussed in Sec. 5-1. Let the thermal environment surrounding the atoms, sometimes called the *surrounding heat bath*, have a temperature that we will denote as T_{bath}. Most commonly this will be the temperature of a crystal or solid in which the atoms are embedded, or possibly the kinetic temperature associated with the external kinetic motions of the atoms in the case of a gas. Then at thermal equilibrium with no signals applied the level populations or internal motions of the atoms will have this same temperature, $T_a = T_{bath}$, and it is this value of temperature that should be used in determining the Boltzmann thermal-equilibrium populations.

THERMODYNAMIC INTERPRETATION

However, if an applied signal is present and there is some degree of saturation, then the atomic populations at steady state will have a hotter atomic temperature, $T_a \geq T_{bath}$. The actual atomic temperature can be calculated from the expression

$$\frac{\Delta \mathcal{N}_{st}}{\mathcal{N}} = \tanh \frac{hf_a}{2kT_a} \tag{8}$$

To express this another way, if the applied signal were to be suddenly turned off, the energy-level populations immediately after turnoff would be appropriate to thermal equilibrium with a heat bath at a hotter temperature, $T'_{bath} = T_a$, instead of the actual bath temperature T_{bath}.

One explanation of this result is that the signal generator connected to the atoms is actually extremely hot. In fact, a thermal source of many millions of degrees would be needed to emit as many watts of electromagnetic radiation to the atoms within the atomic linewidth as does the signal generator. Hence, as shown in Fig. 6-4, the atoms may be viewed as being thermally connected on the one hand to their environment, at temperature T_{bath} with a thermal link of strength $\sim 1/T_1$ and on the other hand to the signal generator, at temperature $T_{gen} \approx \infty$ with a thermal link of strength $\sim W_{12}$.

FIG. 6-4 A thermodynamic model for saturation of the energy-level populations in a two-level system, showing how the three separate thermal reservoirs (thermal environment or bath, atoms, and signal source) are thermally linked by the relaxation and stimulated transition processes.

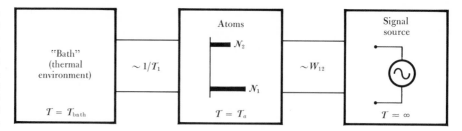

FIG. 6-4 A thermodynamic model for saturation of the energy-level populations in a two-level system, showing how the three separate thermal reservoirs (thermal environment or bath, atoms, and signal source) are thermally linked by the relaxation and stimulated transition processes.

The atomic temperature will then take on a steady-state value somewhere between these two values. The steady-state value will be closer to the bath temperature (negligible saturation) or to the signal source temperature (strong saturation), depending on whether the atoms are more strongly coupled to the surrounding heat bath ($W_{12} \ll 1/T_1$) or to the signal generator ($W_{12} \gg 1/T_1$).

SATURATION POWER FLOW ■ It is also instructive to consider the power flows between signal and atoms and between atoms and surrounding thermal bath in a saturated two-level system. The *net* number of stimulated upward transitions (upward minus downward) per unit time in a collection of atoms is given by $W_{12} \, \Delta N$, and each transition represents the transfer of one quantum hf of energy from the signal to the atoms. Therefore the net power flow from signal to atoms in the case of essentially complete saturation of a transition is given by

$$
\begin{aligned}
P_{\text{sig}\to\text{atoms}} &= W_{12} h f_a \, \Delta N_{\text{st}} \\
&\approx \frac{h f_a \, \Delta N_0}{2 T_1} \qquad W_{12} \gg \frac{1}{T_1}
\end{aligned}
\tag{9}
$$

The population difference ΔN_{st} approaches zero at complete saturation, but in such a way that the product $W_{12} \, \Delta N_{\text{st}}$ approaches a finite and constant value.

By similar arguments, each upward relaxation transition of an atom means one quantum of energy absorbed by the atoms from the thermal surroundings, while each downward relaxation transition means one quantum of energy emitted by the atoms to the thermal surroundings. Hence the net rate of transfer of energy from the atoms to their thermal surroundings is

$$
P_{\text{atoms}\to\text{bath}} = \hbar f_a (w_{21} N_2 - w_{12} N_1)
\tag{10}
$$

But at full saturation we have $N_1 \approx N_2 \approx N/2$, and so the power flow from atoms to bath via relaxation in this limit is

$$
\begin{aligned}
P_{\text{atoms}\to\text{bath}} &\approx \frac{h f_a N}{2}(w_{21} - w_{12}) \qquad W_{12} \gg \frac{1}{T_1} \\
&= \frac{h f_a \, \Delta N_0}{2 T_1} = P_{\text{sig}\to\text{atoms}}
\end{aligned}
\tag{11}
$$

Clearly, the fixed power flow from signal to atoms at full saturation is just equal to the maximum rate at which the atoms can get rid of this energy by passing it along to their thermal surroundings through relaxation processes. In fact, this condition must obviously be equally true under steady-state conditions for any arbitrary degree of saturation.

6-3   RATE EQUATIONS FOR MULTIPLE-ENERGY-LEVEL SYSTEMS

Real atoms and practical maser systems involve multiple energy levels, with multiple transitions at different frequencies among these energy levels. In this section we will see how to extend our analytical methods, specifically the rate equations, to cover the more realistic and complicated case of multiple energy levels.

For carrying out a relatively complete and rigorous quantum-mechanical analysis of a collection of multilevel atoms, the quantum-mechanical *density-matrix approach* is probably the most widely used. This method of analysis is beyond the scope of this book. However, the density-matrix equations of motion for an atomic system are actually not so very complicated, and the more rigorous density-matrix equations turn out to be not so very different from the more approximate equations we will obtain here with simple heuristic arguments.

The approximate approach we will develop in this section amounts in essence to treating each separate transition in a multilevel system as a separate two-level transition and then adding up the various rate-equation terms to find the total rate equation for each level in the multilevel system.

■ Consider a collection of identical multiple-energy-level atoms having various possible transition frequencies among their energy levels. For simplicity let us assume that the transition frequencies are all distinct, i.e., that no two transition frequencies coincide to within a few atomic linewidths or less. Suppose that applied signals are present at or near several of the various transition frequencies f_{mn} between various levels E_n and E_m, as illustrated in Fig. 6-5. Then, provided that none of the applied signals is too strong (a condition we will explain more fully later), the following general principles can be applied:

1. *As far as the stimulated response on any particular transition is concerned, that transition may be treated as if it were simply an elementary two-level transition between the two energy levels E_n and E_m.*

That is, each individual transition may be regarded as either an electric- or magnetic-dipole transition (whichever is appropriate) with a resonance frequency $f_a = f_{mn}$, an atomic lineshape and atomic linewidth $\Delta f_a = \Delta f_{mn}$, a certain oscillator strength F_{mn} or radiative lifetime τ_{mn}, and in agreement with these parameters, a resulting atomic susceptibility $\tilde{\chi}_{mn}(\omega)$ having all the characteristic features developed in our earlier discussions. Each of these above parameters, as well as the tensor polarization properties of $\tilde{\chi}_{mn}$, will be different for each different $n \to m$ transition. In each case, however, the induced response on the transition will be proportional to the population difference $\Delta \mathcal{N}_{nm}$ on the transition, and will be independent of the populations of all of the other energy levels, as well as independent of the presence of any applied signals on other transitions (except in so far as these other signals change the value of $\Delta \mathcal{N}_{nm}$).

In brief, the induced response and resulting circuit back reaction from any single transition is exactly like the response of a two-level transition if we use the appropriate transition parameters and population difference with either an electric-dipole or magnetic-dipole type of model, as appropriate.

2. *Only the populations $\mathcal{N}_n$ and $\mathcal{N}_m$ of the two levels will be directly changed by the presence of an applied signal on that particular transition, and these population changes*

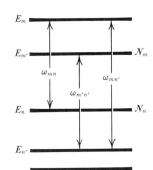

FIG. 6-5 A multilevel system showing the transition frequencies between various energy levels E_m, E_n, $E_{m'}$, etc.

(or, more precisely, rates of change) can be described in the same rate-equation terms as in the equivalent two-level case.

To put this more directly, if a signal is applied to the $m \to n$ transition, there is a stimulated transition probability W_{mn} given in the electric-dipole case by

$$W_{nm} = \frac{F_{mn}}{3} \; \frac{e^2}{2m\hbar\omega_{mn}} \; \frac{1}{\Delta\omega_{mn}} \; \frac{1}{1 + [2(\omega - \omega_{mn})/\Delta\omega_{mn}]^2} |\tilde{E}|^2 \tag{1}$$

and in the magnetic-dipole case by

$$W_{nm} = \left(\frac{ge}{2m}\right)^2 \frac{1}{\Delta\omega_{mn}} \; \frac{1}{1 + [2(\omega - \omega_{mn})/\Delta\omega_{mn}]^2} |\tilde{B}_+|^2 \tag{2}$$

Then the time rates of change of the level populations N_n and N_m due to the applied signal on the $n \to m$ transition may be written as

$$\frac{d}{dt} N_n = -\frac{d}{dt} N_m = -W_{nm}N_n + W_{nm}N_m \tag{3}$$

The populations of all other energy levels will not be directly affected by this particular applied signal (although, as we will see shortly, the directly stimulated changes in the populations N_n and N_m may cause changes in the relaxation rates from these levels to other levels in the system, and this in turn may cause *indirect* changes in the populations of other energy levels).

3. *A signal applied at or near a given transition frequency will excite a significant response on that transition only. Multiple signals applied simultaneously to several different transitions in the same atomic system will not directly interact with each other.*

The essence of this statement is that if several different signals of normal strength are applied simultaneously to a multilevel system, we may calculate the stimulated ac response of each transition independently, without considering any direct influence of one signal on the response caused by another signal. Of course, in evaluating the strength of the response on each transition we must know the population difference on that transition, and the presence of other signals may influence a given response strongly by changing the populations on the relevant transition. In our terms, however, this is an indirect effect; it is not the presence or absence of the other signals that counts, but simply the population difference that is present, regardless of how it is brought about.

RELAXATION PROCESSES IN MULTILEVEL SYSTEMS

■ Before proceeding further, we must also consider the relaxation processes that occur in multilevel systems. These are essentially similar to those in two-level systems. We must distinguish first between transverse and longitudinal relaxation processes, as described in Chaps. 3 and 4—that is, between relaxation processes that broaden the atomic response without changing level populations and relaxation processes in which atoms move from one level to another while exchanging energy with the thermal surroundings of the atoms.

In multilevel atoms, as in two-level, atoms there are purely transverse or line-broadening processes, such as elastic collisions, dipolar interactions, and doppler shifts, all of which serve to broaden the response on a given transition without changing the populations or the internal energy of the atomic system. For our purposes here we need only note that in general these processes give each transition in a multilevel system its own characteristic line-broadening parameter or characteristic transverse relaxation time $T_{2, nm}$. These parameters will in general be different for different transitions even in the same atomic system. There are also the longitudinal relaxation processes in which atoms move from one energy level to another, giving energy to or receiving energy from the thermal surroundings in the process. As in the two-level case, these processes may be purely radiative, representing interaction between the atoms and the surrounding blackbody radiation density, or they may be nonradiative, arising from interactions with a surrounding crystal lattice, walls of a laser tube, or other nonradiative sources.

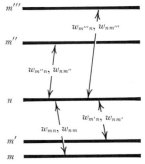

These longitudinal relaxation processes always act to bring the energy-level populations to thermal equilibrium, with a Boltzmann distribution between each pair of levels. While the basic principles are the same, the analytic details are somewhat more complicated in the multilevel case than in the two-level case. Specifically, it is reasonable to assume that in a multilevel system such as Fig. 6-6 every atomic level population may be connected by longitudinal relaxation processes (of varying strength) with every other atomic-energy-level population, both above and below it. From the same physical arguments as in earlier discussions, it is invariably assumed that the relaxation rate from one level E_n to a second level E_m will be given by a *relaxation transition probability* w_{nm} (per atom per unit time), multiplied by the number of atoms N_n available in the originating level. Of course, there will be a similar relaxation process in the reverse direction, with a total rate given by $w_{mn}N_m$. Thus the relaxation processes connecting two specific levels E_n and E_m will give rise to longitudinal-relaxation rate-equation terms given by

FIG. 6-6 Illustrating the fact that any given level E_n is connected by relaxation processes with every other level E_m in the atomic system.

$$\frac{d}{dt} N_n = - \frac{d}{dt} N_m = - w_{nm}N_n + w_{mn}N_m \tag{4}$$

in direct analogy to the two-level system.

If there is to be no net transfer of atoms between these two levels at thermal equilibrium (which we should certainly expect to be the case), then the Boltzmann condition at equilibrium applied to this particular transition requires that

$$- w_{nm} N_{n0} + w_{mn} N_{m0} \equiv 0 \tag{5}$$

or

$$\frac{w_{mn}}{w_{nm}} = \frac{N_{n0}}{N_{m0}} = e^{(E_m - E_n)/kT} \tag{6}$$

This must be true for each transition individually. Just as in the two-level case, the downward relaxation probability on any transition must be greater than the upward relaxation probability by exactly the Boltzmann ratio because of the smaller population in the upper level at thermal equilibrium.

A relaxation process w_{nm} with these properties exists on every available transition in a multilevel system. However, there is no necessary connection whatever between the *magnitudes* of the relaxation rates on different transitions; e.g., there is no necessary connection between the values of w_{nm} and $w_{n'm'}$, where $n \rightarrow m$ and $n' \rightarrow m'$ are different transitions, even in cases where they may share a common level, $n = n'$ or $m = m'$. The values of the w_{nm} factors are determined by the physics of the relaxation processes and can differ widely for different transitions. In practice the relaxation rates are most commonly regarded as parameters to be determined experimentally rather than by calculation. The calculation is exceedingly difficult, and even advanced calculations will usually predict only order-of-magnitude values.

COMPLETE MULTILEVEL RATE EQUATIONS

■ The complete rate equations for a multilevel system are now obtained by simply summing all the stimulated rate-equation terms and all the relaxation terms that represent the transfer of atoms into or out of each of the individual levels in the multilevel system. That is, by summing all the possible stimulated transition terms from a given level E_n to and from all other levels E_m, $m \neq n$, as well as all possible relaxation terms between these levels, we may write the rate equation for level E_n as

$$\frac{d}{dt} N_n = \sum_m - W_{nm}(N_n - N_m) + \sum_m (-w_{nm}N_n + w_{mn}N_m) \qquad (7)$$

$$\underbrace{\qquad\qquad}_{\text{stimulated terms}} \qquad \underbrace{\qquad\qquad\qquad}_{\text{relaxation terms}}$$

If there are M energy levels in all, there will be M such rate equations, one for each of the energy-level populations N_n, $n = 1, 2, \ldots, M$. Except for one additional point to be discussed below, these provide M coupled linear equations for finding the M level populations $N_n(t)$.

EXAMPLE OF A THREE-LEVEL SYSTEM

■ Probably the clearest way to pull together our discussion is to see how the rate equations for a multilevel system are formed in the specific three-level atomic system shown in Fig. 6-7. For completeness there are applied signals at or near all three resonance frequencies, $f_{21} = (E_2 - E_1)/h$, $f_{32} = (E_3 - E_2)/h$, and $f_{31} = (E_3 - E_1)/h$, leading to stimulated transition probabilities W_{21}, W_{32}, and W_{31} on these transitions. Each of these probabilities is, of course, proportional to the respective signal strength, as well as to the other parameters involved in W_{nm}.

The complete three-level rate equations may be written as

$$\frac{d}{dt} N_1 = - W_{12}(N_1 - N_2) - W_{13}(N_1 - N_3)$$
$$- w_{12}N_1 + w_{21}N_2 - w_{13}N_1 + w_{31}N_3$$

$$\frac{d}{dt} N_2 = - W_{12}(N_2 - N_1) - W_{23}(N_2 - N_3)$$
$$- w_{21}N_2 + w_{12}N_1 - w_{23}N_2 + w_{32}N_3 \qquad (8)$$

$$\frac{d}{dt} N_3 = - W_{13}(N_3 - N_1) - W_{23}(N_3 - N_2)$$
$$- w_{31}N_3 + w_{13}N_1 - w_{32}N_3 + w_{23}N_2$$

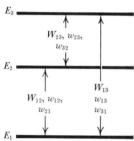

FIG. 6-7 A three-energy-level system showing all possible stimulated and relaxation transitions among the levels.

The terms in these equations are not condensed or organized in any way, but the source of each term should be clear from the format. The stimulated terms are stated first and are followed by the relaxation terms. We have also used the fact that $W_{nm} = W_{mn}$, although this is, of course, not true for w_{nm} and w_{mn}.

RATE-EQUATION SOLUTIONS

■ The rate equations appear to provide M coupled linear equations for the M unknown level populations N_n in an M-level atomic system, and so it would seem possible to solve them for the population variations with time in terms of the applied signals W_{nm}, the relaxation rates w_{nm}, and the M initial conditions on the populations. This is not quite the case, however. In the set of M rate equations there are really only $M - 1$ linearly independent equations, since any one of the equations can be obtained as a linear combination of all the others. The additional Mth equation required to make up a complete solution is provided by the total-population condition

$$\sum_n N_n = N \qquad (9)$$

or, in the three-level case,

$$\mathcal{N}_1 + \mathcal{N}_2 + \mathcal{N}_3 = \mathcal{N} \tag{10}$$

It is essentially because of this condition that the three rate equations are not independent; for example, since $(d/dt)\mathcal{N} = 0$, in the three-level case we have

$$\frac{d}{dt}\mathcal{N}_3 = -\left(\frac{d}{dt}\mathcal{N}_1 + \frac{d}{dt}\mathcal{N}_2\right) \tag{11}$$

The total-population equation (9) plus any choice of $M - 1$ of the rate equations does provide a complete set of coupled linear equations which we can solve for both the transient and steady-state values of the populations $\mathcal{N}(t)$. The nature of these solutions are probably best illustrated by the specific laser and maser examples considered in later chapters.

■ Finally, we need to discuss the conditions under which a simple rate-equation approach remains a valid approach to a multilevel system. The relaxation terms introduced in the simple form above provide what seems to be the simplest reasonable way of representing what are otherwise insolubly complicated phenomena. In this form the equations give solutions which have the right behavior in limiting cases such as thermal equilibrium, and which also agree reasonably well with observed relaxation processes. They contain a certain number of parameters, the relaxation probabilities w_{nm}, which can be treated as unknowns to be determined by experiment. There is no reason to be dissatisfied with the relaxation equations in this form for accurately describing relaxation phenomena under almost all circumstances. More rigorous calculations always reduce to the simple rate-equation form when reasonable approximations are made, and the relaxation terms are invariably written in the form we have developed here.

LIMITATIONS OF THE RATE-EQUATION APPROACH

As for the signal-stimulated rate-equation terms, the use of the stimulated transition probability W_{nm} to describe the effects of an applied signal remains valid as long as the stimulated transition rate W_{nm} is small compared to the transverse dephasing time $T_{2,nm}$ on the same transition, i.e., as long as

$$W_{nm} \ll T_{2,nm}^{-1} \tag{12}$$

This approximation is basically the same as the approximation made in solving the Bloch equations in Chap. 4 by first linearizing the transverse equations for signals "not too large" and then using these solutions in the longitudinal equation to find the much slower quasi-dc variation of the longitudinal component $m_z(t)$. In terms of the transition linewidth, this condition may also be expressed as

$$W_{nm} \ll \Delta\omega_{nm} \tag{13}$$

That is, the rate-equation approach is valid at least for signal perturbations small compared to the perturbations that create the finite linewidth of a transition.

As an aside, the condition for the saturation of a two-level system by an applied signal was found in Sec. 6-2 to be $W_{12}T_1 \gg 1$. For this saturation condition to be met at signal levels low enough that the rate-equation approach itself is still clearly valid requires the simultaneous satisfaction of the two inequalities

$$T_1^{-1} \ll W_{12} \ll T_2^{-1} \tag{14}$$

This can be the case, provided that the relaxation times satisfy the condition

$$T_2 \ll T_1 \tag{15}$$

This condition is, in fact, met by most maser transitions, although there are other particularly narrow transitions for which the relationship $T_1 \approx T_2$ is more accurate. These latter transitions are good candidates for demonstrating various interesting nonlinear or large-signal effects which are not described by the rate equations alone. Such nonlinear effects include the generation of harmonics of applied signals, the generation of intermodulation products in the form of sum and difference frequencies between simultaneously applied signals, parametric amplification and parametric frequency-conversion effects, and other effects characteristic of strongly nonlinear systems. In general, the narrower the atomic linewidth, the lower the applied-signal levels at which such nonlinear effects occur.

Even in typical maser devices at normal signal levels, weak nonlinear and intermodulation effects can be induced and measured in sufficiently careful experiments. Such effects can usually be analyzed by using some appropriate rigorous method of analysis such as the Bloch equations or the density-matrix approach, and then finding the linearized or first-order effects on which we have concentrated our attention so far, feeding these linearized solutions back into the rigorous equations, and then solving for the nonlinear second-order effects as small corrections.

Other nonlinear phenomena such as spin echoes, photon echoes, adiabatic rapid passage, and $180°$ pulses can also be observed at high enough signal levels, where the linearized approach and the rate equations no longer furnish even an approximate description of the atomic dynamics. There is a very large literature on nonlinear atomic responses of various types, of which some examples are listed in Refs. 6-4 through 6-10.

6-4   LOW-FREQUENCY AND HIGH-FREQUENCY RATE-EQUATION APPROXIMATIONS

The general multilevel rate equations are indeed linear, but they are sufficiently complex that their general solutions are algebraically involved even for the three-level case and are hopelessly lengthy for larger numbers of energy levels. Considerable algebraic simplification is possible for two limiting cases: low frequencies (typically microwave frequencies and below), for which the condition $hf_{mn} \ll kT$ holds, and high frequencies (typically infrared and optical frequencies), for which the condition $hf_{mn} \gg kT$ applies. We will now set down the approximate rate-equation forms in these two limiting cases.

LOW-FREQUENCY APPROXIMATION, $hf/kT \ll 1$ ■ If the approximation $hf_{mn}/kT \ll 1$ applies for all the transitions in a multilevel system, the Boltzmann ratios are nearly unity for all pairs of levels and, as illustrated in Fig. 6-8, the energy-level populations are all nearly equal. As a first approximation, the level populations are all nearly equal to $\mathcal{N}_n \approx \mathcal{N}/M$, where M is the total number of energy levels.

By using the Boltzmann ratio $\mathcal{N}_{m0}/\mathcal{N}_{n0} = e^{-hf_{mn}/kT}$, we may write the thermal-equilibrium population difference between any pair of levels in the form

$$\Delta \mathcal{N}_{0,nm} \equiv \mathcal{N}_{n0} - \mathcal{N}_{m0} = \frac{e^{hf_m/kT} - 1}{e^{hf_m/kT} + 1}(\mathcal{N}_{n0} + \mathcal{N}_{m0})$$

$$\approx \frac{hf_{mn}}{kT}\frac{\mathcal{N}}{M} \qquad \frac{hf_{mn}}{kT} \ll 1 \tag{1}$$

The general pair of relaxation terms between any two levels E_n and E_m may then be manipulated into the form

$$-w_{nm}N_n + w_{mn}N_m =$$
$$-\frac{w_{nm} + w_{mn}}{2}\left[(N_n - N_m) - \frac{w_{mn} - w_{nm}}{w_{mn} + w_{nm}}(N_n + N_m)\right] \quad (2)$$

If we define a longitudinal relaxation time $T_{1,nm}$ for the $n \to m$ transition by

$$w_{nm} + w_{mn} = \frac{1}{T_{1,nm}} \quad (3)$$

and make use of the Boltzmann ratio for the relaxation probabilities, then the relaxation terms may be written, without any approximations so far, as

$$-w_{nm}N_n + w_{mn}N_m = -\frac{1}{2T_{1,nm}}\left[\Delta N_{nm} - \frac{e^{hf_{mn}/kT} - 1}{e^{hf_{mn}/kT} + 1}(N_n + N_m)\right] \quad (4)$$

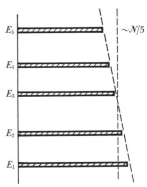

FIG. 6-8 In the low-frequency approximation $hf_{mn} \ll kT$ for all transitions, the level populations are all very nearly the same and approximately equal to the total number of atoms N divided by the number of levels M.

The low-frequency approximation is now made by assuming that if the populations all remain near $N_n \approx N/M$ and the population differences all remain small compared to the populations themselves, then we may write

$$N_n + N_m \approx N_{n0} + N_{m0} \approx 2\frac{N}{M} \quad (5)$$

With this approximation, the relaxation terms are converted into the simpler approximate form

$$-w_{nm}N_n + w_{mn}N_m = -\frac{\Delta N_{nm} - \Delta N_{0,nm}}{2T_{1,nm}} \quad (6)$$

The complete set of rate equations can then be written in the low-frequency approximate form

$$2\frac{d}{dt}N_n(t) = \sum_m -2W_{nm}\Delta N_{nm}(t) - \frac{\Delta N_{nm}(t) - \Delta N_{0,nm}}{T_{1,nm}} \quad (7)$$

In this form the right-hand sides are written entirely in terms of the population differences rather than the populations themselves (although the left-hand sides still involve the populations themselves). This form is often convenient, particularly in finding steady-state solutions where the time derivatives are all set equal to zero, because it is usually the population differences that are of most interest in maser situations.

If we set the left-hand sides of all the rate equations equal to zero, $d/dt = 0$, Eq. (7) then forms a coupled set of linear algebraic equations for the steady-state population differences ΔN_{nm}. However, this set still contains only $M - 1$ linearly independent equations. The set can be completed by using the total-population condition expressed in slightly different form,

$$\sum_n \Delta N_{n,n+1} = \Delta N_{12} + \Delta N_{23} + \cdots + \Delta N_{m-1,m} + \Delta N_{m,1} = 0 \quad (8)$$

to provide the Mth independent equation.

■ The essential feature of the high-frequency limit is that the Boltzmann ratios all become very large compared to unity (or very small, depending on which way they are written). For any two energy levels E_n and $E_m > E_n$, therefore, the upward relaxation

HIGH-FREQUENCY APPROXIMATION, $hf/kT \gg 1$

probability becomes negligible compared to the downward relaxation probability; that is,

$$\frac{w_{nm,\text{up}}}{w_{mn,\text{down}}} = e^{-(E_m - E_n)/kT} \simeq 0 \tag{9}$$

On each transition we can then write in general

$$w_{mn,\text{down}} \simeq \frac{1}{\tau_{nm}} \qquad w_{nm,\text{up}} \simeq 0 \tag{10}$$

where τ_{mn} (or, alternatively, $T_{1,nm}$) is the decay lifetime (radiative plus nonradiative) of the E_m energy level on the $n \to m$ transition.

In writing the rate equations, therefore, as a good first approximation, only downward relaxation terms need be included, and all upward relaxation terms can be neglected, as illustrated in Fig. 6-9. The rate equations then have the general form

$$\frac{d}{dt} N_n(t) = \sum_{\text{all } m} - W_{nm}[N_n(t) - N_m(t)] - \sum_{\substack{\text{lower levels} \\ E_m < E_n}} \frac{N_n(t)}{\tau_{nm}} + \sum_{\substack{\text{higher levels} \\ E_m < E_n}} \frac{N_m(t)}{\tau_{mn}} \tag{11}$$

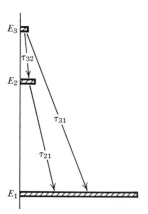

FIG. 6-9 In the high-frequency approximation $hf_{mn} \gg kT$, only the downward-relaxation rates $w_{mn} \equiv 1/\tau_{mn}$ need be taken into account in writing the rate equations.

We will see some of the consequences of this approximation in later chapters. In general, the rate equations are greatly simplified.

Of course, one consequence of this approximation is that if only relaxation is present, without any stimulated terms, all the atoms will eventually end up in the lowest or ground energy level. If the Boltzmann ratios are all large, then the populations of all the upper levels at thermal equilibrium are negligible compared to the ground level, and essentially all the atoms are in the ground level at equilibrium.

PROBLEMS

6-1. Verify, for any arbitrary level of partial saturation, that the rate at which an applied signal delivers energy to a partially saturated two-level atomic system exactly equals the rate at which that same system delivers energy to its thermal surroundings via longitudinal relaxation.

6-2. Suppose that the saturating signal W_{12} applied to a two-level atomic system consists of a steady-signal component plus an additional small-signal component that is amplitude modulated at a low modulation frequency ω_m, so that the stimulated transition probability has the time variation

$$W_{12}(t) = W_a + W_b \cos \omega_m t \qquad W_b \ll W_a$$

The steady signal W_a will cause some average degree of partial saturation of the population difference ΔN, while the time-varying part W_b will cause a similar time variation in the population difference ΔN, so that this can also be written as

$$\Delta N(t) = \Delta N_a + \Delta N_b \cos (\omega_m t + \phi) \qquad \Delta N_b \ll \Delta N_a$$

Using the rate equation for a two-level system and the assumptions that the b components are small compared to the a components in order to linearize the equations, find the population-

difference modulation ΔN_b caused by the signal modulation W_b. Discuss in particular the phase difference between these two quantities and how it varies with the modulation frequency ω_m compared to the relaxation time T_1. *Note:* The variation of this phase angle with ω_m has, in fact, been used as a practical experimental method for measuring T_1.

6-3. Write out the complete rate equations for a three-energy-level system in the low-frequency approximation, assuming applied signals present on all three transitions. Then set all time derivatives to zero, assume that $W_{13} = W_{23} = 0$, and solve for the steady-state population difference $\Delta N_{12,\text{st}}$ as a function of W_{12}. Compare the results with the saturation behavior for the simpler two-level system.

6-4. Compute the saturation behavior of a three-level system in the low-frequency approximation for a signal applied to the $1 \to 3$ transition only, assuming for simplicity that all relaxation times $T_{1,nm}$ are the same. Find the variation of all three population differences with W_{13} and plot them.

6-5. In the results of Prob. 6-4, verify, for any arbitrary degree of saturation, that the energy being delivered from signal to atoms exactly equals the energy being passed on from atoms to thermal surroundings.

6-6. A single-pass traveling-wave system filled with an absorptive two-level atomic medium has a relatively small peak attenuation, say, 10 percent reduction in transmitted power at midband, together with a corresponding atomic phase shift due to the atomic medium. We assume small fractional loss, so that the signal power level, and hence the atomic saturation level at higher powers, will be essentially the same all along the line. Taking this saturation into account, develop an expression for the atomic phase shift in passing through the traveling-wave system as a function of both input frequency and input power level. Compute and plot curves of atomic phase shift versus frequency for several different values of input power, including values both well below and well above the saturation power level for the atomic medium. Discuss these results.

6-7. Consider a tuned-cavity circuit containing internal losses represented by a conductance G_c across the circuit, together with the absorptive effects of a collection of two-level atoms represented by a conductance G_a connected across the circuit. The external coupling line also connected across the circuit has characteristic admittance G_e. For small signals the Q values associated with these three conductances have the relative values $Q_c = 2Q_m = 2Q_e$, where Q_m is the molecular Q associated with the conductance G_a. However, for large signals saturation effects occur in the atomic system, so that G_a, and hence Q_m, changes. Evaluate the power reflected versus the power incident on this cavity over a wide range of incident power levels, for a signal tuned exactly to the cavity resonance frequency.

6-8. Develop an electric-circuit analog, using resistors, capacitors, and batteries, in which the terminal voltages will be the direct analogs of the energy-level populations for the rate equations in the low-frequency approximation.

REFERENCES

6-1. L. J. Curtis, "A diagrammatic mnemonic for calculation of cascading level populations," *Am. J. Phys.*, **36**:1123 (December, 1968). An alternate method for finding transient solutions to multilevel rate equations.

6-2. J. P. Lloyd and G. E. Pake, "Spin relaxation in free radical solutions exhibiting hyperfine structure," *Phys. Rev.*, **94**:579 (May 1, 1954). An early paper discussing the writing of multilevel rate equations and saturation behavior in multilevel systems.

6-3. C. L. Tang, "On maser rate equations and transient oscillations," *J. Appl. Phys.*, **34**:2935 (October, 1963). Some discussion of the range of validity of rate equations.

6-4. F. Bosch, H. Rothe, and E. O. Schulz-DuBois, "Direct observation of difference frequency signal in a traveling-wave maser," *Proc. IEEE*, **52**:1243 (October, 1964).

6-5. D. H. Close, "Strong-field saturation effects in laser media," *Phys. Rev.*, **153**:360 (Jan. 10, 1967).

6-6. J. R. Fontana, R. H. Pantell, and R. G. Smith, "Parametric effects in a two-level electric dipole system," *J. Appl. Phys.*, **33**:2085 (June, 1962).

6-7. A. Javan, "Theory of a three-level maser," *Phys. Rev.*, **107**:73 (Sept. 15, 1957).

6-8. A. Javan and A. Szoke, "Theory of optical frequency mixing using resonant phenomena," *Phys. Rev.*, **137**:A536 (Jan. 18, 1965).

6-9. W. J. Tabor, F. S. Chen, and E. O. Schulz-DuBois, "Measurement of intermodulation and a discussion of dynamic range in a ruby traveling-wave maser," *Proc. IEEE*, **52**:656 (June, 1964). See also the preceding article in this journal.

6-10. C. L. Tang and H. Statz, "Nonlinear effects in the resonant absorption of several oscillating fields by a gas," *Phys. Rev.*, **128**:1013 (Nov. 1, 1962).

CHAPTER SEVEN

MICROWAVE
SOLID-STATE
MASERS

The microwave solid-state maser uses electron-paramagnetic-resonance (EPR) energy levels in certain crystals to obtain extremely low-noise (but also rather low-power and narrowband) amplification at microwave frequencies. In this chapter we will consider this particular type of useful maser device in closer detail.[1] There are several methods, such as adiabatic fast passage or the $180°$ pulse technique, by which we can obtain pulsed maser action with a two-level atomic system. Some of these ideas were known in the early 1950s, when the ammonia molecular-beam maser was the only working maser device. By far the greatest impetus to maser development came in 1956, however, when Bloembergen showed how to create and maintain a con-

[1] Readers interested primarily in optical maser devices may skip this chapter, although many of the ideas developed here are also useful in understanding laser devices.

tinuous population inversion in a three-level system. The same three-level idea had been suggested earlier by Basov and Prokhorov in connection with energy levels in gases but apparently was not exploited or extended to solids.

In the following sections we will describe this three-level maser scheme and show how it can be used for amplification in a cavity-type maser. The important topic of amplification in microwave traveling-wave masers will then be considered, followed by some typical experimental results and some useful practical amplifications for microwave maser amplifiers.[2]

7-1   THE THREE-LEVEL MICROWAVE MASER

This section is concerned with the analysis of the Bloembergen three-level maser scheme, and with the use of this scheme in microwave cavity masers. A preliminary explanation of the three-level maser scheme was given in Chap. 1. We will now develop a quantitative analysis, using the rate equations of Chap. 6.

Consider the three-energy-level system shown in Fig. 7-1a, with radiation applied at the two frequencies $f_{31} \equiv f_p$, where p signifies the *pump* transition, and $f_{32} \equiv f_s$, where s signifies the *amplified-signal* transition. Let the pump radiation be made strong enough to saturate the $3 \to 1$, or pump, transition, so that the level populations N_1 and N_3 become equal. The intermediate-level population N_2 will then adjust itself to some new steady-state (but non-thermal-equilibrium) value determined by the relaxation rates among the levels. As shown in Figs. 7-1b and 7-1c, respectively, the result is a population inversion on one or the other of the $2 \to 1$ and $3 \to 2$ transitions—barring the unlikely (and unlucky) event that all three populations become equal. Let us plan in advance for the $3 \to 2$ transition to be the inverted signal transition and find what conditions are necessary to obtain this result.

In writing the rate equations we assume that $hf/kT \ll 1$ for all three transitions, remembering that this assumption will begin to break down at frequencies in the millimeter-wave range for temperatures of $2°K$ or lower. The low-frequency approximate form for the rate equations (Sec. 6-3) can then be used, including the approximation

$$w_{ij} \approx w_{ji} \approx \frac{1}{2T_{1,ij}} \qquad i,j = 1,2,3 \tag{1}$$

[1] See Ref. 7-3.

[2] Much more extensive coverage of all aspects of microwave solid-state masers is given in the author's earlier book (see Ref. 7-9), from which much of the material in this chapter has been condensed.

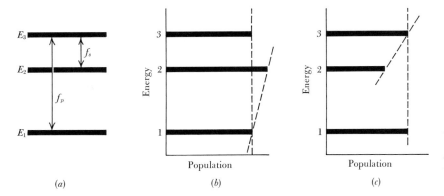

FIG. 7-1 The Bloembergen three-level microwave maser scheme: (a) energy levels, (b) inversion on the 1→2 transition, and (c) inversion on the 2→3 transition.

The complete rate equations with both signals applied are then

$$\frac{d}{dt}\mathcal{N}_1 = -w_{12}(\Delta\mathcal{N}_{12} - \Delta\mathcal{N}_{0,12}) - w_{13}(\Delta\mathcal{N}_{13} - \Delta\mathcal{N}_{0,13}) - W_{13}\,\Delta\mathcal{N}_{13}$$

$$\frac{d}{dt}\mathcal{N}_2 = -w_{21}(\Delta\mathcal{N}_{21} - \Delta\mathcal{N}_{0,21}) - w_{23}(\Delta\mathcal{N}_{23} - \Delta\mathcal{N}_{0,23}) - W_{23}\,\Delta\mathcal{N}_{23}$$

$$\frac{d}{dt}\mathcal{N}_3 = -w_{31}(\Delta\mathcal{N}_{31} - \Delta\mathcal{N}_{0,31}) - w_{32}(\Delta\mathcal{N}_{32} - \Delta\mathcal{N}_{0,32})$$
$$- W_{31}\,\Delta\mathcal{N}_{31} - W_{32}\,\Delta\mathcal{N}_{32} \quad (2)$$

To find the steady-state population differences we can set all time derivatives $d/dt = 0$ and rewrite these equations, with $W_{ij} = W_{ji}$, $w_{ij} \approx w_{ji}$, and $\Delta\mathcal{N}_{ij} \equiv -\Delta\mathcal{N}_{ji}$, in the form

$$\begin{bmatrix} w_{12} & 0 & (w_{13} + W_p) \\ w_{12} & -(w_{23} + W_s) & 0 \\ 0 & (w_{23} + W_s) & (w_3 + W_p) \end{bmatrix} \begin{bmatrix} \Delta\mathcal{N}_{12} \\ \Delta\mathcal{N}_{23} \\ \Delta\mathcal{N}_{13} \end{bmatrix} = \begin{bmatrix} w_{12}\,\Delta\mathcal{N}_{0,12} + w_{13}\,\Delta\mathcal{N}_{0,13} \\ w_{12}\,\Delta\mathcal{N}_{0,12} - w_{23}\,\Delta\mathcal{N}_{0,23} \\ w_{13}\,\Delta\mathcal{N}_{0,13} + w_{23}\,\Delta\mathcal{N}_{0,23} \end{bmatrix} \quad (3)$$

The indices on the $\Delta\mathcal{N}_{ij}$ terms have been interchanged as necessary to make all quantities positive. We are primarily interested, of course, in the inverted population difference $\Delta\mathcal{N}_{32} = -\Delta\mathcal{N}_{23}$ on the signal transition.

SOLUTION FOR FULLY
SATURATED PUMP TRANSITION

■ The general solution of Eq. (3), which we will write down a little later, is somewhat messy. A quick solution may be obtained by assuming that the pump transition rate W_p is strong enough to completely saturate the pump transition, $\Delta\mathcal{N}_{13} = 0$, regardless of any relaxation effects. Since $\Delta\mathcal{N}_{12} = -\Delta\mathcal{N}_{23}$ for full pump saturation, the second rate equation by itself immediately yields

$$\Delta\mathcal{N}_{32} = -\Delta\mathcal{N}_{21} = \frac{w_{12}\,\Delta\mathcal{N}_{0,12} - w_{23}\,\Delta\mathcal{N}_{0,23}}{w_{12} + w_{23} + W_s} \quad (4)$$

With the low-frequency approximations of Sec. 6-3, this result can also be written as

$$\Delta\mathcal{N}_{32} \approx \frac{h\mathcal{N}}{3kT}\,\frac{f_{21}/T_{1,12} - f_{32}/T_{1,23}}{1/T_{1,12} + 1/T_{1,23} + 2W_s} \quad (5)$$

These results show that either the $3 \to 2$ transition or the $2 \to 1$ transition will become inverted, depending on whether the first or the second term in the numerators is larger. The requirement for the $3 \to 2$ transition to be inverted is

$$w_{12}\,\Delta\mathcal{N}_{0,12} > w_{23}\,\Delta\mathcal{N}_{0,23} \quad \text{or} \quad \frac{f_{12}}{T_{1,12}} > \frac{f_{23}}{T_{1,23}} \quad (6)$$

By analogy with parametric-amplifier terminology, the $2 \to 1$ transition is sometimes called the *idler* or *i transition*, so that $f_{21} \equiv f_i$ and $f_s + f_i = f_p$, as in parametric amplifiers. This is definitely not to imply that parametric amplifiers and masers are similar in mode of operation, but merely to choose a convenient name for the remaining transition. The population-inversion condition can then be written as

$$\frac{f_i}{f_s} > \frac{T_{1,i}}{T_{1,s}} \quad \text{or} \quad \frac{f_p}{f_s} > 1 + \frac{T_{1,i}}{T_{1,s}} \quad (7)$$

These conditions are actually valid regardless of which of the $1 \to 2$ or $2 \to 3$ transitions becomes the signal and which the idler.

■ For small applied signals Eq. (5) can be rewritten in the form

INVERSION RATIO

$$\Delta N_{32} = I \frac{hf_s}{kT} \frac{N}{3} = I \Delta N_{0,23} \tag{8}$$

where the *inversion ratio* I is given by

$$I \equiv \frac{\Delta N_{32}}{\Delta N_{0,23}} = \frac{f_p/f_s - [1 + T_{1,i}/T_{1,s}]}{1 + T_{1,i}/T_{1,s}} \tag{9}$$

By definition, the inversion ratio I is the ratio of the inverted population difference ΔN_{32} with the pump on to the thermal-equilibrium population difference $\Delta N_{0,23}$ with the pump off. Note that the inversion ratio depends only on the frequency and relaxation-time ratios, and not on their absolute values. The inversion ratio is of order unity in most cases. For example, in two simple cases the inversion ratio will be

$$I = \begin{cases} \dfrac{f_p}{2f_s} - 1 & \text{if } T_{1,i} = T_{1,s} \\[2ex] \dfrac{f_p}{f_s} - 1 & \text{if } T_{1,i} \to 0 \text{ (optimum)} \end{cases} \tag{10}$$

Even though the relaxation times T_1 themselves may be temperature dependent, the inversion ratio may be nearly independent of temperature.

■ If both W_p and W_s are assumed to be finite and the assumption of complete pump saturation is removed, the exact steady-state solution to the rate equations (3) is

GENERAL SOLUTION FOR PARTIAL PUMP SATURATION

$$\Delta N_{32,\text{st}} = \frac{W_p(w_{12} \Delta N_{0,12} - w_{23} \Delta N_{0,23}) - \Delta N_{0,23}(w_{12}w_{23} + w_{12}w_{13} + w_{13}w_{23})}{W_p(w_{12} + w_{23} + W_s) + W_s(w_{12} + w_{23}) + (w_{12}w_{23} + w_{12}w_{13} + w_{13}w_{23})} \tag{11}$$

With all signals removed, $W_p = W_s = 0$, this expression gives the correct thermal-equilibrium limit $\Delta N_{32} = -\Delta N_{0,23}$. However, for the pump transition to be strongly saturated, obviously the pump rate must be much stronger than the relaxation rates, $W_p \gg w_{ij}$ for all i and j, and also much stronger than the signal, $W_p \gg W_s$. The general result (11) then reduces directly to the fully pump-saturated results (4) or (5).

■ The large number of three-level masers which have been successfully operated since Bloembergen's proposal are overwhelming evidence of the correctness of his analysis. We can also present at least one experimental curve verifying the rate-equation analysis in detail. From the saturation analysis of Chap. 6, we can expect the pump transition to saturate in the fashion

EXPERIMENTAL CONFIRMATION

$$\Delta N_{13} = \Delta N_{0,13} \frac{1}{1 + kP_p} \tag{12}$$

where P_p is the pump power applied and k is a constant which lumps together cavity geometry, transition probability, relaxation rates, and so on. At the same time, if there are no signal saturation effects, the general solution of Eq. (11) for the signal-frequency population difference can be written in the form

$$\Delta N_{32} = \Delta N_{0,23}\left(I - \frac{1 + I}{1 + kP_p}\right) \tag{13}$$

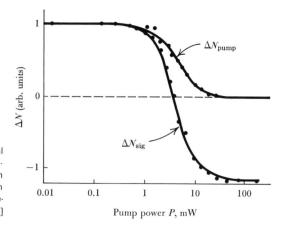

FIG. 7-2   Saturation of the pump transition and inversion of the signal transition, as predicted by the rate-equation analysis for the Bloembergen three-level maser scheme. Maser material is potassium chromicyanide, pump = 8000 MHz, signal = 1700 MHz. [From S. Shapiro and N. Bloembergen, "Relaxation effects in a maser material, K$_3$(CoCr)(CN)$_6$," *Phys. Rev.*, **116**:1453 (1959).]

where I is the inversion ratio and k and P_p are the same as in (12). Figure 7-2 shows curves of the population differences ΔN_{13} and ΔN_{23} versus pump power P as determined experimentally by Shapiro and Bloembergen in a crystal of potassium chromicyanide. A small piece of crystal in a test cavity was used, and the populations were monitored by their paramagnetic-resonance absorption. It is clear that the pump transition saturates and the signal transition inverts with increasing pump power in exactly the fashion predicted. The experimental points are fitted very exactly by curves obtained from Eqs. (12) and (13) with appropriate values of k and the inversion ratio, which is a little over unity in this case. The very close agreement may be taken as detailed confirmation of our entire rate-equation analysis.

CONDITIONS FOR
LARGE INVERSION

■ The inversion and inversion-ratio expressions (4) to (9) show that to guarantee population inversion we want a high pump frequency in relation to the signal frequency, together with a short relaxation time on the idler transition in relation to the signal transition. Obviously from Fig. 7-1, a long signal relaxation time means that the lower signal level E_2 is only weakly coupled to the upper maser level E_3, while a short idler relaxation time means that atoms feeding into the lower maser level E_2 are rapidly equilibrated with the ground level E_1.

In practice the relaxation times are often not known with any accuracy. With the simplest possible assumption, that all the T_1's are equal, the condition for population inversion becomes $f_s/f_i < 1$ or $f_p/f_s > 2$; that is, population inversion occurs on the smaller of the two transitions unless the relaxation times differ in value. A pump–signal-frequency ratio of 3 or 4 is typically sought in practical masers to ensure good population inversion. This makes it difficult to obtain suitable sources of pump power near the upper limit of the microwave range. It is interesting to note, however, that the first three-level maser built[1] actually had $f_p/f_s \approx 2$. The relaxation-time ratio for the signal and idler transitions in this case was altered by artificial means.

The inversion ratio is a number of order unity in most cases, so that the inverted population difference obtained in a microwave maser with the pump on is of the same order as the thermal-equilibrium population difference with the pump off. From Eq. (5) or Eq. (8), the size of the thermal-equilibrium population difference varies inversely with temperature (for $hf/kT \ll 1$). A high operating temperature means small popu-

[1] See Ref. 7-7.

lation difference and small absorption with the pump off, and correspondingly small inverted population difference and small maser gain with the pump on. To obtain a sufficiently large population difference for good maser operation requires low-temperature operation, almost always in the liquid-helium range. Getting around this requirement entails getting around Boltzmann's law—a difficult assignment. Masers have been operated in a few cases at temperatures well above that of helium, but only with substantial sacrifices in performance, owing to the decrease in $\Delta N_{0,23}$ at the higher temperatures.

Note also that once the pump transition becomes fully saturated, pumping harder does not improve the population inversion in any way. In one sense this is an advantage, since it means that the population inversion and the gain in a microwave maser are automatically stabilized against any amplitude fluctuations or ripple in the pump power supplied to the maser material.

■ If we assume that the pump transition is held fully saturated under all conditions, the inverted population difference on the signal transition saturates with increasing signal power W_s in exactly the same way a simple uninverted two-level transition does. That is, Eq. (5) may be rewritten in the form

SIGNAL SATURATION

$$\Delta N_{32} = \frac{w_{12}\,\Delta N_{0,12} - w_{23}\,\Delta N_{0,23}}{w_{12} + w_{23} + W_s} = I\,\Delta N_{0,23}\frac{1}{1 + 2T_{1,\text{eff}}W_s} \tag{14}$$

where the *effective relaxation time* for signal saturation of the inverted transition is

$$\frac{1}{T_{1,\text{eff}}} = \frac{1}{T_{1,s}} + \frac{1}{T_{1,i}} \tag{15}$$

To put this another way, the gain or the inverted population of a microwave maser will saturate in the fashion

$$\Delta N_{32} = \Delta N_{32,\text{small-sig}}\frac{1}{1 + \text{const} \times P_s} \tag{16}$$

where P_s is the signal energy density in the maser material. This is exactly the same form as the saturation of the absorption on a simple two-level transition.

Shortening either $T_{1,s}$ or $T_{1,i}$ will evidently shorten $T_{1,\text{eff}}$ and raise the saturation level of the maser—a matter of some importance, since real microwave masers saturate at inconveniently low signal levels. The equations also make clear the interesting fact that once the pump transition is fully saturated, the signal saturation level does not depend in any way on the pumping level; in particular, the signal saturation level cannot be increased simply by pumping harder, as might at first seem reasonable.

■ Once population inversion has been obtained on a microwave transition in a paramagnetic crystal by the three-level maser scheme, this crystal can be placed in an appropriate microwave cavity, and reflection-type cavity maser amplification can be obtained in exactly the fashion analyzed in detail in Chap. 5. Because the analysis of Chap. 5 applies exactly to the microwave-maser case, we will not repeat it here.

CAVITY MASER AMPLIFICATION

The essential elements of a microwave cavity maser, then, include some sort of waveguide or coaxial type of microwave cavity resonant at the signal frequency, with an input-output coupling line for the signals to be amplified. This cavity must be more or less completely filled with the maser material. At the same time, in order to apply the pumping power efficiently to the maser material, the cavity should also have a higher-order resonant mode at the pump frequency and an input line for the pump power which should be impedance matched to the cavity pump mode. Since reflection-type cavity masers have better performance and stability than transmission-type amplifiers, and since good microwave circulator devices are available, microwave cavity masers are always operated in the reflection mode.

Because of the necessity for helium-temperature operation ($\sim 4°$K) in practical microwave masers, the maser cavity must be placed inside a liquid-helium Dewar flask which is either periodically refilled with helium from a storage Dewar or cooled by a closed-cycle helium refrigerator. Since only very small heat leaks can be tolerated in a helium-cooled system, the signal and pump input lines must be special waveguides or coaxial lines made of extremely thin stainless steel, metallized plastic, or other special material. The entire helium system is almost always surrounded by a second Dewar or heat shield, cooled to liquid-nitrogen temperature ($77°$K). The magnetic field of a few thousand gauss usually required may be supplied either by an external electromagnet or solenoid outside the Dewars, which makes the magnet very heavy and bulky, or by a superconducting solenoid placed around the cavity inside the helium Dewar. The superconducting solenoid can be very lightweight and requires negligible power consumption, but it is somewhat more expensive to fabricate.

From the results of Chap. 5, the midband voltage gain of a microwave cavity maser is given by

$$g_0 = \frac{Q_m + Q_e}{Q_m - Q_e} \tag{17}$$

and the amplifier's 3-dB bandwidth is given by

$$\Delta f_{3\text{dB}} = \frac{1}{g_0 - 1} \frac{2}{Q_m + Q_a} \tag{18}$$

where Q_e is the external Q of the maser cavity as determined by the coupling strength of the signal-input–output line, Q_m is the molecular or maser Q of the maser material in the cavity as determined by the population inversion and other factors, and Q_a is the atomic linewidth Q as determined by the linewidth of the signal atomic transition. We have assumed here, as is usually the case, that internal ohmic and wall losses in the cavity will be negligible, $Q_c \gg Q_e, Q_m$.

Note that in the microwave-maser case the population inversion and the value of Q_m become essentially constant once the pump transition is fully saturated and cannot be adjusted while the maser is in operation. Therefore the midband gain value and the associated bandwidth can be adjusted in operation only by changing Q_e, that is, by changing the amount of coupling of the signal line through some sort of mechanical adjustment.

PRACTICAL CAVITY MASERS ■ Practical cavity masers can use a wide variety of different waveguide and coaxial cavity designs, together with a more limited number of useful microwave maser materials. Figure 7-3 shows a cavity-maser design for a signal frequency of 10,000 MHz, in which the pump and signal modes are both cavity modes in a rectangular cavity completely filled with ruby. The pump and signal external coupling lines are both rectangular waveguides incorporating tapered sapphire transition sections. In building this maser the size of the coupling holes into the cavity from each waveguide had to be carefully determined by trial and error, since no adjustment was possible during operation.

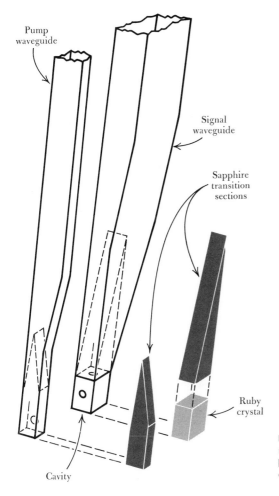

Pump
waveguide

Signal
waveguide

Sapphire
transition
sections

Ruby
crystal

Cavity

FIG. 7-3 An all-waveguide microwave maser-cavity design using a rectangular cavity filled with ruby, where $f_p = 23.5$ GHz and $f_s = 9.3$ GHz. [From T. H. Maiman, "Maser behavior: temperature and concentration effects," *J. Appl. Phys.*, **31**:222 (1960).]

Figure 7-4 shows, as another example, a fairly high-performance 3000-MHz maser cavity. The cavity is essentially a "rectangular-coaxial" or TEM cavity, with the axis of the TEM line running vertically in the figure, and with a break or capacitive gap in the center conductor at the middle of the cavity. Figure 7-5 shows the two resulting lowest-order resonant modes of this cavity. In the signal mode the gap capacitance of the center gap resonates with the inductance of the two shorted TEM-line sections on either side, while the pump mode is essentially a shorted half-wave transmission-line mode, which is unaffected by the center gap, since this mode has no axial current flow at the center of the cavity.

The center conductor of the TEM line is offset to one side of the cavity. It may appear that only a small fraction of the cavity is filled with maser material. However, analysis of the field patterns shows that, in fact, most of the rf stored energy is concentrated in the narrow region occupied by the maser crystal, and the cavity filling factor is actually close to unity. The input line for the pump power at $\sim$10,000 MHz is a slot-coupled waveguide, while the signal line is a coaxial line which is probe coupled directly into the center gap. Among other advantages, this permits easy variation of the signal coupling by mechanically changing the probe insertion. Also, the signal line is

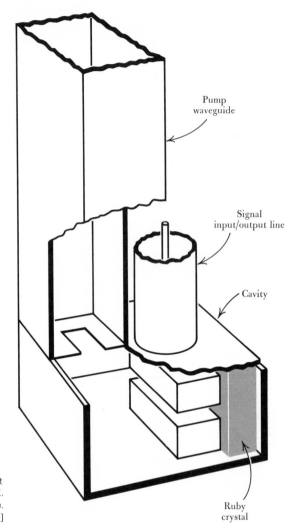

FIG. 7-4 High-filling-factor 3000-MHz cavity maser constructed at Stanford University. [From W. S. C. Chang, J. Cromack, and A. E. Siegman, "Cavity maser experiments using ruby at S-band," *J. Electron. Control,* **6:**508 (1959).]

almost totally decoupled from the pump fields, so that the powerful pump fields do not leak out the signal line and cause possible overloading or interference in the sensitive signal equipment.

MICROWAVE SOLID-STATE
MASER MATERIALS

■ The selection of a microwave maser material is a complicated choice involving consideration of the relaxation times and inversion-ratio performance of the material; the energy levels, particularly their zero-field splitting; the availability and cost of large, high-quality single crystals of the material; and such practical factors as the hardness and water insolubility of the crystal and its ability to stand repeated cooling to helium temperature without cracking. Only a limited number of fully suitable materials have been found, of which one of the best and most readily available is ruby. Ruby has four Zeeman-split levels of the lowest or ground optical energy level ($S = \frac{3}{2}$). The splitting of these levels with an applied dc magnetic field B_0 is different for different angles θ between the dc field and the ruby symmetry or c axis. Figure 7-6 shows these energy levels for the particular case of $\theta = 30°$. There are three different potential operating

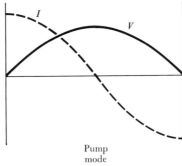

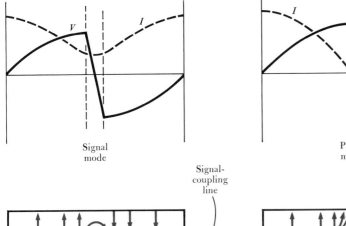

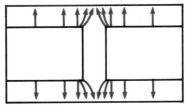

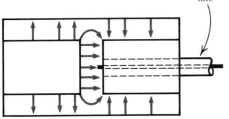

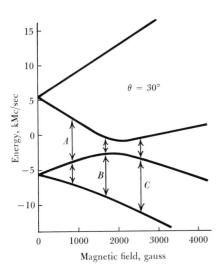

Signal
mode

Pump
mode

Signal-
coupling
line

FIG. 7-5 Voltage and current distributions and electric-field patterns for the signal and pump modes in the rectangular TEM cavity design of Fig. 7-4.

points for a three-level maser with a signal frequency near 3000 MHz and pump frequency near 10,000 MHz.[1]

Given a completed cavity with fixed signal and pump resonances, the value of θ may have to be shifted slightly to make both the signal and pump frequencies coincide with the atomic transition frequencies. One design technique for accomplishing this is the *isofrequency plot*, shown in Fig. 7-7. By using energy-level diagrams such as that

[1] This is, of course, really a four-level system and should be analyzed with the four-level rate equations, but the results are very nearly the same if the fourth level is ignored and the system treated as a simple three-level system.

$\theta = 30°$

FIG. 7-6 The Zeeman energy levels of ruby for an angle $\theta = 30°$ between the c axis and the dc magnetic field, showing three possible operating points for maser action with a signal frequency of 3000 MHz.

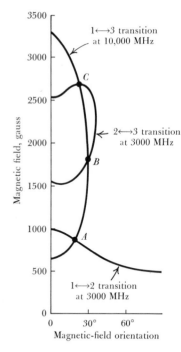

FIG. 7-7 An isofrequency diagram for ruby, showing the loci of magnetic field versus field angle for fixed signal and pump frequencies f_s = 3000 MHz and f_p = 10,000 MHz. The three intersections correspond more or less to the three operating points in Fig. 7-6.

in Fig. 7-6 plotted for several different values of θ (or by using computer solutions for the energy levels as functions of B_0 and θ), we can trace out the loci of (B_0, θ) that yield fixed signal and pump frequencies on different transitions. The intersections of these curves then determine potential points of maser operation, as indicated in Fig. 7-7.

Determining the actual inversion ratio and the strength of the maser action at a potential operating point, such as A, B, or C in Figs. 7-6 and 7-7, is generally an experimental problem. For example, with the cavity of Fig. 7-4, maser action of medium strength was obtained at point C, weaker maser action at point A, and no maser action at point B. At point C the gain and bandwidth of the maser were varied by changing the signal-coupling parameter Q_e. Figure 7-8 shows the gains and bandwidths obtained, in close agreement with a fixed gain-bandwidth product $g_0 \, \Delta f_{3\mathrm{dB}} \approx 4.7$ MHz. This value is typical but not outstanding for a cavity maser at 3000 MHz.

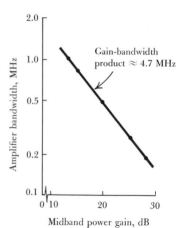

FIG. 7-8 Maser-amplifier performance of the cavity design of Fig. 7-4 at operating point C in Figs. 7-6 and 7-7.

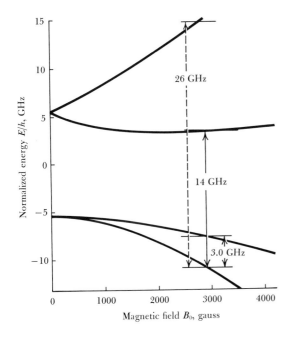

FIG. 7-9 Ruby energy levels for $\theta = 90°$, showing an operating point with a 3000-MHz signal and two possible pumping frequencies.

With the same cavity, measurements were also made at a considerably higher-performance operating point at $\theta = 90°$ in ruby, as shown in Fig. 7-9. In this case the pump frequency was raised from ~10 GHz to ~14 GHz, so that $f_p/f_s \sim 4.7$. The gain-bandwidth product in this case increased to >55 MHz.

Figure 7-9 illustrates another practical point. Instead of pumping on the $1 \to 3$ transition at ~14 GHz, it is possible to pump on the $1 \to 4$ transition at ~26 GHz. Because of the greatly increased f_p/f_s ratio, we might expect even better inversion and better gain-bandwidth product. However, microwave signal sources to provide the required hundred or more milliwatts of pump power are more expensive, shorter lived, and less flexible at 26 GHz than at 14 GHz. Some limited experiments carried out at this higher pumping frequency, although they were constrained by other incidental problems, did in fact indicate that better performance might be achieved with the higher-frequency pumping.

■ As the input signal to a cavity maser is increased, the inverted population difference and the gain of the cavity maser decrease owing to signal saturation effects. The decrease in amplifier gain is predicted by a relatively simple analysis[1] based on Eq. (16). An essential point is that the saturating signal power or power density appearing in Eq. (16) must be neither the input nor the output power from the amplifier, but the signal power density *inside* the maser cavity. Figure 7-10 shows, by way of example, the theoretical and experimental saturation behavior of a typical microwave cavity maser. Note that the maser begins to saturate at an input power level approximately 60 dB below 1 mW, that is, an input power level of only ~10^{-9} W. This very low saturation level is one undesirable attribute of most microwave maser devices.

Figure 7-11 shows a complete packaged maser received system built by the Hughes Research Laboratories. The maser Dewar flask is mounted on a bracket at-

SATURATION

[1] See Ref. 7-9.

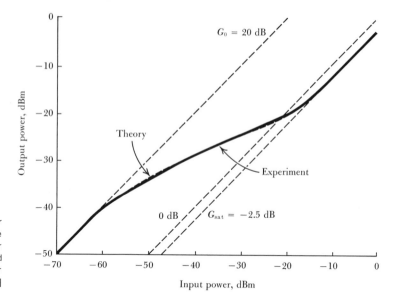

FIG. 7-10 Output power versus input power for a cavity-maser amplifier, showing the saturation of the amplifier gain at higher input power levels. [From F. R. Arams and S. Okwit, "Packaged tunable L-band maser system," *Proc. IRE*, **48**:866 (1960).]

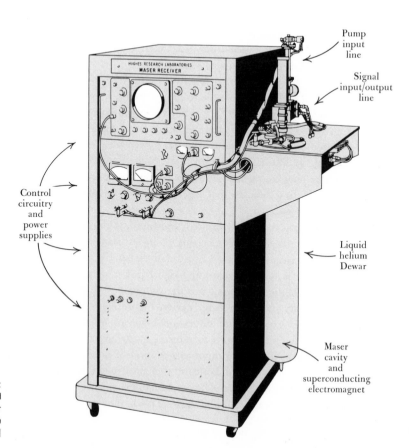

FIG. 7-11 Example of a packaged 10-GHz cavity maser, including power supplies and control circuitry. [From T. H. Maiman, "Maser behavior: temperature and concentration effects," *J. Appl. Phys.*, **31**:222 (1960).]

tached to one side of a rack panel containing the controls, pump-power supply, and additional instrumentation for further amplifying the signal after it leaves the maser preamplifier. Obviously, the maser cavity and Dewar unit could be mounted externally—for example, at the focus of a receiving antenna—and connected to the instrumentation panel by appropriate cables.

■ From Sec. 4-6, the maser Q_m on a magnetic-resonance transition is given by

CALCULATION OF Q_m

$$\frac{1}{Q_m} = \frac{2g^2\beta^2\mu_0}{h} \frac{\Delta\mathcal{N}_{32}}{\Delta f_a} \tag{19}$$

For a real microwave cavity a finite filling factor $\eta \leq 1$ must be included in this expression. The inverted population difference on a transition in an n-level system may be written in terms of the inversion ratio and the thermal-equilibrium population difference, with the $hf/kT \ll 1$ approximation, in the form

$$\Delta\mathcal{N}_{32} = I \Delta\mathcal{N}_{0,23} = I \frac{hf_s}{kT} \frac{\mathcal{N}_v}{n} \tag{20}$$

These quantities must be atomic densities (per unit volume) in the Q_m formula. We note again that

$$\frac{hf}{kT} \simeq \frac{1}{20} \frac{f\,(\text{GHz})}{T\,(°\text{K})} \tag{21}$$

Also, a dimensionless matrix-element factor $\sigma^2 \leq 1$, which measures the transition-probability strength of the real transition against that for an ideal two-level transition, is often inserted in this expression (this factor plays somewhat the same role as the oscillator strength for electric-dipole transitions). With these modifications, the maser Q_m is given by

$$\frac{1}{Q_m} = \frac{2g^2\beta^2\mu_0}{h} \frac{hf_s}{kT} \frac{\mathcal{N}_v}{n} \frac{\eta I \sigma^2}{\Delta f_a} \tag{22}$$

Although all the significant quantities in this expression are discussed elsewhere, a short review at this point may be useful. For best maser performance we want the lowest possible magnetic Q_m, or the highest Q_m^{-1}. Therefore, other factors being equal, maser performance is better at higher frequencies and lower temperatures. The inverse temperature dependence, which traces back to the Boltzmann law, as discussed earlier, is the basic reason that liquid-helium temperatures are commonly required for a useful maser amplifier, although marginal operation has been obtained at much higher temperatures at the higher microwave frequencies.[1]

Note that Q_m^{-1} depends only on the spin *density* $\mathcal{N}_v$, and not on the total number of spins or the size of the maser cavity. Simply increasing the spin density might seem a simple way of improving performance, but there are sharp limitations on how far we can go in this direction. Above some relatively low spin density, the resonance linewidth Δf_a increases directly with the spin density $\mathcal{N}_v$ due to spin-spin, or dipolar, broadening, so that the effects of these two factors on Q_m cancel, and no advantage is gained. Also, above a certain density, *cross-relaxation effects* become significant in de-

---

[1] Note that the T appearing in Eq. (22) and the earlier expressions is the *bath* temperature, or the temperature of the thermal surroundings of the atoms, and not the atomic or spin temperature of the signal transition, which becomes negative when the pump is turned on.

creasing spin-lattice relaxation times and thus increasing the pump-power requirement. More significantly, they also generally cause the inversion ratio I to deteriorate badly at higher concentrations. For one or another of these reasons, acceptable spin densities generally correspond to a quite dilute paramagnetic crystal, typically with less than 1 percent concentration of paramagnetic ions. As the factor n shows, the fewer the number of levels over which these spins are distributed, the better, although this factor in some cases is partially canceled by larger values of σ^2 in multilevel spin systems.

Narrower linewidth Δf_a generally means better maser performance, provided that the linewidth is not so narrow as to limit the maser bandwidth through the Q_a factor in Eq. (18). Typical microwave-maser-crystal linewidths range from a few tens to perhaps a few hundred megacycles.

In choosing a maser material and operating point, it is, of course, important to avoid signal transitions for which σ^2 is small or zero, i.e., weak or forbidden transitions. In general the transition probability for a transition between two adjacent levels is strong, $\sigma^2 \sim 1$, although there are exceptions. Transitions which jump across an intermediate level ($\Delta M = 2$ transitions) are generally weaker, again with some exceptions, and σ^2 for these transitions becomes quite small outside those regions where the energy levels curve strongly owing to strong mixing of the spin states.

We have already seen that the inversion ratio I depends on the relaxation-time ratio and the pump–signal-frequency ratio and is generally improved by higher pump frequencies. Additional methods of improving I are discussed below.

Note that all the factors discussed so far are entirely properties of the maser material, and not of the maser cavity or microwave circuitry. In fact, the only significant property of a simple tuned cavity which affects the maser performance is the filling factor η. We have already noted what is required for $\eta \to 1$: maser crystal everywhere that there is an rf magnetic field and a cavity design which orients the bulk of the rf magnetic field in the optimum direction for inducing transitions.

To gain some idea of typical magnetic Q values, the following typical parameters can be put into Eq. (22):

Maser material: pink ruby, 0.1 percent chromium concentration
$\mathcal{N} = 5 \times 10^{19}$ spins/cm^3
$n = 4$ levels
$f = 3000$ MHz
$T = 4.2°$K
$\Delta f_a = 100$ MHz
$Q_a = 30$
$\sigma^2 = 1$
$I = 2$
$\eta = 1$

The result is the magnetic Q value,

$$Q_m \approx 100 \tag{23}$$

which is in accord with experimentally achieved Q_m values for this maser material in this frequency range. Note that this predicts a gain-bandwidth product

$$g_0 \, \Delta f_{3\text{dB}} \approx \frac{2 f_a}{Q_m + Q_a} \approx 46 \text{ MHz} \tag{24}$$

which is not far from what was obtained in the experiments reported earlier.

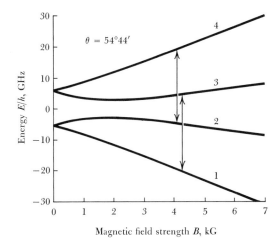

FIG. 7-12 Ruby energy levels for $\cos^2 \theta = 1/3$, or $\theta = 54° \ 44'$. The two arrows indicate that the two pumping frequencies f_{13} and f_{24} are equal for all values of the dc magnetic field.

PUSH-PULL PUMPING METHODS

■ There are a variety of more or less complicated methods for improving the inversion ratio in maser materials, as well as for broadening the frequency-response bandwidth of a cavity maser amplifier. We will discuss only one of these methods here. Figure 7-12 shows the energy-level diagram in ruby for the special case of $3 \cos^2 \theta = 1$, or $\theta = 54°44'$, at which angle the four energy levels are symmetrically distributed about their mean value. Under this condition, it is possible at any field value to look for maser action on the $3 \rightarrow 2$ transition while pumping simultaneously on the $1 \rightarrow 3$ and the $2 \rightarrow 4$ transitions with the same pumping radiation, since the two transition frequencies are equal. Similar operating points can be found elsewhere in ruby and in other maser materials.

The type of double maser pumping possible in this situation is referred to as *push-pull pumping*, as illustrated in Fig. 7-13a. It is left to the reader to write out the rate-equation analysis for this situation; note that in this situation the pump is lifting atoms from the normally most populated lowest level into the upper maser level and is simultaneously lifting atoms out of the lower maser level into the normally least-populated topmost level. A better inversion with push-pull pumping than with normal three-level pumping can be expected and is usually obtained. To put this another way, in the push-pull case inversion can often be obtained even though the signal frequency

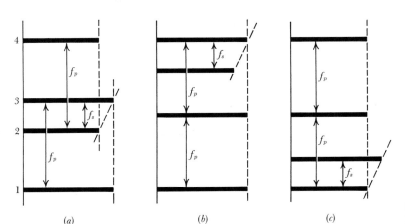

FIG. 7-13 Various forms of push-pull or push-push pumping schemes.

is greater than one-half the pump frequency, so that $f_s/f_i > 1$. There are many extensions of this idea of push-pull, or in some cases push-push, pumping, some of which are illustrated in Fig. 7-13b and c. However, the ruby operating angle shown in Fig. 7-12 turns out to be particularly useful for this purpose.

7-2   MICROWAVE TRAVELING-WAVE MASERS

By distributing a negative-resistance mechanism such as an inverted maser material along a propagating circuit instead of placing it in a resonant cavity, we can avoid the gain-bandwidth limitation inherent in the resonant-cavity approach and obtain a traveling-wave maser which has not only considerably greater bandwidth, but also greater stability, easier tuning, and a number of other advantages. In fact, the advantages of the traveling-wave approach for microwave solid-state masers are so strong that an engineer contemplating the development of a microwave maser at the present time should resist the temptation to build a cavity maser first "just for practice," and should probably begin immediately with the traveling-wave approach.

In this section we will discuss the basic mechanism of traveling-wave amplification in the microwave slow-wave circuits used in masers and illustrate the resulting performance characteristics with some examples of good traveling-wave maser designs.[1]

CHARACTERISTICS OF TRAVELING-WAVE MASERS

■ A microwave traveling-wave maser consists of a microwave slow-wave circuit, of either continuous or periodic type, along which is distributed inverted maser material, as shown schematically in Fig. 7-14. Pump power is applied to the maser material in any of several ways so as to create an inversion according to the three-level maser scheme. The slow-wave circuit then becomes essentially a transmission line with a negative attenuation coefficient. A signal introduced into one end of the slow-wave circuit travels down the circuit and grows exponentially with distance instead of attenuating, as in the usual circuit. The amplified signal then emerges from the other end of the circuit. In practical traveling-wave masers this amplification can often be made unidirectional, so that the circuit amplifies strongly in only one direction and attenuates signals traveling in the reverse direction. The traveling-wave maser then becomes a very stable unidirectional amplifier, a condition not generally possible with a cavity maser amplifier except with the use of an external circulator.

Traveling-wave amplification of plane waves in an inverted medium was discussed in Chap. 5. However, the analysis given there applies only to *plane* waves, and

---

[1] Much more extensive coverage of this topic, including considerable material on the analysis of microwave slow-wave circuits, may be found in chap. 7 of Ref. 7-9.

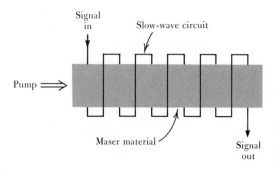

FIG. 7-14   A traveling-wave solid-state maser amplifier.

does *not* apply in general to the more complex waves propagating in a microwave slow-wave circuit. Therefore we must develop a new traveling-wave gain analysis in this section, which we will do first in a simple fashion and then in a somewhat more complicated and rigorous fashion. The gain expressions obtained from these analyses will differ from the plane-wave results of Chap. 5 only in that the *phase velocity* v_ϕ appearing in the plane-wave results will be replaced here by the *group velocity* v_g of the slow-wave circuit. This replacement is simple, but very important. The group-velocity result of this chapter is the truly correct and general result. For a plane wave the group and phase velocities are the same, and we do not have to consider the difference in that particular special case, but for slow-wave circuits in general we must use the rigorous group-velocity result.

■ Let us first consider a simple derivation of traveling-wave maser gain which applies most directly to uniform (nonperiodic) slow-wave circuits. If the voltage wave on a slow-wave circuit or transmission line grows exponentially with distance in the form $|V(z)| = |V(0)|e^{\alpha_m z}$, where α_m is the maser-gain coefficient, then the power carried by the wave increases with distance as $P(z) \propto e^{2\alpha_m z}$ and we can write

SIMPLE GAIN ANALYSIS

$$\frac{d}{dz} P(z) = 2\alpha_m P(z) \tag{1}$$

In a traveling-wave maser the power dP added in length dz comes from the maser crystal. Now, we can relate the power dP emitted by the maser material in a length dz to the stored signal energy $W_s' \, dz$ in that length and to the maser Q_m through the basic definition

$$Q_m \equiv \frac{\omega \times \text{stored energy}}{\text{emitted power}} = \frac{\omega W_s' \, dz}{dP} \tag{2}$$

where W_s' is the stored signal energy per unit length in the line.

It is a general theorem of transmission lines that the power P carried by a transmission line, the stored energy W_s' per unit length of the lines, and the group velocity v_g of the wave on the line are related by

Power flow = stored energy per unit length × group velocity

or

$$P = W_s' v_g \tag{3}$$

(a brief discussion of group velocity is given in Appendix D). Combining Eqs. (1) to (3) leads to the identification

$$\frac{d}{dz} P = 2\alpha_m P = \frac{\omega}{Q_m v_g} P \tag{4}$$

so that the maser-gain coefficient α_m is given by

$$\alpha_m = \frac{\omega}{2Q_m v_g} \tag{5}$$

This is exactly the same result as in the plane-wave analysis of Sec. 5-4, except that the phase velocity v_ϕ in the earlier result is replaced here by the group velocity v_g, which is the more generally correct result.

To convert the exponential gain coefficient α_m to maser power gain in decibels, we write

$$G_{\text{dB}} = 10 \log e^{2\alpha_m L} = 20\alpha_m L \log e = 4.34 \frac{\omega L}{Q_m v_g} \tag{6}$$

where L is the length of the slow-wave circuit. If we define the parameter $\mathcal{N}$ by

$$\mathcal{N} \equiv \frac{\text{circuit length}}{\text{free-space wavelength}} = \frac{L}{\lambda} \tag{7}$$

to express the length of the slow-wave circuit in free-space wavelengths, and we define the *slowing factor* S of the circuit as the ratio of the velocity of light to the circuit's group velocity,

$$S \equiv \frac{\text{velocity of light}}{\text{group velocity}} = \frac{c}{v_g} \tag{8}$$

then we can write Eq. (6) in the form

$$G_{\text{dB}} = 4.34 \frac{2\pi(c/v_g)L/\lambda}{Q_m} = \frac{27 S \mathcal{N}}{Q_m} \tag{9}$$

It is apparent that for high gain we want a high slowing factor—i.e., a low group velocity—and as usual, a *low* value of the maser Q_m.

PERIODIC SLOW-WAVE CIRCUITS ■ Most traveling-wave maser circuits are periodic rather than uniform; i.e., they have some basic period or pitch (for example, the axial spacing between wires in Fig. 7-14). Figure 7-15 shows a more obviously periodic example in which the slow-wave circuit consists of a cascaded sequence of identical resonant cavities, each coupled to the next. The gain analysis above, although it speaks of a wave growing smoothly and exponentially with distance, can also be used for periodic circuits, provided that the

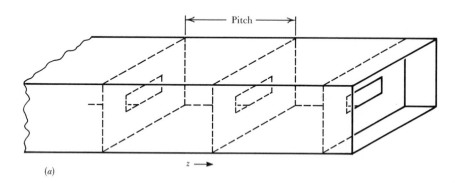

(a)

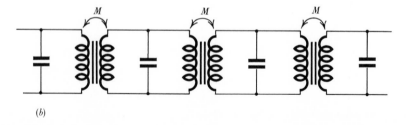

FIG. 7-15 A periodic slow-wave circuit consisting of cascaded coupled resonant cavities. The lumped resonant circuit in (b) provides a good lumped model for analyzing wave propagation in the cascaded resonant-cavity circuit of part (a).

(b)

signal gain per period is small (which is usually the case). If the pitch of the periodic circuit (for example, the length of one cavity in Fig. 7-15) is p, and if ΔP is the power added to the amplifying wave in one period, then clearly

$$\Delta P \equiv P(z + p) - P(z) = \frac{\omega W_s}{Q_m} \tag{10}$$

where W_s is the total stored signal energy in one period. For periodic circuits the transmission-line theorem given in Eq. (3) becomes

$$P = \frac{W_s}{p} v_g \tag{11}$$

Then for small gain per period we can make the approximation

$$\frac{d}{dz} P \approx \frac{\Delta P}{p} = \frac{\omega}{Q_m v_g} P \tag{12}$$

This is essentially the same as Eq. (4) and leads to the same overall gain result if the circuit is many periods long.

■ Let us consider a numerical example to indicate the possibilities of traveling-wave masers. Figure 7-16 shows a 3000-MHz traveling-wave maser amplifier with a "meander line" slow-wave circuit in the form of a flat slotted metal tape, on top of which is placed a slab of ruby as the maser material. The pump power is supplied to the maser material in the form of a conventional waveguide mode in the surrounding waveguide enclosure. The achievable value of maser Q_m in a maser amplifier is primarily a function of the maser material and ought to be roughly the same for the same material in either a cavity or a traveling-wave maser. The following design parameters are quite realizable for a ruby traveling-wave maser at 3000 MHz:

SOME TYPICAL VALUES

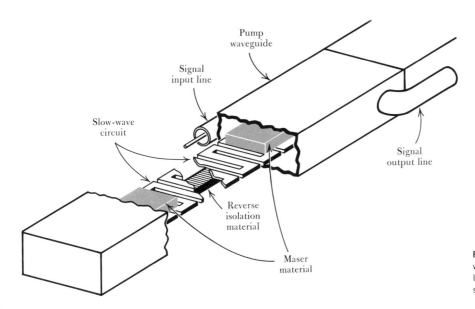

FIG. 7-16 A 3000-MHz traveling-wave maser built at Stanford University, using a meander-line slow-wave circuit.

Frequency: $f = 3000$ MHz
Maser Q: $Q_m = 100$
Slowing factor: $S = 100$
Circuit length: $L = 10$ cm $= 4$ in.
Wavelengths: $\mathcal{N} = 1$

The slowing factor S given here is a reasonable value for the circuit shown or for other typical slow-wave circuits that we will examine later. The midband power gain in decibels is then

$$G_{\mathrm{dB}} = \frac{27 S \mathcal{N}}{Q_m} = 27 \text{ dB} \tag{13}$$

This is a very satisfactory midband gain in a circuit of reasonable physical length. In addition, the effective length of a maser circuit can be increased by doubling the circuit back on itself several times within the same liquid-helium Dewar flask and electromagnet.

Figure 7-17 shows experimental results obtained in a test section of the circuit of Fig. 7-16, with a maser gain $G_{\mathrm{dB}} \approx 17$ dB in a length $L \approx 1.7$ in., slightly better than predicted by Eq. (13). The maser absorption with the pump off is also shown, indicating that the ratio of midband decibel gain to decibel loss, which is equal to the signal inversion ratio I, is ~ 2.3. Note that the bandwidths of these curves are determined entirely by the shape of the atomic transition itself, since there is no narrowband resonant circuit involved in any way.

ALTERNATE DERIVATION OF GAIN ■ The traveling-wave–maser gain expression (5) can be derived in several different ways. The following derivation, which is somewhat more rigorous than the simple derivation just given, brings out the phase-shift as well as amplification effects associated with the maser material. A uniform transmission line or slow-wave circuit in the absence of maser action supports traveling waves which propagate with distance in

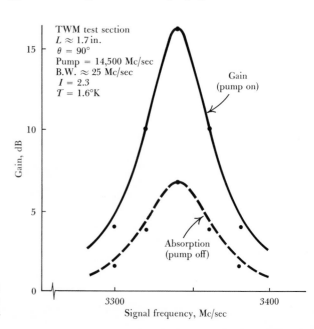

FIG. 7-17 Traveling-wave maser absorption (pump off) and maser gain (pump on) in a short test section using the structure shown in Fig. 7-16.

the form

$$\tilde{u}(z) = \tilde{u}(0)e^{-j\beta z} \tag{14}$$

where β is the propagation constant. A periodic slow-wave circuit with pitch p is somewhat more complicated; it can be shown that all the field components in such a circuit can be written in the form

$$\tilde{u}(z) = \tilde{u}(0)F(z)e^{-j\beta z} \tag{15}$$

where $F(z)$ is periodic in z, with period p; that is, for all z

$$F(z + p) = F(z) \tag{16}$$

If we pick a set of planes spaced one pitch p apart all along the periodic circuit, the fields at successive planes are related by

$$\tilde{u}(z + p) = \tilde{u}(z)e^{-j\beta p} \tag{17}$$

Over a distance L equal to many periods, $L = mp$, this will give

$$\tilde{u}(z + L) = \tilde{u}(z)e^{-j\beta mp} = \tilde{u}(z)e^{-j\beta L} \tag{18}$$

In other words, β plays essentially the same role in the periodic case as it does in the uniform case in giving the net propagation of a wave with distance, except that we must choose some arbitrary reference point within each period and then measure the field amplitude and phase at that same reference point in each successive period.

Given a slow-wave circuit, the propagation constant β can be found by solving the electromagnetic wave equation derived from Maxwell's equations,

$$(\nabla^2 + k'^2)\tilde{u}(x,y,z) = 0 \tag{19}$$

where

$$k'^2 \equiv \omega^2 \mu\epsilon \tag{20}$$

and k' is the plane-wave propagation constant in the dielectric medium surrounding the circuit. The solution of (19) will, of course, be subject to the boundary conditions imposed on the electromagnetic fields by the geometry of the circuit, i.e., the shape of the circuit structure. The quantities μ and ϵ are the magnetic and dielectric permeabilities of the material filling the circuit, which is usually some sort of maser host crystal or dielectric medium. The only factors involved in solving the wave equation (19) to find β are then the plane-wave propagation constant k' (in the dielectric medium) and the boundary conditions or the circuit geometry. Hence we may say in general that the solution will have the form

$$\beta = \beta(k', \text{geometry}) \tag{21}$$

The geometry is fixed for a given circuit, whereas k' varies with changes in ω, μ, or ϵ. Hence we usually leave the dependence on geometry implicit and write this simply as

$$\beta = \beta(k') = \beta(\omega\sqrt{\mu\epsilon}) \tag{22}$$

The frequency dependence of β comes in through the frequency dependence of k'.

The propagation behavior in a slow-wave circuit is thus fully specified by the function $\beta(k')$, which may either be calculated analytically or measured experimentally. This function is often plotted backward as a k-vs.-β curve (or ω-vs.-β curve), as in

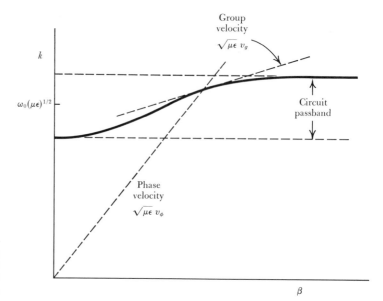

FIG. 7-18 The k-vs.-β curve for wave propagation in a coupled-resonator circuit such as Fig. 7-15. The dashed lines indicate the phase and group velocities at a particular frequency within the circuit passband.

Fig. 7-18, which shows the k-vs.-β curve for a coupled-cavity type of slow-wave circuit like Fig. 7-15. The circuit propagates only in a narrow frequency band, which is smeared out about the resonant frequency of the individual cavities. For this derivation it is not necessary to know in detail the k'-vs.-β curve of a slow-wave circuit, but only to know that a function $\beta = \beta(k')$ does exist. Note that if we pick any point along the k'-vs.-β curve, the shape of the dashed line from the origin to that point is

$$\frac{k'}{\beta} = \frac{\omega(\mu\epsilon)^{1/2}}{\omega/v_\phi} = \frac{v_\phi}{c'} \tag{23}$$

That is, this slope is the circuit *phase* velocity normalized to the velocity of light in the dielectric medium, $c' \equiv (\mu\epsilon)^{-1/2}$. Since the definition of group velocity (see Appendix D) is $v_g \equiv \partial\omega/\partial\beta$, we also have

$$\frac{1}{v_g} = \frac{\partial\beta}{\partial\omega} = \frac{d\beta}{dk'}\frac{\partial k'}{\partial\omega} = \frac{1}{c'}\frac{d\beta}{dk'} \tag{24}$$

or

$$\frac{dk'}{d\beta} = \frac{v_g}{c'} \tag{25}$$

The slope of the k'-vs.-β curve itself gives the circuit group velocity normalized to c', as indicated on Fig. 7-18.

For all maser materials normally used in microwave masers the magnetic permeability μ in the absence of maser action has the free-space value μ_0. The effect of inserting magnetic-dipole maser atoms into the material is to change the magnetic permeability μ_0 by

$$\mu_0 \rightarrow \mu_0[1 + \tilde{\chi}(\omega)] \qquad \text{or} \qquad \Delta\mu = \mu_0\tilde{\chi}(\omega) \tag{26}$$

where $\tilde{\chi}(\omega)$ is the susceptibility due to the maser transition. Adding maser atoms to a slow-wave circuit[1] then causes the propagation constant to change by

$$\beta \rightarrow \beta + \Delta\beta \tag{27}$$

where

$$\Delta\beta = \frac{\partial\beta}{\partial\mu}\,\Delta\mu = \frac{d\beta}{dk'}\frac{\partial k'}{\partial\mu}\,\Delta\mu = \frac{\omega}{2v_g}\,\tilde{\chi}(\omega) \tag{28}$$

Again, this is exactly like the plane-wave analysis of Sec. 5-4, except that the phase velocity there has been replaced by the group velocity. The wave on the slow-wave circuit now propagates as

$$
\begin{aligned}
\tilde{u}(z) &\sim \exp\left[-j(\beta + \Delta\beta)z\right] \\
&= \exp\left[-j\beta z - j\frac{\omega}{2v_g}\chi'(\omega) + \frac{\omega}{2v_g}\chi''(\omega)\right] \\
&= \exp\left[\alpha_m(\omega)z\right]\exp\left\{-j[\beta + \Delta\beta_m(\omega)]z\right\}
\end{aligned}
\tag{29}
$$

For a lorentzian inverted transition,

$$\tilde{\chi}(\omega) = \frac{j}{Q_m}\frac{1}{1 + 2j(\omega - \omega_a)/\Delta\omega_a} \tag{30}$$

and so

$$\alpha_m(\omega) = \frac{\omega}{2v_g}\chi''(\omega) = \frac{\omega}{2Q_m v_g}\frac{1}{1 + [2(\omega - \omega_a)/\Delta\omega_a]^2} \tag{31}$$

and

$$
\begin{aligned}
\Delta\beta_m(\omega) &= \frac{\omega}{2v_g}\chi'(\omega) \\
&= \frac{\omega}{2Q_m v_g}\frac{2(\omega - \omega_a)/\Delta\omega_a}{1 + [2(\omega - \omega_a)/\Delta\omega_a]^2} = \frac{2(\omega - \omega_a)}{\Delta\omega_a}\alpha_m(\omega)
\end{aligned}
\tag{32}
$$

The amount of added phase shift $\Delta\beta_m L$ is directly related to the amount of maser gain $\alpha_m L$.

■ The gain-vs.-frequency profile of a microwave traveling-wave maser is given by the expression developed in Sec. 5-4; for an assumed lorentzian atomic lineshape   BANDWIDTH

$$G_{\mathrm{dB}}(f) = 20\alpha_m(\omega)L\log e = G_{\mathrm{dB}}(f_a)\frac{1}{1 + [2(f - f_a)/\Delta f_a]^2} \tag{33}$$

The amplifier 3-dB bandwidth of the maser is then given by

$$\Delta f_{\mathrm{3dB}} = \Delta f_a\sqrt{\frac{3}{G_{\mathrm{dB}}(f_a) - 3}} \tag{34}$$

Figure 7-19 is another plot of this relationship, showing that even for quite large midband gains the amplifier bandwidth remains at about one-third the atomic linewidth, or larger.

■ In addition to increased bandwidth, microwave traveling-wave masers can provide   NONRECIPROCAL FORWARD GAIN AND REVERSE ISOLATION

[1] We think of the maser host crystal, with its dielectric effects, as being a part of the slow-wave circuit itself and as determining μ and ϵ in the absence of maser action. Adding maser atoms then means putting in the small (but vital) additional effects due to the susceptibility $\tilde{\chi}(\omega)$ of the maser transition itself.

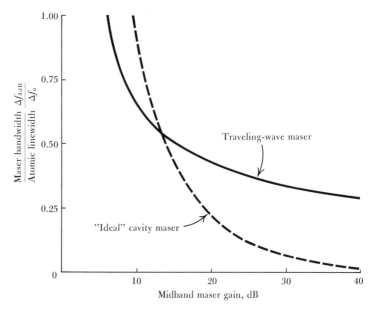

FIG. 7-19 Amplifier bandwidth versus midband gain for a traveling-wave maser and for an ideal cavity maser.

both nonreciprocal forward gain and nonreciprocal reverse isolation or attenuation. That is, the maser amplifier can have high gain in the forward direction only, and still higher attenuation in the reverse direction only. As a result, the amplifier can be unconditionally stable, in that there is no possible combination of mismatches in the amplifier input and output lines that can cause the amplifier to oscillate. This is an important advantage, not shared by many other types of negative-resistance amplifiers.

It was pointed out in Chap. 4 that magnetic-resonance transitions typically have a nonreciprocal type of polarization response to applied ac fields. The transition in many simple cases will respond very strongly to a circularly polarized applied field having positive circular polarization, but only very weakly or not at all to an applied field having the opposite or negative sense of circular polarization. Also, many slow-wave circuits have certain regions in which the rf fields of a forward-traveling wave are circularly polarized, or very nearly so, together with other symmetrically located regions in which the rf fields have exactly the opposite sense of polarization. Moreover, if the direction of travel of the wave is reversed, the sense of the circular polarization in both these regions is reversed.

Suppose that the maser material in a slow-wave circuit is located only in those regions where the circular polarization is optimum for interaction with the maser material when the wave on the circuit is a forward-going wave. Then the forward-going wave on the circuit will have a low value of Q_m and a high gain per unit length (provided that the maser material is a good one). However, the backward-going wave on the same circuit will have the opposite sense of circular polarization in the same region where the maser material is located, and hence the fields of this wave will not interact effectively with the maser atoms. The backward-traveling wave will in effect have a very high value of Q_m, and hence only a very small or zero amplification. The circuit will exhibit nonreciprocal amplification, i.e., sizable gain in the forward direction only. This condition is fairly readily achieved in practical microwave solid-state maser devices.

In addition, material having an absorptive or nonmaser atomic transition at the same frequency can also be placed in the traveling-wave circuit in the symmetrically located regions of the circuit where the polarization is opposite to that in the maser crystal regions. The fields will then have the optimum polarization for this absorbing material, and the amount of absorption will be large only for a wave traveling in the *backward* direction. The circuit will now have nonreciprocal attenuation, often called *reverse isolation,* which will not change the forward gain to any significant extent, but which will cause large attenuation in the backward direction.

The reverse-isolation material can in principle be the same material as the amplifying maser crystal, but with a circuit design such that the reverse-isolation material is shielded from the pumping fields, and hence does not become inverted. Another solution is to use the same maser material, but with a greatly increased density of maser atoms in the crystal. For various reasons, a more heavily doped material will usually not be successfully inverted by the same pump fields that invert the regular maser material. An advantage of this approach is that the absorbing material will automatically track the amplifying material if the maser center frequency is tuned in any way (for example, by changing the value of B_0). A disadvantage is that the reverse-isolation material, even though it is not successfully inverted, still absorbs large amounts of power from the pumping fields.

The most practical choice for a reverse-isolation material usually turns out to be some sort of ferrite material, which exhibits a ferromagnetic (rather than paramagnetic) type of magnetic-resonance absorption. These materials exhibit extremely strong absorption, so that only very small samples are required, have very good nonreciprocal properties, and cannot be inverted in any way and do not absorb any power from the pumping fields. Yttrium iron garnet (YIG) is one common example of the type of ferrite material used for reverse isolation.

The ratio of the maser gain in the forward direction to that in the reverse direction is referred to as the *front-to-back ratio* of the nonreciprocal gain mechanism, and the corresponding ratio in the opposite direction for the reverse isolation is described by the same term. Obviously, a stable high-performance maser amplifier necessitates high front-to-back ratios for both the gain and the reverse isolation, plus a slightly larger amount of reverse isolation than forward gain. This is obtained with success in many practical masers.

■ Consider a thin sheet of material having the unusual properties of perfect electrical conductivity in one direction and zero conductivity in the direction at right angles to this—as if the sheet were made of a very large number of very fine wires laid side by side, but insulated from each other. Such an ideal conducting sheath is shown in the upper left corner of Fig. 7-20. A surface of this type can propagate guided slow waves that propagate in a direction at right angles to the conduction direction, as shown. It can be shown further[1] that the fields above and below this sheath have opposite senses of perfect circular polarization, exactly as desired for nonreciprocal traveling-wave maser circuits.

The conducting sheath serves as an idealized model for a number of practical transversely conducting slow-wave circuits, including particularly the three other circuits shown in Fig. 7-20, all of which have been used successfully in microwave traveling-wave masers. All these circuits can be used in a configuration like that shown in cross section in Fig. 7-21, in which the pump field is applied in a TE_{10} rectangular waveguide mode which is virtually unaffected by the presence of the slow-wave circuit. An experiment using the meander-line circuit has already been illustrated (Fig. 7-16).

SOME PRACTICAL CIRCUIT DESIGNS

[1] See Ref. 7-9, sec. 7-3.

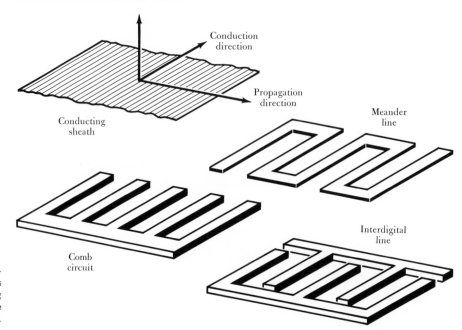

FIG. 7-20 Examples of traveling-wave-maser slow-wave circuits derived from the ideal conducting sheath model shown in the upper left corner.

The comb circuit, in which each of the fingers may be viewed as a quarter-wave transmission-line resonator, short-circuited at one end and open-circuited at the other, is one of the most highly developed and widely used maser slow-wave circuits. Figure 7-22 shows a typical example of a comb-type traveling-wave maser developed and widely used by the Bell Telephone Laboratories.

■ By extending the length of a high-performance traveling-wave maser, perhaps through folding back the circuit, it is sometimes possible to obtain considerably more midband gain than is really necessary in the maser preamplifier, as determined by systems specifications. In this event the excess gain can be traded off for improved amplifier bandwidth by stagger-tuning different sections of the maser.

BROADBANDING AND SATURATION BEHAVIOR IN TRAVELING-WAVE MASERS

For example, the maser can be divided into two equal sections, each with half the overall gain. The center frequencies of these two sections can then be tuned apart by changing the magnetic field strength B_0 or its direction in one of the sections in relation to the other. Figure 7-23a shows the results of such two-stage stagger tuning on one traveling-wave maser. It may or may not be necessary to apply separate pump frequencies to the two sections, depending on the amount of stagger tuning compared to the pump transition's linewidth.

Still greater bandwidth increases can be achieved by using more complex multi-stage stagger-tuning arrangements. Figure 7-23b is an example of the bandwidth increases obtained by stagger tuning the dc magnetic field strength in individual segments along the traveling-wave maser circuit.

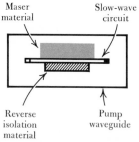

FIG. 7-21 Cross section of typical maser design using one of the conducting-sheath family of slow-wave circuits. The maser material and reverse isolation material go on opposite sides of the circuit, where the rf fields have opposite signs of circular polarization. The pump fields are in the form of a TE_{10} waveguide mode in the surrounding rectangular waveguide.

The gain of a traveling-wave maser saturates with increasing signal power in essentially the same fashion as any other maser device, with one added complexity. Since the signal-power level increases greatly in going from the input to the output end of the traveling-wave amplifier, because of the gain, the power density is highest and the population difference and gain begin to saturate first at the output end of the amplifier. Then, as the input signal is increased still further, the saturation region gradually spreads back along the circuit toward the input end. Thus it is really the output power

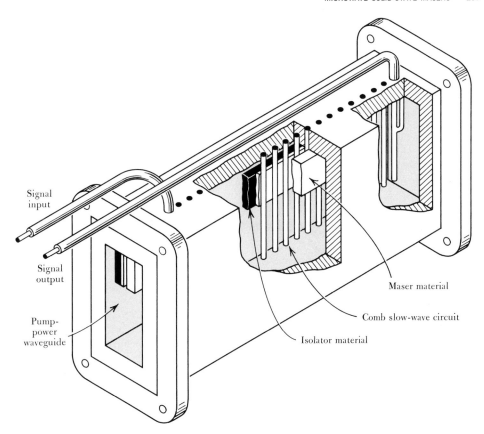

Signal
input

Signal
output

Pump-
power
waveguide

Isolator material

Pump-
power
waveguide

Maser material

Comb slow-wave circuit

Isolator material

level rather than the input power level of the maser that is most important in determining when saturation effects will begin to occur. Figure 7-24 shows the gain-saturation behavior in a typical traveling-wave maser. Note the extremely low input power
level at which saturation effects begin to appear.

7-3 APPLICATIONS OF MICROWAVE SOLID-STATE MASERS

Microwave solid-state masers are relatively complex devices, requiring expensive crystalline maser materials, large magnetic fields, a high-frequency pump source, and
liquid-helium cooling. At the same time, they provide only limited gain, and especially
limited bandwidth, compared to other competitive microwave amplifiers. The interest
in maser amplifiers for practical applications is due entirely to their extraordinarily low
noise factors, lower than those of any other competitive amplifiers. In this section we
will consider briefly the noise performance of microwave maser amplifiers and some
practical applications of the maser's low-noise amplification.

■ The basic noise sources in maser devices and the resulting maser-amplifier noise
performance will be discussed at length in Chap. 11. In this section we will merely
summarize the elementary results for microwave maser amplifiers. Consider a microwave maser amplifier (either cavity or traveling-wave) connected to a signal source,
such as a signal generator or a microwave antenna. The output from the maser amplifier
will then consist of the input power P_{in} multiplied by the amplifier power gain G, plus
some additional amplifier noise power P_n generated in the maser amplifier itself by

FIG. 7-22 A Bell Telephone
Laboratories traveling-wave maser
design using the comb slow-wave
circuit. [From R. W. DeGrasse,
E. O. Schulz-DuBois, and H. E. D.
Scovil, "The three-level solid-
state traveling-wave maser,"
Bell Syst. Tech. J., **38**:305
(1959).]

NOISE PERFORMANCE OF
MICROWAVE MASERS

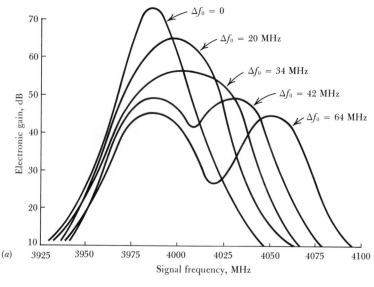

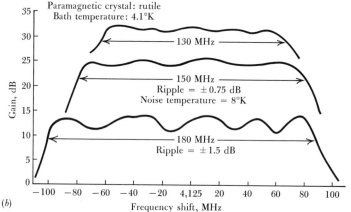

FIG. 7-23 Examples of bandwidth increases obtained by stagger tuning of traveling-wave masers: (a) two-stage stagger tuning and (b) multistage stagger tuning.

spontaneous emission and other noise sources in the maser. Hence the total power output is

$$P_{\text{total}} = GP_{\text{in}} + P_n \tag{1}$$

In many cases of interest the input power P_{in} to be amplified will itself consist of the background thermal noise generated by a source at a temperature T_S. In this case, for microwave frequencies we may write, to a very good degree of approximation,

$$P_{\text{in}} \approx kT_S B \tag{2}$$

where T_S is the thermal-source temperature and B is the bandwidth within which this noise power is measured.

It turns out to be convenient to relate the internally generated amplifier noise power P_n to the amplifier power gain G times a fictitious input noise power, and to write this fictitious input noise power in the form $kT_{\text{eq}}B$, where T_{eq} is then the *equivalent input noise temperature* of the maser. For a maser connected only to a thermal-noise

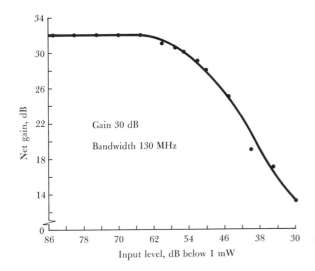

FIG. 7-24 Saturation of the gain of a microwave traveling-wave maser with increasing signal input.

source at temperature T_S, we may then write

$$P_{\text{out}} = GkT_SB + GkT_{\text{eq}}B \tag{3}$$

Obviously, even if the background source is cooled to $T_S = 0°\text{K}$, and hence generates no input noise to the maser, the output from the maser looks as if the maser were connected to a thermal source at temperature T_{eq}. To put this another way, the noisy real maser is equivalent to an ideal noise-free amplifier having no internal noise, but having an unavoidable input noise power $kT_{\text{eq}}B$ added to whatever other signals or noise may come into the amplifier from the signal source.

If the quantity we wish to observe and measure is the background thermal-noise emission kT_SB itself, as is often the case, then obviously for a reasonably accurate measurement the background source temperature T_S must be equal to or greater than the amplifier equivalent input temperature, $T_S \geq T_{\text{eq}}$. Thus T_{eq} also gives an indication of how hot a thermal-noise source must be before its thermal radiation can be measured with a maser as the first-stage amplifier.[1]

The amplifier equivalent input noise temperature can be related to the conventional definition of amplifier *noise figure* F as follows. Consider a matched signal source at temperature T_S which is generating the unavoidable background thermal-noise power kT_SB, as well as some amount of input signal power P_s which is to be measured or detected. Then the ratio of signal power to noise power in the input line to the maser amplifier is

$$\left(\frac{S}{N}\right)_{\text{in}} = \frac{P_s}{kT_SB} \tag{4}$$

The input signal power will be multiplied by the amplifier gain G, while the input noise power kT_SB will be supplemented by the amplifier equivalent input noise power $kT_{\text{eq}}B$, and then both will be multiplied by the amplifier gain G. Thus the signal-noise ratio in the amplifier's output line will be

---

[1] There are a number of radiometric and other signal-processing methods by which we can reduce the minimum measurable background temperature T_s considerably below this level, but T_{eq} still furnishes a good measure of the difficulty of this task and of how much signal processing and measurement time will be required.

$$\left(\frac{S}{N}\right)_{\text{out}} = \frac{GP_s}{G(kT_S + kT_{\text{eq}})B} \tag{5}$$

By definition, the noise figure F is the signal-noise ratio at the amplifier input divided by the signal-noise ratio at the amplifier output, under conditions where the background source temperature T_S is room temperature, $290°\text{K}$; that is,

$$F \equiv \frac{(S/N)_{\text{in}}}{(S/N)_{\text{out}}} = \frac{G(kT_S + kT_{\text{eq}})B}{GkT_SB} = 1 + \frac{T_{\text{eq}}}{300°\text{K}} \tag{6}$$

The equivalent input temperature T_{eq} of a well-designed helium-temperature maser amplifier will be only a few degrees, or perhaps a few tens of degrees Kelvin. The conventionally defined noise figure F is essentially unity in this case. Moreover, maser amplifiers are most likely to be used in situations where the source temperature or background temperature T_S is much lower than room temperature. Under these circumstances the conventional noise figure F is not a very direct measure of the actual noise capability of a maser amplifier. The most common practice is to describe the noise properties of a maser amplifier simply by giving the equivalent input noise temperature T_{eq} of the maser. The noise temperatures and noise figures of some typical microwave receivers are shown in Table 7-1 for comparison.

TABLE 7-1 Microwave-receiver noise figures

Amplifier or receiver	Noise figure F, dB	Noise temperature T_{eq}, °K
Heterodyne receiver with crystal mixer	7	1200
Traveling-wave tube or transistor amplifier	5	625
Ultralow-noise traveling-wave tube	2	170
Microwave solid-state maser	0.16	10

SOME PRACTICAL
APPLICATIONS

■ There is no reason to use a maser amplifier, with its penalties in cost, weight, and performance, in situations where the background noise accompanying the signals to be measured is much greater than the equivalent input noise of the maser itself; that is, in situations where the effective background temperature T_S is much larger than the maser noise temperature, which will typically be $T_{\text{eq}} \approx 10°\text{K}$. This rules out the maser as a useful device for most ordinary laboratory measurements, in which the background temperature is room temperature or warmer. Also, in most ordinary radar systems there is sufficient thermal radiation from the earth and other warm objects within the radar field, and also sufficient background clutter from interference, transmitter leakage and the like, that a maser preamplifier is again not worth its cost and complexity.

Maser amplifiers are uniquely useful, however, in equipment for receiving extremely weak signals from space by means of a large, carefully designed antenna pointed upward at the cold sky. If an antenna is pointed at the sky, away from the sun or any other major noise source, the background sky noise received by the antenna corresponds to a source temperature $T_S = T_{\text{sky}}$, with typical values as a function of microwave frequency and antenna angle as indicated in Fig. 7-25. At low frequencies, below the microwave range, considerable galactic noise comes from the stars in our galaxy.

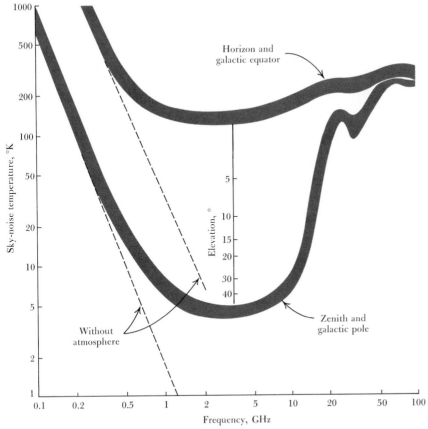

FIG. 7-25 The apparent noise temperature of the sky as detected by an ideal antenna (negligible side lobes or back lobes) under various conditions. The dashed lines at low frequencies are the galactic-noise contributions as seen in the plane of the galaxy and perpendicular to that plane. The total noise increases far above the galactic contribution at higher frequencies largely because of atmospheric absorption. The lower shaded curve is for the best possible case of an antenna pointed at earth's zenith and out of the galactic plane. The upper shaded curve is the worst possible case of an antenna pointed at earth's horizon and in the galactic plane. The elevation scale indicates roughly how the noise would decrease as the antenna is rotated away from the horizon and toward the zenith.

At high frequencies, above the microwave range, the earth's atmosphere becomes partially absorbing and radiates considerable noise back into an antenna. However, over a broad microwave band, from ∼1 to 10 GHz, and for antenna angles more than ∼30° above the horizon, the background sky temperature[1] is not more than ∼10°K.

Figure 7-26 shows two typical installations of maser amplifiers on large steerable antennas pointed at the sky. The antennas are specially designed to have low antenna losses, very short feed lines between the antenna and the maser, and very low side-lobe and back-lobe levels, since these minor lobes will pick up noise from the warm surroundings of the antennas.

The very low background noise and low maser-amplifier noise have proved particularly advantageous in the field of *radio astronomy*. Compared to the cold sky back-

---

[1] Some of this background sky noise is now believed to represent isotropic noise radiation left everywhere in space from the original explosion in the "big-bang" theory of the creation of the universe.

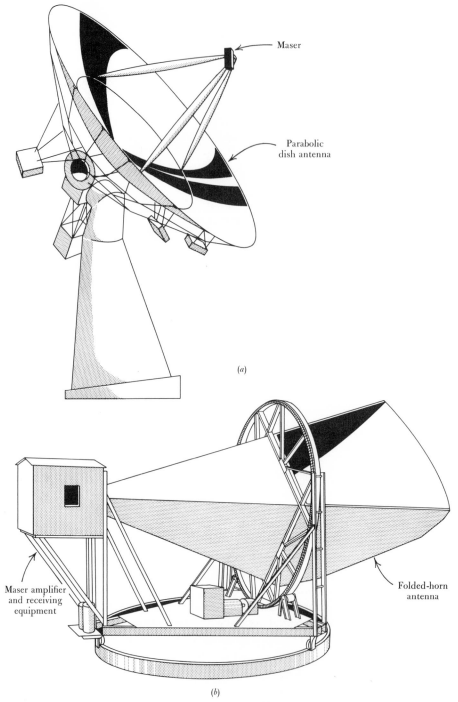

(a)

(b)

FIG. 7-26 Typical maser amplifiers mounted on large steerable antennas: (*a*) A large parabolic dish antenna with a maser package mounted at the focus. (*b*) A folded-horn, or "sugar-scoop," receiving antenna. The latter antenna must be considerably larger to obtain the same receiving aperture, but the maser and other receiving equipment can be mounted close to the ground and in a fixed position, with only a rotary joint required between the maser and the antenna.

ground, a planet is a warm (although an exceedingly small and distant) object. By making extremely careful and accurate measurements of the slight increase in total thermal noise received as an antenna is scanned past the celestial location of a planet, it is possible to measure the microwave noise radiation from the nearer planets such as Venus, and thereby to deduce information about the apparent temperature of the planet, the possible composition of the planetary atmosphere, and so forth. Jupiter, Mars, Saturn, and Venus are among the planets that have been observed in this fashion. It is also possible to observe and study discrete *radio stars*, which emit microwave noise radiation, as well as clouds of interstellar gases such as hydrogen and water vapor that emit at certain distinct frequencies, of which the 1420-MHz ($\lambda = 21$ cm) hydrogen line is the best known.

In the field of *radar astronomy*, special microwave radar systems with microwave maser receivers are able to detect microwave radar echoes from the near planets. Analysis of the doppler shifts in the returned signals can reveal planetary rotation rates and other important astronomical information.

Maser preamplifiers are used in *space communications and telemetry* to receive the weak signals broadcast back to earth in certain microwave telemetry bands by planetary probes and other deep-space vehicles, whose on-board power supplies permit only weak signal transmission. Telemetry and data transmission in high-signal-noise-ratio channels from satellites in earth or moon orbit are similar applications. *Tracking space vehicles* and satellites in orbit is one specialized radar application in which the background noise is very low and in which the maser amplifier's great sensitivity can be put to good use. Another application is *satellite communications*, in which microwave signals carrying multiple telephone and television channels are transmitted from one terrestrial location to another by transmission upward to a satellite and reflection or re-broadcast back to a maser-equipped receiving station.

PROBLEMS

7-1. Consider a three-level microwave maser material in which the pump level is so strong that the pump transition remains fully saturated and $\Delta N_{13} = 0$ regardless of the signal power or the changes in the signal population difference ΔN_{32}, either transient or steady-state. Show that under these conditions the three-level rate equations can be reduced to a single rate equation which governs the transient behavior of the signal population difference ΔN_{32}, and which does not contain the pump transition rate W_p explicitly. Compare this rate equation with the rate equation for an elementary two-level atomic system.

7-2. Carry out a simplified rate-equation analysis of the four-level push-pull pumping scheme of Fig. 7-13a to find the inversion ratio for the push-pull case, assuming arbitrary relaxation times among the levels, but assuming that the pump transitions are fully saturated, so that $\Delta N_{13} = \Delta N_{24} = 0$ at all times.

7-3. Carry out a general rate-equation analysis of the four-level push-pull maser pumping scheme shown in Fig. 7-13a for arbitrary levels of signal and pump power, assuming all relaxation times equal. Find the net population difference on the pump

transitions and on the signal transitions as a function of the pump power level, and compare with Eqs. (12) and (13) and Fig. 7-2 in Sec. 7-1.

7-4. Suppose that the atomic linewidth Δf_a for a microwave maser transition can be artificially broadened or narrowed without changing any of the other parameters describing the maser atoms. If a microwave cavity maser is described by certain values of $Q_m = Q_{m0}$ and $Q_a = Q_{a0}$ for the starting value of linewidth $\Delta f_a = \Delta f_{a0}$, how much can the gain-bandwidth product of the maser amplifier be increased by changing Δf_a, and what change in Δf_a is required to accomplish this?

7-5. Using Eq. (16) of Sec. 7-1 for the saturation of the population difference ΔN_{32}, and hence for the saturation of Q_m^{-1} in a three-level system, analyze the saturation behavior of the midband gain of a cavity maser amplifier as the input signal power is increased. *Warning:* Note that the signal power which saturates the inverted atomic population is neither the amplifier input power nor the output power, but rather the signal power level *inside* the maser cavity.

7-6. A high-gain traveling-wave microwave maser with a lorentzian atomic transition is to be stagger tuned by dividing it into two cascaded sections, each having the same linewidth and half the overall gain, but with an adjustable frequency detuning Δf_0 between the center frequencies of the two sections. Write out the gain-frequency expression for the stagger-tuned maser and investigate the resulting increase in amplifier bandwidth and decrease in midband gain. For example, find the value of detuning which will give a maximally flat gain response, i.e., the value for which a dip in the center of the overall-gain curve will just begin to appear. If possible, program the gain expression for a computer and plot curves of gain versus frequency with detuning as a parameter, similar to Fig. 7-23a.

REFERENCES

7-1. F. R. Arams and S. Okwit, "Packaged tunable *L*-band maser system," *Proc. IRE,* **48**:866 (1960). Example of a packaged maser system for field applications.

7-2. N. G. Basov and A. M. Prokhorov, "Possible methods of obtaining active molecules for a molecular oscillation," *Sov. Phys. JETP,* **1**:184 (1955). An early proposal for the three-level maser scheme in gas molecules.

7-3. N. Bloembergen, "Proposal for a new type solid-state maser," *Phys. Rev.,* **104**:324 (1956). The original proposal of the three-level solid-state maser concept, still good reading.

7-4. W. S. C. Chang, J. Cromack, and A. E. Siegman, "Cavity maser experiments using ruby at *S*-band," *J. Electron. Control,* **6**:508 (1959). High-performance cavity design.

7-5. R. W. DeGrasse, E. O. Schulz-DuBois, and H. E. D. Scovil, "The three-level solid-state traveling-wave maser," *Bell Syst. Tech. J.,* **38**:305 (1959). A good general discussion of traveling-wave maser design and experimental results.

7-6. T. H. Maiman, "Maser behavior: temperature and concentration effects," *J. Appl. Phys.,* **31**:222 (1960). Operation at higher than usual temperatures, in the liquid-nitrogen range.

7-7. H. E. D. Scovil, G. Feher, and H. Seidel, "The operation of a solid-state maser," *Phys. Rev.,* **105**:762 (1957). The first experimental operation of a three-level solid-state maser.

7-8. S. Shapiro and N. Bloembergen, "Relaxation effects in a maser material, $K_3(CoCr)(CN)_6$," *Phys. Rev.,* **116**:1453 (1959). Some detailed experiments on three-level maser inversion.

7-9. A. E. Siegman, *Microwave Solid-state Masers,* McGraw-Hill, New York, 1964. Extensive and detailed coverage of all aspects of these devices.

OPTICAL RESONATORS
AND
LENS WAVEGUIDES

The cavity resonators used for optical masers usually consist of two flat or curved mirrors set up facing each other, so that a quasi-planar optical wave can bounce back and forth between the two mirrors in the manner shown in Fig. 1-1. Optical resonators of this type have many features in common with lens waveguides or optical transmission lines, in which a light beam is transmitted with little or no loss through a repeated series of identical lenses mounted in a line. In this chapter we will discuss the important features of optical resonators and of the equivalent lens waveguides.

Many important features of optical resonators and lens waveguides can be derived very simply from geometric or ray optics, without taking into account any of the diffraction effects caused by the wave nature of light. We will develop the elementary ray-optics approach and some of its important consequences before we consider a more detailed diffraction description, particularly a full description of the gaussian modes characteristic of stable optical resonators and lens waveguides.

8-1   PERIODIC FOCUSING SYSTEMS: RAY APPROACH

Consider the situation in Fig. 8-1a, where a ray of light (or possibly a particle, such as an electron or an ion) is traveling approximately in the z direction, but with a trajectory having a small transverse displacement $r(z)$ away from the z axis, and also a small slope $r'(z) \equiv dr/dz$ with respect to the z axis. The displacement r may represent displacement in either the x or the y direction. As far as the following analysis is concerned, the ray can represent a light ray, a sound wave, an electron, an ion, or any other particle that normally propagates in a straight line. Our results will, in fact, apply equally well to optical resonators or lens waveguides, the periodic focusing of electron beams, the focusing of ion beams in particle accelerators, and various other cases.

Let us analyze the propagation of this ray in a few simple situations. When such a ray propagates unhindered from $z = z_1$ to $z = z_2 = z_1 + L$, as in Fig. 8-1b, the ray displacement and slope at the output plane z_2 are related to the input displacement and slope at z_1 by the equations

$$r_2 = r_1 + Lr_1' \qquad r_2' = r_1' \tag{1}$$

Similarly, Fig. 8-1c shows that if the ray passes through a thin convergent lens of focal length f, the input and output quantities (just before and just after the thin lens) are related by

$$r_2 = r_1 \qquad r_2' = r_1' - \frac{1}{f}r_1 \tag{2}$$

The second equality can be checked rapidly by noting that if the ray passes through the center of the lens ($r_1 = 0$), its slope should be unchanged ($r_2' = r_1'$), while a ray entering the lens parallel to the axis ($r_1' = 0$) at any finite transverse displacement r_1 should be bent inward by just enough that it will pass through the focal point of the lens ($r_2' = -r_1/f$).

RAY MATRICES ■ The changes in the displacement r and slope r' of a ray as it passes through an optical element may be generally summarized in matrix form as

$$r_2 = Ar_1 + Br_1' \qquad r_2' = Cr_1 + Dr_1' \tag{3}$$

or

$$\mathbf{r_2} = \mathbf{M}\mathbf{r_1} \qquad \mathbf{r} = \begin{bmatrix} r \\ r' \end{bmatrix} \qquad \mathbf{M} = \begin{bmatrix} A & B \\ C & D \end{bmatrix} \tag{4}$$

FIG. 8-1 (a) A general ray trajectory, and its behavior in passing through (b) a straight section and (c) a thin lens.

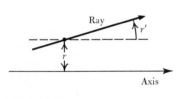

(a)

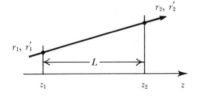

(b)

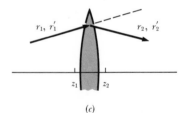

(c)

where the vector quantity **r** summarizes the two ray quantities $\mathbf{r} \equiv (r, r')$, and the ray matrix $\mathbf{M} = (A, B, C, D)$ summarizes the ray-transformation properties of the optical element. Table 8-1 shows the ray matrices for the straight section and the thin lens just described, together with the ray matrices for a number of additional simple optical elements. In each case these matrices are based on the *paraxial,* or small-angle,

---

TABLE 8-1
Ray matrices for simple optical elements

1. Straight section

   Length L

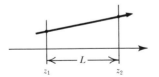

$$\begin{bmatrix} 1 & L \\ 0 & 1 \end{bmatrix}$$

2. Thin lens

   Focal length f

   ($f > 0$, converging; $f < 0$, diverging)

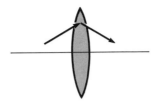

$$\begin{bmatrix} 1 & 0 \\ -1/f & 1 \end{bmatrix}$$

3. Flat dielectric interface

   Refractive indices n_1, n_2

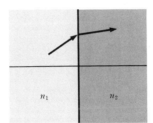

$$\begin{bmatrix} 1 & 0 \\ 0 & n_1/n_2 \end{bmatrix}$$

4. Curved dielectric interface

   Radius R

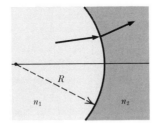

$$\begin{bmatrix} 1 & 0 \\ \dfrac{n_2 - n_1}{n_2 R} & \dfrac{n_1}{n_2} \end{bmatrix}$$

5. Curved mirror

   Radius of curvature R

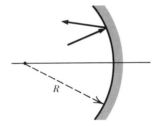

$$\begin{bmatrix} 1 & 0 \\ -2/R & 1 \end{bmatrix}$$

approximations; i.e., the angle between the trajectory and the axis is always small enough to fall within the $\sin\theta \approx \tan\theta \approx \theta$ approximation, and the displacements from the axis are in all cases small compared to the radii of curvature of the refractive and reflective surfaces.

The final entry in this table shows that reflection of a ray from a curved mirror of radius R has the same effect as passage of the ray through a thin lens of focal length $f = R/2$, provided the slope of a ray is always defined with respect to its forward direction of travel. This is very important in establishing the connection between optical resonators and lens waveguides.

RESONATOR g PARAMETERS   ■ Figure 8-2a shows a typical optical resonator formed by two curved mirrors with radii of curvature R_1 and R_2 spaced a distance L apart (for each mirror, $R > 0$ implies that the mirror is concave toward the resonator). From the above identification between a curved mirror and a thin lens we can deduce that the behavior of a ray upon repeated bounces back and forth between these two mirrors will be exactly the same as the behavior of a ray passing through an iterated sequence of lenses spaced at intervals L

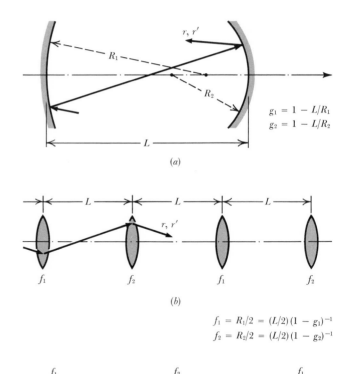

$$g_1 = 1 - L/R_1$$
$$g_2 = 1 - L/R_2$$

(a)

(b)

$$f_1 = R_1/2 = (L/2)(1 - g_1)^{-1}$$
$$f_2 = R_2/2 = (L/2)(1 - g_2)^{-1}$$

Half lens   Full lens   Half lens

(c)

FIG. 8-2 (a) A typical optical resonator. (b) The equivalent periodic lens waveguide. (c) The basic unit for analysis: a single symmetric period of the lens waveguide, extending from the midplane of one lens to the midplane of the next identical lens one period further down the line.

with alternate focal lengths $f_1 = R_1/2$ and $f_2 = R_2/2$, as shown in Fig. 8-2b. Thus the ray properties of the resonator in Fig. 8-2a should be entirely equivalent to the ray properties of the iterated lens waveguide of Fig. 8-2b.

It will turn out to be very convenient to describe the curvatures and spacing of a two-mirror optical resonator, or the equivalent lens waveguide, in terms of their g *parameters,* defined by

$$g_1 \equiv 1 - \frac{L}{R_1} \qquad g_2 \equiv 1 - \frac{L}{R_2} \tag{5}$$

Figure 8-2b expresses the lens focal lengths f_1 and f_2 in terms of the lens spacing L and these two g parameters.

■ Let us now analyze the behavior of a ray upon repeated bounces in an optical reso- nator, as in Fig. 8-2a, or upon passage through repeated sections in a lens waveguide, as in Fig. 8-2b. In particular, we wish to know whether the system is *stable* or *unstable;* i.e., we wish to know whether after many bounces the ray will still be reasonably close to the axis of the system or whether it will have diverged outward a large distance from the axis.

We must first consider the net transformation of a ray in passing through one complete round trip inside the resonator or one full period of the iterated periodic lens waveguide. It will simplify the analysis somewhat if we consider one full symmetric period of the system, such as the symmetric transformation from the midplane of one lens to the midplane of the next identical lens, as shown in Fig. 8-2c. When a ray passes through such a series of optical elements in cascade, the total or overall ray transformation of r and r' can be computed by successive application of the individual (A,B,C,D) matrices, that is, successive multiplication of the ray vector by the individual ray matrices. If this procedure is applied to the sequence of elements shown in Fig. 8-2c, the resulting overall transformation for one full period (length $2L$) is

$$\begin{bmatrix} r_1 \\ r_1' \end{bmatrix} = \begin{bmatrix} 1 & 0 \\ -1/2f_1 & 1 \end{bmatrix} \begin{bmatrix} 1 & L \\ 0 & 1 \end{bmatrix} \begin{bmatrix} 1 & 0 \\ -1/f_2 & 1 \end{bmatrix} \begin{bmatrix} 1 & L \\ 0 & 1 \end{bmatrix} \begin{bmatrix} 1 & 0 \\ -1/2f_1 & 1 \end{bmatrix} \begin{bmatrix} r_0 \\ r_0' \end{bmatrix} \tag{6}$$

output   second   free   middle   free   first   input
               half-lens   space   lens   space   half-lens

If the lens parameters are expressed in terms of g_1 and g_2, and the matrix multiplications in Eq. (6) are carried out, this expression for one period of the lens waveguide, or one complete bounce in the optical resonator, may be reduced to

$$\mathbf{r}_1 = \begin{bmatrix} r_1 \\ Lr_1' \end{bmatrix} = \begin{bmatrix} 2g_1g_2 - 1 & 2g_2 \\ 2g_1(g_1g_2 - 1) & 2g_1g_2 - 1 \end{bmatrix} \begin{bmatrix} r_0 \\ Lr_0' \end{bmatrix} = \mathbf{M}_{\text{total}}\mathbf{r}_0 \tag{7}$$

where we have redefined **r** very slightly by multiplying r' by the half-period L in order to make the ray matrix entirely dimensionless.

We must now look for the *normal modes,* or *eigenmodes,* of this system by asking if there exist any values of the input vector $\mathbf{r}_0$ such that the output vector after one period will just equal the input vector multiplied by some constant λ. That is, we must determine whether there are any input vectors $\mathbf{r}_0$ and constants λ that will, together, exactly satisfy the requirement

$$\mathbf{r}_1 = \mathbf{M}_{\text{total}}\mathbf{r}_0 = \lambda\mathbf{r}_0 \tag{8}$$

for this particular total ray matrix. This is equivalent to finding solutions to the matrix equation

$$\left\{ \begin{bmatrix} 2g_1g_2 - 1 & 2g_2 \\ 2g_1(g_1g_2 - 1) & 2g_1g_2 - 1 \end{bmatrix} - \begin{bmatrix} \lambda & 0 \\ 0 & \lambda \end{bmatrix} \right\} \begin{bmatrix} r_0 \\ Lr_0' \end{bmatrix} = 0 \tag{9}$$

The mathematical procedure for finding possible values of the constant λ, called the *eigenvalues* of the problem, consists of setting the determinant formed from the total matrix in Eq. (9) equal to zero, or

$$\begin{vmatrix} (2g_1g_2 - 1) - \lambda & 2g_2 \\ 2g_1(g_1g_2 - 1) & (2g_1g_2 - 1) - \lambda \end{vmatrix} = 0 \tag{10}$$

which gives the quadratic equation for the eigenvalues,

$$\lambda^2 - 2(2g_1g_2 - 1)\lambda + 1 = 0 \tag{11}$$

The two eigenvalues or solutions of this equation are then

$$\lambda = \lambda_a, \lambda_b = (2g_1g_2 - 1) \pm \sqrt{4g_1g_2(g_1g_2 - 1)} \tag{12}$$

Along with these two eigenvalues λ_a and λ_b, there will be two *eigenvectors* $\mathbf{r}_a$ and $\mathbf{r}_b$, such that either will satisfy the basic *eigenequation*

$$\mathbf{M}_{\text{total}}\mathbf{r}_a = \lambda_a\mathbf{r}_a \qquad \mathbf{M}_{\text{total}}\mathbf{r}_b = \lambda_b\mathbf{r}_b \tag{13}$$

We will not work out the values of $\mathbf{r}_a$ and $\mathbf{r}_b$ explicitly here, since we do not need them for this analysis. However, the techniques for finding $\mathbf{r}_a$ and $\mathbf{r}_b$ should be well known to readers familiar with matrix eigenvalue problems.

It is an important property of the eigenvectors $\mathbf{r}_a$ and $\mathbf{r}_b$ that they form a mathematically complete set; that is, any arbitrary input vector $\mathbf{r}_0$ may be written as a sum of $\mathbf{r}_a$ and $\mathbf{r}_b$ components in the form

$$\mathbf{r}_0 = C_a\mathbf{r}_a + C_b\mathbf{r}_b \tag{14}$$

where C_a and C_b are expansion coefficients. Then, since passage through one section of the lens waveguide simply multiplies each eigenvector by its respective eigenvalue, the output ray after one section (or one complete trip around the resonator) is given by

$$\mathbf{r}_1 = \lambda_a C_a\mathbf{r}_a + \lambda_b C_b\mathbf{r}_b \tag{15}$$

In fact, it is easy to calculate the output even after an arbitrary number n of complete periods, since each eigenvector component is simply multiplied by its own eigenvalue to the nth power; i.e., the output is

$$\mathbf{r}_n = \lambda_a^n C_a\mathbf{r}_a + \lambda_b^n C_b\mathbf{r}_b \tag{16}$$

The nature of the eigenvalues λ_a and λ_b obviously determines the essential features of ray propagation in the system.

STABLE SYSTEMS, $0 \leq g_1g_2 \leq 1$ ■ In the particular example we are considering, if the g parameters satisfy the condition $0 \leq g_1g_2 \leq 1$, the eigenvalues may be written as

$$\lambda_a, \lambda_b = (2g_1g_2 - 1) \pm j\sqrt{4g_1g_2(1 - g_1g_2)} \tag{17}$$

and this may also be written as

$$\lambda_a, \lambda_b = \cos\theta \pm j\sin\theta = e^{\pm j\theta} \tag{18}$$

where

$$\theta = \cos^{-1}(2g_1g_2 - 1) \qquad 0 \leq g_1g_2 \leq 1 \tag{19}$$

The eigenvalues in this case are complex numbers with magnitude unity and phase angle $\pm\theta$. Since $\lambda^n = (e^{\pm j\theta})^n = e^{\pm jn\theta}$, propagation of an arbitrary initial ray through n periods of a lens waveguide, or through n bounces in an optical resonator, will lead to an output of the form

$$\mathbf{r}_n = C_a e^{jn\theta}\mathbf{r}_a + C_b e^{-jn\theta}\mathbf{r}_b = (C_a\mathbf{r}_a + C_b\mathbf{r}_b)\cos n\theta + j(C_a\mathbf{r}_a - C_b\mathbf{r}_b)\sin n\theta \tag{20}$$

In particular, the displacement of the ray at the $(2n)$th lens, where n is any arbitrary integer, will be given by an expression of the form

$$r_n = r_0 \cos n\theta + S_0 \sin n\theta \tag{21}$$

where S_0 is related to the initial ray slope. As illustrated in Fig. 8-3a, the ray in this case oscillates back and forth in sinusoidal fashion about the system axis, with a maximum excursion determined entirely by the entrance conditions r_0 and r_0'. Thus the focusing system is stable in the sense that while a ray oscillates about the axis, it always remains within a bounded maximum excursion. The usefulness of the g parameters is in part the simplicity of the associated stability criterion; i.e., if

$$0 \leq g_1g_2 \leq 1 \tag{22}$$

the focusing system is stable. We will see other aspects of this stability criterion later.
■ In optical resonators or lens waveguides with $g_1g_2 < 0$ or $g_1g_2 > 1$ the eigenvalues have the form

UNSTABLE SYSTEMS, $g_1g_2 < 0$ or $g_1g_2 > 1$

$$\lambda_a, \lambda_b = (2g_1g_2 - 1) \pm \sqrt{4g_1g_2(1 - g_1g_2)} \tag{23}$$

which may be written as

$$\lambda_a, \lambda_b = e^{+\alpha_a}, e^{-\alpha_b} \qquad g_1g_2 < 0 \text{ or } g_1g_2 > 1 \tag{24}$$

In contrast to the stable situation, the trajectory of an arbitrary ray in this case will be of the form

$$r_n = a_0 e^{+\alpha_a n} + b_0 e^{-\alpha_b n} \tag{25}$$

As illustrated in Fig. 8-3b, a ray in such an unstable system will diverge exponentially with increasing number of sections or bounces and will eventually pass out of the system

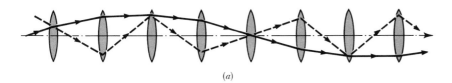

(a)

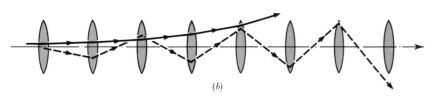

(b)

FIG. 8-3 (a) Ray propagation in a stable periodic-focusing system. The solid and dashed lines show two different types of stable oscillatory behavior, depending on the focusing properties of the lenses. (b) Ray propagation in an unstable system.

or intercept some limiting boundary of the system. The solid and dashed lines show two different forms of unstable behavior, depending on whether the lenses are individually divergent (solid line) or individually convergent but overly powerful (dashed line).

EXAMPLES OF OPTICAL RESONATORS

■ The stability analysis just presented applies equally well to sequences of electron lenses focusing an electron beam, optical lens waveguides, or optical resonators. Table 8-2 shows some specific examples of optical resonator configurations, ranging from the marginally stable *plane-parallel system* ($g_1 = g_2 = 1$), to the *confocal* system ($g_1 = g_2 = 0$), and on to the again marginally stable *spherical* or *concentric system* ($g_1 = g_2 = -1$). For simplicity only symmetric systems ($R_1 = R_2$) are illustrated. Obviously, a flat mirror placed at the midplane of any of these systems would yield another resonator with essentially the same behavior, and there are innumerable other nonsymmetric stable configurations ($R_1 \neq R_2$) not shown here. It appears that for g_1 and g_2 both positive, the ray uses multiple bounces to "walk" slowly back and forth across the resonator axis, while for g_1 and g_2 both negative, the ray crosses the system axis once each bounce.

STABILITY DIAGRAM

■ Although the geometric or ray-optics approach cannot predict many of the details of resonator behavior revealed by the more rigorous diffraction analysis in the following sections, the stability criterion developed here is basic and retains its validity even in more rigorous analyses. This stability criterion,

$$0 \leq g_1 g_2 \leq 1 \qquad \text{stable resonators}$$
$$g_1 g_2 < 0 \text{ or } g_1 g_2 > 1 \qquad \text{unstable resonators} \tag{26}$$

can be represented graphically by the stability diagram of Fig. 8-4. Any optical resonator, or any periodic focusing system, may be represented by a point on the $g_1 g_2$ plane, where $g_1 \equiv 1 - L/R_1 = 1 - L/2f_1$ and $g_2 \equiv 1 - L/R_2 = 1 - L/2f_2$. The resonator or focusing system will be stable only if this point falls within the shaded region of Fig. 8-4. The planar, confocal, and concentric resonators are indicated specifically on the diagram of Fig. 8-4*a*.

In Fig. 8-4*b* the mirror curvatures appropriate to various regions have been overlaid on the stability diagram. It is particularly interesting to note that a system with two convergent mirrors can still be unstable if the mirror convergence is too strong. Such a system is "overfocused," so to speak, as in the more-than-concentric resonator in the lower left corner of the diagram. The diagram also shows that it is possible in some cases to have a stable resonator with one divergent, or defocusing, mirror, if the other mirror or lens has the proper convergence (neither too weak nor too strong) to make the overall system stable.

ADDITIONAL TOPICS IN THE RAY APPROACH

■ The ray approach developed here may be applied to a number of additional topics, some of which have received considerable attention recently.[1]

Ducting in focusing media: Consider a dielectric medium such as that shown in Fig. 8-5, in which the index of refraction varies across a transverse cross section, with a maximum value n_0 at the axis. Situations of this type arise in inhomogeneous laser rods (or even in homogeneous laser rods as a result of uneven heating by pumping radiation), in gas laser tubes and gas-filled pipes, in certain optical waveguides, and in naturally occurring ducts for sound waves in the ocean or for radio waves in the

---

[1] For more details on the ray approach in general see Refs. 8-11 and 8-19.

TABLE 8-2
Typical resonator configurations

1. Plane parallel
   $R_1 = R_2 = \infty$
   $g_1 = g_2 = 1$
   $\cos \theta = 1$
   $\theta = 0$

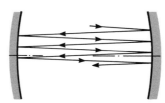

2. Slightly concave
   $R_1 = R_2 = $ large
   $g_1 = g_2 \lesssim 1$
   $\cos \theta = 1 - \delta$
   $\theta \approx \sqrt{2\delta}$

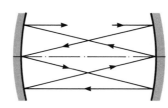

3. "Focal" resonator
   (Focus of each
   mirror on other mirror)
   $R_1 = R_2 = 2L$
   $g_1 = g_2 = 1/2$
   $\cos \theta = -1/2$
   $\theta = 3\pi/4$

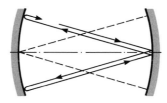

4. Confocal resonator
   (Focal points
   of mirrors coincide)
   $R_1 = R_2 = L$
   $g_1 = g_2 = 0$
   $\cos \theta = -1$
   $\theta = \pi$

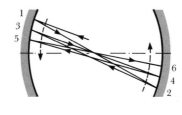

5. Near concentric
   $L/2 < (R_1, R_2) < L$
   $g_1 = g_2 \approx -1$
   $\cos \theta = -1 + \delta$
   $\theta \approx \pi + \sqrt{2\delta}$

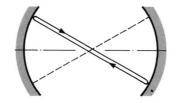

6. Concentric (Spherical)
   $R_1 = R_2 = L/2$
   $g_1 = g_2 = -1$
   $\cos \theta = 1$
   $\theta = 2\pi$

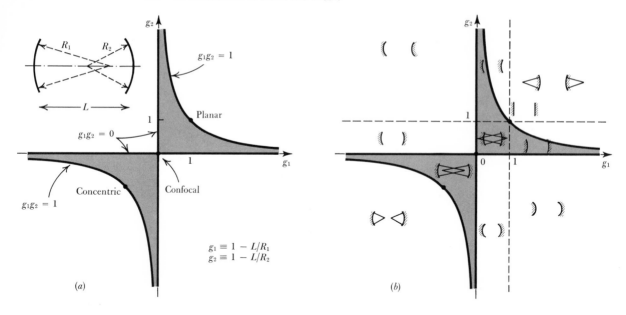

$$g_1 \equiv 1 - L/R_1$$
$$g_2 \equiv 1 - L/R_2$$

(a)   (b)

FIG. 8-4 The stability diagram for optical resonators and lens waveguides; all systems falling in the shaded regions are stable: (a) general features of the stability diagram and (b) examples of mirror configurations corresponding to different regions of the $g_1 g_2$ plane.

ionosphere. If the index of refraction has a maximum on the axis, then the first term in a Taylor series expansion of the index with radius will have the form

$$n(r) = n_0(1 - \tfrac{1}{2}\alpha r^2) \tag{27}$$

A ray propagating through a medium with a transversely varying index will always be gradually bent or refracted from low-index toward high-index regions. In simple terms, a ray or beam with a small but finite width will be slightly slowed or retarded on the high-index side compared to the low-index side, and hence will be bent slightly toward the high-index side. The equations governing the trajectory $r(z)$ of such a ray are

$$\frac{d}{dz} r(z) \equiv r'(z) \qquad \text{by definition}$$

$$\frac{d}{dz} r'(z) = \frac{1}{n(r)} \frac{d}{dr} n(r) \approx -\alpha r(z) \qquad \text{refractive bending} \tag{28}$$

Combining these equations leads to

$$\frac{d^2}{dz^2} r(z) + \alpha r(z) = 0 \tag{29}$$

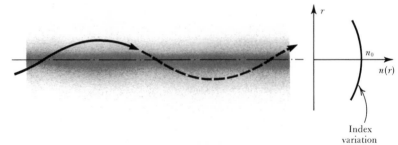

FIG. 8-5 Sinusoidal oscillation of a ray trajectory about the axis in a "duct" having an index maximum along the axis.

with the solution

$$r(z) = r_0 \cos \left(\alpha^{1/2}z\right) + \frac{r_0'}{\alpha^{1/2}} \sin \left(\alpha^{1/2}z\right) \tag{30}$$

In such a ducting medium the ray oscillates sinusoidally back and forth across the axis of the duct, with a period that depends on the strength of the focusing effect in the duct.

It is apparent that a duct with an index maximum on the axis always traps a ray and causes sinusoidal transverse oscillations, while an "antiduct" having an index minimum on axis will cause $r(z)$ to have an exponentially diverging behavior; i.e., the ray will rapidly diverge outward from the axis. If a duct were sliced into a large number of thin transverse slices, each such slice would be essentially a weakly convergent thin lens. From this viewpoint, the duct becomes essentially a continuous version of a periodic focusing system. The theory of ducting has many applications to mode distortion in laser rods and tubes and to wave propagation in inhomogeneous media.[1]

Optical delay lines and memory elements: If a narrow collimated laser beam is introduced into an optical resonator system with the proper initial displacement and initial slope—perhaps through a small off-axis hole in one mirror—the beam can make a large number of bounces, following ray paths such as those of Table 8-2, before leaving through another exit hole (see also Fig. 8-6). In this way a very long optical delay line (≥ 1000 m) can be folded into a very short physical length (≤ 1 m). In addition to its use as a broadband delay line, this system can also be used as an optical memory for coded modulation signals or pulses applied to the incident light beam. The dynamics of ray bounces are obviously important in understanding these systems. Astigmatic systems, which have different mirror curvatures and focusing properties in the x and y transverse directions, are of particular interest in these applications.[2]

Aberrations and random errors in lens waveguides: It now appears feasible to transmit high-information-capacity light beams over long distances with small power losses (< 1 dB/mile) with lens waveguides having low-loss lenses of small diameter (a few centimeters) spaced some hundreds of meters apart in underground pipes or tunnels. Since the construction and alignment of such a system can never be perfect, a combination of ray optics and statistics has been used to analyze the effects on ray propagation of small random errors in lens position, spacing, or focal length. The effects of random errors or aberrations in the lenses themselves must also be considered.[3]

Gas lenses: A tube filled with gas, with a temperature or density gradient across the tube cross section, furnishes, in effect, a thick but weak lens. Gas lenses of this type are of interest for use in lens waveguides because of their extremely low scattering and reflection losses. A combination of gas kinetics and thermodynamics and the theory of rays in ducts are needed to analyze these novel and ingenious types of lenses.[4]

Connection between ray optics and diffraction theory: The ray-optics approach is successful in predicting useful results because it represents essentially the zero-wavelength limit ($\lambda \rightarrow \infty$) of the more rigorous diffraction theory. There are a number

---

[1] See, for example, Refs. 8-15, 8-23, 8-24, and 8-27.

[2] For some striking photographs of the spot patterns and beam trajectories on successive bounces in such a delay line see Ref. 8-9.

[3] See Refs. 8-2, 8-8, and 8-21 to 8-23.

[4] See Refs. 8-8 and 8-23.

of analyses that explore the connections between the ray theory and wave theory of light propagation, or that attempt to extend the ray theory to obtain still more detailed results.[1]

DEMONSTRATION OF THE
OPTICAL DELAY LINE

■ Good-quality silvered telescope mirrors as large as 3 in. in diameter, with focal lengths of perhaps 30 in. (available for a few dollars from hobby stores or amateur-astronomy supply houses) can be mounted on simple spring-loaded adjustable mounts to make a large optical resonator or optical delay line, as shown in Fig. 8-6. The small collimated beam from an inexpensive He-Ne laser is then injected into the resonator, with a small piece of flat mirror used as an injection mirror at the edge of one of the larger mirrors. Adjustment of the beam-injection conditions and the mirror alignment will give the various types of periodically repeating beam patterns shown in Fig. 8-4 or Table 8-2. If each mirror is mounted on a heavy block and a straightedge or rail is used as a guide, the mirror spacing can be varied even on a lecture table to create any of the typical resonator configurations shown in Table 8-2. A little chalk dust or smoke of the type used in toy train engines will make the beam patterns dramatically visible in a darkened room. Another simple way of displaying the beam pattern at any cross section, without fouling the mirrors with dust or smoke, is to rapidly sweep a thin screwdriver blade (or perhaps a series of thin wires coming out radially from a rotating shaft) transversely across the resonator, producing a bright spot as the blade intercepts each beam in succession. This makes a striking and dramatic demonstration (see also Prob. 8-3).

8-2 GAUSSIAN LIGHT BEAMS: DIFFRACTION APPROACH

To obtain a detailed description of the optical modes in resonators and lens guides, we will now develop a more rigorous analysis based on diffraction theory. When we take into account the wave nature of light, we find ourselves led to the very basic and important concept of a *gaussian spherical light wave* or *light beam*.

BASIC DIFFRACTION PROBLEM:
HUYGENS' PRINCIPLE

■ Consider an optical wave propagating more or less along the $+z$ direction, so that it may be written as

$$u(x,y,z,t) = \text{Re} \left[\tilde{u}(x,y)e^{j(\omega t - \beta z)} \right] \tag{1}$$

Then the basic problem of diffraction theory or optical beam propagation may be expressed as follows: given the complex wave amplitude $\tilde{u}_0(x_0, y_0)$ across an input plane

[1] See Refs. 8-11, 8-15, and 8-27.

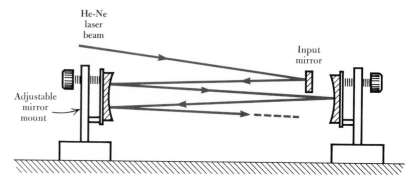

He-Ne
laser
beam

Input
mirror

Adjustable
mirror
mount

FIG. 8-6 Demonstration setup for an optical delay line or optical lens waveguide.

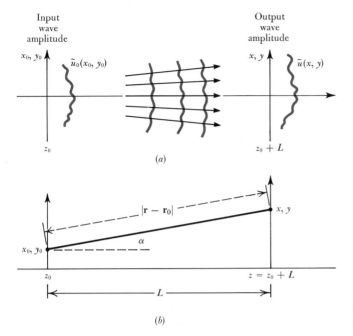

FIG. 8-7 (a) The basic optical diffraction problem and (b) the geometry for analyzing it by Huygens' principle.

z_0, as shown in Fig. 8-7a, find the complex amplitude and phase $\tilde{u}(x, y)$ of the wave across any later output plane $z = z_0 + L$.

For optical problems in which the characteristic dimensions are many wavelengths in size, and in which the transverse variations of $\tilde{u}(x, y)$ are slow compared to a wavelength, this solution may be calculated by *Huygens' principle*. If we use $\mathbf{r}_0 = (x_0, y_0, z_0)$ to denote an arbitrary point on the input plane, then the complex wave amplitude $\tilde{u}(\mathbf{r})$ at an arbitrary point $\mathbf{r} = (x, y, z)$ on the output plane will be given in terms of the input wave amplitude $\tilde{u}_0(\mathbf{r}_0)$ by

$$\tilde{u}(\mathbf{r}) = \frac{j}{\lambda} \iint_{\substack{\text{input} \\ \text{plane}}} \tilde{u}_0(\mathbf{r}_0) \frac{1 + \cos \alpha}{2} \frac{e^{-jk|\mathbf{r}-\mathbf{r}_0|}}{|\mathbf{r} - \mathbf{r}_0|} \, dx_0 \, dy_0 \qquad (2)$$

where the various geometric quantities are as indicated in Fig. 8-7b. Since we are concerned only with relatively narrow and highly collimated light beams, we may immediately make a number of simplifying approximations to this general expression:

1. Since only small angles α will be involved, we neglect entirely the obliquity factor $(1 + \cos \alpha)/2 \approx 1$.
2. We replace $|\mathbf{r} - \mathbf{r}_0|$ by $(z - z_0) \equiv L$ in the denominator, since this is not a critical factor.
3. In the exponential we use the expansion

$$k|\mathbf{r} - \mathbf{r}_0| = k[(z - z_0)^2 + (x - x_0)^2 + (y - y_0)^2]^{1/2}$$
$$\approx k\left[L + \frac{(x - x_0)^2}{2L} + \frac{(y - y_0)^2}{2L} + \cdots\right] \qquad (3)$$

and keep only the terms shown. This expansion is sometimes called the *Fresnel degree of approximation*. If the maximum transverse dimension of the light beam is approximately equal to a, then neglecting higher-order terms means neglecting terms of order

$$\frac{k(x - x_0)^4}{4L^3} \approx \frac{\pi}{2} \frac{a^4}{L^3 \lambda} \tag{4}$$

These terms will have negligible effect in the exponent if they are much smaller than $\pi/2$, which will be true if

$$\frac{a^2}{L\lambda} \ll \left(\frac{L}{a}\right)^2 \tag{5}$$

This is the case in most optical resonators of interest to us.

With the three approximations above, the simplified Huygens integral becomes

$$\tilde{u}(x, y) = \frac{je^{-jkL}}{\lambda} \iint_{\substack{\text{input} \\ \text{plane}}} \tilde{u}_0(x_0, y_0) e^{-j(k/2L)[(x-x_0)^2 + (y-y_0)^2]} \, dx_0 \, dy_0 \tag{6}$$

Note that this has the form of a convolution of the input wave $\tilde{u}_0(x_0, y_0)$ with a complex gaussian kernel or weighting function of the form e^{-jx^2}.

GENERAL SPHERICAL WAVES   ■ Consider next an ideal uniform spherical wave emanating from a point P, as in Fig. 8-8a. The phase distribution of this wave across a transverse plane at distance R from point P is

$$\tilde{u}(x, y) = e^{-jk(R^2 + x^2 + y^2)^{1/2}} \approx e^{-jk[R + (x^2 + y^2)/2R + \cdots]}$$
$$= e^{-jkR} \, e^{-jk(x^2 + y^2)/2R} \tag{7}$$

Thus, if a wave has a transverse phase variation across a plane of the form

$$\phi(x, y) = k\frac{x^2 + y^2}{2R} = \frac{\pi}{R\lambda}(x^2 + y^2) \tag{8}$$

we recognize it as a spherical wavefront with radius of curvature R.

The basic building blocks of our analysis turn out to be *spherical* waves having a *gaussian* variation in amplitude across the wavefront, as shown in Fig. 8-8b. Any wave with a gaussian transverse amplitude distribution may be written as

$$|\tilde{u}(x, y)| = e^{-(x^2 + y^2)/w^2} \tag{9}$$

where w is commonly called the *spot size* of this gaussian distribution. If we wish to normalize this to unit power flow, we may write

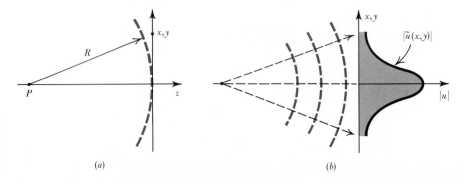

FIG. 8-8 (a) An elementary spherical wave and (b) a spherical wave with a gaussian transverse-amplitude variation across the wavefront.

(a)   (b)

$$|\tilde{u}(x,y)| = \sqrt{\frac{2}{\pi}} \frac{1}{w} e^{-(x^2+y^2)/w^2} \tag{10}$$

in which case the total power flow is

$$\iint |\tilde{u}(x,y)|^2 \, dx \, dy = 1 \tag{11}$$

More generally, we may write a complete *gaussian spherical wave* in the form

$$\tilde{u}(x,y) = \underbrace{\sqrt{\frac{2}{\pi}} \frac{1}{w}}_{\substack{\text{normalizing} \\ \text{factor}}} \underbrace{\exp\left(-j\frac{\pi}{\lambda}\frac{x^2+y^2}{R}\right)}_{\substack{\text{spherical wave} \\ \text{of radius } R}} \underbrace{\exp\left(-\frac{x^2+y^2}{w^2}\right)}_{\substack{\text{gaussian distribution} \\ \text{with spot size } w}} \tag{12}$$

If we combine the two separate exponents, we may write the total exponent in the form

$$-j\frac{\pi}{\lambda}\frac{x^2+y^2}{R} - \frac{x^2+y^2}{w^2} = -j\frac{\pi}{\lambda}\left(\frac{1}{R} - j\frac{\lambda}{\pi w^2}\right)(x^2+y^2) = -j\frac{\pi}{\lambda}\frac{x^2+y^2}{\tilde{q}} \tag{13}$$

The gaussian spherical wave can then be written in the compressed form

$$\tilde{u}(x,y) = \sqrt{\frac{2}{\pi}} \frac{1}{w} \exp\left(-jk\frac{x^2+y^2}{2\tilde{q}}\right) = \sqrt{\frac{2}{\pi}} \frac{1}{w} \exp\left(-j\frac{\pi}{\lambda}\frac{x^2+y^2}{\tilde{q}}\right) \tag{14}$$

where we have implicitly defined a *complex radius of curvature* $\tilde{q}$, given by

$$\frac{1}{\tilde{q}} \equiv \frac{1}{R} - j\frac{\lambda}{\pi w^2} \tag{15}$$

The one complex number $\tilde{q}$ contains both the radius of curvature R and the spot size w of the gaussian spherical wave. We will use the gaussian spherical form extensively in the following discussions.

■ Let us assume a gaussian *plane* wave at an input plane $z_0 = 0$,

PROPAGATION OF GAUSSIAN SPHERICAL WAVES

$$\tilde{u}_0(x_0, y_0) = \sqrt{\frac{2}{\pi}} \frac{1}{w_0} \exp\left(-j\frac{k}{2}\frac{x_0^2 + y_0^2}{\tilde{q}_0}\right) \tag{16}$$

where

$$\frac{1}{\tilde{q}_0} = -j\frac{\lambda}{\pi w_0^2} \qquad \tilde{q}_0 = j\frac{\pi w_0^2}{\lambda} \tag{17}$$

and then apply the simplified Huygens principle (6) to calculate $\tilde{u}(x,y)$ at a later plane z. We must thus evaluate

$$\tilde{u}(x,y,z) = \sqrt{\frac{2}{\pi}} \frac{j}{w_0\lambda} \frac{\exp(-jkz)}{z} \int_{-\infty}^{\infty}$$

$$\exp\left\{-j\frac{k}{2z}[(x-x_0)^2 + (y-y_0)^2]\right\} \exp\left[-j\frac{k}{2\tilde{q}_0}(x_0^2 + y_0^2)\right]$$

$$dx_0 \, dy_0 \quad (18)$$

If we complete the squares in the exponent, we can obtain, for example,

$$\frac{1}{z}(x - x_0)^2 + \frac{1}{\tilde{q}_0}x_0{}^2 = \frac{1}{\tilde{q}_0 + z}x^2 + \left(\frac{1}{\tilde{q}_0} + \frac{1}{z}\right)(x_0 - \beta x)^2 \qquad (19)$$

where $\beta = \tilde{q}_0/(\tilde{q}_0 + z)$. We then have

$$\tilde{u}(x, y, z) = \sqrt{\frac{2}{\pi}}\frac{\exp(-jkz)}{w_0 \lambda z}\exp\left(-j\frac{k}{2}\frac{x^2 + y^2}{\tilde{q}_0 + z}\right)$$
$$\iint_{-\infty}^{\infty}\exp\left\{-j\frac{k}{2}\left(\frac{1}{\tilde{q}_0} + \frac{1}{z}\right)[(x_0 - \beta x)^2 + (y_0 - \beta y)^2]\right\}dx_0\,dy_0 \qquad (20)$$

By changing variables x_0 and y_0 to $x_1 = x_0 - \beta x$ and $y_1 = y_0 - \beta y$, respectively, and then changing the coordinates from rectangular coordinates $dx_1\,dy_1$ to polar coordinates $r_1\,dr_1\,d\theta_1$, we can evaluate this integral and obtain

$$\frac{j}{w_0\lambda z}\iint_{-\infty}^{\infty}\exp\{\ldots\}\,dx_0\,dy_0 = \frac{1}{w_0}\frac{1}{1 - j\lambda z/\pi w_0{}^2} = \frac{1}{w(z)}e^{j\psi(z)} \qquad (21)$$

where

$$w(z) = w_0\sqrt{1 + \left(\frac{\lambda z}{\pi w_0{}^2}\right)^2} \qquad \psi(z) = \tan^{-1}\frac{\lambda z}{\pi w_0{}^2} \qquad (22)$$

Therefore, given a plane-wave input at $z = 0$

$$\tilde{u}_0(x_0, y_0) = \sqrt{\frac{2}{\pi}}\frac{1}{w_0}\exp\left(-j\frac{k}{2}\frac{x_0{}^2 + y_0{}^2}{\tilde{q}_0}\right) \qquad (23)$$

the output at any later plane z is

$$\tilde{u}(x, y, z) = \sqrt{\frac{2}{\pi}}\frac{1}{w(z)}\exp\{-j[kz - \psi(z)]\}\exp\left[-j\frac{k}{2}\frac{x^2 + y^2}{\tilde{q}(z)}\right] \qquad (24)$$

with the following identifications:

$$\tilde{q}(z) = \tilde{q}_0 + z = z + j\frac{\pi w_0{}^2}{\lambda}$$
$$\frac{1}{\tilde{q}(z)} = \frac{1}{R(z)} - j\frac{\lambda}{\pi w^2(z)} = \frac{1}{z + j\pi w_0{}^2/\lambda} \qquad (25)$$
$$R(z) = z + \left(\frac{\pi w_0{}^2}{\lambda}\right)^2\frac{1}{z}$$
$$w(z) = w_0\sqrt{1 + \left(\frac{\lambda z}{\pi w_0{}^2}\right)^2}$$
$$\psi(z) = \tan^{-1}\frac{\lambda z}{\pi w_0{}^2}$$

The input plane, where the beam wavefront is planar and the spot size is w_0, we will henceforth refer to as the *waist*.

This result has some very important consequences. A beam starting as a gaussian plane wave at a waist will remain in the form of a gaussian spherical wave with complex curvature $\tilde{q}(z)$ at all later planes z, as shown in Fig. 8-9a. The radius of curvature of this diverging wave as a function of distance from the waist is given by

$$R(z) = z\left[1 + \left(\frac{\pi w_0^2}{\lambda z}\right)^2\right]$$

$$\approx z \qquad z \gg \frac{\pi w_0^2}{\lambda} \tag{26}$$

Thus at sufficiently large distances from the waist the wave has a spherical wavefront, with its center of curvature located essentially at the waist. Furthermore, since the spot size of the beam as a function of distance from the waist is given by

$$w(z) = w_0\sqrt{1 + \left(\frac{\lambda z}{\pi w_0^2}\right)^2}$$

$$\approx \frac{\lambda z}{\pi w_0} \qquad z \gg \frac{\pi w_0^2}{\lambda} \tag{27}$$

at large distances from the waist the beam diverges linearly with distance, at a constant cone angle θ. As illustrated in Fig. 8-9b, this cone angle depends on the spot size w_0 at the waist [although the curvature $R(z)$ at large distances does not depend on w_0].

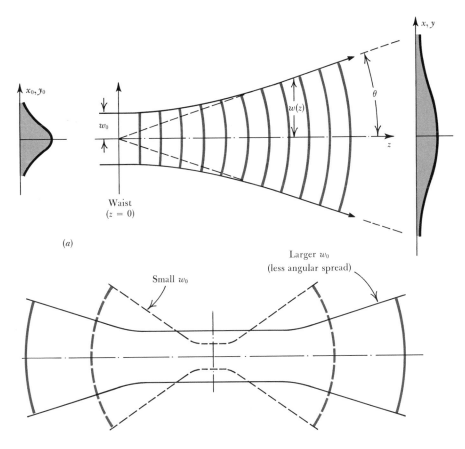

(a)

(b)

FIG. 8-9 (a) Outward propagation of a gaussian beam from a waist located at $z = 0$. (b) The angle at which a gaussian beam converges to or diverges from a waist is inversely related to the spot size w_0 at the waist.

■ We see that any beam having a gaussian spherical distribution at one plane will always propagate so as to remain a gaussian spherical wave at all other planes (henceforth, for brevity, we will simply write *gaussian* to mean *gaussian spherical*). Suppose that at a given plane z a beam has a gaussian wavefront with complex curvature $\tilde{q}_1$, representing wavefront curvature R_1 and spot size w_1. This beam can always be traced backward (or forward, if it happens to be a converging beam) to an appropriate waist located a distance z_1 behind the given plane (or in front of it for a converging beam). From our results above, the complex curvature $\tilde{q}_1$ is related to the waist spot size and the distance z_1 from the waist to the plane by the equation

$$\left(\frac{1}{R_1} - j\frac{\lambda}{\pi w_1{}^2}\right)^{-1} = \tilde{q} = \tilde{q}_0 + z_1 = z_1 + j\frac{\pi w_0{}^2}{\lambda} \tag{28}$$

But by equating the real and imaginary parts of the complex expression, we can also solve in reverse to find the distance z_1 back to the waist and the waist spot size w_0 in terms of the given wavefront parameters R_1 and w_1. The resulting expressions are

$$z_1 = \mathrm{Re}\left(\frac{1}{R_1} - j\frac{\lambda}{\pi w_1{}^2}\right)^{-1} = \frac{R_1}{1 + (\lambda R_1/\pi w_1{}^2)^2}$$
$$w_0 = \frac{w_1}{\sqrt{1 + (\pi w_1{}^2/\lambda R_1)^2}} \tag{29}$$

Every gaussian beam can be similarly traced back (or forward) to a unique real or virtual waist at a unique axial position.

Having traced the beam back to its waist, we can then trace it back out analytically to any other plane z_2, where the complex curvature will be $\tilde{q}_2 = \tilde{q}_0 + z_2$, as shown in Fig. 8-10. By eliminating the waist parameter $\tilde{q}_0$ from the expressions $\tilde{q}_1 = \tilde{q}_0 + z_1$ and $\tilde{q}_2 = \tilde{q}_0 + z_2$, we obtain

$$\tilde{q}_2 = \tilde{q}_1 + (z_2 - z_1) = \tilde{q}_1 + L \tag{30}$$

as the basic law of propagation for the complex curvature $\tilde{q}(z)$ versus distance. Thus, given any gaussian beam with wavefront curvature R_1 and spot size w_1 at one plane, we can find its curvature R_2 and spot size w_2 at a plane a distance L farther along by equating the real and imaginary parts of the complex equation $\tilde{q}_2 = \tilde{q}_1 + L$ to find w_2 and R_2 in terms of w_1 and R_1.

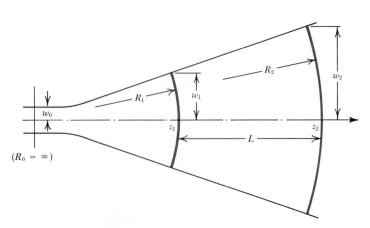

FIG. 8-10 A gaussian wavefront with curvature R_1 and spot size w_1 can be traced backward to a waist with spot size w_0 and infinite curvature ($R_0 = \infty$) or forward to another gaussian wavefront with curvature R_2 and spot size w_2.

Alert readers may already have raised the objection that our derivation of gaussian beam propagation away from the input plane at a waist in Eqs. (16) to (27) is based on the Fresnel approximation of Eqs. (3) to (6), which apparently is valid only for distances sufficiently far from the input plane that $L \gg (\pi a^4/2\lambda)^{1/3}$. Yet we are treating the gaussian beam solutions as if they applied not only far from the input plane, but all the way back to and even through the waist. The gaussian beam solutions do, in fact, remain valid through the waist and all along the z axis, even if the Fresnel approximation in our derivation does not. We chose to start the derivation in Eq. (16) at a waist simply because the algebra is slightly simpler. However, we could have started the derivation at any point—for example, with a converging gaussian beam well before a waist—and followed this beam down into and through the waist, so that the Fresnel approximation would be valid all through the waist (the reader may wish to verify this for himself). The expressions for $w(z)$ and $R(z)$ versus z measured from the waist would all remain exactly the same, and in general the predicted gaussian beam propagation remains exactly the same no matter where the input plane for the derivation is chosen.

■ The properties of gaussian spherical waves form interesting generalizations of the properties of ordinary uniform spherical waves. As Fig. 8-11 indicates, a spherical wave with curvature R_1 at plane z_1 will have curvature R_2 at plane z_2 given by

$$R_2 = R_1 + (z_2 - z_1) \tag{31}$$

The generalized counterpart for gaussian waves is, as just derived,

$$\tilde{q}_2 = \tilde{q}_1 + (z_2 - z_1) \tag{32}$$

An ordinary spherical wave passing through a thin lens of focal length f has its curvature changed according to the lens law,

Ordinary spherical waves

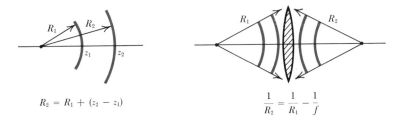

$$R_2 = R_1 + (z_2 - z_1) \qquad\qquad \frac{1}{R_2} = \frac{1}{R_1} - \frac{1}{f}$$

Gaussian spherical waves

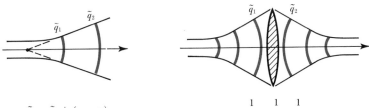

$$\tilde{q}_2 = \tilde{q}_1 + (z_2 - z_1) \qquad\qquad \frac{1}{\tilde{q}_2} = \frac{1}{\tilde{q}_1} - \frac{1}{f}$$

FIG. 8-11 There is an exact correspondence between transformation laws and lens laws for ordinary spherical waves (top) and gaussian spherical waves (bottom).

$$\frac{1}{R_2} = \frac{1}{R_1} - \frac{1}{f} \tag{33}$$

A gaussian wave has its wavefront curvature changed according to the same law, while its spot size is unchanged through the thin lens. Therefore the same law for gaussian beams may be written more generally as

$$\frac{1}{\tilde{q}_2} = \frac{1}{\tilde{q}_1} - \frac{1}{f} \tag{34}$$

The close identification between elementary spherical waves and gaussian spherical waves is evident. Note that in the lower portion of Fig. 8-11 the relative sizes of the waists have been exaggerated. Under most conditions the beam waists will be very small, approaching in strongly focused cases the idealized point sources of the ordinary spherical waves.

PROPERTIES OF GAUSSIAN LASER BEAMS
■ We have already seen (Sec. 1-5) that some of the most important aspects of laser beams are related to their directionality and spatial-mode properties. This includes particularly their properties with regard to collimation into highly straight and directional beams, leading to important applications in precision alignment, surveying, aiming, and the like; radiation into very small far-field angles, leading to very sharp antenna patterns and very small illuminated areas even at large ranges; and focusing into extremely small spots at close distances, leading to a very large energy density (incident power or energy per unit area) in the small region of the focus. We will see in the following section that most well-designed lasers emit an output beam that is very close to an ideal gaussian spherical beam. In the following paragraphs we will discuss in more detail the important collimation and focusing properties of gaussian light beams.[1]

GAUSSIAN-BEAM APERTURE SIZE
■ Gaussian beams must in many cases be passed through finite-sized apertures, such as laser mirrors, collimating or focusing lenses, or telescopes. We need to know, therefore, how large the aperture must be in terms of the gaussian spot size w for virtually all the gaussian beam's energy to be transmitted.

If the amplitude variation of a gaussian beam across a transverse cross section is given by $\tilde{u}(r) = (2/\pi)^{1/2}(1/w)\, e^{-r^2/w^2}$, then the fraction of the total intensity I_0 transmitted through a circular aperture of radius a (aperture diameter $d = 2a$) is given by

$$\frac{I(a)}{I_0} = \iint_{\text{aperture}} |\tilde{u}(r)|^2 \, dA = \frac{2}{\pi w^2}\int_0^a 2\pi r e^{-2r^2/w^2}\, dr = 1 - e^{-2a^2/w^2} \tag{35}$$

Figure 8-12 shows this power-transmission ratio plotted against the aperture-radius–spot-size ratio a/w. Evidently an aperture of radius equal to the gaussian spot size (aperture diameter $d = 2a = 2w$) will transmit ~86 percent of the total beam power. There will be in this case some slight distortion of the gaussian beam profile in the far-field region beyond the aperture because of the diffraction effects of the finite aperture, but these effects will be relatively minor.

As a rule of thumb, we can say that an aperture of diameter three times the gaussian spot size will pass ~99 percent of the gaussian beam power, and the diffraction

---

[1] The basic properties of gaussian light beams are extensively discussed by Kogelnik (Refs. 8-13 to 8-17), as well as by many other writers. Ref. 8-16 gives a general survey of gaussian beams, with extensive references.

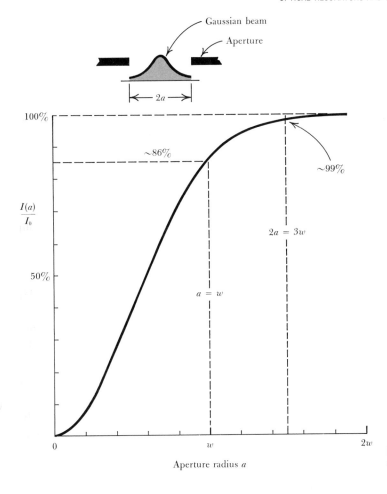

FIG. 8-12 Power transmission of a gaussian beam of spot size w through a circular aperture of radius a.

effects of this aperture on the subsequent beam profile will be completely negligible. Such an aperture with $2a = 3w$ provides a very conservative aperture design for transmitting an undistorted gaussian beam.

■ As a gaussian beam propagates outward from a waist, its diameter, or spot size, at first stays nearly constant, and begins to diverge linearly with distance at large distances. In many practical laser applications what is wanted is a pencil laser beam, which remains collimated to as small a diameter as possible for as long a distance as possible. Unfortunately, there is an inverse tradeoff between the diameter or the waist size at which the beam is collimated and the distance or range over which the beam will remain collimated at this diameter, as illustrated by Fig. 8-9.

A collimated laser beam is simply a particularly long gaussian-beam waist, as illustrated in Fig. 8-13. We define the collimated or waist region rather arbitrarily as extending between the points where the spot size $w(z)$ has increased by $\sqrt{2}$ over the value w_0 at the waist, or the beam area has doubled. Beyond these limits the beam continues spreading nearly linearly with distance and hence is no longer a parallel or collimated beam.

The distance z_R from the beam waist to the $\sqrt{2}\, w_0$ point is given by the equation

GAUSSIAN-BEAM COLLIMATION: RAYLEIGH RANGE

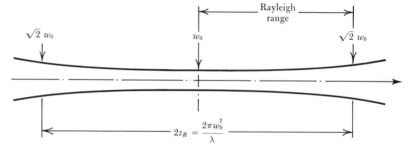

FIG. 8-13 A collimated gaussian beam is really just a long slender beam waist of length $2z_R$. The Rayleigh range z_R is defined as the distance from the waist to the point where the beam area has doubled.

$$w(z) = w_0\left(1 + \frac{\lambda z}{\pi w_0{}^2}\right)^{1/2} = \sqrt{2}\, w_0 \qquad (36)$$

or

$$z = z_R = \frac{\pi w_0{}^2}{\lambda} \qquad (37)$$

The quantity $z_R = \pi w_0{}^2/\lambda$ is sometimes called the *Rayleigh range*. The waist region then extends for roughly one Rayleigh range on either side of the origin. Obviously, the smaller the spot size of the beam, the more rapidly the beam diverges and the smaller the distance over which it remains collimated with a near-constant diameter and a near-planar wavefront.

The way to obtain the longest possible collimated beam is obviously to start with a transmitting aperture of diameter $d = 3\sqrt{2}\, w_0$ located at the point corresponding to $z = -z_R$ in Fig. 8-13, and focus the emitted beam just sufficiently to obtain the same spot size two Rayleigh ranges away, with a waist halfway in between. Figure 8-14 shows the resulting collimated beam range $2z_R$ plotted against the transmitting aperture diameter (defined on the conservative criterion $3a = 2w$) for two particularly important laser wavelengths. A visible beam coming from an aperture diameter $d = 10$ cm, or 4 in., will remain collimated to approximately that diameter for about 6 km, or ≈ 4 miles. Note also that Fig. 8-14 presents a conservative picture in that a beam of spot size w_0 appears to the eye to be considerably smaller than $3w_0$ in diameter. In alignment applications the centerline of a gaussian spot can be located photoelectrically to an accuracy of only one-thousandth of w_0 or less because of the large signal-noise ratio possible in the photodetection process.

FAR-FIELD BEAM ANGLE AND SPOT SIZE

■ Closely related to the Rayleigh range z_R is the far-field divergence of a gaussian beam for distances $z \gg z_R$. The far-field beam spread is important in transmitting laser beams over long distances, as in optical communications, laser radars, and similar applications. The output mirror of a laser, or any other aperture through which a gaussian beam is radiated, may be considered as an optical antenna. We wish to define the antenna properties of this optical antenna.

At large distances z from a waist a gaussian beam wavefront is essentially a spherical wave radiated from a quasi-point source at the waist. The far-field half-angle θ of the beam may be defined (see Fig. 8-9a) as

$$\theta \equiv \frac{w(z)}{z} \approx \frac{\lambda}{\pi w_0} \qquad z \gg z_R \qquad (38)$$

This is a more precise form of the usual relationship for an antenna, which says that the beam angle is $\theta \approx \lambda/d$, where λ is the wavelength and d is the antenna aperture diameter. As another measure of beam divergence, the solid angle Ω occupied by the

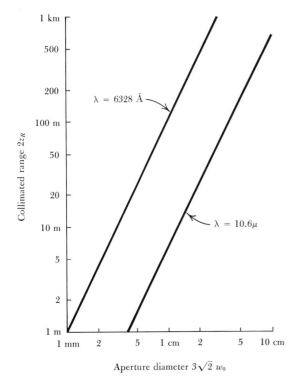

Aperture diameter $3\sqrt{2}\,w_0$

FIG. 8-14 The full length of the collimated-beam region or beam waist possible with a transmitting aperture of specified diameter for two common laser wavelengths, using the conservative aperture-diameter criterion $d = 3w$.

beam (out to one spot size, or out to the $1/e^2$ level in intensity) may be written as

$$\Omega \equiv \pi\theta^2 = \frac{\pi w^2(z)}{z^2} = \frac{\lambda^2}{\pi w_0^2} \tag{39}$$

If we define the spot size at the waist as $A_0 = \pi w_0^2$, using the same criterion for beam diameter, then the above result becomes

$$A_0\Omega = \lambda^2 \tag{40}$$

This is the gaussian-beam version of the general antenna principle that a radiating aperture of area A will have a radiation pattern with a minimum far-field beam spread Ω given by $A\Omega \geq \lambda^2$.

In the optical case the important point is, of course, that any reasonable aperture A is very much larger than λ^2 in size, and hence the far-field beam angles become exceedingly small (the optical antennas are extremely directional, and have extremely high antenna gains). The beam area and solid angle in Eqs. (39) and (40) are defined on the basis of diameter $d = 2w$ and will thus contain only $\sim$86 percent of a full gaussian beam. To be conservative, let us instead define areas and beam angles on the basis of a diameter $d = 3w$ (99 percent beam transmission):

$$A_0' \equiv \frac{\pi(3w_0)^2}{4} \quad = \text{transmitting aperture area}$$

$$A_1'(R) \equiv \frac{\pi[3w(R)]^2}{4} \quad = \text{far-field beam area at range } R \tag{41}$$

$$\Omega' \equiv \frac{A_1'(R)}{R^2} \quad = \text{far-field beam solid angle}$$

Then the conservative version of Eq. (40) is

$$A_0' \Omega' \approx 5\lambda^2 \tag{42}$$

for the beam angle and

$$A_1' = R^2 \Omega' \approx \frac{5R^2\lambda^2}{A_0'} \tag{43}$$

for the far-field beam area. In terms of spot diameters, these relations are

$$w(R) \approx \frac{R\lambda}{\pi w_0} \tag{44}$$

or if we define $d(R) \equiv 3w(R)$ and $d_0 \equiv 3w_0$,

$$d(R) \approx \frac{3\lambda}{d_0} R \tag{45}$$

To give a simple example, for a transmitting aperture of diameter $d_0 = 10$ cm, or ≈ 4 in., and a wavelength $\lambda = 6328$ Å, the far-field beam angle is $\Omega' \approx 2.5 \times 10^{-10}$ sterad, and the far-field beam diameter is $d \approx 10$ m at $R = 500$ km, or ≈ 300 miles. With the same 4-in. diameter transmitting aperture on earth, the diameter of an illuminated spot on the moon ($R \approx 4 \times 10^5$ km) will be only $d \approx 10$ km, or ≈ 6 miles.

Given an initial collimated gaussian beam (coming from a laser, for example) whose initial diameter is smaller than the desired transmitting-aperture diameter d_0, how can the beam size be expanded to the desired d_0? The answer is simply to pass the beam through an M-power telescope focused at infinity, as in Fig. 8-15, where M is the necessary beam expansion ratio. The effects of an M-power telescope on beam parameters are

Initial beam diameter $\propto M$

Initial beam area $\propto M^2$

Far-field spot diameter $\propto 1/M$ (46)

Far-field solid angle $\propto 1/M^2$

Use of a keplerian telescope has the advantage that a small pinhole aperture placed at the focal point can also filter out spurious beams generated in the laser by multiple reflections from the laser-tube walls, mirror front and back surfaces, and the like. Figure 8-15 also shows a typical commercial beam-expanding telescope available for attachment to the output end of an He-Ne 6328-Å laser.

FOCUSING TO A SPOT   ■ The final important property of a gaussian laser beam is the fact that it can be focused into an extremely small spot with an extremely high energy density, making it possible to drill tiny holes, make tiny cuts or welds, inspect tiny areas, make very-high-density recordings, and generally carry out operations in areas only a wavelength or two in size. As shown in Fig. 8-16, the problem of focusing a gaussian beam is essentially the far-field beam problem in reverse, since the focused spot is simply a beam waist produced by a sharply converging beam. As seen from the focus or waist of spot size w_0, the focusing lens in Fig. 8-16 is in the far field. For a collimated beam of spot size w incident before the lens, the lens will be located at a distance z equal to its focal length f behind the focus, and the two spot sizes will then be related by

$$w_0 = \frac{f\lambda}{\pi w} \tag{47}$$

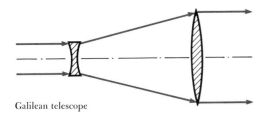

Galilean telescope

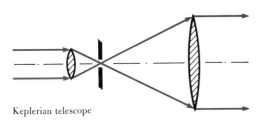

Keplerian telescope

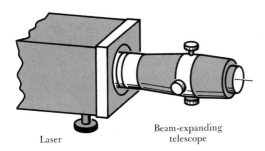

Laser

Beam-expanding telescope

FIG. 8-15 A telescope of either the galilean or keplerian type, focused at infinity, can be used to expand the beam size and thus change the far-field beam properties.

Under our conservative design criteria, the focusing lens must have a diameter $d = 3w$ to pass the incident beam. However, since ~86 percent of the energy will be focused into an area of diameter $2w_0$, we might say that the focused spot will have a full diameter defined as only $d_0 \approx 2w_0$. This focused-spot diameter is then given by

$$d_0 \approx \frac{2f\lambda}{d} \tag{48}$$

The f *number* or f *stop* of a focusing system is defined as

$$f\# \equiv \frac{f}{d} \approx \frac{f}{3w} \tag{49}$$

The focused-spot size is then given by

$$d_0 \approx 2f\#\lambda \tag{50}$$

Focusing systems with f numbers of unity or even a little less are available,[1] and hence the focused-spot size for an ideal gaussian beam is only a wavelength or two in diameter for $f\# \sim 1$.

[1] With f numbers as low as unity the beam convergence angles become large, and this begins to violate the small-angle assumptions inherent in the basic gaussian beam analysis. More exact methods of calculation, however, show that the gaussian beam formulas still give fairly accurate answers down to values of $f\# \gtrsim 1$, and extremely accurate answers for all values of $f\# \gtrsim 2$.

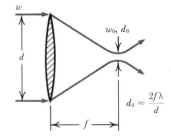

FIG. 8-16   A gaussian beam can be focused to a spot of diameter $d \approx 2f^{\#}\lambda$, where $f^{\#}$ is the f number of the focusing system.

PHASE FACTOR ■ One additional aspect of a gaussian beam is that the total phase shift along the axis of the beam, from the waist ($z = 0$) to plane z, is given by the expression

$$\phi(z) \equiv \int_0^z \beta(z) \, dz = kz - \psi(z) = kz - \tan^{-1}\frac{z}{z_R} \tag{51}$$

This differs from the simple free-space phase shift kz for an elementary plane or spherical wave by the factor $\psi(z)$, which builds up from $\psi = 0$ at $z = 0$ to $\psi \to 90°$ for $z \gg z_R$, with most of the change taking place within the waist region $z \lesssim z_R$.

This added-phase-shift contribution in the gaussian-beam case may be explained as follows. The wave equation for any electromagnetic signal is $(\nabla^2 + k^2)\tilde{u}(x,y,z) = 0$. If we assume that the wave amplitude may be written as $\tilde{u}(x,y,z) = \tilde{u}(x,y)e^{-j\beta z}$, then the wave-equation operator may be written in symbolic form as

$$\nabla^2 + k^2 = \nabla_{xy}^2 + \frac{\partial^2}{\partial z^2} + k^2 = \nabla_{xy}^2 - \beta^2 + k^2 = 0 \tag{52}$$

where ∇_{xy}^2 is the laplacian operator with respect to the xy coordinates only. Turning this around, we have for the z-direction propagation constant β

$$\beta(z) = \sqrt{k^2 + \nabla_{xy}^2} \approx k + \frac{\nabla_{xy}^2}{2k} \tag{53}$$

The z-directed propagation constant $\beta(z)$ differs somewhat from the plane-wave value k because of the transverse derivatives ∇_{xy}^2 of the fields, just as the phase velocity in an ordinary waveguide differs from the usual free-space phase velocity. This difference is most pronounced for a gaussian beam near the waist, where the beam is smallest and the transverse variations largest. The net result is the added-phase-shift term $-\psi(z)$.

COLLINS CHART ■ Another useful method of analyzing gaussian light beams is the *Collins chart*. Any single gaussian beam, such as that in Fig. 8-9b, may be described by its waist spot size w_0, or, equivalently, by its Rayleigh length $z_R = \pi w_0^2/\lambda$. In terms of the parameter z_R, the spot-size and curvature variations along the beam (with distance z measured from the beam waist) are given by

$$w^2(z) = w_0^2\left[1 + \left(\frac{z}{z_R}\right)^2\right] = \frac{\lambda z_R}{\pi}\left[1 + \left(\frac{z}{z_R}\right)^2\right]$$

$$R(z) = z + \frac{z_R^2}{z} \tag{54}$$

Consider a rectangular coordinate system in which the coordinates are $x \equiv \lambda/\pi w^2$ and $y \equiv 1/R$. Each point in this xy plane then corresponds to a certain complex curvature wR for a gaussian wavefront. The gaussian beam expressions above may then be combined into the single expression

$$\left(\frac{\lambda}{\pi w^2} - \frac{1}{2z_R}\right)^2 + \left(\frac{1}{R}\right)^2 = \left(x - \frac{1}{2z_R}\right)^2 + y^2 = \left(\frac{1}{2z_R}\right)^2 \tag{55}$$

This is the equation for a circle in the xy plane, with center at the point $\frac{1}{2}z_R$ on the x axis and radius $\frac{1}{2}z_R$. Therefore, as shown in Fig. 8-17a, the locus in the xy plane of the complex curvatures along a given gaussian beam is simply a circle with center at $\frac{1}{2}z_R$ and radius $\frac{1}{2}z_R$. The distance coordinate z is a parameter along this circle. The waist, $z = 0$, is the point ($x = x_{\max} = 1/z_R$, $y = 0$). The points at the top and bottom of the circle, ($x = x_{\max}/2 = \frac{1}{2}z_R$, $y = \pm y_{\max} = \pm\frac{1}{2}z_R$), correspond to distances $z = \pm z_R$ from the waist. The origin corresponds to $z \to \infty$, so that $w^2 \to \infty$ and $R \to \infty$.

A different gaussian beam, with a different waist parameter z_R, corresponds to a different circle in this same plane. The set of all possible gaussian beams, characterized by all possible spot sizes w_0 or Rayleigh ranges z_R, forms a family of circles, as indicated by the solid circles in Fig. 8-17b. At the same time the points corresponding to

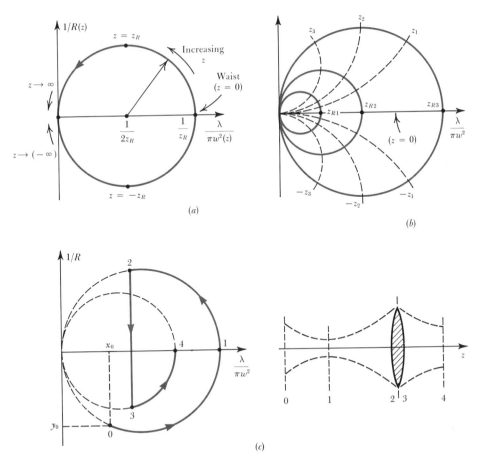

FIG. 8-17 (a) As a gaussian beam propagates through free space, its complex curvature $\bar{q}$ follows the circular trajectory shown. (b) The family of such trajectories corresponding to gaussian beams of different waist sizes forms the Collins chart. (c) Typical gaussian beam propagation problem described on the Collins chart.

different distances z_1, z_2, and z_3 along these beams are characterized by the dashed circles also shown in Fig. 8-17b. The circle corresponding to a fixed distance z from the waist of any gaussian beam has its center at the point $\frac{1}{2}z$ on the y axis and passes through the origin.

This type of circle diagram, called a *Collins chart,* may be used to describe and even to solve gaussian beam-propagation problems, as illustrated in the example of Fig. 8-17c. As shown on the circle diagram and the accompanying sketch, a hypothetical beam originates with a certain initial curvature and spot size, which together locate the starting point 0. As the beam travels forward in z, it converges to a waist (point 1) and then diverges to a lens (point 2). The transformation through the lens leaves the spot size unaltered and changes only $R = y^{-1}$, as represented by the vertical transition between points 2 and 3 on the circle diagram. The beam then converges to another larger waist at point 4.

Readers familiar with transmission-line theory will notice that the Collins chart of Fig. 8-17b has exactly the same construction as the familiar Smith chart; indeed, a Smith chart with its axes properly relabelled becomes a Collins chart and may be used to plot gaussian beam transformations, as in Fig. 8-17c. Collins diagrams can be useful in diagraming and understanding gaussian beam problems, and even in obtaining rough graphical results, although numerical calculations may still be necessary for sufficient accuracy. The Collins chart can also be recast into several other mathematically equivalent forms.[1]

GAUSSIAN BEAMS IN DUCTS   ■ Consider again a region in which the dielectric constant or index of refraction varies transversely with a maximum on axis, as shown in Fig. 8-5. If the index of refraction in this duct is given by $n(x) = n_0(1 - \frac{1}{2}\alpha x^2)$, then the dielectric constant is $\epsilon(x) = n^2(x)\epsilon_0 \approx n_0^2\epsilon_0(1 - \alpha x^2)$. We will consider only x variations for simplicity, since the y variations are exactly analogous. With certain approximations we will not discuss here, the wave equation in this region then becomes

$$[\nabla^2 + \omega^2\mu_0\epsilon(x)]\tilde{u}(x,y) = [\nabla^2 + n_0^2k^2(1 - \alpha x^2)]\tilde{u}(x,y) = 0 \tag{56}$$

If an assumed wavefront of the form $\tilde{u}(x,z) = e^{-j\beta z}e^{-x^2/w_0^2}$ is substituted into this wave equation, it is found that the only allowed solution is a wave of the form

$$\tilde{u}(x,z) = e^{-x^2/w_0^2}e^{-j\beta z} \tag{57}$$

where the propagation constant is $\beta = \sqrt{n_0^2k^2 - 2/w_0^2} \approx n_0k$ and the gaussian spot size is

$$w_0 = \sqrt{\frac{\lambda}{\pi n_0\alpha^{1/2}}} \tag{58}$$

In other words, the duct will trap or propagate a certain gaussian planar guided wave having a certain definite size w_0 which is inversely related to the curvature of the $n(x)$ variation. One way of viewing this wave-trapping phenomenon is to think of it as an exact balance between the diverging tendencies of the gaussian wave due to diffraction, and the converging or focusing tendencies of the duct due to the $n(x)$ variation.

Further extensions of this ducting analysis are possible. For example, it can be shown that if one launches a gaussian wave with the wrong spot size or complex curva-

[1] See Refs. 8-4 and 8-20.

ture in a duct, then the wave will alternately converge and diverge, oscillating in quasi-sinusoidal fashion about the allowed gaussian spot size w_0.[1]

8-3   MODE PROPERTIES OF STABLE OPTICAL RESONATORS

In this section we will apply the gaussian light-beam theory of the preceding section to develop the basic mode properties of stable optical resonators. Such resonators, with their characteristic low-diffraction-loss gaussian mode patterns, are used in the great majority of practical optical masers.

■ When two curved optical mirrors of appropriate curvature and spacing are set up facing each other, the lowest-order resonant or cavity mode of this optical resonator is a *gaussian light beam* of appropriate curvature and spot size trapped between the two mirrors. Perhaps the easiest way to demonstrate this fact is to approach the problem backward, by starting with a gaussian light beam and fitting resonator mirrors to it.

GAUSSIAN BEAMS AND STABLE RESONATORS

Consider some typical gaussian light beam, with a waist of spot size w_0 at $z = 0$ and with spot sizes w_1 and w_2 and radii of curvature R_1 and R_2 at two other arbitrary planes $z = z_1$ and $z = z_2$ along the beam, as shown in Fig. 8-18. If we place at these two planes z_1 and z_2 curved mirrors whose radii of curvature R_1 and R_2 are exactly matched to the beam wavefronts and whose diameters are considerably larger than the beam spot sizes, these mirrors will reflect the gaussian beam exactly back on itself at each end. As a result, the gaussian beam will be forced to bounce back and forth between the two mirrors, forming a standing wave, without changing its spot sizes or curvatures with time. In other words, this trapped gaussian beam will form a standing-wave resonant mode in the optical cavity formed by the two mirrors.

It can be seen immediately that the shape of the resonant mode, that is, the variation of spot size and wavefront curvature along the axis of the resonator, will not depend on the mirror diameters $2a_1$ and $2a_2$ at all (provided that $a_1 \gg w_1$ and $a_2 \gg w_2$), but only on the mirror radii R_1 and R_2 and their spacing $L = z_2 - z_1$. Furthermore, for $a_1 \gg w_1$ and $a_2 \gg w_2$ the amount of energy lost by leakage past the edges of the mirrors on each bounce will be very small, and so the resonator losses due to leakage or diffraction will be small despite the completely open sides of this cavity. As we will see shortly, for typical laser-mirror curvatures and spacings the resulting gaussian modes are very much more slender and threadlike than those in Figs. 8-9, 8-10, and 8-18, where the transverse sizes are considerably exaggerated for illustration. Real laser mirrors are easily made larger in diameter than the gaussian-mode spot sizes.

■ We have approached the problem of gaussian resonator modes by starting with an assumed gaussian beam and then fitting appropriate resonator mirrors to it. However,

FINDING THE APPROPRIATE GAUSSIAN BEAM

[1] See Ref. 8-27.

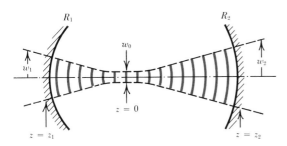

FIG. 8-18 A stable optical resonator is obtained by placing mirrors with the proper curvatures R_1 and R_2 at the proper planes z_1 and z_2 along a gaussian beam.

the actual optical-resonator problem more commonly appears in the opposite form: given two predetermined laser mirrors of curvature R_1 and R_2 spaced apart a distance L, find the appropriate (and unique) gaussian beam that will just fit between these mirrors in the manner shown in Fig. 8-18 (this includes finding the spot sizes w_1 and w_2, waist spot size w_0, waist location, and so forth). This problem can be solved by applying the general gaussian beam formula $R(z) = z + z_R^2/z$ to find the wavefront curvature along the beam and requiring that this curvature match the mirror curvature at each end; i.e.,

$$z_1 + \frac{z_R^2}{z_1} = -R_1 \qquad z_2 + \frac{z_R^2}{z_2} = R_2$$
$$z_2 - z_1 = L \tag{1}$$

The left-hand mirror curvature R_1 is preceded by a minus sign in the first equation, since the resonator sign convention for the left-hand mirror is the reverse of the sign convention used in the gaussian light-beam analysis. We have used the Rayleigh length $z_R \equiv \pi w_0^2/\lambda$ to characterize the waist parameter of the gaussian beam.

These equations can now be solved to find the unknown gaussian beam parameters z_1, z_2, and z_R in terms of the specified resonator-mirror parameters R_1, R_2, and L. With the resonator g parameters g_1 and g_2 substituted for the mirror curvatures R_1 and R_2, these results are

$$z_1 = -\frac{g_2(1 - g_1)}{g_1 + g_2 - 2g_1g_2} L$$
$$z_2 = +\frac{g_1(1 - g_2)}{g_1 + g_2 - 2g_1g_2} L = z_1 + L \tag{2}$$
$$z_R^2 \equiv \left(\frac{\pi w_0^2}{\lambda}\right)^2 = L^2 \frac{g_1g_2(1 - g_1g_2)}{(g_1 + g_2 - 2g_1g_2)^2}$$

We can further apply gaussian beam theory to find the gaussian spot sizes at the two mirrors:

$$w_1^2 \equiv w^2(z_1) = w_0^2\left[1 + \left(\frac{z_1}{z_R}\right)^2\right] = \frac{L\lambda}{\pi} \sqrt{\frac{g_2}{g_1(1 - g_1g_2)}}$$
$$w_2^2 = \frac{L\lambda}{\pi} \sqrt{\frac{g_1}{g_2(1 - g_1g_2)}} \tag{3}$$

We see immediately that if either $g_1g_2 \to 0$ or $g_1g_2 \to 1$, the spot size at least at one of the two mirrors blows up, and the gaussian theory is obviously no longer valid. Equation (1) has a solution in the form of a finite gaussian beam only if the optical resonator satisfies the stability requirement

$$0 \le g_1g_2 \equiv \left(1 - \frac{L}{R_1}\right)\left(1 - \frac{L}{R_2}\right) \le 1 \tag{4}$$

But, this is exactly the same as the stability criterion of Eq. (26) in Sec. 8-1, derived from the geometric ray approach. In other words, the range of validity of the gaussian resonator-mode solutions is exactly the same as the stable regime predicted by the simple ray approach of Sec. 8-1.

SYMMETRIC STABLE
RESONATORS
■ Before we pursue these general arguments further, it may be helpful to discuss some specific resonator configurations. Consider a general symmetric resonator with equal

mirror curvatures, $R_1 = R_2 = R$, so that $g_1 = g_2 = g = 1 - L/R$. The waist of the gaussian resonant mode is then obviously in the center of the resonator, with waist and mirror spot sizes given by

$$w_0 = \left(\frac{L\lambda}{2\pi}\right)^{1/2}\left(\frac{1+g}{1-g}\right)^{1/4} \qquad w_1 = w_2 = \left(\frac{L\lambda}{\pi}\right)^{1/2}\left(\frac{1}{1-g^2}\right)^{1/4} \qquad (5)$$

All these symmetric resonators lie on the line with slope $+45°$ through the origin in the g-plane stability diagram (Fig. 8-4), with an allowed range of $g = +1$ (plane-mirror case), through $g = 0$ (concentric case), to $g = -1$ (concentric, or spherical, case). Table 8-3 illustrates how the resonator mode changes shape as the g value is varied over this range, for example, by steadily increasing the mirror curvatures while keeping the mirror spacing fixed. Note that the waist size steadily decreases from $w_0 \to \infty$ as $g_1 \to +1$ to $w_0 \to 0$ as $g_1 \to -1$, while the end-mirror spot size de-

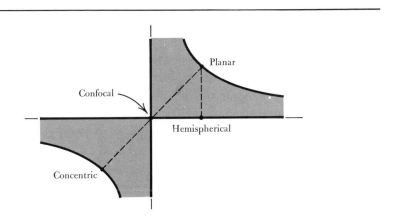

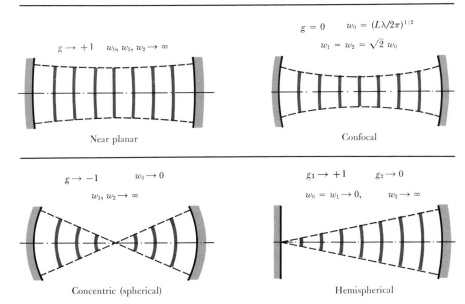

TABLE 8-3
Typical stable optical resonators

creases from $w_1 \to \infty$ as $g_1 \to +1$ to a minimum value $w_1 = \sqrt{L\lambda/\pi}$ at $g = 0$, and then increases again to $w_1 \to \infty$ as $g_1 \to -1$.

The spot sizes in stable resonators are generally on the order of the quantity $(L\lambda/\pi)^{1/2}$ multiplied by a function $f(g_1,g_2)$, which does not deviate too far from unity in many practical cases. The characteristic size of the modes in the transverse direction for typical optical infrared wavelengths is

$$
\begin{aligned}
L = 1 \text{ m}, \lambda = 1 \ \mu \qquad & \sqrt{\frac{L\lambda}{\pi}} \approx 0.6 \text{ mm} \\
L = 10 \text{ cm}, \lambda = 1 \ \mu \qquad & \sqrt{\frac{L\lambda}{\pi}} \approx 0.18 \text{ mm}
\end{aligned}
\tag{6}
$$

The spot sizes are generally very small, and the gaussian beam modes are very long and slender for all reasonable resonator dimensions.

CONFOCAL RESONATORS ■ The confocal resonator is a particularly interesting case, since it is located at a singular point (the origin) in the g-plane stability diagram. At every other point on the stable-region boundary, including points arbitrarily close to the confocal point, one or both of the end-mirror spot sizes becomes infinite. For the symmetric confocal resonator, however, the end-mirror spot sizes are not only finite, $w_1 = w_2 = (L\lambda/\pi)^{1/2} = 2^{1/2}w_0$, but they have the smallest value of any stable symmetric system.

A general unsymmetric confocal resonator will be formed by any two mirrors whose focal points coincide. Since the focal point of a curved mirror is located halfway between the center of curvature and the mirror itself, the general unsymmetric confocal condition is $R_1 + R_2 = 2L$, or, in terms of g values,

$$
\frac{1}{1 - g_1} + \frac{1}{1 - g_2} = 2
\tag{7}
$$

The g values satisfying this relationship all lie in the unstable portion of the g plane, except for the special case $g_1 = g_2$. In other words all unsymmetric confocal resonators are unstable, and only the exactly symmetric case is stable.

HALF-SYMMETRIC (ONE-PLANE-MIRROR) RESONATORS ■ Another elementary system is the half-symmetric system, in which one mirror is plane and the other is curved, so that $g_1 = 1$ and $g_2 = g$. This is called half-symmetric because it is equivalent to half of a symmetric system that is twice as long. The waist in this case is at the left-hand mirror, and the spot sizes are

$$
w_0 = w_1 = \sqrt{\frac{L\lambda}{\pi}} \left(\frac{g}{1 - g}\right)^{1/4} \qquad w_2 = \sqrt{\frac{L\lambda}{\pi}} \left[\frac{1}{g(1 - g)}\right]^{1/4}
\tag{8}
$$

The allowed range of $g_2 = g$ is now from $+1$ to 0, corresponding to a vertical line between the points $(1,1)$ and $(1,0)$ in the stability diagram.

HEMISPHERICAL RESONATORS ■ The hemispherical, or half-concentric, resonator, also illustrated in Table 8-3, is a particular type of half-symmetric resonator that is widely used in laser devices. As the mirror spacing in this case approaches the mirror curvature, $L \to R$, the spot size at one end diverges, $w_2 \to \infty$, while the spot size at the other end becomes very small, $w_1 \to 0$. Practical lasers are built with a length L just slightly less than R. Very slight changes in resonator length are then used to adjust the larger spot size w_2, so that the lowest-order gaussian mode just fills the laser tube or mirror. A semiempirical rule is that best performance will be obtained from a laser tube or mirror of diameter $2a$, under most conditions, if the mode size w is adjusted so that $2a \approx 3.5w$ to $4.0w$ at the mirror or other limiting aperture.

■ Any curved-mirror resonator of reasonable transverse size whose g_1 and g_2 parameters fall well within the stable region on the stability diagram will have a gaussian lowest-order mode pattern following the rules described above, with a spot size $w(z) \ll a$ (transverse mirror size $2a$). Since these gaussian modes are much smaller than the mirrors in transverse cross section, they will have very small diffraction losses past the edges of the mirrors. The shape of the gaussian mode will be determined only by the mirror curvatures, and is essentially unaffected by the transverse size or shape of the end mirrors.

As the g_1 and g_2 parameters approach the boundary of the stable region at any point, the waist spot size w_0 will approach zero (except at a few singular points such as $g_1 = g_2 = 0$ or 1), and either one or both of the end-mirror spot sizes w_1 and w_2 will approach infinity. As soon as the mirror parameters come close enough to the stable-unstable boundary that the spot size at either end approaches the mirror size, w_1 or $w_2 \approx a$, we can expect that the simple gaussian beam analysis will fail, or at least begin to lose validity. That is, the simple gaussian-beam description can no longer be fully valid, because a gaussian wave impinging on at least one of the ends will suffer a large loss and will be severely distorted upon reflection.

The gaussian mode picture is thus valid everywhere inside the stable region predicted by ray theory, except in a narrow boundary region where the mode size predicted by the gaussian analysis exceeds the mirror sizes. The width of this rather fuzzy boundary region depends on the mirror transverse diameter and increases as the mirror size is decreased. The boundary region is, however, typically very narrow for mirrors of practical size; i.e., the stability diagram remains a very accurate picture for most practical cases.

The mode shapes for resonators lying in the boundary region, or even entirely outside the stable region, can be determined only from more elaborate analyses, which we will discuss later. The mode shapes depart from the simple gaussian shape and become more complicated, depending on both the mirror curvatures and the mirror sizes and shapes. The diffraction losses past the mirror edges also increase substantially, although not as much as might be thought.

■ Most commercially available, small, inexpensive He-Ne lasers are specified to oscillate *uniphase;* i.e., they are designed to oscillate only in a single gaussian lowest-order transverse mode. The gaussian intensity profile of the beam from such a laser can readily be verified with the simple demonstration apparatus shown in Fig. 8-19. Since the beam emerging from the laser output mirror is usually quite small ($\sim$1 mm diameter), the beam is diverged with a simple lens. A slowly rotating motor-driven mirror (a few revolutions per second) is then used to sweep the beam profile across a slit aperture in front of a photodetector. The photodetector output is displayed against time on an oscilloscope, and the gaussian profile of the beam can readily be verified. The oscilloscope may be internally triggered, or a separate photodevice may be used to pretrigger the oscilloscope sweep externally.

■ In some laser experiments it becomes necessary to focus the gaussian output beam emitted by one laser back down into a second optical resonator, such as a regenerative laser amplifier, a passive optical filter cavity (interferometer cavity), or perhaps a lens waveguide system. In these cases the original gaussian laser beam, characterized by its waist size and waist location, must be transformed by appropriate lenses or other optical elements so that it will converge down to the waist size and waist location characteristic of the second optical system. This transformation of the beam from one

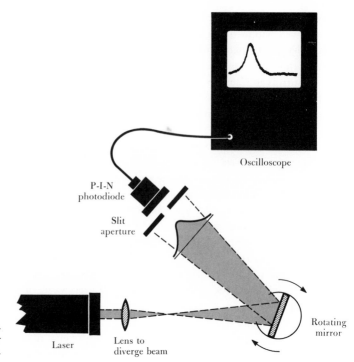

Oscilloscope

P-I-N
photodiode

Slit
aperture

Rotating
mirror

Laser

Lens to
diverge beam

FIG. 8-19 Demonstration apparatus for observing the gaussian transverse intensity profile of a laser
beam.

resonator into a beam that matches up with a second gaussian system is referred to as *gaussian mode matching.*

For proper mode matching the laser beam entering the second system must have both the proper radius of curvature and the proper spot size at the system's input. The simplest way to achieve this is to trace the original gaussian laser beam forward and the required gaussian beam for the second system backward to find the point at which the spot sizes of the two beams are identical (if such a point can be found). Given the two radii of curvature at this point, we can then calculate the focal length f of the thin lens necessary to match one beam exactly into the other. Of course, in a real problem it may not be convenient to place a lens at this point, or a lens of the necessary focal length may not be available. More complicated multiple-lens transformations must then be considered, or the spacing between the original laser and the second system must be varied. The Collins chart can be helpful in diagraming the beam transformations through the various optical elements involved.

Through incorrect design or improper alignment, the gaussian beam entering an optical system, such as a cavity resonator or a lens waveguide, may not be matched to the system, and may have the wrong spot size, wrong curvature, or a tilt or offset from the system axis. Then an incident lowest-order gaussian beam will excite in the second system a mixture of lowest plus higher-order modes of the second system.[1]

STABLE MULTIELEMENT
RESONATORS

■ Stable gaussian resonator modes can also exist in more complex multielement optical resonators, such as resonators containing internal lenses, ring resonators with more than two mirrors, or resonators with internal dielectric interfaces, as illustrated in

---

[1] Calculations of the cross coupling between modes in situations of this sort have been carried out, for example, by Kogelnik (see Ref. 8-13).

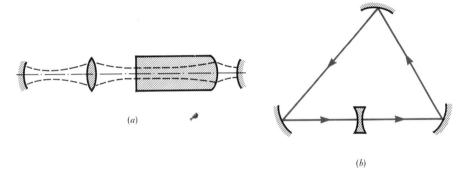

(a)

(b)

FIG. 8-20 Examples of more complex optical resonators, with intracavity elements, or forming closed rings.

Fig. 8-20. The problem of finding the right gaussian beam profile to match all the wavefront conditions becomes more complicated than in the simple two-mirror resonator, but can be handled by the following method.

Consider an arbitrary black-box optical system containing one or more lenses, dielectric interfaces, or other beam-modifying elements, as shown in Fig. 8-21a. With the ray approach of Sec. 8-1 it is possible to work out the overall ray matrix, or (A,B,C,D) matrix, of this optical black box so that its overall effects are summarized by

$$r_2 = Ar_1 + Br_1' \qquad r_2' = Cr_1 + Dr_1' \tag{9}$$

Let us consider how an ideal spherical wave will propagate through this black box. Since an optical ray is essentially a vector normal to the optical wavefront, it is evident from the geometry of Fig. 8-21b that the wavefront curvature R and the ray parameters r and r' are related by

$$r' = \frac{r}{R} \qquad \text{or} \qquad R = \frac{r}{r'} \tag{10}$$

Therefore the input and output wavefront curvatures for the optical black box may be related by

$$R_2 = \frac{r_2}{r_2'} = \frac{Ar_1 + Br_1'}{Cr_1 + Dr_1'} = \frac{AR_1 + B}{CR_1 + D} \tag{11}$$

In connection with Fig. 8-11, we saw that, at least for free-space propagation and for a simple lens, the complex curvature $\bar{q}$ obeys exactly the same propagation laws as does the wavefront radius R in geometrical optics. However, this relationship holds

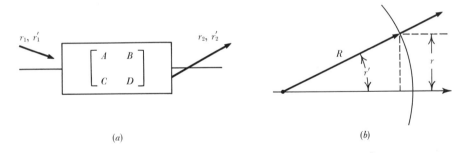

(a)

(b)

FIG. 8-21 Evaluation of ray propagation or gaussian-beam propagation through an arbitrary optical system.

for *any* optical system if $\tilde{q}$ is substituted for R in Eq. (11). That is, if a gaussian beam with complex curvature $\tilde{q}_1$ is sent into the input of the black box of Fig. 8-21a, the complex curvature at the output can be obtained simply from the (A,B,C,D) ray matrix of the system by writing

$$\tilde{q}_2 = \frac{A\tilde{q}_1 + B}{C\tilde{q}_1 + D} \tag{12}$$

There is obviously a close connection between ordinary ray optics and gaussian beam propagation, even though the former completely neglects and the latter fully includes the wave nature of light.

The gaussian mode of any complex optical resonator can now be found by first evaluating the total (A,B,C,D) matrix, starting from any arbitrary point inside the resonator and making one complete trip around the resonator. Then a stable gaussian mode with $\tilde{q} = \tilde{q}_1$ starting at that point must, after one round trip, come back to the starting point with the same $\tilde{q}$ value $\tilde{q}_0 = \tilde{q}_2 = \tilde{q}_1$ if the mode is to be a closed stationary mode of the resonator. That is, the stable mode (if there is one) must satisfy

$$\tilde{q}_2 = \frac{A\tilde{q}_1 + B}{C\tilde{q}_1 + D} = \tilde{q}_1 \tag{13}$$

which can immediately be solved to give

$$\tilde{q}_1 = \frac{(A - D) \pm \sqrt{(A - D)^2 + 4BC}}{2B} \tag{14}$$

With the aid of a general property of all ray matrices,

$$AD - BC = 1 \tag{15}$$

the gaussian solution can be rewritten as

$$\frac{1}{\tilde{q}_1} = \frac{D - A}{2B} - j\sqrt{\frac{4 - (A + D)^2}{4B^2}} = \frac{1}{R_1} - j\frac{\lambda}{\pi w_1{}^2} \tag{16}$$

Since the mode must have a finite real spot size w_1, the general criterion for the existence of a stable mode is that the round-trip ray matrix must obey the condition

$$\left(\frac{A + D}{2}\right)^2 \leq 1 \tag{17}$$

The stable mode curvature R_1 and spot size w_1 at the selected starting point are then given by Eq. (16), and the complex curvature at other locations around the resonator can readily be determined.

8-4 HIGHER-ORDER GAUSSIAN BEAM MODES AND RESONATOR MODES

The elementary gaussian beam developed in Sec. 8-2 and used in Sec. 8-3 is actually only the simplest or lowest-order mode in a complex family of higher-order gaussian beams or modes. In this section we will extend gaussian beam analysis to higher-order transverse modes and then use these higher-order transverse modes to analyze some important additional properties of optical resonators.

■ We noted in Sec. 8-2 that the Huygens integral which transforms an optical wave from one cross-sectional plane to another has, when reduced to the Fresnel degree of approximation, the form of a convolution integral between the input waveform and a complex gaussian function of the form e^{-jx^2}. The elementary gaussian (gaussian spherical) waveform developed in Sec. 8-2 is the simplest type of waveform that will reproduce itself upon passing through the reduced Huygens integral; that is, a gaussian input to Eq. (6) of Sec. 8-2 yields a gaussian output. A gaussian wave can thus reproduce itself unchanged in shape upon repeated bounces in a stable optical resonator (although the wave amplitude will decrease slightly on each bounce, since there is some diffraction loss from the resonator).

There are, however, more complicated waveforms that will also reproduce themselves through this same transformation. In fact, such waveforms comprise a doubly infinite sequence of higher-order beam modes, often called *higher-order Hermite-gaussian modes,* since these higher-order modes all retain the common feature of a gaussian-spherical exponent as part of their transverse dependence.

Although we will not carry out the algebra here, it can be shown that the basic integral transformation

$$\tilde{u}(x,y,z) = \frac{je^{-jkz}}{z\lambda} \iint \tilde{u}_0(x_0, y_0)e^{-j(k/2L)[(x-x_0)^2+(y-y_0)^2]} \, dx_0 \, dy_0 \tag{1}$$

is satisfied not only by the elementary gaussian form of $\tilde{u}(x, y, z)$, but also by each member of the doubly infinite set of waves and modes

$$\tilde{u}_{mn}(x, y, z) = \sqrt{\frac{1}{2^{m+n}m!n!}} \frac{1}{w(z)} H_m\left(\frac{\sqrt{2}x}{w(z)}\right) H_n\left(\frac{\sqrt{2}y}{w(z)}\right) e^{-j(k/2)(x^2+y^2)/\tilde{q}(z)}$$
$$\times e^{-jkz+j(n+m+1)\psi(z)} \qquad m, n = 0, 1, 2, \ldots \tag{2}$$

where $w(z)$, $\tilde{q}(z)$ and $\psi(z)$ are given by exactly the same expressions as before, and where $H_n(x)$ is the Hermite polynomial

$$H_n(x) \equiv (-1)^n e^{x^2} \frac{\partial^n}{\partial x^n} e^{-x^2} \tag{3}$$

The integers m and n, with $m, n = 0, 1, 2, \ldots$, label the various members of this sequence of higher-order modes.

Each of these higher-order transverse modes retains the same transverse form at every longitudinal position z, except for a change in transverse scaling due to the factor $w(z)$ accompanying every factor x or y. As written, the modes are normalized so that

$$\iint_{-\infty}^{\infty} |\tilde{u}_{mn}(x, y)|^2 \, dx \, dy = 1 \tag{4}$$

independently of m, n, or the longitudinal coordinate z. If the scaling factor is set equal to $w(z) = \sqrt{2}$ for simplicity, the transverse-mode patterns have the general form

$$\tilde{u}_{mn}(x, y) \sim H_m(x)H_n(y)e^{-(x^2+y^2)/2} \tag{5}$$

The first three Hermite polynomials are

$$H_0(x) = 1 \qquad H_1(x) = 2x \qquad H_2(x) = 4x^2 - 2 \tag{6}$$

Even-numbered polynomials are thus symmetric and odd numbers are antisymmetric, and in general the mth-order polynomial contains m zeros, or nulls. Figure 8-22 shows the first three Hermite polynomials and the associated mode-pattern variations along the x or y axes. The lowest-order mode ($m,n = 0,0$) is simply the elementary gaussian mode treated in previous sections. In general the mth-order mode contains m nulls, or zeros, and $m - 1$ peaks, or lobes, with the outermost lobe being the strongest.

If a light beam consisting of one of these modes is photographed, each lobe appears as an exposed spot in the photograph, as illustrated by the typical results obtained with a real laser shown in Fig. 8-23. Note that the m and n index values vary quite independently. A special case is the linear combination of equal amounts of the $\tilde{u}_{10}$ and $\tilde{u}_{01}$ modes, which provides a circularly symmetric "doughnut" mode, with a node or hole exactly on axis. Although this is not usually a desirable mode, it often appears in real laser oscillators when the mode-control aperture is not quite small enough to limit oscillation to the $\tilde{u}_{00}$ mode as desired.

CIRCULAR COORDINATES   ■ The higher-order gaussian modes may also be written in circular polar coordinates in the *gaussian-Laguerre form*

$$\tilde{u}_{pl}(r,\theta,z) = \frac{2}{\sqrt{1 + \delta_{0l}}} \frac{p!}{\pi(l + p)!} \frac{1}{w(z)} \left(\frac{\sqrt{2}r}{w(z)}\right)^l L_p^l\left(\frac{2r^2}{w^2(z)}\right)$$
$$\times \begin{pmatrix} \cos l\theta \\ \sin l\theta \end{pmatrix} e^{-j(k/2)r^2/\tilde{q}(z)} e^{-jkz + j(2p+l+1)\psi(z)} \quad (7)$$

where p and l are an alternative set of integer indices, L_p^l is the associated Laguerre polynomial, and δ_{0l} is 1 for $l = 0$ and 0 for $l > 0$. Although the hermitian and Laguerre functions are quite different in appearance, either set can equally well be

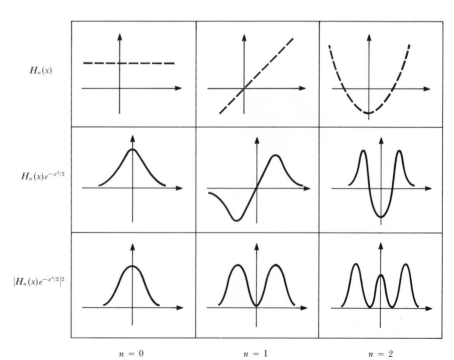

FIG. 8-22 Mode shapes for the three lowest-order Hermite-gaussian modes.

$H_n(x)$

$H_n(x)e^{-x^2/2}$

$|H_n(x)e^{-x^2/2}|^2$

$n = 0$ $n = 1$ $n = 2$

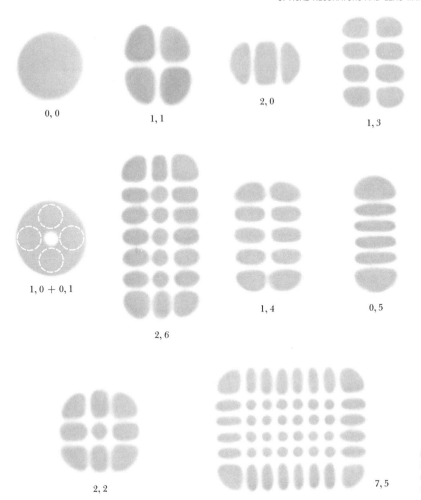

0, 0

1, 1

2, 0

1, 3

1, 0 + 0, 1

2, 6

1, 4

0, 5

2, 2

7, 5

FIG. 8-23 Examples of higher-order Hermite-gaussian optical-resonator modes as photographed in the output beam of a laser oscillator.

used as a complete set for expanding any arbitrary overall laser-beam profile. Each of the circular (p,l) Laguerre modes represents a linear combination of a certain number of the rectangular (m,n) Hermite modes, or vice versa. The Laguerre modes generally have a circularly symmetric form with a certain number of radial and circumferential nodal lines.

As a practical matter, the presence of Brewster-angle windows, as well as any slight misalignments or mirror tilts, usually cause any real laser to oscillate in mode patterns having the rectangularly symmetric Hermite form rather than the circularly symmetric Laguerre form. Therefore we will use the rectangular form for our future discussions. However, the $\tilde{u}_{pl}(r,\theta)$ forms have also been demonstrated in special experiments using internal laser mirrors and very careful mirror alignment; a few of the resulting circularly symmetric laser-beam patterns are illustrated in Fig. 8-24.

■ The stable optical resonator mirrors with the curvatures R_1 and R_2 discussed in Sec. 8-3 will reflect higher-order gaussian beams as well as the lowest-order gaussian beams, since the wavefront-curvature and spot-size parameters are entirely independent of the mode indices m and n. All the analytical results of Sec. 8-3 thus apply equally

HIGHER-ORDER OPTICAL RESONATOR MODES

well to either lowest-order or higher-order beams. That is, any stable optical resonator can support resonances having the higher-order $\tilde{u}_{mn}(x, y)$ gaussian transverse-mode patterns as well as the $\tilde{u}_{00}$ mode already discussed. Lasers can, and generally do, oscillate in any of these higher-order modes. Finding appropriate transverse-mode-control techniques so as to obtain laser oscillation only in a single controlled transverse mode —usually the lowest-order, or $\tilde{u}_{00}$, mode—is one of the major practical problems in laser design.

Note that when a laser oscillates in any stable higher-order gaussian mode, its transverse-mode pattern will have exactly the same appearance, except for changes in size, at every plane both inside and outside the laser. There is no distinction between near-field and far-field mode patterns, or diffraction patterns in the gaussian case, except in the variation of the scale factor $w(z)$ for $z \ll z_R$ or $z \gg z_R$.

■ Most real laser devices tend to oscillate not only in higher-order modes, but in many such modes at once. Figures 8-22 and 8-23 illustrate the general fact that the higher-order modes extend farther out in the transverse direction and have more of their energy at greater distances from the axis than do lower-order modes. Practical laser rods or tubes are generally larger in cross section than typical gaussian-mode spot sizes. Hence a laser can often oscillate in various low-order modes, using primarily the inverted atoms near the laser axis, and can simultaneously oscillate in one or more higher-order modes, using primarily the inverted atoms farther out from the axis. Slight misalignments, tilts, or imperfections (such as dust specks) in the laser mirrors also often seem to favor higher-order modes.

Single-mode oscillation, which is limited to the usually desired lowest-order mode, can be obtained only by somehow favoring the lowest-order mode, as for example by making the gain strongest on axis, or by somehow increasing the losses for the higher-order modes (possible because of the larger average diameter of the higher-order modes).

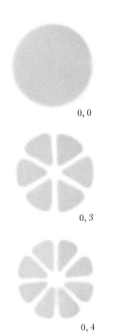

0, 0

0, 3

0, 4

FIG. 8-24 Various circularly symmetric gaussian-Laguerre modes obtained in a special internal-mirror laser oscillator.

Suppose the transverse size of an optical resonator is defined by a limiting aperture of diameter $2a$ (which may be the edge of one of the mirrors, or the outer wall of a laser rod or laser tube, or even an iris placed inside the resonator for mode-control purposes). For a given set of mirror curvatures and gaussian modes, all the mode losses will increase as the aperture radius a is reduced toward the mode size w, since more and more energy will be scraped off or lost around the edges. This loss, although generally small for all modes, will be larger for the higher-order modes because of their larger transverse spread. Under some conditions it is possible in this way to suppress all higher-order modes, allowing oscillation in the $\tilde{u}_{00}$ mode only. The previously mentioned empirical choice of $2a \approx 3.5w$ to $4.0w$ seems in many cases to provide sufficient loss to suppress the next-higher $\tilde{u}_{10}$ and $\tilde{u}_{01}$ modes with no significant effect on the $\tilde{u}_{00}$ mode.

This type of mode control may be obtained in practice by using an adjustable iris within the resonator to reduce the aperture diameter $2a$. As a widely used alternative, the rapid variation of w_2 with mirror spacing for spacings $L = R_2 - \delta L$ in the hemispherical resonator (Table 8-3) can provide a convenient method of adjusting spot size during operation, so as to fill an iris or aperture at the w_2 end of the laser.

■ Up to this point we have not given any attention to the resonance frequencies of gaussian optical resonators. In so far as the gaussian beams in these resonators are similar to plane waves, the resonance frequencies are given by the axial-mode expressions in Sec. 5-4. The resonance condition is $2kL = q2\pi$; that is, the resonant frequencies are the axial modes,

$$f_q \approx q\frac{c}{2L} = q\,\Delta f_{\text{axial}} \tag{8}$$

where q is the number of half-wavelengths along the resonator axis (generally a very large number). These resonance frequencies are fairly closely spaced, and to first order, the gaussian shapes of the modes and the axial resonance frequencies are entirely independent of one another.

To develop a more exact expression for the resonant-mode frequencies in a stable resonator we must make use of the exact phase-shift expression for a gaussian beam. The basic condition for resonance is that the round-trip phase shift must be a multiple of 2π, or the one-way phase shift must be an integer multiple of π. In terms of the axial-phase-shift expression for a gaussian beam, Eq. (51) of Sec. 8-2, this requires that

$$\phi(z_2) - \phi(z_1) = q\pi \tag{9}$$

Since the phase shift for a $\tilde{u}_{mn}$ mode is $\phi(z) = kz - (n + m + 1)\psi(z)$, where $\psi(z) = \tan^{-1}(z/z_R)$, the exact resonance condition becomes

$$\phi(z_2) - \phi(z_1) = \frac{2\pi fL}{c} - (n + m + 1)[\psi(z_2) - \psi(z_1)] = q\pi \tag{10}$$

which leads to

$$f_q = \left[q + (m + n + 1)\frac{\psi(z_2) - \psi(z_1)}{\pi}\right]\frac{c}{2L} \tag{11}$$

With the gaussian resonator-mode expressions for z_1 and z_2, it is possible to show (after considerable algebra) that

$$\cos[\psi(z_2) - \psi(z_1)] = \sqrt{g_1 g_2} \tag{12}$$

Hence the final result for the resonance frequency of the qth axial mode in the mnth transverse-mode pattern is

$$f_{qmn} = \left[q + (m + n + 1)\frac{\cos^{-1}\sqrt{g_1 g_2}}{\pi}\right]\frac{c}{2L} \tag{13}$$

The resonant frequency does depend to some extent on the particular transverse-mode pattern $\tilde{u}_{mn}$ under consideration. This is best illustrated by some typical cases. For example, for a *near-planar resonator* with two identical and nearly flat mirrors $(R \to \infty)$, we may write $g = 1 - L/R$, $L/R \ll 1$, and hence $\cos^{-1}(g_1 g_2)^{1/2} = \cos^{-1}(1 - L/R) \approx \alpha$, where $\alpha = 2L/R \ll \pi$. The resonant-mode spectrum is then given by

$$f_{qnm} = \left[q + (n + m + 1)\frac{\alpha}{\pi}\right]\frac{c}{2L} \tag{14}$$

as shown in Fig. 8-25a. Each axial mode is separated by the relatively large axial-mode spacing $\Delta f_{\text{axial}} = c/2L$. However, each axial mode is split into a set of transverse-mode resonance frequencies spaced by the much smaller amount $(\alpha/\pi)\,\Delta f_{\text{axial}}$.

If the mirror curvature is increased at fixed spacing, starting from the near-planar case, the transverse mode spacing for a given axial mode increases; i.e., the arrays of

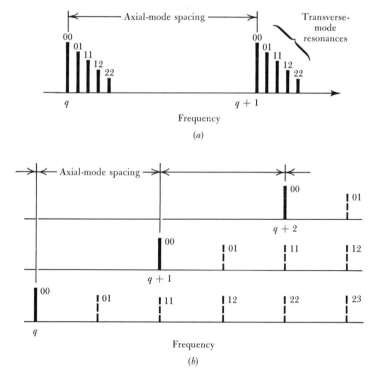

FIG. 8-25 Transverse-mode resonant frequencies f_{qmn} of optical resonators: (a) near-planar (or near-concentric) case and (b) confocal case.

higher-order transverse modes in Fig. 8-25a expand toward the right, while the axial-mode intervals remain the same. When the mirror curvatures reach the *confocal condition* $R_1 = R_2 = L$, the result is $g_1 = g_2 = 0$, and $\cos^{-1}(g_1 g_2)^{1/2} = \pi/2$. The mode frequencies then become

$$f_{qmn} = \left[q + \frac{(m+n+1)}{2}\right]\frac{c}{2L} \tag{15}$$

As shown in Fig. 8-25b, the symmetric higher-order (m,n) modes associated with a given q value are shifted upward in integral multiples of the axial-mode spacing and lie directly on top of axial modes of higher q value, while the antisymmetric (m,n) modes are shifted by $\frac{1}{2}\Delta f_{\text{axial}}$ and lie halfway between the higher axial modes.

As the mirror curvature increases still more, the quantity $g_1 g_2$, having gone from $+1$ down to zero, begins to move back toward $+1$, and so the transverse mode spacing decreases from $\frac{1}{2}\Delta f_{\text{axial}}$ back toward zero. The mode spectrum for a *near-concentric resonator* is thus essentially the same as the near-planar case shown in Fig. 8-25a.

MEASUREMENT OF TRANSVERSE-MODE BEAT FREQUENCY

■ When a laser beam containing two or more closely spaced oscillation frequencies falls on a photodetector, such as a photomultiplier tube or photodiode, the photodetector output will contain not only a dc component proportional to the total intensity of the laser signal, but also *beat-frequency,* or *heterodyne, components* at each of the different frequencies between the various oscillation components present (provided that the photodetector response is fast enough to follow the difference frequencies present). For example, if a cw gas laser oscillates simultaneously in a number of different transverse modes and the laser beam is simply directed onto a photodetector and the photodetector output applied to a radio receiver or rf-spectrum analyzer, the difference frequencies between the various transverse modes can be observed.[1]

These small frequency shifts between transverse modes depend directly on the small added phase shifts of a gaussian beam, and these phase shifts are in turn related to the transverse field variations and mode patterns of the gaussian beam analysis. Therefore measurement of these small frequency shifts really provides a rather stringent test of the entire gaussian mode theory. If the transverse-mode patterns were significantly distorted from the predicted values by some unexpected effect in a real laser, then the transverse-mode frequencies would also inevitably be shifted.

■ Although the loss in an optical resonator and the resulting cavity Q are important cavity parameters, no quantitative results for the diffraction losses in gaussian resonators are given in this section. The reason is that for a resonator well inside the stable region, the losses due to diffraction, that is, the energy losses due to leakage past the mirror edges, are so small as to be negligible (typically $\ll 1$ percent per bounce). For such resonators other loss mechanisms, such as finite mirror reflectivity, internal scattering losses, and imperfect Brewster-angle windows, usually dominate over diffraction losses.

RESONATOR LOSSES

If an exactly gaussian lowest-order beam reflects from a circular mirror of diameter $2a$ (or passes through an aperture of the same diameter), the fractional energy loss at the mirror edges will be $\delta = e^{-2a^2/w^2}$, which is less than 1 percent if the aperture radius a is greater than ~ 1.5 times the spot size w. However, as we will discuss in the following section, the modes in an optical resonator, although remaining accurately gaussian in the central portion of the mirrors, always make subtle adjustments in their amplitude and phase patterns near the mirror edges in such a way as to minimize the diffraction losses per bounce. Because of these small adjustments, their diffraction losses are even smaller than the simple estimate just given.

The only cases for which resonator diffraction losses become sizable (≥ 5 percent per bounce) are those resonators lying within or outside the boundary region of the stability diagram. For these resonators the gaussian analysis no longer remains accurate in any event. In the following section we will discuss methods of solution for such resonators and show some numerical results for the resulting diffraction losses.

8-5 PLANAR AND RELATED RESONATORS: FOX AND LI APPROACH

The gaussian-beam approach to optical resonators ceases to be valid when the spot size predicted by this approach begins to equal or exceed the mirror size, i.e., whenever the resonator g parameters fall in the boundary of, or even entirely outside, the stable region of the g plane. Discussion of these nongaussian resonators, including the basic example of two plane-parallel mirrors, requires a more complex analysis, in most cases entailing extensive computer calculations before useful results can be obtained. In

---

[1] Careful measurements of this type have been carried out with various types of gas lasers, with excellent agreement between theory and experiment. Rigorously speaking, the different transverse-mode patterns are spatially orthogonal, and the overlap integrals that determine the beat amplitudes between different transverse modes are, in a strict calculation, all zero. However, the orthogonality is easily broken down, and the beats can be made to appear either by spatially inhomogeneities in the photodetector or by inserting an edge or some other sort of aperture into the laser beam.

this section we will outline this more general method of analysis and summarize some of the numerical results for important practical resonators.

RESONATOR INTEGRAL
EQUATION

■ To analyze any arbitrary curved-mirror resonator rigorously (at least to the level of rigor represented by Huygens' principle) we begin with the optical resonator geometry indicated in Fig. 8-26. Instead of analyzing directly the energy loss with time for a standing wave in this resonator, it is simpler and essentially equivalent to analyze the energy loss with distance for a traveling wave. We may view such a wave either as bouncing repeatedly back and forth between the mirrors or as traveling down the equivalent periodic lens waveguide (see Fig. 8-2).

Let us suppose initially that there exists on the left-hand mirror in Fig. 8-26 a wave amplitude[1] $\tilde{u}_0(x_0, y_0)$. Then, using Huygens' principle in the Fresnel approximation and taking into account the added path lengths due to the mirror curvatures, we can write the wave amplitude $\tilde{u}'(x, y)$ on the right-hand mirror surface as

$$
\tilde{u}'(x, y) = \frac{je^{-jkL}}{L\lambda} \iint \exp\left\{ -jk\left[\frac{(x - x_0)^2 + (y - y_0)^2}{2L} \right. \right.
$$
$$
\left. \left. - \frac{x_0^2 + y_0^2}{2R_1} - \frac{x^2 + y^2}{2R_2} \right] \right\} \tilde{u}(x_0, y_0)\, dx_0\, dy_0
$$
$$
= \iint \tilde{K}(x, y: x_0, y_0)\tilde{u}(x_0, y_0)\, dx_0\, dy_0 \tag{1}
$$

where the integral is over the surface of the first mirror and $\tilde{K}(x, y: x_0, y_0)$ is the Huygens kernel implicitly defined by the first line. If we then ask what new distribution $\tilde{u}''(x, y)$ will be produced back on the left-hand mirror by the distribution $\tilde{u}'(x, y)$ on the right-hand mirror, the result is

$$
\tilde{u}''(x, y) = \frac{je^{-jkL}}{L\lambda} \iint \exp\left\{ -jk\left[\frac{(x - x_1)^2 + (y - y_1)^2}{2L} \right. \right.
$$
$$
\left. \left. - \frac{x_1^2 + y_1^2}{2R_2} - \frac{x^2 + y^2}{2R_1} \right] \right\} \tilde{u}'(x_1, y_1)\, dx_1\, dy_1
$$
$$
= \iint \tilde{K}(x_1, y_1: x, y)\tilde{u}'(x_1, y_1)\, dx_1\, dy_1 \tag{2}
$$

[1] Note that there will be a phase difference $\Delta\phi(x, y) = k(x^2 + y^2)/2R_1$ between the phase distribution of a wave directly on the surface of a mirror of radius R and the phase distribution on a perpendicular xy plane located at the mirror position, such as we have considered previously.

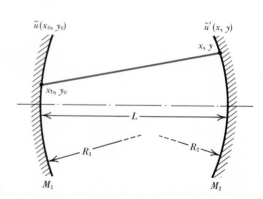

FIG. 8-26 Geometry for analyzing an optical resonator.

where the integral is now over the right-hand mirror surface and $\tilde{K}$ is the same kernel (note the change in order of the arguments). Combining these results yields, after some minor rearranging,

$$\tilde{u}''(x, y) = \iint dx_0 \, dy_0 \left[\iint dx_1 \, dy_1 \, \tilde{K}(x_1, y_1: x, y)\tilde{K}(x_1, y_1: x_0, y_0) \right]\tilde{u}(x_0, y_0)$$

$$= \iint \tilde{L}(x, y: x_0, y_0)\tilde{u}(x_0, y_0) \, dx_0 \, dy_0 \tag{3}$$

where $\tilde{L}$ is the combined kernel function

$$\tilde{L}(x, y: x_0, y_0) \equiv \iint \tilde{K}(x_1, y_1: x, y)\tilde{K}(x_1, y_1: x_0, y_0) \, dx_1 \, dy_1 \tag{4}$$

The overall wave transformation given by the integration using this kernel function describes mathematically the propagation of a wave through one complete round trip between the mirrors or through one complete section of the equivalent lens waveguide.[1]

■ An essential property of each single mode in a resonator is that its transverse amplitude pattern or shape should not change with time, although its absolute amplitude may decrease owing to energy losses. Thus if the initial wave amplitude $\tilde{u}(x, y)$ above is to correspond to a normal mode of the resonator, after one complete round trip the transformed wave amplitude $\tilde{u}''(x, y)$ should have exactly the same form as the original wave amplitude $\tilde{u}(x, y)$, except that it is multiplied by a complex constant $\tilde{\gamma}$, which takes into account energy losses ($|\tilde{\gamma}|^2 < 1$) and phase shifts in the round trip. That is, if $\tilde{u}(x, y)$ is to be a resonator mode, it must satisfy the requirement

DEFINITION OF MODE

$$\tilde{u}''(x, y) = \tilde{\gamma}\tilde{u}(x, y) = \iint \tilde{L}(x, y: x_0, y_0)\tilde{u}(x_0, y_0) \, dx_0 \, dy_0 \tag{5}$$

This is an integral equation for the unknown mode function $\tilde{u}(x, y)$ and constant $\tilde{\gamma}$. There is in fact a certain set of allowed solutions, or eigensolutions, $\tilde{u}_{mn}(x, y)$ and associated eigenvalues $\tilde{\gamma}_{mn}$ that will satisfy this integral equation with the kernel[2] $\tilde{L}(x, y: x_0, y_0)$. The functions $\tilde{u}_{mn}(x, y)$ are then the transverse modes of the resonator; and the eigenvalues $\tilde{\gamma}_{mn}$ determine the resonator losses of these modes. Specifically, the round-trip power transmission in the resonator is $|\tilde{\gamma}_{mn}|^2$, and so the average one-way power transmission must be $|\tilde{\gamma}_{mn}|$. The fractional power loss per bounce (or per one-way pass, as defined in Sec. 5-5) due to diffraction is then

$$\delta_{mn} = 1 - |\tilde{\gamma}_{mn}| \tag{6}$$

Given this parameter, the resonator Q due to diffraction losses can be calculated from the expressions of Sec. 5-5.

■ In applying Huygens' principle we calculate the amplitude $\tilde{u}'(x, y)$ at any point (x, y) on an output plane by adding up contributions $\tilde{u}(x_0, y_0)$ from points (x_0, y_0) on an input plane, with each contribution weighted by a phase factor $e^{-jk(r-r_0)}$. For

FRESNEL NUMBER N

---

[1] In fact, the wave transformation from one mirror surface to the opposite mirror and back to the same surface is exactly equivalent to the wave transformation from one lens midplane to the next similar lens midplane, as shown in Fig. 8-2c. The lens midplane is equivalent to the mirror surface.

[2] This kernel is mathematically more difficult than many of the kernels usually treated in the theory of integral equations, and there are some considerable mathematical difficulties in proving rigorously that this particular integral equation does have a set of eigensolutions. However, practical experience has made it clear that such solutions do exist. See Ref. 8-3.

example, if an observer were to stand at the center of one mirror in a plane-mirror optical resonator and look back toward the other mirror, he would see the phase factor for an input point at radius $r_0 = (x_0, y_0)$ as $e^{-jk(x_0{}^2+y_0{}^2)/2L} = e^{-j\pi r_0{}^2/L\lambda}$. Each time the exponent of this factor increases by π, the weighting factor by which $\tilde{u}(x_0, y_0)$ is multiplied changes sign. Each annular region or range of r_0 for which $m\pi \leq \pi r_0{}^2/L\lambda \leq (m+1)\pi$ holds is a *Fresnel zone* on the input plane, as seen from the output plane.[1]

The number N of Fresnel zones on one plane mirror of diameter $2a$, as viewed from the center of the next mirror—or, equivalently, the number N of sign changes in the weighting factor $e^{-j\pi r_0{}^2/L\lambda}$ from the center to the edge of the input mirror—is determined by the condition $\pi a^2/L\lambda = N\pi$, or

$$N = \frac{a^2}{L\lambda} \tag{7}$$

This parameter N, called the *Fresnel number*, provides a meaningful dimensionless parameter for expressing the size of the mirrors in an optical resonator (or the size of the lenses in a lens guide). Although the Fresnel number N applies most directly to plane circular mirrors, it is used much more widely in resonator analyses as a convenient measure of mirror size for both plane and curved mirrors, with both circular (diameter $2a$) and square (width $2a$) cross sections.

THE FOX AND LI METHOD OF
SOLUTION

■ The integral equation for the resonator modes, Eq. (5), turns out to be extremely intractable in the general case. For stable resonators of large size the limits of integration in the equation may be set at infinity, and the equation is then solved by the gaussian modes of Sec. 8-4. However, for the cases of interest to us in this section, marginally stable systems with finite mirror sizes, the solution becomes much more difficult.

Various mathematical approaches (all involving computer calculations at one stage or another) have been applied to these equations. Perhaps the simplest and most graphic of these is the iterative computer approach, first applied by Fox and Li to demonstrate the nature of these solutions, and used extensively since then.[2] In the Fox and Li approach an initial amplitude function $\tilde{u}_0(x, y)$ is chosen arbitrarily, and the integral transformation is applied, with the aid of an electronic computer, to compute the new amplitude after one bounce,

$$\tilde{u}_1(x, y) = \iint \tilde{L}(x, y : x_0, y_0)\tilde{u}_0(x_0, y_0)\, dx_0\, dy_0 \tag{8}$$

The new function $\tilde{u}_1(x, y)$ is then used as input to the integral transformation to compute another function $\tilde{u}_2(x, y)$, and so forth. The computation process is repeated (iterated) until the wave amplitude converges to a function $\tilde{u}_n(x, y)$ which does not change in form on further transformation, i.e., which satisfies

$$\tilde{u}_{n+1}(x, y) = \iint \tilde{L}(x, y : x_0, y_0)\tilde{u}_n(x_0, y_0)\, dx_0\, dy_0 = \tilde{\gamma}_n\tilde{u}_n(x, y) \tag{9}$$

This function must then be one of the eigenfunctions, or normal modes, that satisfies the integral equation.

[1] See any standard optics text for more on Fresnel zones.

[2] Other important analytical approaches to the same problem include the Schmidt expansion method used by Heurtley and Streiffer (Ref. 8-10) and an approach based on waveguide theory used by Vainshtein (Ref. 8-28).

This method of solution has a simple and direct physical interpretation. The assumed initial function $\tilde{u}_0(x, y)$ can be viewed as an input distribution applied to the input end of a long lens waveguide. This arbitrary input may be broken down into, or will excite, a mixture of all the lowest- and higher-order modes in the lens waveguide or resonator. Each computer iteration then corresponds to forward propagation of this mixture of modes through another section of the lens guide. As the wave propagates through many sections, modes with higher losses relative to the lowest-loss mode of the system will be attenuated. Eventually, after many sections, the higher-order modes will be filtered out, and only the lowest-loss normal mode will remain.

This method, then, will always converge to the lowest-loss mode of the system; this is, however, also the mode of most interest for laser applications. Actually, by injecting a symmetric (even) input function we can find the lowest-loss even mode, and by injecting an antisymmetric (odd) input function we excite only antisymmetric modes and thus find the lowest-loss antisymmetric mode.[1]

Figures 8-27 and 8-28 illustrate some typical Fox and Li computer results for a uniform[2] initial distribution $\tilde{u}_0(x, y) = 1$ applied to a resonator system with square mirrors of width $2a$. The dashed lines in Fig. 8-27a are the amplitude and phase distributions across the mirror after one bounce, i.e., the amplitude and phase of $\tilde{u}_1(x)$. The solid lines show the steady-state results obtained after approximately 300 bounces. The right-hand plots show similar steady-state results for the three Fresnel numbers $\mathcal{N} = 0.5$, 2.5, and 6.25. Figure 8-28 is a plot of the amplitude reduction or attenuation per bounce at the midpoint of the mirror versus the iteration or bounce number for the computer run that produced Fig. 8-27a. Early in the calculation the loss varies irregularly from bounce to bounce because the different transverse modes excited in the initial mode mixture interfere, constructively and destructively, with each other. Later in the calculation, as the higher-loss modes gradually drop out, the loss per bounce settles down to the expected constant attenuation, or loss per bounce for the one remaining lowest-loss mode, as expressed by the constant factor γ.

Repeated computer runs of this type give the lowest-loss mode patterns and mode losses for resonators with mirrors of arbitrary shape and curvature. As an example of such results, Fig. 8-29a shows the power loss per bounce for the lowest-loss symmetric (0,0) and antisymmetric (1,0) modes as a function of the mirror size, i.e., the Fresnel number $\mathcal{N} = a^2/L\lambda$, both for planar circular mirrors and for the confocal mirror case. Figure 8-29b extends the circular-plane-mirror results to larger Fresnel number values. For any value of $\mathcal{N} \geq 1$ the confocal case has essentially gaussian modes and vanishingly small diffraction losses. The planar mirrors, by contrast, have a lowest-order mode with a roughly cosine (or Bessel function) transverse variation, with small additional ripples as in Fig. 8-27. The losses in the planar case are considerably higher than in the confocal case, although they also drop below 1 percent per bounce for $\mathcal{N} \geq 20$. In either case the losses for higher-order transverse modes are significantly higher than for the lowest-loss lowest-order mode.

■ In the gaussian mode analysis of Secs. 8-2 and 8-4 we found that a gaussian beam had a total phase shift from, say, plane z to plane $z + L$ given by $(2\pi f L/c) -$

PHASE SHIFTS AND RESONANT FREQUENCIES

---

[1] By further tricks it is also possible to extract from the calculation the next-higher-loss symmetric and antisymmetric modes.

[2] In the absence of any better choices, we usually simply apply a uniform input $\tilde{u}_0(x, y) = 1$ to start the calculation.

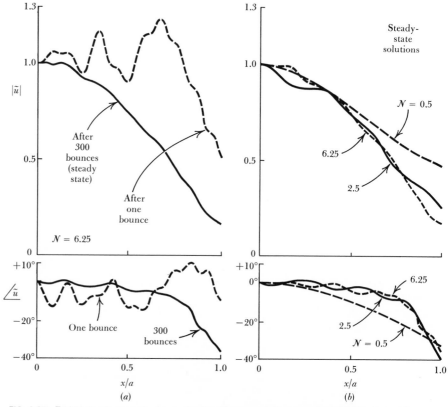

FIG. 8-27 Typical results from the Fox and Li iterative-computation procedure. (a) The dashed lines show the amplitude and phase angle of the complex wave function $\tilde{u}(x)$ across a flat laser mirror after just one bounce, starting with a uniform initial distribution $\tilde{u}_0(x) = 1$. The solid lines show the unchanging steady-state distribution of $\tilde{u}(x)$ after 300 (or more) bounces. (b) Similar steady-state wave functions across the laser mirror for three different values of Fresnel number N.

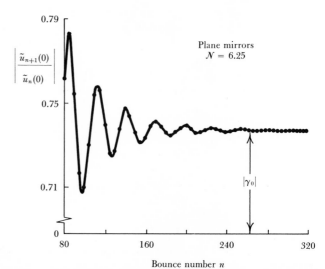

FIG. 8-28 Attenuation per bounce at mirror midpoint versus bounce number in the Fox and Li computation procedure, showing how the iterative procedure settles down to a steady state as the higher-loss modes are filtered out.

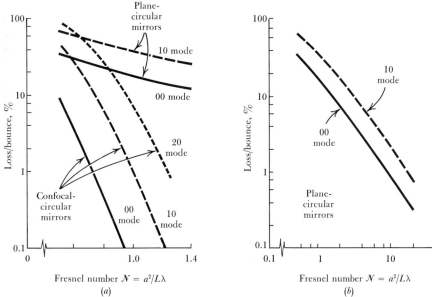

FIG. 8-29 (a) Power loss per bounce in percent versus Fresnel number $N = a^2/L\lambda$ for plane circular mirrors and for confocal circular mirrors, for the lowest and next higher-order modes. (b) Additional results at larger N for the plane-mirror case.

$(n + m + 1)[\psi(z + L) - \psi(z)]$, where the $\psi(z)$ phase factor accounted for the slight difference between the propagation constant $\beta(z)$ of the gaussian wave and the free-space or plane-wave propagation constant $k = 2\pi L/c$. The various lowest- and higher-order modes of nongaussian resonators also possess corresponding phase shifts which can be determined from the Fox and Li analysis. That is, when we write and solve the equation

$$\tilde{u}''_{mn}(x, y) = \iint \tilde{L}(x, y: x_0, y_0)\tilde{u}_{mn}(x_0, y_0)\, dx_0\, dy_0 = \tilde{\gamma}_{mn}\tilde{u}_{mn}(x, y) \qquad (10)$$

the complex eigenvalue $\tilde{\gamma}_{mn}$ expresses both the attenuation and phase shift of the round-trip transformation. We may define the phase angle of $\tilde{\gamma}_{mn}$ by

$$\angle\, \tilde{\gamma}_{mn} = 2kL + \psi_{mn} \qquad (11)$$

where ψ_{mn} is the round-trip phase factor. The $2kL$ factor is usually cancelled out of both $\tilde{\gamma}_{mn}$ and $\tilde{L}$ before the numerical calculations are carried out, leaving ψ_{mn} as the resulting phase angle for $\tilde{\gamma}_{mn}$. As before, the resonant frequencies f_{mnq} of a cavity are given by[1]

$$\frac{4\pi f q L}{c} + \psi_{mn} = q2\pi \qquad (12)$$

or

$$f_{mnq} = [q + (2\pi)^{-1}\psi_{mn}]\frac{c}{2L} \qquad (13)$$

■ The Fox and Li iterative computer approach has a number of significant advantages. By making appropriate changes in the kernel and in the ranges of integration, this

EVALUATION OF THE FOX AND LI APPROACH

[1] In several instances Fox and Li have plotted results for the phase angle $-\psi_{mn}/2$ versus the Fresnel number N.

technique can provide answers not only for uniform curved mirrors, but for mirrors of arbitrary surface contour and transverse shape, including distorted and tilted mirrors, mirrors with irregularities and defects, and mirrors with coupling holes or nonuniform reflectivity. For all these cases it automatically yields the important low-loss mode.[1]

The disadvantages of the method are primarily expense and the limited generality of the results. In computing the field at an output position x, for accuracy the input must be evaluated at positions x_0 spaced closely enough that the path length $|x - x_0|$ in the kernel increases by no more than, say, $\lambda/20$ between points. This means that the input, and the output, must be evaluated at $10N$ or more separate points across the mirror. Each complete forward step then requires $(10N)^2$ or more computations of the integrand. A complete computer run may require several hundred forward steps, and the output of this run is only a single datum point for a single set of system parameters. Any small change in any system parameter then requires a completely new run. Large investments in computer time are required to obtain results for any extensive range of variables. Unfortunately, the integral equation (5) for resonator modes has proved to be so mathematically intractable, even for a comparatively simple case such as two plane mirrors, that the Fox and Li approach or some similar computer-based approach seems to be the only available way to pull answers out of this integral equation.

UNSTABLE OPTICAL
RESONATORS

■ As a final resonator topic, let us consider briefly the high-loss optical resonators that lie completely outside the stable region in the stability diagram of Fig. 8-4 and correspond to unstable or divergent lens waveguides, rather than to convergent or stable periodic focusing systems. Two typical examples of unstable optical resonators are shown in Fig. 8-30, along with a stable gaussian resonator mode for comparison.

The mode in an unstable resonator consists in general of two opposite, diverging spherical waves, with more or less uniform amplitudes across the wavefronts out to the edges, as shown by the middle sketch of Fig. 8-30. There is no similarity to the gaussian modes of the stable resonator. The resonator losses, in the form of energy coupled out past the outer edges of one or both mirrors, are generally large. However, for reasonable designs these losses can be kept small enough (20 to 40 percent per bounce) that laser action in an unstable resonator is still possible with many high-gain laser systems, such as ruby and Nd-glass lasers and the argon-ion and CO_2 gas lasers.

The unstable type of resonator can be useful, in fact, in high-gain, high-power,

FIG. 8-30   Mode patterns in unstable and stable optical resonators.

[1] See Refs. 8-5 to 8-7.

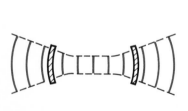

Stable resonator

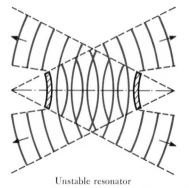

Unstable resonator

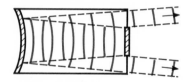

"Cassegrainian" unstable resonator

and large-diameter laser devices. It is difficult to obtain a single large-diameter lowest-order gaussian mode in a stable resonator system without adjusting the resonator g values precariously close to the border of instability. However, the unstable resonator is easily designed to have as large a mode diameter as is required to fill a laser tube or laser rod simply by making the mirrors as large as required. As shown in the final sketch of Fig. 8-30, all the energy output from the resonator can easily be taken from one end of the resonator. Rather than being considered as a loss mechanism, this output can be regarded as the useful laser output beam. This type of output is often referred to as *diffraction coupling*. Many high-gain lasers give maximum power output with the fairly large degree of output coupling obtained with an unstable resonator. Although the output mode is an annular ring in the near field, this transforms in the far field into a single main-beam lobe with no hole on the axis, much like the antenna beam from a cassegrainian microwave antenna.

Finally, although the properties of higher-order modes in unstable optical resonators are rather complex,[1] with proper design the losses for the higher-order modes can be made even larger than the losses for the lowest-order mode. Then a laser with an unstable resonator can have good transverse-mode selection even with a large Fresnel number or large laser diameter, something difficult to obtain with the usual stable gaussian modes. Some encouraging experimental results with the unstable optical resonator for a CO_2 laser have recently been reported.[2]

PROBLEMS

8-1. A certain optical black box has a front entrance plane and various lens and mirrors inside it, such that an optical ray entering the reference plane eventually comes back out through the same plane with a total ray transformation given by a known total ray matrix, or (A,B,C,D) matrix. Suppose this black box is to be replaced by a single curved mirror of radius R_{eq} located an appropriate distance L_{eq} behind (or, if necessary, in front of) the entrance plane of the black box. Find the required radius R_{eq} and position L_{eq} of the single curved mirror.

8-2. The mirrors used in real gas lasers are, of course, not just thin sheets, but curved surfaces ground onto one side of a rather thick cylinder or plug of quartz or optical glass. Thus it is necessary in real lasers to take into account the change in wavefront curvature due to refraction when the beam crosses the glass-air interface at the mirror's outer surface. Many laser manufacturers supply *collimating mirrors,* on which the outer surface has just the correct curvature to convert the laser's output beam to a collimated beam (a plane wave). Consider a confocal He-Ne laser 15 cm long (between the inner mirror faces), having fused quartz mirrors 1 cm thick ($n_0 = 1.456$ for fused quartz). What radius of curvature on the outer surface is necessary to make these collimating mirrors?

8-3. Write a computer program to compute and plot on the printer the position of the beam spot on successive bounces for

an optical delay line such as Table 8-2 or Fig. 8-6. Allow for arbitrary ray-injection conditions and for astigmatic mirrors, i.e., mirrors having different curvatures R_x and R_y in the x and y transverse directions. Print integers to mark the first six or eight bounce locations and asterisks to mark the beam positions on all successive bounces. Experiment with obtaining the complex patterns shown in Ref. 8-9.

8-4. Make a series of sketches showing two mirrors facing each other, with the mirror spacing fixed. Assuming that the center of curvature C_1 of the right-hand mirror is located in the following positions, indicate by cross hatching those sections of the axis within which the center of curvature C_2 of the left-hand mirror must be located in order to have a stable resonator:

(*a*) C_1 located between the two mirrors

(*b*) C_1 located to the left of the left-hand mirror

(*c*) C_1 located to the right of the right-hand mirror (i.e., a divergent right-hand mirror)

8-5. An optical cavity of length L is formed by two end mirrors, both having the same radius of curvature R, plus a convergent lens of focal length f located at the midpoint of the cavity. Set up the necessary analysis and find the stability conditions for this resonator in terms of L, R, and f. Sketch the general variation of spot size with distance along the axis in-

[1] See Refs. 8-25 and 8-26.

[2] See Ref. 8-18.

side the resonator, indicating the waist or waists (if any) inside the resonator. Develop expressions for the spot sizes at the end mirrors and at the waists (if any exist). Indicate the behavior of this system on a Collins chart.

8-6. In certain practical applications, such as harmonic generation with a nonlinear crystal inside a laser cavity, it is desirable to have a relatively large spot diameter in the portion of the cavity occupied by the laser rod, but a very small spot diameter at some other point in the cavity, say, the point at which the beam passes through the nonlinear crystal. It is also desirable that the adjustments to obtain this be noncritical; i.e., that a very small spot diameter be obtained at some point inside the cavity while still keeping the overall resonator well within its stability region. The use of a focusing lens inside the cavity (with a good antireflective coating to eliminate surface reflections from the lens) is often suggested as a method of achieving this.

To evaluate this approach, consider a laser cavity of fixed total length L, consisting of one curved mirror of radius R, one flat mirror (infinite radius), and a lens of focal length f located at a variable distance L_1 from the flat mirror. Evaluate the range of lens positions L_1 over which the cavity will remain stable for fixed R, L, and f. Discuss the behavior of the spot sizes within the cavity, particularly the location and size of any waists, as the lens is moved over its stable range. In general, does it appear possible to obtain a very small waist at some point within a cavity and still remain well away from the boundary of the stability region for that cavity?

8-7. In setting up a gas laser with two curved mirrors of the same nominal radius R (in reality the two mirrors are never exactly identical) and variable spacing L, we sometimes find that in the region near confocal spacing ($L \approx R$) there is a narrow range of L over which the laser will not oscillate, although it will oscillate quite well at either slightly larger or slightly smaller values of the spacing L. What might be the reason for this somewhat mysterious (but frequently observed) behavior?

8-8. An He-Ne 6328-Å gas laser ~ 1 m long is to be designed with a hemispherical cavity, i.e., one flat mirror and one curved mirror with $R = 1$ m. A micrometer screw is to be used to vary the exact cavity length over a small range ΔL, so that the cavity length will be $L = R - \Delta L$, where $\Delta L \ll L$. In this way the spot size w_2 at the curved-mirror end can be varied to make w_2 in the same range as the 1-mm radius of an aperture at the spherical-mirror end of the laser.

(a) Making use of the fact that $\Delta L \ll L$ and R, develop a simple expression for w_2 as a function of ΔL.

(b) Over what range of ΔL must the micrometer screw move the curved mirror if w_2 is to vary from 1 mm to all larger values? Plot w_2 versus ΔL over this range.

(c) When $w_2 = 1$ mm, what will be the value of w_1 at the flat-mirror end of the laser?

8-9. In a near-hemispherical optical resonator of length L with one plane mirror and one curved mirror of radius R, where $L = R(1 - \delta)$ and $\delta \ll 1$, both the output spot size w_2 and the transverse-mode frequency spacing depend on the small length adjustment δ. Assuming $\delta \ll 1$, derive a simple relationship between w_2 in millimeters and the transverse-mode frequency interval in megahertz. Put in some typical numbers for a resonator of $R = 1$ m and a resonator of $R = 10$ cm.

8-10. For an optical resonator of length L with one flat mirror and one curved mirror of radius R, evaluate the length–mirror-curvature ratios L/R at which there will be exactly 2, 3, 4, ... transverse-mode spacings in each axial-mode frequency interval.

8-11. The output beam from a laser oscillator 1 m long, whose two mirrors have 2-m radii of curvature, is to be matched into an interferometer cavity 5 cm long, whose two mirrors have 10-cm radii of curvature. The end mirrors of the two units are 50 cm apart. If they are to be matched with a single lens, what focal length is required, and where must the lens be located?

8-12. In Prob. 8-10, suppose that the only lens available has $f = 1$ m, but that the spacing between the units is allowed to vary. At what spacings between the laser, the lens, and the interferometer will matching be achieved?

8-13. As a rough first estimate, develop formulas for the power losses in stable optical resonators having circular mirrors of finite diameter a by using the standard gaussian field expressions and calculating the fraction of the energy in the assumed gaussian patterns that is lost by spillover past the edges of the mirrors.

Note: The losses predicted by this procedure, although small, will still be considerably larger than the real losses. In stable resonators with mirror diameters larger than a spot size or two, the real modes follow the predicted gaussian mode patterns quite accurately over most of the central region of the mirror where the mode amplitude is large, but the exact mode pattern close to the edge of the mirror, where the gaussian is small, deviate from the gaussian patterns and become even smaller, so that the exact mode losses are reduced considerably below the simple gaussian spillover predictions.

8-14. Consider the $\tilde{u}_{22}(x, y)$ higher-order gaussian mode in rectangular coordinates. Develop a formula and write a computer program to trace out the constant-amplitude contours in the xy plane for this mode, and make an isoamplitude contour map or model.

8-15. In an experiment carried out at the Bell Telephone Laboratories a powerful gaussian laser beam was passed through a laser amplifier, and certain interesting power-dependent focusing effects were observed. The incident laser beam was powerful enough to cause at least partial saturation of the amplifying transition in the laser amplifier, and because the signal fields are strongest at the center of a gaussian incident beam, the degree of saturation was largest on the axis of the amplifier tube, decreasing radially outward. When the saturation took place, it was found that the amplifier tube began to act as a (weak) lens, with the sign of this lens effect (convergent or divergent) depending on whether a weak probing beam used to observe the lens effect had a frequency slightly above or slightly below the atomic center frequency.

Explain the physical causes of this effect, and in particular, predict whether the lens should be convergent or divergent above and below the laser center frequency. (For simplicity, assume that the gain profile is uniform across the amplifier-tube cross section before saturation, and that the atomic transition is homogeneously broadened.)

REFERENCES

8-1.   D. W. Berreman, "Convective gas light guides or lens trains for optical beam transmission," *J. Opt. Soc. Am.*, **55**:239 (March, 1965).

8-2.   D. W. Berreman, "Growth of oscillations of a ray about the irregularity wavy axis of a lens light guide," *Bell Syst. Tech. J.*, **44**:2117 (November, 1965).

8-3.   J. A. Cochran, "The existence of eigenvalues for the integral equations of laser theory," *Bell Syst. Tech. J.*, **44**:77 (January, 1965). See also H. Hochstadt, "On the eigenvalue of a class of integral equations arising in laser theory," *SIAM Rev.*, **8**:62 (January, 1966).

8-4.   S. A. Collins, Jr., "Analysis of optical resonators involving focusing elements," *Appl. Optics*, **3**:1263 (November, 1964). See also S. A. Collins, Jr., and D. T. M. Davis, Jr., "Modes in a triangular ring resonator," *Appl. Optics*, **3**:1314 (November, 1964).

8-5.   A. G. Fox and T. Li, "Resonant modes in a maser interferometer," *Bell Syst. Tech. J.*, **40**:453 (March, 1961).

8-6.   A. G. Fox and T. Li, "Modes in a maser interferometer with curved mirrors," in P. Grivet and N. Bloembergen (eds.), *Quantum Electronics III*, vol. 2, p. 1263, Columbia University Press, New York, 1964.

8-7.   A. G. Fox and T. Li, "Modes in a maser interferometer with curved and tilted mirrors," *Proc. IEEE*, **51**:80 (January, 1964).

8-8.   D. Gloge, "Experiments with an underground lens waveguide," *Bell Syst. Tech. J.*, **46**:721 (April, 1967).

8-9.   D. R. Herriott and J. J. Schulte, "Folded optical delay lines," *Appl. Optics*, **4**:883 (August, 1965).

8-10.   J. C. Heurtley and W. Streifer, "Optical resonator modes: circular reflectors of spherical curvature," *J. Opt. Soc. Am.*, **55**:1472 (November, 1965).

8-11.   W. K. Kahn, "Ray theory of optical resonators and beam waveguides," in *Quasi-Optics*, Polytechnic Institute of Brooklyn Symposia Series, vol. 14, p. 399, Polytechnic Press/Wiley, New York, 1964.

8-12.   W. K. Kahn, "Geometrical optical derivation of formula for the variation of the spot size in a spherical mirror resonator," *Appl. Optics*, **4**:758 (June, 1965).

8-13.   H. Kogelnik, "Matching of optical modes," *Bell Syst. Tech. J.*, **43**:334 (January, 1964).

8-14.   H. Kogelnik, "Imaging of optical modes-resonators with internal lenses," *Bell Syst. Tech. J.*, **44**:455 (March, 1965).

8-15.   H. Kogelnik, "On propagation of gaussian beams of light through lenslike media," *Appl. Optics*, **4**:1562 (December, 1965).

8-16.   H. Kogelnik, "Modes in optical resonators," in A. K. Levine (ed.), *Lasers: A Series of Advances*, vol. 1, p. 295, Marcel Dekker, New York, 1966.

8-17.   H. Kogelnik and T. Li, "Laser beams and resonators," *Proc. IEEE*, **54**:1312 (October, 1966).

8-18.   W. F. Krupke and W. R. Sooy, "Properties of an unstable confocal resonator/CO_2 laser system," *IEEE J. Quantum Electron.*, **QE-5**:575 (December, 1969). See also Y. A. Anan'ev, N. A. Sventsitskaya, and V. E. Sherstobitov, "Properties of a laser with an unstable resonator," *Sov. Phys. JETP*, **28**:69 (January, 1969).

8-19.   N. Kurauchi and W. K. Kahn, "Rays and ray envelopes within stable optical resonators containing focusing media," *Appl. Optics*, **5**:1023 (June, 1966).

8-20.   T. Li, "Dual forms of the gaussian beam chart," *Appl. Optics*, **3**:1315 (November, 1964).

8-21.   D. Marcuse, "Propagation of light waves through a lens waveguide with curved axis," *Bell Syst. Tech. J.*, **43**:741 (March, 1964).

8-22.   D. Marcuse, "Statistical treatment of light-ray propagation in beam-waveguides," *Bell Syst. Tech. J.*, **44**:2065 (November, 1965).

8-23.   D. Marcuse, "Properties of periodic gas lenses," *Bell Syst. Tech. J.*, **44**:2083 (November, 1965).

8-24.   S. E. Miller, "Light propagation in generalized lens-like media," *Bell Syst. Tech. J.*, **44**:2017 (November, 1965).

8-25.   A. E. Siegman, "Unstable optical resonators for laser applications," *Proc. IEEE*, **53**:277 (March, 1965).

8-26.   A. E. Siegman and R. Arrathoon, "Modes in unstable optical resonators and lens waveguides," *IEEE J. Quantum Electron.*, **QE-3**:156 (April, 1967).

8-27.   P. K. Tien, J. P. Gordon, and J. R. Whinnery, "Focusing of a light beam of gaussian field distribution in continuous and periodic lens-like media," *Proc. IEEE*, **53**:129 (February, 1965).

8-28.   L. A. Vainshtein, "Open resonators for lasers," *Sov. Phys. JETP*, **18**:471 (February, 1964).

CHAPTER NINE

DOPPLER BROADENING: HOMOGENEOUS AND INHOMOGENEOUS TRANSITIONS

In Chap. 3 we discussed a number of basic line-broadening mechanisms for atomic transitions, including lifetime broadening, collision broadening, and dipolar broadening. In this chapter we will introduce some additional line-broadening mechanisms that are important for optical-frequency transitions, particularly doppler broadening for atomic transitions in gases. Before doing this, however, we will introduce and describe the important concepts of homogeneous versus inhomogeneous broadening in atomic transitions and their effects on laser behavior.

9-1 HOMOGENEOUS VERSUS INHOMOGENEOUS LINE BROADENING

There are certain line-broadening mechanisms that operate by broadening the response of each individual atom equally, while other broadening mechanisms operate by shifting or spreading out the center frequencies of individual atoms, thereby broadening the overall response of a collection without broadening the response of individual atoms. These two different types of line-broadening effects are classified as *homogeneous* and *inhomogeneous*, respectively. The distinction between homogeneous and inhomogeneous broadening of atomic transitions has major effects on the laser and maser behavior of these transitions, as we will see later. In this section we will discuss in more detail some of the important features and differences of homogeneous and inhomogeneous atomic transitions.

■ The essential feature of a homogeneously broadened atomic transition is that every atom in the collection of atoms has the same center frequency and the same atomic lineshape and frequency response, so that a signal applied to the transition has exactly the same effects on all the atoms in the collection. The differences between homogeneous and inhomogeneous transitions show up most clearly in the saturation behavior of these transitions.

HOMOGENEOUS BROADENING

The meaning of homogeneous broadening is perhaps most clearly illustrated by a hypothetical (but entirely realistic) experiment. Suppose that both the absorptive susceptibility $\chi''(\omega)$ and the reactive susceptibility $\chi'(\omega)$ of a homogeneously broadened line in a collection of atoms are being continuously monitored versus frequency by some weak tunable probing signals or test signals, while at the same time a strong saturating signal is applied to the atoms at some fixed frequency f_{sat} within the atomic linewidth. Figure 9-1 illustrates such an experiment. From Chap. 6 we know that a strong signal applied to a transition causes the population difference $\Delta \mathcal{N}$ on that transition to decrease from its small-signal value toward zero for a sufficiently strong applied signal. The atomic response—that is, the susceptibilities χ'' and χ', or the maser gain and phase shift—in turn depends directly on the population difference $\Delta \mathcal{N}$. The important point about a homogeneous transition is that the population difference, and hence the entire atomic response, will saturate uniformly under the influence of a sufficiently strong signal applied anywhere within the atomic linewidth.

Figure 9-1 shows how, as the saturating signal level is increased and the population difference thereby decreased, the measured responses $\chi''(\omega)$ and $\chi'(\omega)$ at all other frequencies decrease in direct proportion to $\Delta \mathcal{N}$ without changing in shape or in linewidth. The transition saturates uniformly across its width. Applying a strong signal anywhere within the atomic linewidth causes saturation of the atomic response all

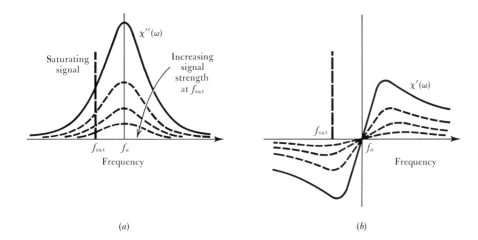

(a) (b)

FIG. 9-1 When a strong saturating signal is applied to a homogeneously broadened transition at a frequency f_{sat} anywhere within the atomic line, the atomic response, including both $\chi''(\omega)$ and $\chi'(\omega)$, saturates uniformly without changing shape or width.

across the atomic line. Of course, the transition is most easily saturated (i.e., the least saturating power is required to obtain a given degree of saturation) if the saturating signal is tuned exactly to the line center. The saturation behavior of $\Delta \mathcal{N}$ is of the general form

$$\Delta \mathcal{N} = \Delta \mathcal{N}_{\text{small-sig}} \frac{1}{1 + \text{const} \times W_{ij}} \tag{1}$$

and the stimulated transition probability in turn contains the lineshape

$$W_{ij} = \text{const} \times \text{lineshape} \times \text{signal power}$$

$$\propto \text{const} \times \frac{1}{1 + [2(\omega - \omega_a)/\Delta\omega_a]^2} \times \text{signal power} \tag{2}$$

For a given signal power level, W_{ij} is reduced as the frequency is tuned away from the atomic line center. Nonetheless, a strong saturating signal even well to the side of the atomic transition will, if it is strong enough, saturate the entire transition uniformly across its lineshape.

INHOMOGENEOUS
BROADENING

■ The inhomogeneously broadened case is more complex. The essential feature of an inhomogeneously broadened transition is that different atoms or groups of atoms within the same collection have slightly different resonance frequencies on the same transition, owing to doppler shifts or a number of other possible types of inhomogeneities. As a result, the overall response of the collection is broadened, or smeared out in frequency, because of the smearing out of center frequencies of individual atoms. An applied signal at a given frequency within the overall linewidth interacts strongly only with those atoms whose shifted resonance frequencies lie close to the applied-signal frequency. The applied signal has little or no effect on atoms whose shifted resonance frequencies are more than a few natural linewidths away in frequency. In short, an applied signal does not have the same effect on all the atoms in an inhomogeneously broadened collection.[1]

A particularly simple idealized low-frequency experiment is probably the best way to illustrate these concepts. Figure 9-2a shows a magnetic-resonance experiment in which a long, narrow sample of magnetic-dipole material is placed inside a matching rf coil, and this coil is then placed in an inhomogeneous dc magnetic field in which the field strength B_0 varies along the length of the sample. Since the magnetic-dipole resonance frequency is proportional to B_0, the resonance frequency f_a' of each little increment of length along the sample is slightly shifted in relation to adjacent sections.

When a test signal is applied to this coil in order to measure the magnetic-resonance response of the sample, a magnetic-resonance response will be excited only from those atoms in the small region along the sample where the local magnetic field strength B_0' and local resonance frequency f_a' match the applied-signal frequency; that is, $f_s \approx f_a' = g\beta B_0'$. As the signal frequency is varied, the region of strongest response moves along the sample, from one end to the other. Since the entire sample is inside a single coil, however, a response will be observed from the coil over the entire tuning range f_{a1} to f_{a2} in Fig. 9-2b, corresponding to the full range of variation of B_0 from B_{01} to B_{02}. An experimenter looking into the coil with measuring apparatus will thus see a continuous *inhomogeneously broadened* atomic response that is considerably wider in

---

[1] The concept of inhomogeneous versus homogeneous broadening seems to have been originated by Portis (Ref. 9-3).

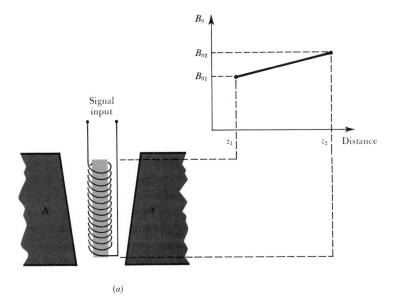

(a)

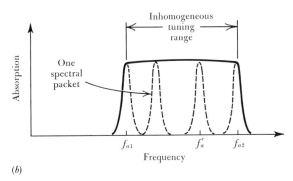

(b)

FIG. 9-2 (a) A magnetic-resonance experiment using a spatially inhomogeneous dc magnetic field. (b) The resulting inhomogeneously broadened overall response.

frequency than the response from any single small segment or any single atom of the sample.

■ In describing an inhomogeneously broadened transition we must consider both the *homogeneous linewidth,* the width of the response of any single atom in the collection as determined by whatever homogeneous broadening mechanisms may be present, and the *inhomogeneous linewidth,* which is determined by the spread or range of smearing of the individual atomic center frequencies as determined by whatever inhomogeneous broadening mechanism is responsible. Homogeneous broadening mechanisms almost invariably lead to a lorentzian, or very nearly lorentzian, lineshape for atomic response. However, as Fig. 9-2 illustrates, the inhomogeneous smearing out of a transition can lead to almost any lineshape. The supposed near-uniform spreading out of center frequencies in Fig. 9-2 leads to a nearly square shape for the inhomogeneously broadened response. In many cases, such as doppler broadening, the inhomogeneous mechanism, whatever it is, is a random kind of quantity which obeys the central-limit theorem and therefore has a gaussian probability distribution. The resulting lineshape is then also a nearly gaussian lineshape, as we will see in the doppler-broadening example of the following section.

SPECTRAL PACKETS

A signal applied to an inhomogeneous transition interacts strongly only with those atoms whose resonance frequencies lie within about one homogeneous linewidth on each side of the applied signal frequency. The region of the sample in Fig. 9-2 that is affected by a given applied signal will be only about a homogeneous linewidth or two wide. Therefore, as a convenient simplified description, an inhomogeneously broadened transition is often divided—at least for purposes of discussion—into a set of adjacent frequency bands or groups of atoms, each representing those atoms whose shifted resonance frequencies f_a' lie within a given band one or two homogeneous line-widths wide on the frequency scale. In the magnetic-resonance field, where the concept of inhomogeneous broadening was first developed,[1] these individual groups were called *spin packets*. As a more general term to be used for any type of inhomogeneous transition at any frequency, we will speak of these groups of atoms as *spectral packets*. The total response of an inhomogeneously broadened collection of atoms is the sum of the responses of the individual spectral packets. The number of spectral packets in a collection is the overall inhomogeneous linewidth divided by the individual-atom ho-mogeneous linewidth (give or take a factor of 2). An applied signal interacts strongly only with that spectral packet within which the applied-signal frequency is located.

In our simple example of Fig. 9-2 the different spectral packets are actually phys-ically separated in space along the magnetic-dipole sample. This is not usually the case, however. More commonly the atoms associated with different spectral packets are phys-ically intermingled in random fashion throughout the entire collection of atoms. The inhomogeneous broadening mechanism of doppler broadening, for example, is the dif-ferent doppler shifts of atomic resonance frequencies caused by different thermal ve-locities of the atoms in a gas. The atoms having these different velocities are, of course, completely intermingled throughout the entire gas volume instead of being somehow sorted out in space by their velocities.

SATURATION CHARACTERISTICS AND HOLE-BURNING
■ The saturation characteristics of an inhomogeneous transition are very different from those of a homogeneous transition, and the differences are important. Suppose that the saturation experiment of Fig. 9-1 is repeated for an inhomogeneously broadened transi-tion. Then a major point is that a strong applied signal will saturate the population difference only for those atoms, or those spectral packets, with which the signal strongly interacts. As the saturating signal increases in strength, only the spectral packet, or packets, immediately adjacent to the strong signal will be saturated. The spectral pack-ets at other more distant frequencies will be essentially unchanged, since more distant packets are almost unaffected by the strong signal. As a result, with increasing saturat-ing power, the strong saturating signal will in essence burn a "hole" in the atomic-absorption curve, as shown in Fig. 9-3. It can be shown that this hole is at first approxi-mately two homogeneous linewidths wide and becomes steadily deeper with increasing signal strength, as the packet or packets in direct synchronism with the saturating sig-nal become more heavily saturated. The hole eventually "touches bottom," after which its width increases slowly with further increases in signal strength, because a saturating signal of sufficient strength can saturate packets that are even somewhat more than a linewidth or so away from it. This kind of hole burning has been clearly demonstrated at both conventional and optical frequencies.

This type of hole is burned only in the absorptive $\chi''(\omega)$ curve. The reactive $\chi'(\omega)$ effects are more complicated. First of all, because the reactive susceptibility is

[1] See Ref. 9-3.

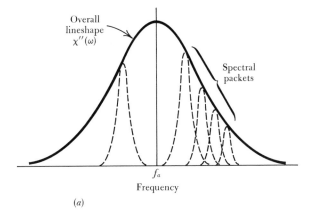

(a)

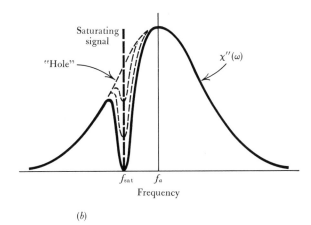

(b)

FIG. 9-3 (a) An inhomogeneously broadened atomic transition, showing some of the spectral packets within the overall linewidth. (b) Applying a strong saturating signal at f_{sat} will burn a "hole" in the absorption profile or $\chi''(\omega)$ curve for the transition.

zero at line center, $\chi'(\omega) = 0$ at $\omega = \omega_a'$, a spectral packet makes no contribution to the total $\chi'(\omega)$ value at its own frequency. Thus saturating a given packet does not change the $\chi'(\omega)$ at the center of that packet. However, a spectral packet does contribute to the susceptibility $\chi'(\omega)$ a few homogeneous linewidths away on either side. These contributions are of opposite sign on each side because of the asymmetric shape of $\chi'(\omega)$ (see Fig. 2-3). Thus the effect of saturating a given spectral packet on the $\chi'(\omega)$ curve at other frequencies is roughly as indicated in Fig. 9-4.

■ An inhomogeneously broadened transition is obviously more complex than a homogeneous transition, since it really consists of a number of more or less independent homogeneous transitions or spectral packets, each having different center frequencies. The susceptibility of a homogeneous transition can be completely described under all conditions of saturation by giving only the lineshape function or the linewidth Δf_a and the instantaneous population difference $\Delta \mathcal{N}$ on the transition. For an inhomogeneous transition, particularly under conditions where one or several holes are burned in the transition, it is necessary to give the homogeneous linewidth of the individual packets, the overall inhomogeneous broadening or spreading out of the center frequencies of these packets, and in the most general case a separate value of population difference $\Delta \mathcal{N}'$ for each separate spectral packet. With multiple applied signals the degree of saturation of each packet must be kept track of separately.

SUMMARY OF HOMOGENEOUS VERSUS INHOMOGENEOUS BROADENING

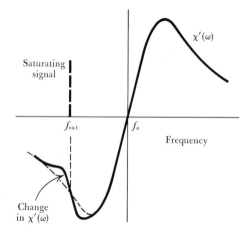

FIG. 9-4 Burning a hole at $f = f_{sat}$ in the inhomogeneous line causes a small change in $\chi'(\omega)$ which is zero right at f_{sat} but has a finite value within a homogeneous linewidth or two on either side of f_{sat}.

If the inhomogeneous broadening, or smearing out of the packet center frequencies, is substantially greater than the homogeneous linewidth of a single packet, so that there are many spectral packets within the overall line, then the transition is said to be *strongly inhomogeneously broadened.* Several different, noninteracting holes can be burned in such a transition, since the hole widths will be only a small fraction of the overall linewidth. The opposite limit is the case where the amount of inhomogeneous frequency shifting is zero, or at least small compared to the homogeneous linewidth. In this case a signal applied anywhere saturates the entire line, and no holes can be burned in the line; the transition is essentially homogeneous. Finally, there can be intermediate cases in which the amount of inhomogeneous broadening is about the same as, or perhaps a little larger than, the homogeneous linewidth. A hole can be burned in the transition to some extent, but the hole width will be a sizable fraction of the total linewidth. This intermediate case can be the most complicated of all to analyze. Ruby lasers happen to be homogeneously broadened in most cases; helium-neon gas lasers are strongly inhomogeneously broadened, and many CO_2 lasers fall in the category of transitions which are intermediate between fully homogeneous and strongly inhomogeneous.

Some further points concerning the characteristics of inhomogeneous transitions and their effects on laser oscillation will be discussed later.

9-2   DOPPLER BROADENING OF ATOMIC TRANSITIONS

The atoms in a gas undergo rapid but random motions owing to the brownian kinetic motion characteristic of any collection of particles in thermal equilibrium at a finite temperature. The random doppler shifts associated with these random motions in turn cause the apparent resonance frequencies of the atoms to be shifted randomly, so that the overall frequency response of the collection of atoms is broadened. This type of inhomogeneous *doppler broadening* provides the dominant broadening mechanism for many infrared- and optical-frequency laser transitions.

DOPPLER SHIFT FOR A
MOVING ATOM

■ Doppler shifts occur whenever a moving emitter or a moving receiver interacts with a traveling wave of radiation—for example, when a moving atom interacts with a wave of signal radiation in a laser. The doppler effect is basically a relativistic one, requiring a relativistic analysis. However, a first-order expression for doppler shift which is more than sufficiently accurate for all practical purposes can easily be obtained from a simple nonrelativistic derivation.

Figure 9-5a shows an atom moving with vector velocity $\mathbf{u}$ while interacting with a traveling wave. Let the direction in which the wave is traveling define the z direction; then it is only the component of the atomic velocity parallel to the wave, u_z, that is significant in causing a doppler shift. Figure 9-5b shows a wave of wavelength λ moving in the $+z$ direction at the velocity of light, c, together with an atom moving in this direction at velocity u_z. Because the atom is moving through the wave, the apparent frequency f' of the wave, as seen from the atom, differs from the frequency f of the wave as measured in the laboratory. During a time period T, the wave moves a distance cT to the right. The number of cycles of the wave that would pass by a stationary atom during this time period is $N = cT/\lambda = fT$, since $c = f\lambda$. However, since the atom itself is moving, it moves a distance u_zT to the right during this same time. Therefore there are a certain number of cycles $\Delta N = u_zT/\lambda$ that will not actually pass by the atom. The apparent frequency f' then becomes

$$f' = \frac{N - \Delta N}{T} = \frac{cT - u_zT}{\lambda T} = \left(1 - \frac{u_z}{c}\right)f \tag{1}$$

where $N - \Delta N$ is the number of cycles and T is the time interval. A rigorous relativistic analysis gives a more complicated formula which reduces to this same result as long as $u_z \ll c$.

For a signal wave to elicit maximum response from a moving atom, the apparent signal frequency f' must equal the atomic resonance frequency f_a, or

$$f' = \left(1 - \frac{u_z}{c}\right)f = f_a \tag{2}$$

If this expression is inverted, the requirement for resonant interaction in terms of the laboratory frequency f is

$$f = \frac{f_a}{1 - u_z/c} \approx \left(1 + \frac{u_z}{c}\right)f_a \tag{3}$$

To put this another way, the apparent resonance frequency of the moving atom from the laboratory frame of reference appears to be shifted from f_a to a new value f_a', given by

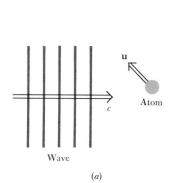

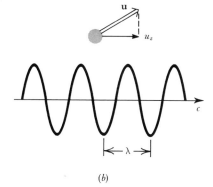

FIG. 9-5 Geometry for analysis of doppler-shift effects: (a) moving atom encountering a traveling wave, (b) only the component of atomic velocity parallel to the wave is significant in evaluating the doppler shift.

$$f'_a = \left(1 + \frac{u_z}{c}\right)f_a = f_a + \delta f_a \tag{4}$$

where $\delta f_a = (f_a/c)u_z$ is the doppler shift for that particular atom.

RANDOM DOPPLER
BROADENING

■ The atoms or molecules in a gas have random thermal-velocity components in all directions. If we consider some large number N of atoms in a gas, we find that the number of atoms, dN, with a velocity component u_z lying in the narrow range du_z between u_z and $u_z + du_z$ is given (from statistical mechanics) by the gaussian or maxwellian distribution

$$dN(u_z) = N\sqrt{\frac{M}{2\pi kT}}e^{-Mu_z{}^2/2kT}\,du_z \qquad -\infty < u_z < \infty \tag{5}$$

where M is the mass of the atom or molecule and T is the temperature associated with the kinetic motion of the gas atoms. Figure 9-6 is a sketch of this function, showing how the area under the curve in any narrow range du_z gives the number of atoms having a z-directed velocity component in that range. The mean-square z velocity of the atoms can be calculated from this curve by multiplying $u_z{}^2$ by the fractional number of atoms moving at that particular value of u_z and integrating over all positive and negative values of u_z. The result is

$$\langle u_z{}^2 \rangle = \frac{\int_{-\infty}^{\infty} u_z{}^2\,dN(u_z)}{\int_{-\infty}^{\infty} dN(u_z)} = \sqrt{\frac{M}{2\pi kT}}\int_{-\infty}^{\infty} u_z{}^2 e^{-Mu_z{}^2/2kT}\,du_z = \frac{kT}{M} \tag{6}$$

The average kinetic energy associated with the z component of motion only is then

$$\tfrac{1}{2}M\langle u_z{}^2\rangle = \tfrac{1}{2}kT \tag{7}$$

This agrees with the general rule that there is an average kinetic energy of $\tfrac{1}{2}kT$ associated with each component of kinetic motion in a gas, or $\tfrac{3}{2}kT$ for all three cartesian components.

Suppose a signal is applied to this collection of atoms; for example, an optical wave passing down a gas laser tube. Each atom in the gas is traveling at some different velocity u_z and therefore has its apparent resonance frequency doppler shifted by the amount $\delta f_a = (f_a/c)u_z$. Each atom thus has a doppler-shifted response centered at

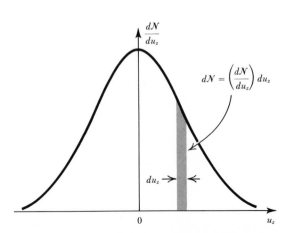

FIG. 9-6 Probability density distribution of z-directed atomic velocities (maxwellian distribution), showing evaluation of the number of atoms dN whose z velocities lie in a narrow range du_z centered at u_z.

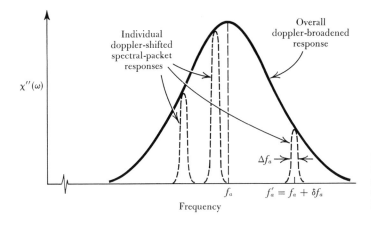

Individual doppler-shifted spectral-packet responses

Overall doppler-broadened response

$\chi''(\omega)$

Δf_a

f_a $f_a' \equiv f_a + \delta f_a$

Frequency

FIG. 9-7 The absorption lines of individual atoms (each of which has the homogeneous linewidth Δf_a) are shifted about by random doppler shifts δf_a to produce the overall smeared-out or doppler-broadened absorption line shown.

$f_a' = f_a + \delta f_a$, with a natural linewidth Δf_a which is determined by lifetime broadening, collisions, or whatever homogeneous mechanism is important in the particular atomic collection. It seems reasonable to assume that the natural or homogeneous width of the individual atomic responses will not be significantly changed by the atomic motions.

Suppose, as a first example, that the doppler shifts δf_a suffered by the various atoms are, on the average, large compared to the natural linewidth Δf_a. Then the total response of the collection of atoms, including the doppler-shift effects, will be a broadened collection of many individual responses whose individual center frequencies are spread over a sizable range, as illustrated in Fig. 9-7. Moreover, the midband value of this response will be proportionally reduced in relation to its value without the doppler broadening, because only those few atoms in the unshifted spectral packet, i.e., those few atoms moving very slowly in the z direction, will respond to an applied signal at the line center, rather than all the atoms, as would have been the case without the doppler effects.

The result of strong random doppler shifts, then, is a sizable doppler broadening of the atomic transition, accompanied by a sizable reduction in the peak value of the response in relation to the case of no doppler broadening. This is clearly an inhomogeneous type of broadening.

■ To express the steady-state response of a collection of atoms in the presence of doppler broadening, we must write the response to an applied signal of an individual atom whose apparent resonance frequency is doppler shifted by an amount δf_a, multiply this response by the number of atoms having that particular doppler shift, and then sum (or, rather, integrate) this expression over all atoms (all possible values of the doppler shift). Suppose that a collection of atoms without doppler broadening has a susceptibility

ANALYTIC EXPRESSIONS

$$\tilde{\chi}(\omega) = j\chi_0'' \frac{1}{1 + 2j(\omega - \omega_a)/\Delta\omega_a} \tag{8}$$

The susceptibility contribution of a single atom moving with an axial velocity u_z may be written as

$$\tilde{\chi}(\omega: \delta\omega_a') = j\frac{\chi_0''}{\mathcal{N}} \frac{1}{1 + 2j(\omega - \omega_a - \delta\omega_a)/\Delta\omega_a} \tag{9}$$

where the doppler shift in radian-frequency units for that particular atom is

$$\delta\omega_a = \frac{\omega_a}{c} u_z = 2\pi \, \delta f_a \tag{10}$$

The maxwellian expression (5) for the number of atoms having axial velocity u_z or a doppler shift $\delta\omega_a$ can then be written in the form

$$d\mathcal{N}(\delta\omega_a) = \frac{\mathcal{N}}{\sqrt{2\pi\langle\delta\omega_a{}^2\rangle}} \, e^{-\delta\omega_a{}^2/2\langle\delta\omega_a{}^2\rangle} \, d(\delta\omega_a) \tag{11}$$

where the mean-square doppler shift $\langle\delta\omega_a{}^2\rangle$ is

$$\langle\delta\omega_a{}^2\rangle = \left(\frac{\omega_a}{c}\right)^2 \langle u_z{}^2\rangle = \left(\frac{\omega_a}{c}\right)^2 \frac{kT}{M} \tag{12}$$

or

$$\frac{\langle\delta\omega_a{}^2\rangle}{\omega_a{}^2} = \frac{kT}{Mc^2} \tag{13}$$

Doppler shifts much larger than $\langle\delta\omega_a{}^2\rangle^{1/2}$ are not very probable.

The total doppler-broadened response is now obtained by multiplying the response of an atom with doppler shift $\delta\omega_a$ by the number of atoms having that shift and integrating over all values of $\delta\omega_a$. The result is

$$\widetilde{\chi}(\omega) = \int_{\text{all atoms}} \widetilde{\chi}(\omega : \delta\omega_a) \, d\mathcal{N}(\delta\omega_a)$$

$$= \int_{-\infty}^{\infty} \underbrace{\frac{j\chi_0''}{\mathcal{N}} \frac{1}{1 + 2j(\omega - \omega_a - \delta\omega_a)/\Delta\omega_a}}_{\substack{\text{lorentzian response of a} \\ \text{single doppler-shifted atom}}}$$

$$\times \underbrace{\frac{\mathcal{N}}{\sqrt{2\pi\langle\delta\omega_a{}^2\rangle}} \, e^{-\delta\omega_a{}^2/2\langle\delta\omega_a{}^2\rangle} \, d(\delta\omega_a)}_{\substack{\text{number of atoms having a} \\ \text{particular doppler shift } \delta\omega_a}} \tag{14}$$

This is the general analytical form for the inhomogeneously broadened response of a doppler-broadened atomic transition, valid for any arbitrary ratio of doppler broadening to natural or homogeneous broadening.

Unfortunately, the integral in Eq. (14) is mathematically intractable and cannot be easily evaluated in any closed form.[1] To carry the analysis any further, various approximations must be made, of which the two cases of most interest are the limiting cases of very small and very large amounts of doppler broadening (relative to the homogeneous linewidth).

The case of negligible doppler broadening, $\langle\delta\omega_a{}^2\rangle \ll \Delta\omega_a$, is almost trivial. If the average doppler shift is small compared to the natural resonance linewidth of the atoms, then these small doppler shifts should have little effect. Mathematically, in this limit the maxwellian or gaussian factor becomes much narrower than the lorentzian term, and acts essentially like a delta function $\delta(\delta\omega_a)$. The general expression (14) then reduces back to the simple lorentzian form

[1] See Refs. 9-2 and 9-4.

$$\tilde{\chi}(\omega) \approx j\chi_0'' \frac{1}{1 + 2j(\omega - \omega_a)/\Delta\omega_a} \qquad \langle \delta\omega_a{}^2 \rangle \ll \Delta\omega_a{}^2 \tag{15}$$

The amount of doppler broadening disappears from the expression entirely, as seems only reasonable.

The opposite limit is when the doppler shifts are on the average large compared to the individual atomic linewidths, $\langle \delta\omega_a{}^2 \rangle \gg \Delta\omega_a{}^2$. In this case the line becomes strongly inhomogeneously broadened, and the gaussian factor becomes wide compared to the individual lorentzian response. The mathematics of this case still remain fairly difficult. The imaginary part $\chi''(\omega)$, which of course determines the absorption or gain lineshape of the transition, can be written as

$$\chi''(\omega) = \frac{\chi_0''}{\mathcal{N}} \int_{-\infty}^{\infty} \frac{1}{1 + [2(\omega - \omega_a - \delta\omega_a)/\Delta\omega_a]^2}$$
$$\frac{\mathcal{N}}{\sqrt{2\pi\langle\delta\omega_a{}^2\rangle}} e^{-\delta\omega_a{}^2/2\langle\delta\omega_a{}^2\rangle} \, d(\delta\omega_a) \tag{16}$$

It is now the lorentzian factor that is the narrower one, and that can be replaced by a delta function, $\delta(\delta\omega_a - \omega + \omega_a)$, with appropriate normalization. Within this degree of approximation, the absorptive-susceptibility expression becomes

$$\chi''(\omega) \approx \sqrt{\frac{\pi \Delta\omega_a{}^2}{8\langle\delta\omega_a{}^2\rangle}} \chi_0'' e^{-(\omega-\omega_a)^2/2\langle\delta\omega_a{}^2\rangle} \qquad \langle\delta\omega_a{}^2\rangle \gg \Delta\omega_a{}^2 \tag{17}$$

This is the widely used expression for the gaussian lineshape of a doppler-broadened transition (or any other transition that is strongly inhomogeneously broadened by some sort of gaussianly distributed random frequency shifts).

Even with this same approximation, it is not possible to write any similar closed-form approximate expression for the reactive susceptibility $\chi'(\omega)$ of a strongly doppler-broadened transition. Although the χ'' part of the lorentzian susceptibility can be replaced by a delta function in evaluating (14), the χ' part cannot, and there is no approximate analytic way of evaluating the general integral expression (14) to find the reactive susceptibility $\chi'(\omega)$.

■ The strongly doppler-broadened lineshape for $\chi''(\omega)$ thus has the gaussian frequency dependence

$$\chi''(\omega) \propto e^{-(\omega-\omega_a)^2/2\langle\delta\omega_a{}^2\rangle} \tag{18}$$

where $\langle \delta\omega_a{}^2 \rangle$ is the mean-square linewidth of the gaussian resonance curve. For consistency with the definition of linewidth in the lorentzian case, we may wish to define a doppler linewidth $\Delta\omega_d \equiv 2\pi \Delta f_d$ by the same convention as the lorentzian linewidth, i.e., the full linewidth between half-power points. The doppler susceptibility $\chi''(\omega)$ will be down to half its peak value for frequency shifts of

$$\frac{(\omega - \omega_a)^2}{2\langle\delta\omega_a{}^2\rangle} = \ln 2 \tag{19}$$

Therefore the full linewidth or doppler linewidth $\Delta\omega_d$ between these points will be related to the mean-square linewidth $\langle \delta\omega_a{}^2 \rangle$ by

$$\Delta\omega_d = 2\sqrt{2 \ln 2\langle\delta\omega_a{}^2\rangle} = \sqrt{8 \ln 2\langle\delta\omega_a{}^2\rangle} \tag{20}$$

or

DOPPLER LINEWIDTH
AND LINESHAPE

$$\frac{\Delta\omega_d}{\omega_a} = \frac{\Delta f_d}{f_a} = \sqrt{8 \ln 2 \frac{kT}{Mc^2}} \tag{21}$$

In terms of this half-power doppler linewidth, the doppler-broadened susceptibility takes the form

$$\chi''(\omega) = (\pi \ln 2)^{1/2} \frac{\Delta\omega_a}{\Delta\omega_d} \chi_0'' \exp\left[-(2 \ln 2)^2 \left(\frac{\omega - \omega_a}{\Delta\omega_d}\right)^2 \right]$$

$$\Delta\omega_d \gg \Delta\omega_a \tag{22}$$

and it is useful to remember that $(\pi \ln 2)^{1/2} \simeq 1.48$. The exponent is now in a somewhat cumbersome form because the half-power linewidth $\Delta\omega_d$ is not as natural a parameter for a gaussian response as is the mean-square linewidth or variance $\langle \delta\omega_a^2 \rangle$.

It is apparent from expressions (17) and (22) that in the strongly doppler-broadened limit, $\Delta\omega_d \gg \Delta\omega_a$, the peak response is reduced below the value it would have for no broadening by the ratio

$$(\pi \ln 2)^{1/2} \frac{\Delta\omega_a}{\Delta\omega_d} \simeq 1.48 \frac{\Delta\omega_a}{\Delta\omega_d}.$$

This is in agreement with the physical argument given a few paragraphs back.

Although no simple analytic expressions are available for $\chi'(\omega)$ in the doppler-broadening case, this function can be calculated numerically.[1] The result looks in general much like the same quantity for the lorentzian case, i.e., peaks of opposite sign located roughly one-half linewidth on either side of line center, and with approximately half the amplitude of the χ'' peak. Figure 9-8 is a plot of $\chi''(\omega)$ and $\chi'(\omega)$ versus ω for a strongly doppler-broadened transition. The general similarity to the lorentzian case is apparent.

There are, however, some significant differences between the lorentzian and the

[1] Ref. 9-4 gives various numerical tabulations of this quantity.

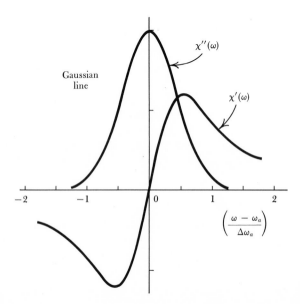

FIG. 9-8 The real and imaginary parts of the susceptibility $\bar{\chi}(\omega)$ for a gaussian or strongly doppler-broadened atomic resonance.

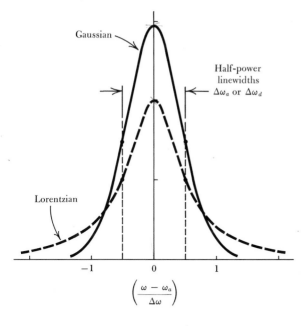

FIG. 9-9 A comparison of the gaussian and lorentzian lineshapes, given equal half-widths for the two curves and equal areas under the two curves. Note the wide, slowly decaying "wings" characteristic of the lorentzian curve.

doppler-gaussian lineshapes, particularly for the absorption profile $\chi''(\omega)$. These two $\chi''(\omega)$ curves are plotted for comparison in Fig. 9-9, with the same half-power linewidths and the same areas under each curve. The doppler curve drops off to essentially zero beyond about one full linewidth from center on either side, while the lorentzian curve is characterized by much more slowly decreasing wings far from line center. With the equal-area normalization, the peak value of the gaussian line is larger by the factor $(\pi \ln 2)^{1/2} \approx 1.48$ because more of its total area is concentrated close to the center of the line.

■ The doppler-broadened linewidth in conventional frequency units is given by

TYPICAL NUMERICAL VALUES

$$\Delta f_d = \frac{\Delta\omega_d}{2\pi} = \sqrt{8 \ln 2 \frac{kT}{Mc^2}} f_a = \sqrt{8 \ln 2 \frac{kT}{M\lambda^2}} \tag{23}$$

The doppler width obviously varies directly as the transition frequency f_a and as the square root of the kinetic temperature $T^{1/2}$, and varies inversely as the square root of the atomic or molecular mass $M^{1/2}$. It is convenient to remember that the thermal energy kT corresponds to $\sim\frac{1}{40}$ eV, or 25 meV, for room temperature $T = 290°$K, while the self-energy Mc^2 for a proton or hydrogen atom is $\sim10^9$ eV, or 1000 MeV.

To pick some common examples, the doppler linewidth of the 6328-Å He-Ne laser transition, given a temperature $T \approx 400°$K and an atomic mass of 20 for the Ne atom, is about

$$\Delta f_d \approx 1.5 \times 10^9 = 1500 \text{ MHz} \tag{24}$$

Since this is about ten times larger than the lifetime or collision-broadened homogeneous linewidth for typical He-Ne laser conditions, the He-Ne laser transition is definitely inhomogeneously broadened by doppler effects. Experimental results are in good agreement with this calculation.

For the CO_2 10.6-μ laser transition, the doppler linewidth is much reduced because of the lower transition frequency f_a. With $T \approx 300°$K and the CO_2 molecular mass of 44, the doppler linewidth is predicted as only

$$\Delta f_d \approx 50 \text{ MHz} \tag{25}$$

However, we found in Sec. 3-4 that the collision-broadened homogeneous linewidth for this transition varies with CO_2 pressure roughly as

$$\frac{\Delta f_a \text{ (MHz)}}{\text{Pressure (torr)}} \approx 6.5 \text{ MHz/torr} \tag{26}$$

Therefore the linewidth-vs.-pressure curve for the CO_2 transition has the form shown in Fig. 3-10, changing over from predominantly doppler broadened and inhomogeneous well below 5 torrs of pressure to predominantly pressure broadened (i.e., collision broadened), and hence homogeneous, well above 5 torrs. When pressure broadening of the He, N_2, and other gases present in the CO_2 laser is taken into account, the total pressure broadening is usually about the same as, or perhaps twice, the doppler broadening, and the CO_2 laser transition is essentially a homogeneously broadened transition.

In the argon-ion and other similar ion lasers the kinetic temperature of the atoms is considerably higher than in the He-Ne laser, presumably because the ion laser discharge is excited with much higher current and much more pumping energy per unit volume. The doppler widths of visible argon-ion laser transitions appear to be as large as 6000 MHz.

9-3 OTHER BROADENING MECHANISMS FOR OPTICAL-FREQUENCY TRANSITIONS

Optical-frequency transitions in *gases* can be broadened by lifetime, collision, or doppler broadening, all of which we have now discussed. Optical-frequency transitions in *solids* may be broadened by lifetime broadening, dipolar broadening, a certain type of thermal fm broadening, or by random inhomogeneities. In this section we will discuss briefly these last three broadening mechanisms.

DIPOLAR BROADENING
■ We saw in Chaps. 3 and 4 that dipolar broadening arises from interactions between the magnetic or electric dipolar fields of neighboring atoms, leading to results very similar to collision broadening, including a linewidth that increases with increasing density of atoms. Since dipolar broadening represents a kind of coupling between atoms, so that excitation applied to one atom is distributed to or shared with other atoms, dipolar broadening is a homogeneous broadening mechanism.

There are a large number of solid-state laser systems that involve rare-earth ions in various host crystal lattices or even in glass host materials. Some of these systems can still operate successfully as laser systems even at rare-earth ion concentrations as high as 5 percent, or perhaps even 15 percent. Dipolar broadening can then become a significant source of line broadening at these higher concentrations. Complications arise, however, because at these higher concentrations it becomes much more difficult to grow the laser materials as good strain-free single crystals. Hence other broadening effects caused by random imperfections may also increase sharply at higher concentrations, owing to the decreased crystalline perfection of strongly doped crystals.

RANDOM INHOMOGENEITIES
■ The energy levels of laser ions in crystals—including the rare-earth ions and particularly the Cr^{3+} ion in ruby—are perturbed or shifted in energy by the crystalline electric fields at the site of the laser ion caused by the other surrounding ions in the crystalline lattice (this is particularly true of ruby, and the Cr^{3+} ion energy levels in ruby are

totally different from the levels of a free Cr^{3+} ion). Therefore, if there are random variations or changes in the crystalline surroundings from laser ion to laser ion, there may be small shifts in the exact energy-level spacings and transition frequencies from ion to ion. These random variations may be caused by dislocations, interstitial foreign atoms, lattice strains, missing atoms, and other sorts of localized crystal defects in the laser host crystal.

Like doppler broadening, these defects and variations do not (at least, not necessarily) broaden the response of an individual atom, but they do cause the exact resonance frequencies of different atoms to be slightly different, so that the overall response of the collection of atoms is smeared out in frequency. Thus random crystal imperfections or inhomogeneities can be a source of inhomogeneous broadening in a solid-state laser crystal.

As might be expected, the magnitude of these broadening effects can vary considerably from sample to sample, depending on how the crystal was grown, what annealing techniques were employed, the concentration both of laser ions and of other impurities, and so forth. In general, large ion concentrations often lead to poorer crystal quality, and hence to increased inhomogeneity broadening.

The distributions of random quantities such as defects often exhibit a gaussian probability density, owing in essence to the operation of the central-limit theorem. The line broadening due to these random quantities may then exhibit a more or less gaussian sort of response in many, though by no means all, cases. If so, the same sort of gaussian analysis as in the doppler-broadening case will apply equally well to the random-inhomogeneity case.

■ The final major form of line broadening is thermal fm broadening, the broadening mechanism which is responsible for the linewidth of the important laser transition in ruby, as well as in many other solid-state laser systems. The Cr^{3+} ions in laser ruby are fairly well dispersed,[1] and dipolar broadening of the laser transition is negligible. The exact R_1 transition frequency of the Cr^{3+} ion does, however, depend rather critically on the immediate lattice surroundings of the ion, particularly the spacing to the nearby oxygen ions surrounding the chromium ion. For example, a mechanical squeeze applied to a ruby crystal will distort the crystal structure very slightly, and this distortion then has sufficient effect on the chromium energy levels to tune the laser transition by a small but easily measurable amount.

In thermal equilibrium at temperature T, the immediate lattice surroundings of the chromium ion undergo small but rapid variations, owing to the thermal lattice vibrations or heat vibrations in the crystal. The tuning effects of these thermal vibrations then cause a thermal broadening of the ruby resonance line. Figure 9-10 shows the measured atomic linewidth of the laser transition in a low-concentration ruby crystal as a function of temperature. At very low temperatures, below $\sim 100°K$, the lattice vibrations or thermal motions are small. The ruby linewidth is then essentially independent of temperature, and is in fact determined primarily by the random inhomogeneity effects described above. At higher temperatures, however, the linewidth suddenly begins to increase rapidly with increasing temperature and with increasing thermal agitation of the crystal lattice. This increase can be predicted from appropriate theories of the lattice vibrations and their effects on the Cr^{3+} ion; the experimental

THERMAL FM BROADENING

---

[1] In typical pink laser ruby with 0.05 percent Cr^{3+} concentration, the density of Cr^{3+} ions is $N_v \approx 2.5 \times 10^{19}$ ions/cm³, and the average distance between Cr^{3+} ions is ≈ 30 Å.

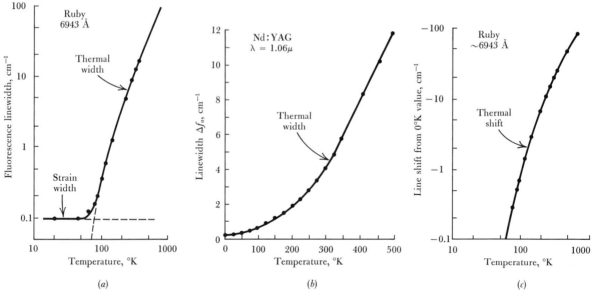

FIG. 9-10 (a) The linewidth of the 6943-Å laser transition in ruby plotted against temperature, showing inhomogeneity (strain) broadening at lower temperatures, changing over to thermal fm broadening at higher temperatures. (b) Linewidth of the 1.06-μ laser transition in Nd:YAG plotted against temperature, showing thermal broadening over essentially the entire temperature range. (c) Thermal shift of the center of the ruby laser transition away from its low temperature value, as caused by thermal fm effects. [From D. E. McCumber and M. D. Sturge, "Linewidth and temperature shift of the R lines in ruby," *J. Appl. Phys.*, **34**:1682 (June, 1963).]

results shown in Fig. 9-10a are in very good agreement with these more complicated theories of thermal fm broadening.

The important 1.06-μ laser transition in the Nd-YAG laser crystal is also broadened predominantly by thermal broadening, as shown in Fig. 9-10b. In this relatively high-quality host crystal the broadening effects of crystalline inhomogeneities are small, and so thermal broadening continues to be the dominant mechanism even down to quite low temperatures.

The thermal lattice vibrations are, for the most part, very rapid vibrations, with frequencies extending to 10^{12} Hz or higher. Therefore their effect on an atomic transition is not just a static resonance shift, as in the crystalline inhomogeneity case. Rather, the thermal vibrations shift the resonance frequency of each atom back and forth at a very rapid rate, much more rapid than any of the other time constants or stimulated transition rates that affect the atom. One way of describing this is to say that the resonance frequency of each individual atom gets shifted through all possible values within the thermally broadened linewidth in a time short compared to anything else that happens to the atom. As a result, an applied signal anywhere within the thermally broadened linewidth is felt equally by all the atoms. In other words, this thermal broadening mechanism is essentially a homogeneous broadening mechanism. The response of each individual atom is homogeneously broadened by being given thermal fm noise-modulation sidebands that spread out over the thermally broadened linewidth. Whatever the description, thermal fm broadening is definitely a homogeneous type of broadening mechanism.

The various possible lattice distortions and vibrations in ruby generally tend to shift the transition frequency f_a more toward lower frequencies than toward higher frequencies. Therefore, as a side effect, the thermal vibrations cause not only a thermal broadening, but also a sizable thermal shift in the average transition frequency toward lower frequency values with increasing temperature. Figure 9-10c plots this shift for ruby. The experimental results are again in good agreement with the theory, giving further confirmation for the general picture of the thermal effects on the atomic transition.

The thermal shift in ruby is sufficient to tune the R_1 transition from about 6934 Å at liquid-nitrogen temperature to about 6943 Å at room temperature. In constructing a ruby laser-oscillator–laser-amplifier chain it is necessary to take care that the temperatures of the laser oscillator and amplifier track each other sufficiently well to keep the oscillation frequency within the amplifier passband. Note that when ruby atoms are pumped from the ground level up into the upper pump bands, these atoms then drop down to the metastable upper laser level by emitting phonons of lattice vibrational energy into the crystal lattice. With the emission of these phonons, the ruby crystal is heated essentially instantaneously throughout the entire pumped volume. As a result, there can be a considerable temperature change in the ruby, and a considerable thermal shift of the laser transition, even during a single laser pulse. If the output spectrum of a ruby laser is plotted against time during a single pulse (this is a fairly difficult experiment), the individual cavity modes or axial modes of the laser will be seen to shift in frequency at one tuning rate owing to thermal shifts in the cavity length and the ruby index of refraction. At the same time, the overall envelope of the ruby multimode oscillation spectrum will be seen to shift in frequency at a different tuning rate, because of the thermal tuning of the center frequency of the ruby transition and the associated atomic gain curve.

9-4 EFFECTS OF INHOMOGENEOUS BROADENING ON LASER OPERATION

The different properties of homogeneously and inhomogeneously broadened transitions, especially their differing saturation characteristics, have important effects on the behavior of laser oscillators using these transitions. While we will not be discussing the detailed properties of laser oscillators until the following chapter, we will extend our discussion of homogeneously and inhomogeneously broadened transitions in this section to some of their effects on laser oscillators.[1]

■ By way of a quick review, we note once again that homogeneous mechanisms are those that broaden the response of all atoms in a collection equally, so that an applied signal affects all atoms in the same way and the transition saturates uniformly across its full width under the influence of a strong applied signal anywhere within the transition. *Homogeneous broadening mechanisms* include lifetime or T_1 broadening, collision or pressure broadening, dipolar interactions, and thermal fm broadening.

HOMOGENEOUS VERSUS INHOMOGENEOUS BROADENING MECHANISMS

Inhomogeneous mechanisms, by contrast, broaden the overall response of a collection of atoms by shifting the resonance frequencies of individual atoms. An applied signal interacts only with those atoms in the spectral packet that is shifted into resonance with the applied signal, and a strong applied signal saturates only that

---

[1] Those with only limited familiarity with laser properties may want to study Chap. 10 first and then come back to this section later.

particular packet, or perhaps a few closely adjacent spectral packets, thereby burning a hole into the absorption profile of the transition. Important examples of *inhomogeneous frequency-shifting mechanisms* include spatially inhomogeneous dc magnetic fields, crystalline strains, defects, and inhomogeneities, and doppler broadening.

Most visible and near-IR gas laser transitions are inhomogeneously broadened by doppler broadening, while longer-wavelength IR gas lasers may be homogeneously broadened by pressure broadening. Solid-state lasers may be inhomogeneously broadened by crystalline defects at low temperatures, but are usually homogeneously broadened by thermal fm effects at normal temperatures. The microwave EPR transitions used in microwave solid-state masers are usually homogeneously broadened by dipolar effects, although the inhomogeneous contribution due to crystalline imperfections may also be important. Certain high-resolution NMR transitions can have extraordinarily small homogeneous linewidths. Such narrow transitions are almost always inhomogeneously broadened owing to variations in the dc magnetic field strength B_0 across the sample. In such cases very large, carefully aligned polished magnetic-pole faces are used, with very small gaps. Even so, in some instances the most important source of broadening is still the minute variation in B_0 due to small random variations in magnetic permeability caused by the magnetic-domain microstructure in the magnetic-pole faces.

HOMOGENEOUS SINGLE-MODE
LASER OSCILLATION

■ The type of saturation of a laser transition has important consequences for the mode behavior of that laser. Consider, for example, a regenerative traveling-wave system such as Fig. 5-21, having a number of axial-mode resonances within the atomic linewidth, so that the overall gain profile has the appearance of Fig. 5-24. Suppose that the transition is homogeneously broadened and that the inverted population difference ΔN and the single-pass laser gain are gradually increased, for example, by increasing the laser pumping strength. At some point the gain of the most favored axial mode (the one nearest line center) will become infinite, and at this point the favored axial mode will break into coherent laser oscillation. As we will see in more detail in the following chapter, the laser oscillation in this mode will then build up to a power level at which the saturation effects due to the laser oscillation just balance the laser pumping rate, so as to keep the round-trip gain for the favored mode exactly unity. Further increases in pumping will be counterbalanced by stronger laser oscillation, and hence stronger saturation effects, but the essential point is that the population difference and the single-pass gain cannot go beyond the threshold values, at least not in steady-state oscillation.[1]

Now, if the transition is homogeneous, then once the favored mode reaches threshold, the steady-state gain cannot increase further, either for the favored mode *or for any other mode*. Therefore in a fully homogeneous transition only the most preferred mode should ever be able to reach threshold, and no other mode should then be able to reach its own (slightly higher) threshold; only one mode should ever be able to oscillate. Aside from some complexities having to do with spatial differences between modes, which we will discuss shortly, the argument just given is indeed verified by experimental results in CO_2 lasers, Nd-YAG lasers, some injection lasers, and various

---

[1] The gain of the favored mode can exceed the threshold value, $\tilde{g}_1{}^2 r_1 r_2 > 1$, on a transient basis. However, if it does, the signal level in the laser will build up exponentially with time. Steady-state oscillation, i.e., at a steady power level, requires $\tilde{g}_1{}^2 r_1 r_2 \equiv 1$.

other systems which have homogeneously broadened transitions, and which at least tend to oscillate only in a single axial mode at a time.

■ The above argument for the single-mode behavior of homogeneous transitions is completely bypassed with a strongly inhomogeneous laser transition. With an inhomogeneous transition, when the most favored mode reaches threshold and begins oscillating, saturation occurs only in the spectral packet centered at that axial mode. With further increases in pumping strength, the inverted-population difference and the gain at other frequencies, due to other packets, can still increase even though the oscillating packet "sticks" at the unity-round-trip-gain level. Hence other axial modes using other packets can successively reach threshold.

In those inhomogeneously broadened laser systems with inhomogeneous linewidths broad enough to contain many axial modes, simultaneous oscillations at many axial modes within the linewidth are both expected theoretically and observed experimentally. Figure 9-11 shows the kind of multimode oscillation typically observed in a visible gas laser, together with the saturated single-pass gain profile to be expected in a case such as this. Basically, another hole is burned, and the single-pass gain is saturated down to the threshold level (determined by cavity losses) for each oscillating mode.[1]

Single-frequency laser oscillation, which is necessary, or at least desirable, in many laser applications, can be obtained from an inhomogeneous transition only by reducing the cavity length L, thereby increasing the axial mode space $\Delta f_{\text{axial}} = c/2nL$ until there is only one axial mode within the atomic linewidth, or by using some other more complicated type of axial-mode suppression. Unfortunately, reducing the cavity length in this fashion also severely limits the laser power output, and the various other axial-mode-control schemes are complicated and often difficult to make and to adjust.

■ The population difference, and hence the susceptibility, of a homogeneous atomic transition saturates with increasing applied-signal strength in the general fashion

$$\frac{\tilde{\chi}_{\text{sat}}}{\tilde{\chi}_{\text{unsat}}} = \frac{\Delta \mathcal{N}_{\text{sat}}}{\Delta \mathcal{N}_{\text{unsat}}} = \frac{1}{1 + W(t)/W_{\text{sat}}} \tag{1}$$

[1] The single-pass gain may exceed the threshold level between modes without oscillation resulting, because the necessary round-trip-oscillation-phase condition is satisfied only at the axial-mode frequencies.

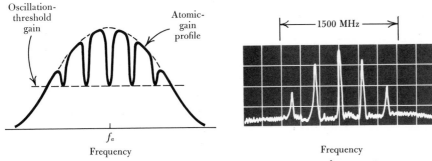

FIG. 9-11 Five simultaneously oscillating axial modes in a typical He-Ne 6328-Å laser oscillator, as observed with a scanning optical-spectrum analyzer; and the form of the atomic gain profile that might be expected in this case, with a separate hole burned into the inhomogeneous gain curve by each separate oscillation frequency.

where $W(t)$ is the signal power density in the volume occupied by the atoms and W_{sat} is the signal power density at which the transition becomes half saturated. The value of W_{sat} depends on the relaxation time T_1; on the various factors in the stimulated transition probability, including the transition matrix element and the atomic lineshape; and on the geometry of the experimental situation.

When a strong applied signal burns a hole in an inhomogeneous line by saturating those spectral packets located close to the signal frequency, each individual spectral packet saturates with increasing signal strength in the same fashion as above. We might therefore expect the degree of saturation of χ'' right at the signal frequency to follow the same law. However, the net gain or value of χ'' as seen by the applied saturating signal consists of the response from the spectral packet right on resonance, which is most strongly saturated, plus weaker contributions from closely neighboring packets, which are both off resonance and also not so strongly saturated as the central packet. A detailed analysis of this saturation for a strongly inhomogeneous line shows that, to a good approximation, the gain or the χ'' value as seen by the strong hole-burning signal itself saturates with increasing power density in the form

$$\frac{\chi''_{\text{sat}}}{\chi''_{\text{unsat}}} = \frac{1}{\sqrt{1 + W(t)/W'_{\text{sat}}}} \tag{2}$$

where $W(t)$ is again the applied-signal power density and W'_{sat} is another saturation power level that depends on various physical parameters of the system. As in the homogeneous case, the response decreases with increasing signal strength, but not quite so rapidly at higher power levels.

Expression (2) gives the saturation behavior only right at the center of the hole. Other test signals at other frequencies will experience some different degree of saturation if they are within the linewidth of the hole (about two homogeneous linewidths wide if the degree of saturation is not too strong), and little or no saturation if they are far enough outside the linewidth of the hole.

REACTIVE AND
FREQUENCY-PULLING EFFECTS

■ An inhomogeneously broadened laser system can oscillate simultaneously at multiple frequencies, which are usually separated by integer multiples of the axial-mode interval for the laser cavity. The frequency intervals between these oscillations can be measured with high accuracy by letting the multiple oscillation outputs fall on an appropriate high-frequency photodetector and observing the resulting heterodyne beat frequencies, or axial-mode beats (this can readily be done as a simple demonstration with almost any He-Ne laser, a PIN photodiode or photomultiplier tube, and a spectrum analyzer or rf receiver). Since the axial-mode beat frequencies typically fall in the range of ~ 100 MHz to ~ 1 GHz, depending on cavity length, the exact beat frequency can be measured with great precision with conventional radio-frequency measuring equipment.

Now, the burning of a hole in one part of an inhomogeneous laser transition due to a laser oscillation at that frequency can have small but easily observable frequency-shifting effects on the exact oscillation frequency of another simultaneous laser oscillation elsewhere in the inhomogeneous line, some distance away in frequency and well outside the hole width of the first oscillation. To understand these small frequency-shifting effects due to hole burning in inhomogeneous lines, the following points must be taken into account:

1. An atomic transition, or a single spectral packet, with resonance frequency f'_a, causes a reactive susceptibility on both sides of the resonance frequency, and this

reactive susceptibility will cause a small but perceptible shift in the exact resonance frequency f'_c of a cavity mode located on either side of f'_a, as compared to the unshifted cavity resonance frequency without the atoms present.

2. We saw earlier in the cavity-frequency-pushing experiment of Fig. 2-9 that an absorptive atomic transition always *pushes* the cavity resonance frequency. That is, inserting an absorptive collection of atoms causes the cavity frequency to shift (slightly) in a direction away from the atomic transition frequency. Conversely, an emissive transition always *pulls* the cavity frequency toward the atomic transition frequency, as we found in Chap. 5 in calculating the shifted axial-mode frequencies of a regenerative traveling-wave amplifier.

3. For a lorentzian line the χ'' or gain contribution due to a given transition or packet falls off with frequency separation from the line center approximately as $1/(f-f'_a)^2$ if the signal frequency f is more than a homogeneous linewidth or two away from the packet frequency f'_a. The reactive χ' contribution, however, falls off only as about $1/(f-f'_a)$ at large frequency separations. We might expect, therefore, that the reactive effects of a packet (or of a hole) might be felt considerably farther away in frequency than the gain effects.

To consider a specific case, suppose, as shown in Fig. 9-12, that one laser cavity mode located at f_{c1} within an inhomogeneous laser transition is already oscillating when another cavity mode located at f_{c2} acquires enough gain to begin oscillating and to burn a new hole at f_{c2}. Before the second mode starts oscillating, the first mode will already be oscillating at a shifted or pulled cavity frequency f'_{c1} owing to the net pulling effects of all the spectral packets in the line. Note that packets located symmetrically on either side of a given frequency will pull symmetrically in opposite directions if they have the same population difference $\Delta \mathcal{N}'$. The net pulling effect at any given frequency within a homogeneous line is the difference between the weighted pulling effects of all the packets above and below that frequency. The overall curve for a doppler-broadened line, as shown in Fig. 9-8, is just the result of this weighted effect before any holes are burned in the line.

When the hole is burned at f_{c2} the population difference on that particular spectral packet is reduced as a result of the saturation. Therefore the pulling effect of that particular packet at f_{c2} on the previously existing oscillation at f_{c1} (or f'_{c1}) is reduced. The first oscillation will no longer be pulled quite as much toward f_{c2}, and hence will shift back to a slightly more distant frequency f''_{c1}. In other words, a newly created hole

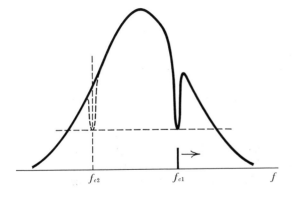

FIG. 9-12 The frequency of an already existing oscillation at f_{c1} will change slightly, owing to the change in total frequency-pushing (or -pulling) effects, when a new oscillation starts and a new hole is burned in the transition at frequency f_{c2}.

has a *pushing* effect on other cavity frequencies located elsewhere in the line. Introducing a hole takes away some emissive atoms, and this is just like introducing some new absorptive atoms at the hole frequency. The nature of this pushing effect of a hole is also illustrated by Fig. 9-4.

The operation of this effect is easily observed by observing the beat frequencies between adjacent axial modes in, say, a 1-m 6328-Å He-Ne laser, with an rf spectrum analyzer used to observe the 150-MHz axial-mode beats. Each of the axial modes is pushed or pulled slightly by the various other holes burned in the neon laser line, and these pushing effects change with time as various modes come into or drop out of oscillation. As a result, the nominal 150-MHz beats are not exactly the same between modes q and $q + 1$, between modes $q + 1$ and $q + 2$, between modes $q + 2$ and $q + 3$, and so forth. These beats are shifted slightly in frequency, in a randomly time-varying fashion, by amounts of $\sim$100 kHz. The beat as displayed on the spectrum analyzer will show several spectral lines extending over a band of $\sim$100 kHz about the center frequency of $\sim$150 MHz. Only when just two modes are oscillating (or when certain special mode-locking effects occur) will these beats coalesce into a single clean beat.

DOPPLER HOLE-BURNING EFFECTS: DOUBLE HOLES

■ The phenomena connected with hole-burning effects in inhomogeneously broadened transitions sometimes seem to spiral in complexity. Without trying to consider all these phenomena, let us examine two of the more important ones. One of these phenomena arises in doppler-broadened gas laser transitions. The basic analysis of doppler shifting and broadening presupposes an interaction between a moving atom and a *traveling* electromagnetic wave, rather than a standing wave as in the usual two-mirror laser resonant cavity. Therefore in the standing-wave cavity-laser case we must break the standing cavity wave into its two component traveling waves moving in the positive and negative z directions along the cavity axis.

Consider a resonant cavity mode at a frequency f_c located off-center on the atomic gain profile, so that $f_c \neq f_a$. Then, as illustrated at the top of Fig. 9-13, the wave at frequency f_c moving to the right will interact most strongly with those atoms whose z-directed velocity is near to

$$\frac{u_z}{c} = \frac{f_c - f_a}{f_a} \tag{3}$$

These are the atoms that have the correct doppler shift to be in resonance with the positive-traveling wave. However, when this same wave or cavity energy is traveling to the left, it will interact most strongly with those atoms having a z-directed velocity given by

$$\frac{-u_z}{c} = \frac{f_c - f_a}{f_a} \tag{4}$$

as illustrated at the center of Fig. 9.13. Thus there are two groups of atoms, with equal and opposite z velocities, that will both interact equally strongly with the standing cavity wave at f_c.

If this cavity mode is strong enough to burn a hole in the transition, it will obviously burn equal and opposite holes at two symmetrically located positions on opposite sides of the u_z velocity distribution, or on both sides of the transition's gain-frequency profile, as shown at the bottom of Fig. 9-13, even though the cavity frequency f_c is on only one side of the line. Thus for a laser oscillating in two or more modes we must take into account the gain-reduction effects and the frequency-pulling effects of

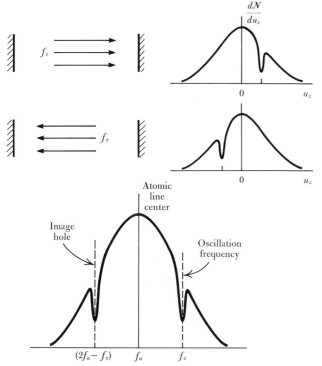

FIG. 9-13 Top: The hole burned in the maxwellian velocity distribution in a gas laser by a wave at frequency f_c traveling to the right within the laser cavity. Center: The symmetrically located hole burned by the same wave traveling to the left in the laser cavity. Bottom: The two symmetrically located holes burned in the doppler-gain profile by the total standing wave at the single oscillation frequency f_c.

not just one, but of two symmetrically located holes associated with every oscillation frequency present. Obviously, this considerably complicates any analysis of laser action in the case of doppler broadening.

■ The existence of the double holes in a doppler-broadened transition is confirmed indirectly, but effectively, by the power-output curve observed when the frequency of a single laser cavity mode is scanned across the gain profile of a laser transition. To perform this experiment the laser must be made short enough, or must be mode-controlled in some other way, such that only a single axial mode within the atomic gain profile can oscillate. The frequency of this mode can be scanned across the line by, for example, mounting one of the laser cavity mirrors on a piezoelectric crystal and changing the cavity length slowly. The resulting power-output curve for an He-Ne laser has the form shown in Fig. 9-14. When the cavity frequency is on either side of line center two holes are burned, and in essence the laser is able to take power out of two sets of spectral packets, or out of two velocity groups in the u_z velocity distribution. However, when the cavity frequency comes into line center the two holes coalesce into one, and laser power is taken from only a single spectral packet. This results in a slight but definite dip in laser power output at line center, which was first explained in a very important analysis of laser behavior by Willis E. Lamb and has become widely known as the *Lamb dip*. The presence or absence of a Lamb dip has become a sensitive test of whether or not a given laser transition is inhomogeneously broadened.[1]

THE LAMB DIP

FIG. 9-14 The Lamb dip observed in a gas laser when the frequency of a single oscillating cavity mode is tuned across an inhomogeneously doppler-broadened gain profile.

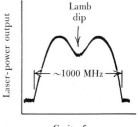

[1] However, the presence of isotope shifts due to multiple gas isotopes, as well as Zeeman splitting of the transition by a magnetic field and certain other effects, can smear out and eliminate the Lamb dip even in a strongly inhomogeneously broadened transition.

Laser cavities are sometimes built as *ring lasers,* in which the laser beam follows a closed, racetrack type of path around three or more mirrors, forming a closed path. The laser mode in this case can be a pure traveling wave running in either direction around the ring, rather than a standing wave, as in the two-mirror cavity. In a ring laser oscillating in a single unidirectional traveling-wave mode, the wave is a pure traveling wave in one direction only, and hence should burn only a single hole in the maxwellian velocity profile and in the doppler-broadened gain curve. No Lamb dip is expected in this case, and in fact none is observed.

SPATIAL-INHOMOGENEITY
EFFECTS

■ The standing-wave pattern of the E field strength between the laser mirrors for a single axial mode in a standing-wave laser cavity is shown at the top of Fig. 9-15. The E field strength has zeros, or null points, spaced every half-wavelength along the axis of the laser cavity. In an electric-dipole type of laser material the degree of saturation of the inverted population difference is proportional to the E field strength squared. Therefore in the standing-wave laser cavity the laser atoms located near the peaks of the E field pattern will be most strongly saturated, while those atoms located near the nulls will not experience any stimulated transitions or be saturated at all.

If we assume, as is reasonable, that the laser material is uniformly pumped and that population inversion is uniform along the laser cavity, then the saturation effects of a single laser mode will tend to burn up this inverted population difference only at the E field peaks, and not at the nulls. The resulting partially saturated distribution of inverted atoms along the laser cavity axis will look something like the middle sketch of Fig. 9-15. As the pumping rate is increased in this situation, even for a homogeneously broadened atomic transition, the amount of inverted population difference in the peak E-field regions is held at or near the threshold value by laser saturation effects, but the amount of population inversion in the E-field null regions will continue to in-

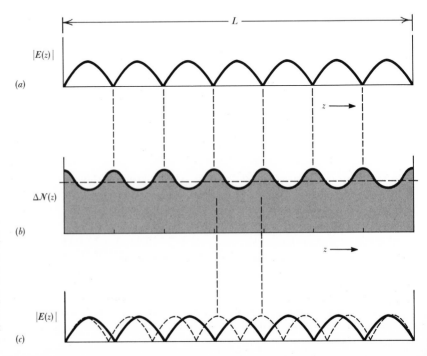

FIG. 9-15 Effects of spatially inhomogeneous saturation in a laser cavity: (a) the standing-wave pattern of electrical field strength for a single axial mode in a laser cavity, (b) the resulting spatially inhomogeneous saturation of the inverted-population difference, and (c) E-field maxima of the next adjacent axial mode in regions left unsaturated by the first oscillating axial mode.

crease with increased pumping, since there will be no saturation effects at the null points.

The next-higher-frequency axial mode will have an E field pattern with a slightly smaller wavelength, as shown by the dashed line at the bottom of Fig. 9-15, so that one additional half-wavelength can be fitted in between the laser mirrors; that is, $L = (q + 1)\lambda/2$ rather than $L = q\lambda/2$. As a result, the two axial modes become spatially a half-wavelength out of phase in the center region of the laser cavity. Exactly the same thing happens if we consider the next-lower-frequency axial mode rather than the next-higher-frequency axial mode.

The sketches in Fig. 9-15 should make clear that in the central region of the laser cavity the E fields of the next adjacent axial mode on either side—the fields responsible for inducing transitions and obtaining gain—are strongest exactly in the region where the first mode leaves a large and growing unsaturated population inversion available to provide gain. Even though the first mode is already oscillating and causing strong saturation effects, by pumping slightly harder it is possible to provide enough inverted population in the null regions of the first mode to permit the second mode, which has just the right axial variation, to reach threshold and also begin oscillating. Therefore, even though the laser transition may be completely homogeneous by our earlier definitions, it may act as an inhomogeneous transition and permit the onset of simultaneous multimode oscillations because of the *spatial-inhomogeneity effects* illustrated in Fig. 9-15.

Although Fig. 9-15 illustrates this effect only for two adjacent axial modes, the general argument can be extended to multiple axial modes. For example, an axial mode and the second-adjacent axial modes on either side will be spatially in phase at the center of the laser cavity but will become a half-wavelength out of phase at points one-quarter and three-quarters of the way along the cavity axis. This spatial-inhomogeneity explanation for multimode oscillation behavior, even in otherwise homogeneous laser transitions, is very important in many solid-state lasers. Ruby, for example, should have a highly homogeneous transition, according to the thermal-fm-broadening explanation of the previous section; yet ruby lasers typically oscillate simultaneously in two or three to perhaps dozens of axial modes. Several experiments have shown that this behavior can be attributed to spatial inhomogeneity. These effects add another dimension of complexity, the spatial variation, to laser analysis and very greatly complicate the resulting equations.

Finally, we may note that the traveling wave in a ring laser cavity has no standing-wave nulls, and hence no spatial-inhomogeneity effects. Thus a unidirectional ring laser is one way of avoiding not only the image hole-burning effects in inhomogeneous gas lasers, but also the spatial-inhomogeneity effects in homogeneous solid-state lasers. This point has been verified in experiments with unidirectional ruby ring lasers, for example. However, there are also difficulties with ring lasers, chiefly in that back scattering from imperfections inside the ring tends to make the ring oscillate in a *closed* standing-wave mode, two oppositely traveling waves locked together to form a standing wave, rather than in the desired unidirectional traveling-wave mode.

PROBLEMS

9-1. Some types of spectrometers used to observe atomic transitions provide as output a signal proportional to $(d/d\omega)\chi''(\omega)$ rather than $\chi''(\omega)$ or $\chi'(\omega)$. This quantity will have two peaks of opposite sign on each side of line center, and it is natural to define a linewidth $\Delta\omega'_d$ as the full width between these two peaks. Find the conversion factor between this linewidth $\Delta\omega'_d$ and the full-width-at-half-power linewidth $\Delta\omega_d$ for a strongly doppler-broadened transition.

9-2. When a strong monochromatic signal is slowly scanned across an inhomogeneously broadened line while χ'' is measured at that saturating frequency, the measured value of χ'' decreases at higher power levels because of saturation effects. However, if the same signal is scanned across the line with the apparatus adjusted to measure χ' at the saturating frequency, the measured value of χ' does not saturate at higher power levels (at least, not nearly so much as does χ''). Explain this difference in the saturation behavior.

9-3. Figure 3-10 illustrates the changeover from doppler broadening to collision broadening with increasing gas pressure for the 10.6-micron laser transition in CO_2 molecules. The extrapolated doppler and collision contributions to the absorption curve appear to intersect at a pressure of ~5.2 torrs, while the extrapolated linewidths from these two regions intersect at ~8.0 torrs. Explain this apparent discrepancy.

9-4. *Computer problem* Suppose a hypothetical inhomogeneously broadened transition has an exactly square or uniform distribution of resonance frequencies over a full range $\Delta\omega_S$ instead of the gaussian distribution characteristic of doppler broadening. Compute and plot the overall atomic responses $\chi''(\omega)$ and $\chi'(\omega)$ for this case for various ratios of the inhomogeneous spreading $\Delta\omega_S$ to the homogeneous linewidth $\Delta\omega_a$ (the integration involved can be done analytically). From the numerical results find the resulting full-width-at-half-power linewidths of $\chi''(\omega)$ and compare these to the root-mean-square expression $[\Delta\omega_a^2 + \Delta\omega_S^2]^{1/2}$, which might be taken as a good first guess for the overall linewidth in an inhomogeneously broadened transition.

9-5. *Computer problem* Write computer programs to evaluate and plot the exact results for $\chi''(\omega)$ and $\chi'(\omega)$ for a doppler-broadened line with arbitrary ratio of doppler spreading to homogeneous linewidth. Compare the resulting full-width-at-half-power linewidths for the $\chi''(\omega)$ curves to the expression $[\Delta\omega_a^2 + \Delta\omega_d^2]^{1/2}$.

9-6. The axial modes in a regenerative traveling-wave amplifier with 5 percent mirror transmission at each end are spaced by exactly one-third the doppler linewidth of the strongly doppler-broadened transition used in the amplifier. One of the modes is tuned exactly to the atomic line center. Plot the overall decibel gain of the first two adjacent modes on one side of the center against the decibel gain of the centermost mode, assuming that the single-pass gain of the amplifier is slowly turned up toward the oscillation threshold value.

9-7. One axial mode at a frequency f_{c1} which is slightly higher than the atomic center frequency f_a is already oscillating in a strongly doppler-broadened gas laser. A second mode located at f_{c2}, where f_{c2} is less than f_a and considerably farther from line center than f_{c1}, begins oscillating. In which direction will the frequency of the original oscillation at f_{c1} move? Explain in detail.

9-8. One of the experiments used to test the spatial-inhomogeneity explanation in ruby employed a ruby rod, with the silver mirrors evaporated directly on the rod ends. A metal-foil "cigar band" was wrapped around the middle 10 or 20 percent of the ruby rod to shield it from the pumping light and thus prevent it from becoming inverted, and changes in the spacing of the oscillating axial modes were observed. What sort of mode spectrum would you predict? Why?

REFERENCES

9-1. D. E. McCumber and M. D. Sturge, "Linewidth and temperature shift of the R lines in ruby," *J. Appl. Phys.*, **34**:1682 (June, 1963).

9-2. A. C. G. Mitchell and M. W. Zemansky, *Resonance Radiation and Excited Atoms*, Cambridge University Press, New York, 1961. See especially pp. 99 and 160.

9-3. A. M. Portis, "Electronic structure of F centers: saturation of the electron spin resonance," *Phys. Rev.*, **91**:1071 (1953). First introduction of the concepts of inhomogeneous versus homogeneous broadening.

9-4. W. J. Surtees, "Calculation of combined doppler and collision broadening," *J. Opt. Soc. Am.*, **55**:893 (July, 1965).

OPTICAL
MASERS (LASERS)

The preceding chapters have provided us with enough background information to study the operation of optical maser or laser oscillators in some detail. In this chapter we will discuss and analyze many of the basic properties of lasers, including laser pumping methods, basic conditions and rate equations for laser oscillation, laser saturation, power output, and the oscillation threshold region, and amplitude fluctuations and "spiking" in lasers. We will also discuss a lumped-circuit model for the laser cavity. The basic equations and elementary analytical results will be presented for each of these properties and then illustrated with appropriate practical examples and experimental results.

10-1   LASER PUMPING METHODS

We are concerned in this section with how the necessary population inversion for laser action is obtained in typical laser devices. The Bloembergen three-level pumping scheme for microwave solid-state masers was described in Chap. 7. The pumping methods for optical masers are simpler than the microwave pumping method in some respects, but also more complicated in others. We can gain considerable understanding of how laser devices are pumped and how their population differences are inverted by studying some simplified but fairly realistic models.

OPTICAL-FREQUENCY
APPROXIMATIONS

■ The pumping and laser processes in real optical masers typically involve a very large number of energy levels, with complex excitation processes and cascaded relaxation processes among all these levels (particularly in gas lasers). Also, real laser devices use many diverse forms of excitation, such as direct optical pumping with various types of flashlamps and arc lamps, excitation by electron impact or by collision with other excited atoms in a gas discharge, excitation by chemical reactions, and direct current excitation. Despite these complexities, simple three-level and four-level analytical models are still very useful and surprisingly accurate in predicting laser pumping characteristics.

Another basic characteristic of laser devices is that $hf_{mn}/kT \gg 1$ for virtually all the transitions involved. For example, the quantity $T_{eq} \equiv hf/k \sim 25{,}000°\text{K}$ for a frequency f in the visible range, and so $hf/kT \gg 1$ holds very well under almost all conditions for optical and infrared transitions. Therefore, as we learned in Sec. 6-4, with this condition the upward relaxation rate on any transition is very much smaller than the downward relaxation rate; that is, $w_{nm,\text{up}} \ll w_{mn,\text{down}}$. As a good approximation, all upward-relaxation terms may be neglected completely in writing atomic rate equations, and only the downward relaxation from any given level into lower-lying levels need be considered. This relaxation occurs essentially by spontaneous emission, or fluorescence, either of photons only (purely radiative relaxation) or of photons plus phonons or other forms of energy (nonradiative relaxation). This approximation also implies that all upper-energy-level populations will be zero at thermal equilibrium, with all the atoms located in the ground energy level.

ELEMENTARY FOUR-LEVEL
LASER SYSTEM

■ As a first example, we will consider the laser pumping process in the most elementary four-energy-level system. Figure 10-1a shows a complex set of multiple energy levels such as might be found in many real laser systems—for example, in a typical solid-state system such as a rare-earth ion in a crystal lattice. The upward arrows indicate upward pumping in this system at various rates, caused by optical pumping or any other pumping process, and the downward arrows indicate various decay or relaxation processes. The heavy arrow indicates the supposed laser transition in this system.

For purposes of analysis this complex collection of levels may be simplified to the four-level atomic system shown in Fig. 10-1b. Such a four-level system furnishes a simple but quite accurate analytical model for many real lasers, such as the Nd^{3+} ion in various host crystals, as well as for certain gas laser systems.

Level 4 in this simplified model represents the combination of all the higher energy levels lying above the upper laser level in the real atomic system. We assume that some pumping process lifts atoms from the ground level 1 into level 4. This is equivalent to pumping into any of the multiple upper levels in the real atom. Atoms may be raised to these upper levels, and thus to the equivalent level 4, by absorbing incident pumping light from a pulsed flashlamp or a continuously operating pump

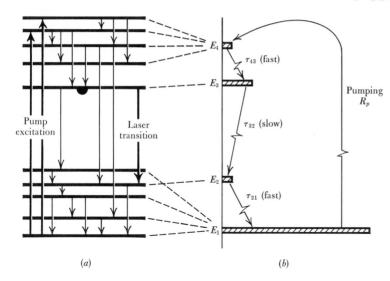

FIG. 10-1   (a) A complex multi-energy-level system such as might be used in a real optical maser. (b) This system reduced to an idealized four-level laser system for purposes of analysis.

lamp, as in various optically pumped solid-state lasers, or they may be excited upward by electron impact, as in many gas lasers. The pumping process may be even more complex, involving cascaded multiple-energy steps, or perhaps energy transfer between different kinds of colliding atoms, as in the He-Ne laser. In any event, all these details may be compressed here into a single *pumping rate* R_p into the excited level E_4.

In most lasers of the four-level type only a very small fraction of the total number of atoms are lifted into the higher energy levels during laser action, and the ground-level population remains essentially constant at $N_1 \approx N$. Thus, instead of writing the pumping term from level 1 to level 4 in the rate equations as $(d/dt)N_4 = W_p(N_1 - N_4)$, where W_p is some pump-induced transition rate, we will simply write the total pumping rate as

$$\left(\frac{d}{dt}N_4\right)_p = W_p(N_1 - N_4) \approx W_p N = R_p \tag{1}$$

where R_p is the net pumping rate in atoms excited per second.[1]

Level 3 is the upper laser level in the simplified four-level model. The following analysis is simplest, and the resulting laser action is most efficient, when all the upper levels represented by level 4 of the model relax rapidly and entirely into the upper laser level 3, with little or no relaxation directly down to any of the lower levels. This is a fairly valid approximation in many real systems (we will see a little later what happens in those cases where it is not valid). If the relaxation from level 4 to level 3 occurs at a (rapid) rate $w_{43} \equiv 1/\tau_{43}$, then the total rate equation for level 4 is

$$\frac{d}{dt}N_4 = R_p - \frac{N_4}{\tau_{43}} \tag{2}$$

The steady-state solution for the population of level 4 [obtained by setting $(d/dt)N_4 = 0$] is then

---

[1] This particular assumption is not valid in the three-level laser system, which we will discuss a little later.

$$N_4 = R_p\tau_{43} = W_p\tau_{43}N$$

$$\approx 0 \qquad \text{for } \tau_{43} \text{ very short} \tag{3}$$

In this section we will write all relaxation rates in the form $w_{mn} \equiv 1/\tau_{mn}$, and we will set all rate-equation time derivatives to zero in order to obtain the steady-state populations of the levels under conditions of continuous pumping.

While the upper pump level 4 is assumed to have very fast relaxation into level 3, the upper laser level 3 is assumed to be metastable, i.e., to have a slow relaxation rate or a very long relaxation time (this is sometimes indicated on energy-level diagrams by a black semicircle under the line representing the energy level, as in Fig. 10-1a). The simplest situation occurs when the upper laser level 3 relaxes primarily into the lower laser level 2, so that the rate equation and its steady-state solution for level 3 are

$$\frac{d}{dt}N_3 = \frac{N_4}{\tau_{43}} - \frac{N_3}{\tau_{32}} = 0 \tag{4}$$

and

$$N_3 = \frac{\tau_{32}}{\tau_{43}}N_4 = R_p\tau_{32} = W_p\tau_{32}N$$

$$\gg N_4 \qquad \text{for } \tau_{32} \gg \tau_{43} \tag{5}$$

Note that the metastable level population N_3 will be much larger than the upper pump level population N_4 if the relaxation time of the metastable level is much longer. Essentially no atoms can accumulate in level 4 because they drop to level 3 by fast $4 \rightarrow 3$ relaxation as soon as they are lifted up; however, a large number of atoms can accumulate in the metastable level 3 because of its long lifetime.

Level 2 in the model is the lower laser level, and level 1 represents the ground level plus any other low-lying levels in the real laser system outside of the lower laser level. Following the same line of argument, the rate equation and its steady-state solution for level 2 are

$$\frac{d}{dt}N_2 = \frac{N_3}{\tau_{32}} - \frac{N_2}{\tau_{21}} \tag{6}$$

and

$$N_2 = \frac{\tau_{21}}{\tau_{32}}N_3 = R_p\tau_{21} = W_p\tau_{21}N$$

$$\approx 0 \text{ for } \tau_{21} \text{ very short} \tag{7}$$

A short lifetime τ_{21} or rapid $2 \rightarrow 1$ relaxation rate will make the lower-laser-level population N_2 very small. In fact, for this idealized four-level model the population difference on the $3 \rightarrow 2$ laser transition is given by

$$\Delta N_{32} \equiv (N_3 - N_2) = R_p(\tau_{32} - \tau_{21}) = W_p(\tau_{32} - \tau_{21})N$$

$$\approx W_p\tau_{32}N \qquad \tau_{21} \ll \tau_{32} \tag{8}$$

A population inversion on the $3 \rightarrow 2$ laser transition will be guaranteed (that is, $\Delta N_{32} > 0$) provided only that the relaxation rate w_{21} out of the lower level 2 is faster than the relaxation rate w_{32} from the upper level 3 into the lower level 2. In this case the existence of a population inversion depends only on the simple relaxation-time ratio and is independent of the total pumping rate R_p. However, the *size* of the inverted population difference $\Delta \mathcal{N}_{32}$ is directly proportional to the pumping rate R_p (and also to the metastable lifetime τ_{32}).

Thus, as a first conclusion, we may say that if the right relaxation-time ratio exists between any two levels (such as 3 and 2) in an energy-level system—and this is, in fact, not uncommon in real atomic systems—then a laser population inversion should be possible. If so, then obtaining a large enough inversion for successful laser operation becomes primarily a matter of pumping hard enough.

■ Figure 10-2 shows the energy levels of three typical rare-earth ions, chosen from at least 10 such ions that will operate essentially as four-level optically pumped lasers. The optical energy levels of rare-earth ions are caused by the electrons in the partially filled inner $4f$ shell in these atoms. Different arrangements of the $4f$ electrons in the various available states of the partially filled $4f$ shell lead to different quantum energy levels for the atom as a whole. Furthermore, because this is an inner shell and is well shielded against external influences by the electrons occupying two surrounding outer filled shells (the $5p$ and $6d$ shells), the quantum energy levels and the laser transitions caused by the $4f$ electrons of a given rare-earth ion remain almost unchanged no matter in what host crystal lattice the rare-earth ion is placed. The $4f$ electrons essentially do not feel the strong crystalline electric fields caused by the other neighboring ions in a typical crystal lattice. The energy levels of the Nd^{3+} ion, for example, remain very nearly the same as in Fig. 10-2 for Nd^{3+} ions in a CaF_2 crystal, in YAG, in glasses, and even in certain liquid host materials.

The energy levels of the real rare-earth ions are considerably more complex than the simple four-level model, but the model still gives a very good description of their laser properties. As seen in Fig. 10-2, there are in each case a large number of higher energy levels, which together may be viewed as comprising the upper pump level 4, lying above a single comparatively sharp and metastable level which corresponds to the upper laser level 3. This metastable level is generally the lowest level in an upper group of levels. Then, considerably closer to the ground state, there are additional groups of levels, some one (or more) of which serves as the lower laser level 2.

RARE-EARTH IONS AS FOUR-LEVEL LASER SYSTEMS

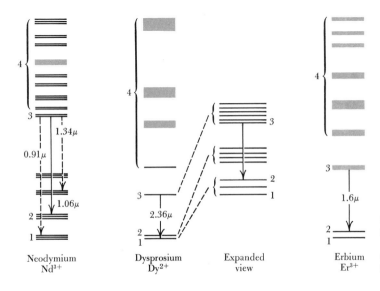

FIG. 10-2 Energy levels and some of the possible laser transitions for three typical rare-earth laser ions. Not all details of the energy levels are shown, although an expanded view is given of some of the dysprosium Dy^{2+} sublevels.

In typical rare-earth systems such as Fig. 10-2 the various $4 \rightarrow 3$ transition frequencies, as well as the various $2 \rightarrow 1$ transition frequencies, all fall within the frequency range of the lattice vibration spectrum of the host crystal lattice. Therefore all these transitions can relax extremely rapidly by *direct nonradiative decay*, i.e., by emitting a phonon to the lattice vibrations, with τ_{43}, $\tau_{21} \approx 10^{-8}$ to 10^{-11} sec. However, the larger $4 \rightarrow 2$, $4 \rightarrow 1$, $3 \rightarrow 2$, and $3 \rightarrow 1$ energy gaps in these atoms often correspond to transition frequencies that are higher than the highest possible vibration frequency of the crystal lattice. Such transitions cannot relax via simple single-phonon spontaneous emission, since the lattice simply cannot accept phonons at those high frequencies. These transitions must then relax either by radiative (photon) emission, or by multiple-phonon processes (simultaneous emission of several lower-frequency phonons within the available lattice bands). Since both these processes are relatively weak compared to direct single-phonon relaxation, the high-frequency transitions will have much slower relaxation rates ($\tau_{32} \approx 10^{-5}$ to 10^{-3} sec in many cases). Therefore the various levels lumped into level 4 will all relax or feed mostly into level 3, while level 3 itself is metastable and long-lived because there are no other levels located close below it into which it can decay directly.

OPTICAL PUMPING OF
SOLID-STATE LASERS

■ Solid-state (and liquid) lasers, such as the ruby and various rare-earth lasers, are usually optically pumped either by a pulsed flashlamp, in a configuration such as that in Fig. 1-26 for pulsed operation, or by a continuous high-intensity lamp, in a configuration such as that in Fig. 1-30 for cw operation (such cw pump lamps include tungsten iodide–filament lamps and mercury-, xenon-, and krypton-arc lamps). One important feature of the four-level laser system then becomes apparent. For good laser action the upper laser level 3 should be a sharp energy level, with a narrow linewidth and only a weak radiative connection to the ground level 1. But this also means that any attempt to pump atoms directly from level 1 into the upper laser level 3 (as in the microwave maser case) by means of a broadband thermal light source or gas-discharge light source would be extremely inefficient, if not impossible. By contrast, the upper pump levels 4 can be (and often are) comparatively broad bands rather than sharp energy levels. These broad absorption or pumping bands can then absorb a much greater fraction of the broad energy spectrum radiated by the pumping lamp,[1] while still funneling all the atoms thus excited down into the narrow metastable level 3.

A second practical pumping consideration is that the pump light should be able to penetrate through most of the volume of a typical laser rod, rather than being absorbed entirely within a thin layer on the outside of the rod. Thus a weak broad pump absorption band is better than a strong narrow absorption line for this reason as well.

When a typical rare-earth laser ion is strongly pumped, excited atoms accumulate in the metastable level 3. With sufficient upper-level population, laser action can then occur between level 3 and one of the various lower laser levels in Fig. 10-2. The specific level that will be the lower laser level 2 in a real system is determined by several considerations. The different possible $3 \rightarrow 2$ laser transitions will have different atomic linewidths and radiative lifetimes, and hence different amounts of laser gain per unit amount of population inversion. Other factors being equal, laser oscillation is obviously

---

[1] Even with these broader pump-absorption bands, a large fraction of the light output from typical pump lamps is still not absorbed by the laser material and hence is wasted in most practical cases. Methods for increasing the pumping efficiency in laser devices by changing either the emission spectrum of the pumping lamp or the spectrum of the laser material absorption are still very much needed.

favored for the transition with the largest laser gain. This transition can often be identified in advance by exciting the laser crystal with below-threshold pump excitation levels, measuring the fluorescent emission from the upper laser level, and noting which of the various possible transitions has the strongest below-threshold fluorescent emission.

The various possible lower laser levels 2 in some cases lie very close to the ground level. The approximation $hf_{21} \equiv E_2 - E_1 \gg kT$ is then not so strongly satisfied for these levels, and as a result they will have some small but noticeable populations at thermal equilibrium with the pump off. When the pump is turned on, population inversion for the transitions to these levels cannot be obtained until the upper-level population N_3 becomes larger than the thermal-equilibrium populations of these levels. Hence this consideration favors the higher-lying members of the group of potential lower levels 2, since their thermal-equilibrium populations are lowest. Since these thermal-equilibrium populations are changed by cooling the laser crystal, the particular lower level that will terminate the laser action can sometimes be changed by changing the operating temperature of the laser crystal.

Finally, for laser oscillation to occur with the minimum amount of population inversion, the laser cavity must have low internal losses, and the end mirrors must have medium to high reflectivity at the laser wavelength. In systems where laser oscillation is possible on several different transitions (as in the Nd^{3+} ion in Fig. 10-2) the particular wavelength that oscillates can be determined in some cases by control of the mirror reflectivity at different wavelengths, or by various other schemes that make the internal cavity losses different at the different possible laser wavelengths.

The actual laser wavelength that occurs in a rare-earth laser system represents a combination of these and other factors and is often determined by experiment rather than prediction.

■ We will now carry out a more exact analysis of the optically pumped four-level laser system, without so many simplifying assumptions, in order to indicate some of the important parameters of these systems. Consider an optically induced pump transition probability W_p between levels 1 and 4, where W_p is proportional to the pumping light intensity falling on the laser material. The N_4 rate equation becomes

OPTICALLY PUMPED FOUR-LEVEL SYSTEM: MORE EXACT ANALYSIS

$$\frac{d}{dt} N_4 = W_p(N_1 - N_4) - \frac{N_4}{\tau_4}$$
$$= W_p(N_1 - N_4) - (\tau_{43}^{-1} + \tau_{42}^{-1} + \tau_{41}^{-1})N_4 \tag{9}$$

Here we will use the convention that τ_n is the total lifetime of level n due to relaxation to all lower levels, or τ_n^{-1} is the total relaxation probability from level n to all lower levels, while τ_{nm} is the relaxation probability from level n to a specific lower level m. Hence for level 4, as a typical example,

$$\frac{1}{\tau_4} \equiv \frac{1}{\tau_{43}} + \frac{1}{\tau_{42}} + \frac{1}{\tau_{41}} \tag{10}$$

The steady-state solution for level 4, $(d/dt)N_4 = 0$, is then

$$N_4 = \frac{W_p \tau_4}{W_p \tau_4 + 1} N_1$$
$$\approx W_p \tau_4 N \qquad W_p \tau_4 \ll 1 \tag{11}$$

As a practical matter, the quantity $W_p\tau_4$ is usually much less than unity for most pumping power levels.

The next two rate equations are

$$\frac{d}{dt}N_3 = \frac{N_4}{\tau_{43}} - \frac{N_3}{\tau_3} = \tau_{43}^{-1}N_4 - (\tau_{32}^{-1} + \tau_{31}^{-1})N_3 \tag{12}$$

$$\frac{d}{dt}N_2 = \tau_{42}^{-1}N_4 + \tau_{32}^{-1}N_3 - \tau_{21}^{-1}N_2$$

The first of these gives

$$N_3 = \frac{\tau_3}{\tau_{43}}N_4 \tag{13}$$

In a good laser system the $4 \to 3$ relaxation is fast, while level 3 is presumably long-lived ($\tau_3 \gg \tau_{43}$), so that (13) implies $N_3 \gg N_4$ at steady state. The N_2 rate equation then gives

$$N_2 = \left(\frac{\tau_2}{\tau_{32}} + \frac{\tau_{43}\tau_2}{\tau_{42}\tau_3}\right)N_3 = \beta N_3 \tag{14}$$

If the quantity β (which depends only on relaxation-time ratios, as per the expression in parentheses) is less than unity, the steady-state result is a population inversion on the $3 \to 2$ transition even for vanishingly small pump powers (this disregards any possible thermal population of the lower laser level 2, as mentioned above). If the lifetime of level 3 is long enough, i.e., if τ_3, and hence τ_{32}, is very long, then inversion is virtually certain. Whether the inverted population density will be large enough to sustain laser action in a practical cavity is another matter.

Combining all the above equations leads to the general expression for inverted population,

$$\Delta N_{32} \equiv N_3 - N_2 = \frac{(1 - \beta)\eta W_p\tau_3}{1 + [(1 + \beta) + 2(\tau_{43}/\tau_3)]\eta W_p\tau_3}N \tag{15}$$

where the pumping *efficiency factor* η, defined by

$$\eta \equiv \frac{\tau_4}{\tau_{43}} \leq 1 \tag{16}$$

tells what fraction of the total atoms excited to level 4 drop from there to level 3, thus becoming potentially useful for laser action. Small η obviously requires a correspondingly larger pump power W_p. The inversion obtained for a given W_p depends very much on the *branching ratios*, the relative relaxation rates for the atoms along the various possible downward relaxation paths. The inversion also depends in an important way on the fluorescent lifetime τ_3 of the upper laser level.

In a very good laser material τ_3 will be much longer than τ_{43}, and the efficiency will be high, $\eta \to 1$, and $\beta \to 0$. For these limits Eq. (15) reduces to

$$\frac{N_3 - N_2}{N} = \frac{(1 - \beta)\eta W_p\tau}{1 + (1 + \beta)\eta W_p\tau} = \frac{W_p\tau}{1 + W_p\tau} \tag{17}$$

where $\tau \equiv \tau_3$ is the observed fluorescent lifetime of the laser transition.

A parameter often used in evaluating laser materials is the *fluorescent quantum efficiency* of the laser and pump transitions, defined as the ratio of the radiative fluorescent photons emitted on the desired laser transition to the pump photons absorbed on the pump transition(s) in a below-threshold fluorescence experiment. For the four-level case this parameter, which we will label η_0, is equivalent to

$$\eta_0 = \frac{\tau_{3,\text{total}}}{\tau_{32,\text{rad}}}\eta \tag{18}$$

If we write $\tau_{32,\text{rad}}$ as simply τ_{rad} for the laser transition, the inversion formula (17) may be rewritten in an alternative form as

$$\frac{N_3 - N_2}{N} = \frac{(1 - \beta)\eta_0 W_p \tau_{\text{rad}}}{1 + (1 + \beta)\eta_0 W_p \tau_{\text{rad}}} \tag{19}$$

The parameters τ in Eq. (17) and η_0 in Eq. (19) are subject to more or less direct experimental observation, while the parameters τ_{rad} and η are not directly measurable, but must be determined indirectly. Thus Eqs. (17) and (19) are equally convenient (or inconvenient) formulations for expressing the population inversion in terms of measurable quantities.

■ It is also possible to obtain population inversion in a simple three-energy-level laser system, such as that shown in Fig. 10-3, with laser action on the $2 \to 1$ transition caused by pumping (of sufficient strength) on the $1 \to 3$ transition. We will see that this three-level system appears to have some major disadvantages (in terms of required pump power for inversion) in relation to the four-level system discussed above. The reason for discussing the three-level system here at all is that the 6943-Å ruby laser— the first laser to be operated and still perhaps the single most important solid-state laser—is an almost ideal example of an elementary three-level laser system. OPTICALLY PUMPED THREE-LEVEL SYSTEMS

In the basic three-level system of Fig. 10-3 atoms are lifted out of level 1 and into level 3 by a strong pumping signal on the $1 \to 3$ transition. The $3 \to 2$ transition should then have a very short relaxation time τ_{32}, so that the atoms will very rapidly drop down and accumulate in the metastable upper laser level 2. With fast enough

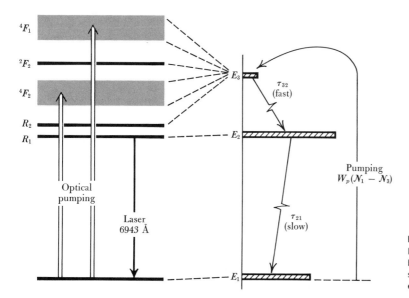

FIG. 10-3 The pumping processes and the laser transition in an elementary three-level laser system, of which the ruby laser system shown at the left is a preeminent example.

$3 \rightarrow 2$ relaxation, the population of the upper pump level 3 will always remain small, and reverse pumping from level 3 back down to level 1 will not become a problem, even though more than half the total number of atoms in the system may be lifted up out of level 1 and into level 2. A vital aspect of the three-level system, in fact, is that the atoms are in effect pumped directly from level 1 into the metastable level 2 with only a momentary pause as they pass through level 3.

The three-level system thus has the same advantage as the four-level system in that the upper pump level 3 may in reality be a group of broad multiple-absorption bands, so as to make good use of the broadband light from a typical optical pump source, while the upper laser level 2 can be the kind of narrow and long-lived level that is best for laser action. The major disadvantage of the three-level system is that slightly more than half the total atoms must be lifted up out of the ground level 1 and into the upper laser level 2 before any population inversion or laser action at all can be obtained on the $2 \rightarrow 1$ transition.

The pumping process in a three-level system can be represented by a pump-stimulated transition probability W_p between levels 1 and 3 that is presumably proportional to the pump light flux falling on the laser material. Then the rate equation for the upper pump level 3 in this system is

$$\frac{d}{dt} N_3 = W_p(N_1 - N_3) - \frac{N_3}{\tau_3} \tag{20}$$

The rate equation for the upper laser level 2 is

$$\frac{d}{dt} N_2 = \frac{N_3}{\tau_{32}} - \frac{N_2}{\tau_2} \tag{21}$$

Any assumption that $N_1 \approx N$ in the presence of strong pumping is not at all valid in this system, and the basic identity

$$N_1 + N_2 + N_3 = N \tag{22}$$

must be used as the third rate equation for the system.

The exact steady-state solutions to the rate equations (20) to (22) are then

$$N_3 = \frac{W_p \tau_3}{1 + W_p \tau_3} N_1 \qquad N_2 = \frac{\tau_2}{\tau_{32}} N_3 \qquad N_1 = N - N_2 - N_3 \tag{23}$$

The population inversion on the $2 \rightarrow 1$ laser transition may be written as

$$\frac{N_2 - N_1}{N} = \frac{(1 - \beta)\eta W_p \tau_2 - 1}{(1 + 2\beta)\eta W_p \tau_2 + 1}$$
$$\approx \frac{W_p \tau_2 - 1}{W_p \tau_2 + 1} \qquad \beta = 0, \eta = 1 \tag{24}$$

where the relaxation-time ratio β and pumping-efficiency factor η in this case are defined by

$$\beta \equiv \frac{\tau_{32}}{\tau_2} \qquad \eta = \frac{\tau_3}{\tau_{32}} \tag{25}$$

It is clear from Eq. (24) that a necessary condition for inversion to be possible is again $\beta < 1$, with the best case being $\beta \rightarrow 0$. However, we now have the additional requirement that the pumping power W_p exceed a minimum, or threshold, value given by

$$W_{p,\text{inversion}} \geq W_{p,\text{threshold}} \equiv \frac{1}{(1 - \beta)\eta\tau_2} \tag{26}$$

before any inversion at all can be obtained. This is the minimum pump power required to raise more atoms up and into the upper laser level 2 than are left behind in the ground or lower laser level 1.

As in the four-level case, a quantum fluorescent-efficiency factor η_0 for the three-level system can be defined by

$$\eta_0 \equiv \frac{\text{fluorescent photons emitted}}{\text{pump photons absorbed}} = \frac{\tau_{2,\text{total}}}{\tau_{2,\text{rad}}}\eta \tag{27}$$

Using this, and writing the radiative lifetime $\tau_{2,\text{rad}}$ of the laser transition as simply τ_{rad}, we can convert Eq. (24) to the alternative form

$$\frac{N_2 - N_1}{N} = \frac{(1 - \beta)\eta_0 W_p\tau_{\text{rad}} - 1}{(1 + 2\beta)\eta_0 W_p\tau_{\text{rad}} + 1} \tag{28}$$

in analogy with the four-level result, Eq. (19).

■ If we assume the optimum conditions $\beta = 0$ and $\eta = 1$ in each case and simply write the laser transition's radiative lifetime as τ in either case, then the inverted population difference ΔN versus pump level W_p in the three-level and four-level cases may be written as

COMPARISON OF THREE-LEVEL AND FOUR-LEVEL SYSTEMS: THE RUBY LASER

$$\frac{\Delta N}{N} = \begin{cases} \dfrac{W_p\tau}{W_p\tau + 1} & \text{four-level system} \\[2mm] \dfrac{W_p\tau - 1}{W_p\tau + 1} & \text{three-level system} \end{cases} \tag{29}$$

These expressions are plotted in Fig. 10-4. Other factors being equal, four-level laser systems should have very much lower pump-power thresholds than three-level systems, and in fact this is almost always the case experimentally.

The well-known three-level ruby laser system is, however, a somewhat special case and an exception to this rule, since the ruby laser can have a fairly low pulsed laser threshold, as well as a low enough cw pumping threshold that useful cw laser

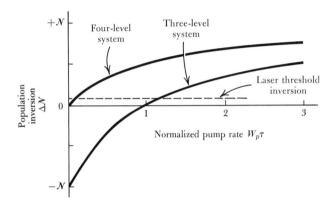

FIG. 10-4 A comparison of population inversion on the laser transition versus normalized pumping rate for the idealized four-level and three-level laser systems. The dashed line indicates that there will be some threshold level of inversion required to obtain oscillation in a laser cavity.

operation is possible. The ruby laser achieves its continuing success because of an unusually favorable combination of all the "other factors," particularly the following:

1. The ruby Cr^{3+} ion has unusually broad and well-located pump absorption bands, which make unusually efficient use of the pumping radiation emitted by available pump lamps.
2. The fluorescent quantum efficiency from these pumping bands into the 6943-Å laser transition is very close to unity.
3. The laser transition in ruby has an atomic linewidth that is unusually narrow for an ion in a solid (see Fig. 9-10).
4. The laser transition also has an unusually long and almost purely radiative fluorescent lifetime ($\approx 4 \times 10^{-3}$ sec).
5. On the practical side, artificial ruby can be grown as good-sized crystals which have high crystal quality, low optical distortion, high optical-power-handling capacity, and good thermal conductivity (for carrying away heat absorbed from the pump light in high-power and high-average-power applications).

Even if its performance were less good, the ruby laser would probably continue to be attractive because its output lies in the visible range, where sensitive photodevices are available, in contrast to most rare-earth four-level lasers, whose outputs are in the near-infrared region, where available photodetectors are not as good.

EXPERIMENTAL VERIFICATION: ■ In the three-level laser it is theoretically possible, with sufficiently hard pumping, to
THE THREE-LEVEL RUBY LASER lift virtually all the atoms in the system into the upper laser level 2, thus obtaining almost total inversion of the $2 \rightarrow 1$ transition. To verify this prediction, and to test the three-level rate-equation analysis generally, we may consider a set of experimental results obtained in a pulsed ruby laser amplifier. In these experiments a ruby laser rod without any end mirrors was pumped by a short but intense pump flash whose duration was considerably shorter than the fluorescent decay time of the ruby crystal.[1] The transmission gain, or loss, of the ruby laser rod just at the end of this pump pulse was measured by using a separate ruby laser oscillator as a probe-signal source.

In ruby the $3 \rightarrow 2$ relaxation time is so extremely short that the atoms lifted into level 3 may be assumed to relax instantaneously to level 2, and the population N_3 may be assumed to be zero at all times. Thus all the atoms may be assumed to be located in levels 2 and 1 only. The rate equations for the ruby system may then be reduced to

$$\frac{d}{dt}N_1 = -W_p N_1 + \frac{N_2}{\tau} = -\frac{d}{dt}N_2$$
$$N_1 + N_2 = N \tag{30}$$

Defining the inverted population difference as $\Delta N \equiv N_2 - N_1$, we can further combine these equations into the single rate equation

$$\frac{d}{dt}\Delta N(t) = \frac{d}{dt}[N_2(t) - N_1(t)] = -(W_p + \tau^{-1})\Delta N(t) + (W_p - \tau^{-1})N \tag{31}$$

The population difference at the end of a square pump pulse of length T_p, starting from the thermal-equilibrium initial condition $\Delta N(t = 0) = -N$, is given by the transient solution

[1] As a practical matter $\tau_2 \approx 4.3$ msec in ruby, and so a pump flash of a few hundred microseconds was used.

$$\frac{\Delta \mathcal{N}(t)}{\mathcal{N}} = \frac{\mathcal{N}_2(t) - \mathcal{N}_1(t)}{\mathcal{N}} = \frac{W_p\tau - 1}{W_p\tau + 1} - \frac{2W_p\tau}{W_p\tau + 1} e^{-(W_p + 1/\tau)T_p} \tag{32}$$

For strong pumping, $W_p \gg 1/\tau$, which is the case in these experiments, the single-pass gain down the rod at the end of the pump pulse is $G_{\mathrm{dB}} \propto \Delta \mathcal{N}$, while the single-pass absorption loss down the rod before the pump pulse is applied is $L_{\mathrm{dB}} \propto \mathcal{N}$. These quantities just before and just after the pump pulse are related to each other and to the total energy $W_p T_p$ in the pump flash by the ratio of the pumped gain G_{dB} to the unpumped loss L_{dB},

$$\frac{G_{\mathrm{dB}}}{L_{\mathrm{dB}}} = \frac{\Delta \mathcal{N}(T_p)}{\mathcal{N}} \approx 1 - 2e^{-W_p T_p} \qquad W_p\tau \gg 1, \ T_p \ll \tau \tag{33}$$

Figure 10-5 shows experimental results for gain-loss ratio versus pump-energy input for ruby rods of two different lengths, as compared to the analytical expression (33). For the maximum pump-energy input used in these experiments the net decibel gain is nearly 90 percent of the net insertion loss of the rod without pumping. This implies that nearly 95 percent of the atoms must have been lifted into the upper laser level,

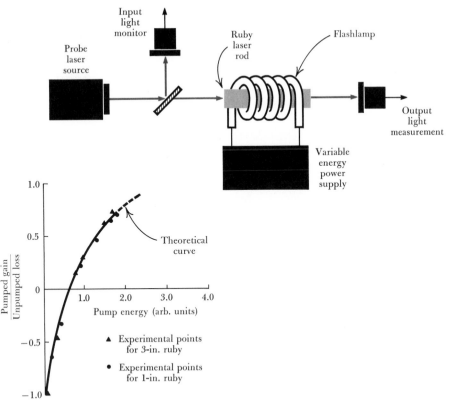

FIG. 10-5 Peak gain of a ruby laser rod (without any surrounding laser mirrors) at the end of a short but intense pumping pulse, compared to the unpumped attenuation in the same rod, as a function of the total energy in the pumping pulse. The data, measured using the experimental arrangement shown, demonstrates nearly complete inversion of the laser transition for high enough pump energies. [From J. E. Geusic and H. E. D. Scovil, "A unidirectional traveling-wave optical maser," *Bell Sys. Tech. J.,* **41**:1371 (July, 1962).]

leaving only 5 percent still in the ground energy level, in agreement with our theoretical predictions.

■ Atoms and ions in gases typically have extremely complex energy-level structures, with many sharp energy levels and a great many possible transitions among these levels. Atoms excited into any given upper level can cascade downward by relaxation into and then out of many different lower levels, with many different (and generally unknown) relaxation transition probabilities w_{mn} among all these levels. Moreover, the energetic electrons in a gas discharge not only lift atoms from the ground level into many different higher energy levels, with different excitation rates for each level; they also excite atoms out of these excited states into still other excited states, both higher and lower in energy. In addition, complicated exchanges of energy between atoms occur as a result of collisions among atoms of both the same kind and different kinds.

The result is that the exact pumping processes in many gas lasers are extremely complicated, and a complete description is usually not possible. Only a broad outline of the most important processes can be given.

Another complication is that the rates of excitation of atoms by electron impact in gas discharges depend not only on the electron density (number of electrons per unit volume) in the discharge, but also in a rather sensitive fashion on the electron energy distribution; the higher-energy electrons in the tail of this distribution are usually most important. At the same time, the electron energy distribution, and especially its high-energy tail, depend fairly strongly on many other discharge characteristics, such as gas pressures, excitation level, and impurities. As a result, the excitation or pumping rate R_p into a given excited level may or may not change in direct proportion to the dc discharge current or the rf power input to a gas discharge. Moreover, all these quantities usually have a sizable spatial variation, both across the discharge-tube radius and along its axis.

Another relevant factor in gas-discharge excitation is radiation trapping. An excited atom in a gas discharge may be able to relax back to the ground level only by radiative decay, i.e., by the emission of a fluorescent photon. If, however, the transition involved is sufficiently narrow and strongly allowed, and the ground-state population of that particular kind of atom is sufficiently large, the fluorescent photon emitted by the excited atom may have a very high probability of immediate reabsorption by another nearby ground-state atom before it can escape from the laser tube. This will be the case if the absorption of the gas on that particular transition is sufficiently strong that the net absorption is large even in a single pass across the laser-tube diameter. Then, since one atom comes down in energy but another is immediately lifted back up, there is no net relaxation in the process, but only a transfer from one atom to another. When this occurs the excited state will, for all practical purposes, have a radiation-trapped effective lifetime that is much longer than its true relaxation time without radiation trapping. With sufficiently strong radiation trapping, such a level will act much like a metastable level. In some cases the lower level in a gas laser transition may not empty out as rapidly as would be desired because its lifetime is increased by radiation trapping.

Because of all these complexities, the pumping processes in most gas lasers have not yet been studied in detail or described in any but a qualitative fashion. Perhaps the best that can be said here is that in many cases the pumping behavior of gas lasers is more or less like a four-level laser system, as described earlier. Electron excitations or collisions with other atoms lift the laser atoms into excited energy levels. These atoms relax or trickle downward, tending to accumulate in the more metastable levels. Population inversions then do occur between certain longer-lived (or more effectively excited) upper levels and other less highly populated lower levels.[1] For the commercially important gas lasers, such as He-Ne, argon-ion, cadmium-ion, and CO_2 lasers, systematic experiments have been made to determine the best values for gas mixes and pressures, tube diameters, and excitation methods. Spectroscopic studies and various theoretical considerations can also usually determine at least roughly the transitions and levels most important for the pumping processes in each major type of gas laser. More information than this, however, is usually not available.

■ The helium-neon laser was the first gas laser and is probably still the most common one. It is also a system with an interesting, reasonably simple, and fairly well-understood pumping mechanism. Let us consider this laser system briefly, as a typical example of some of the important aspects of gas-laser excitation. Figure 10-6 shows the important energy levels for the He-Ne laser system (which was also described in Sec. 1-4). The He atom has two very long-lived metastable upper levels of importance here: the He 2^3S_1 level, which coincides almost exactly in energy with the Ne $2s_2$ upper level for the 1.15-μ laser transition, and the He 2^1S_0 level, which coincides almost exactly with the Ne $3s_2$ level that serves as the upper level for both the 3.39-μ and the 6328-Å laser transitions. We will concentrate here on the pumping processes for these last two transitions; the 1.15-μ transition is excited in much the same general fashion.

We can label the He ground-state and 2^1S_0-level populations as $\mathcal{N}_0$ and $\mathcal{N}_4$, respectively, and label the Ne ground-state and $3s_2$-level populations as $\mathcal{N}_1$ and $\mathcal{N}_3$, respectively, as in Fig. 10-6. The two lower levels for the 3.39-μ and 6328-Å transi-

PUMPING PROCESSES IN THE
HELIUM-NEON LASER

---

[1] Just as an example, sufficient inversion for successful laser operation has been obtained on at least 54 different transitions in the neutral neon atom alone, at wavelengths from 0.594 μ in the visible to 57.4 μ in the far-infrared region.

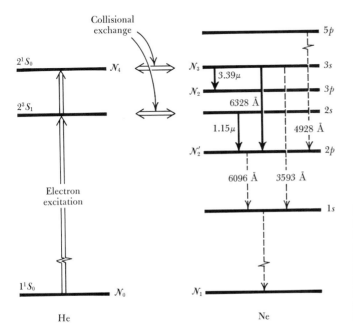

FIG. 10-6 Important energy levels for the He-Ne laser system. Solid arrows are laser transitions and dashed arrows are observable fluorescence lines monitored in certain diagnostic experiments (cf. Fig. 10-7). Note that the energy levels are not entirely to scale (the ground levels N_0 and N_1 should be much lower in energy relative to the other levels). Not all the levels (especially higher levels) are shown, and most of the levels shown are actually groups of multiple closely spaced levels not resolved in the figure.

tions are denoted as N_2 and N_2', respectively. Now, in typical He-Ne lasers the helium pressure and density are five to ten times as large as the corresponding neon values. Also, He atoms are found to be much more readily excited by electron impact than Ne atoms. Therefore one major effect of the discharge excitation (either dc or rf) in an He-Ne laser tube is to excite many He atoms and thus to build up a sizable atomic population in the long-lived He 2^1S_0 level. The rate at which He atoms are lifted from level 0 to level 4 in Fig. 10-6 is proportional to the electron density in the discharge, and it is known from separate experiments that the electron density in such He-Ne discharges is directly proportional to the dc discharge current I. Hence the excitation rate from level 0 into level 4 may be expressed as $k_1 I N_0$, where k_1 is some (unknown) proportionality constant. However, atoms are also excited by electron impact *out* of level 4 into still other He levels, giving a loss rate for level 4 of $-k_2 I N_4$, where k_2 is another constant. There is also relaxation out of level 4 at a (very slow) rate expressed by a lifetime τ_4. The total rate equation for the He level 4 is then

$$\frac{d}{dt} N_4 = k_1 I N_0 - k_2 I N_4 - \frac{N_4}{\tau_4} + \left(\frac{dN_4}{dt} \right)_{\text{coll}} \tag{34}$$

where the last term accounts for collision processes in which excited He atoms in level 4 collide with unexcited Ne atoms in level 1, or vice versa, with a resulting transfer of energy from the excited to the unexcited atom during the collision.

Collisions of this type, sometimes called *collisions of the second kind,* occur with high probability in He-Ne laser mixtures and play a vital role in the laser pumping process. Consider those collisions in which an excited He atom (level 4) collides with a ground-state Ne atom (level 1), with the He atom then dropping down to level 0 and the Ne atom being excited up to level 3. The rate at which such collisions occur should be directly proportional both to the density of excited He atoms N_4 and to the density of ground-state Ne atoms N_1; that is, it should vary as the product $N_1 N_4$. But there is also the reverse process, in which a ground-state He atom (density N_0) collides with an excited Ne atom (density N_3), and the energy exchange occurs in the opposite direction. This process should occur with probability $N_0 N_3$. The net rate of loss to level 4 due to collisions in both directions should then give a rate-equation term of the form

$$\left(\frac{dN_4}{dt} \right)_{\text{coll}} = -k_3 N_1 N_4 + k_3 N_0 N_3 \tag{35}$$

The proportionality constant k_3 must be the same for collisions in either direction as a consequence of the principle of detailed balancing.

Since each such He-Ne collision that destroys an He metastable also creates an excited Ne atom, and vice versa, the rate equation for the upper Ne laser level 3 may be written as

$$\frac{d}{dt} N_3 = -\left(\frac{dN_4}{dt} \right)_{\text{coll}} - \frac{N_3}{\tau_3} = k_3 N_1 N_4 - k_3 N_0 N_3 - \frac{N_3}{\tau_3} \tag{36}$$

This equation includes direct relaxation τ_3 out of the excited Ne level, but does not include any electron-excitation rates into or out of the level, since these rates are believed to be small compared to the collision and decay terms shown.[1]

---

[1] Although these terms are of small importance in the He-Ne laser mixture, where collisional excitation is strong, they are presumably not completely zero because laser action is still possible (although much weaker), even in a pure Ne discharge with no He atoms present to provide collisional excitation.

The three preceding rate equations may be solved simultaneously in the steady state $(d/dt = 0)$ to give

$$N_4 = \frac{k_1 N_0 I}{k_2 I + [k_3 N_1/(k_3 N_0 \tau_3 + 1) + 1/\tau_4]} \tag{37}$$

and

$$N_3 = \frac{k_3 N_1 \tau_3}{k_3 N_0 \tau_3 + 1} N_4 \tag{38}$$

Note that the ground-state populations N_0 and N_1 are, to first order, constants independent of discharge current I, since only a very minute fraction of the atoms of either type are excited into the upper energy levels in a typical laser discharge. Therefore the Ne upper-level population N_3 is predicted to vary in direct proportion to the He metastable density N_4, and both of these are predicted to vary with discharge current I in the form

$$N_4, N_3 = \frac{K_1 I}{K_2 I + K_3} \tag{39}$$

where K_1, K_2, and K_3 are new constants. These populations increase linearly with current at first, but eventually saturate at high enough currents where the electrons destroy the metastable N_4 atoms via the $K_2 I$ term as fast as they create them from the ground level via the $K_1 I$ term.

The population of an excited energy level can often be monitored by observing the intensity of some fluorescent-emission line that originates on the level of interest.[1] Some data of this type for various He-Ne laser levels are shown in Fig. 10-7.[2] In particular, the solid curve in Fig. 10-7a marked "6328 Å" represents the fluorescent intensity at that wavelength out the side of the laser tube versus the discharge current, under nonlasering conditions (laser mirrors blocked). Hence this curve shows how the neon upper-level population N_3 depends on the discharge current I. The dots superimposed on this curve come from a separate absolute measurement of the He metastable population N_4 versus I (the two curves have been scaled vertically to coincide). It seems clear that N_3 and N_4 are indeed directly proportional, as predicted by Eq. (38), and that both do vary with discharge current I in the form predicted by Eq. (39).

The two lower curves marked "6096 Å" and "3593 Å" in Fig. 10-7a show that the lower-level populations N_2 and N_2' for the 3.39-μ and 6328-Å laser transitions, respectively, both increase approximately linearly with discharge current (note that the population differences between the various curves in this figure are not significant, since each curve is plotted to a different arbitrary scale). Exactly how the lower levels N_2 and N_2' are populated is not known. Possible mechanisms include direct electron excitation from the Ne ground level, relaxation down into these levels from the neon $3s_2$ level, and/or relaxation into these levels from still higher Ne levels, which are

---

[1] A monochromator and a suitable photodetector are used to identify the particular emission line desired among all the light being radiated by the discharge. Note that it is very difficult to measure absolute population by this method, because of the difficulty of calibrating the detection apparatus for absolute intensity and because it is necessary to know the radiative lifetime of the transition, a parameter which is often unavailable. Hence only relative population values are usually obtained. This method also fails if the transition involved is strongly self-trapped by radiation trapping.

[2] See Ref. 10-18.

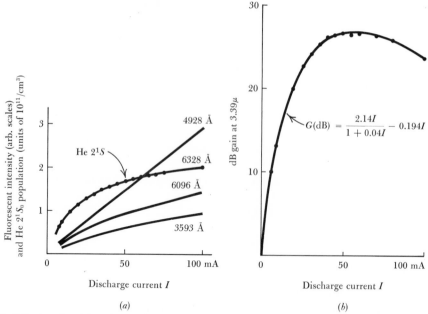

FIG. 10-7 Experimental results showing the pumping and excitation processes in the He-Ne laser system. (a) The solid curves show fluorescent intensity on the various transitions in Fig. 10-6, and hence the relative populations of the associated upper levels, as a function of discharge current I under nonlaser conditions (mirrors blocked). Circled datum points are population of the metastable He 2^1S level versus I measured by an independent method. (b) Measured small-signal gain of the 3.39-μ laser transition versus discharge current. [From A. D. White and E. I. Gordon, "Excitation mechanisms and current dependence of population inversion in He-Ne lasers," *Appl. Phys. Letters*, **3**:197 (Dec. 1, 1963).]

themselves populated by direct electron excitation. The 4928-Å curve, for example, shows that the higher-lying Ne 5p-level population increases exactly linearly with the discharge current.

The population difference, and hence the laser gain on either of these laser transitions, should now vary with dc discharge current in the form

$$\text{Gain} \propto \mathcal{N}_3 - \mathcal{N}_2 = \frac{K_1 I}{K_2 I + K_3} - K_4 I \tag{40}$$

Figure 10-7b is a plot of measured small-signal decibel gain versus discharge current for an He-Ne laser tube measured at 3.39 μ and fitted to a curve of the predicted theoretical form. The good agreement, at least in the shape of the curve, is evident.

These typical solid-state and gas laser systems illustrate the kinds of pumping and relaxation mechanisms that must be taken into account in any detailed discussion of the pumping mechanisms in various laser systems. There are additional pumping mechanisms, such as chemical laser pumping, that have not been even mentioned here, but in general the concepts of excitation of atoms to upper levels, followed by downward relaxation and the buildup of population inversion on certain favored transitions are expected to apply broadly to all different types of laser systems and laser pumping mechanisms.

10-2   LASER OSCILLATION CONDITIONS: GAIN AND POPULATION INVERSION

The pumping methods described in the preceding section, or any other suitable pumping methods, can be used to obtain population inversion on various suitable laser transitions. The next major step in developing a laser oscillator is to find a suitable optical resonator structure for containing and controlling the laser oscillation, and then to find the required population inversion and frequency conditions necessary to reach the oscillation threshold in such a resonator.

The optical resonator configurations described in Chap. 8 provide suitable optical cavity modes for almost all types of lasers. For purposes of analysis, the modes in these optical cavities may be represented by elementary uniform plane waves traveling back and forth along the resonator axis, as in the analyses of Secs. 5-4 and 5-5. In this section we will extend the analysis of Sec. 5-5 to find the basic cavity parameters and oscillation conditions for an elementary laser oscillator.

■ The essential features of an elementary laser oscillator, as shown in Fig. 10-8, begin with two laser mirrors spaced a distance L apart and having voltage-reflection coefficients r_1 and r_2, or power-reflection coefficients $R_1 = r_1^2$ and $R_2 = r_2^2$. Between the mirrors is a laser material having a voltage-gain coefficient[1] $\alpha_m(\omega)$ due to the laser transition, and possibly a loss coefficient α_0 due to absorption, scattering, and any other internal loss effects. The propagation constant in the laser medium, leaving aside the laser transition, is $\beta_0 = n_0\omega/c$, but there is also a phase-shift or propagation coefficient $\Delta\beta_m(\omega)$ due to the laser transition, which as we will see, can have significant frequency-pulling effects. For simplicity the laser material may be assumed to fill the entire region between the two laser mirrors.

BASIC ANALYSIS

The basic condition for steady-state laser oscillation in this system is that the net complex gain in one round trip around the laser's internal feedback loop must be exactly unity. In mathematical terms, this is

$$r_1 r_2 e^{2[\alpha_m(\omega)-\alpha_0]L} e^{-2j[\beta_0+\Delta\beta_m(\omega)]L} = e^{-jq2\pi} \tag{1}$$

where q may be any integer (we know from Chap. 5 that each value of q refers to another axial mode of the laser cavity). The instantaneous round-trip gain inside a laser cavity can be either greater or less than unity on a *transient* basis, but in this case the internal laser signals will experience a net growth or a net decay on each round trip, and hence

---

[1] In this book all coefficients α always refer to *voltage* (i.e., wave-amplitude) gain or loss, rather than power gain or loss. Note, however, that α is often used in the literature to refer to the exponential power-gain or power-decay coefficient.

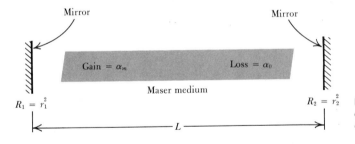

$R_1 = r_1^2$ Maser medium $R_2 = r_2^2$

Gain = α_m Loss = α_0

Mirror   Mirror

L

FIG. 10-8 Analytical model for an elementary laser oscillator, showing the essential elements for analysis of laser oscillation.

the laser oscillation level will either build up or die out with time. For sustained oscillation at a steady ocillation level, the net round-trip gain can only be exactly unity.

The oscillation condition (1), since it is a complex expression, really expresses two separate conditions: the *magnitude* of the round-trip gain must be unity, and the total round-trip *phase shift* must be an integral multiple of 2π. The magnitude condition determines the required round-trip gain, the threshold population inversion, and the threshold pump power required. The phase-shift condition determines the frequency-pulling effects and the exact frequency at which oscillation will occur, as we will see in the next section.

THRESHOLD VERSUS STEADY-
STATE OSCILLATION

■ We refer more or less interchangeably to the *threshold values* or the *steady-state oscillation values* for the laser gain and the laser population inversion. The reason is that condition (1) determines equally well both the threshold condition at which laser oscillation can just begin and the steady-state condition that must prevail in an oscillating laser whose oscillation level is stable, i.e., neither growing nor decaying with time. As the pump power is turned up from zero in a laser oscillator such as that in Fig. 10-8, the population inversion and gain are at first too small to satisfy Eq. (1). The round-trip gain in the laser cavity is less than unity, and no signals can build up. At some larger threshold pumping value the net round-trip gain will just reach unity, so that the cavity is on the verge of oscillation. The laser gain and population inversion at this point are properly referred to as the *threshold values.* If the laser is pumped still harder, the oscillations will build up to some appropriate steady-state level (after some transient buildup interval). But at the steady-state oscillation level the laser round-trip gain must again be exactly unity, so that the oscillations will neither grow nor decay from that steady-state level. In other words, as far as the laser gain and the related population inversion are concerned, the steady-state values are the same as the threshold values. Harder pumping above threshold will in general mean a still larger steady-state oscillation level, but the values of gain and of population inversion for steady state always stick at, and are the same as, their threshold values to just reach oscillation.

In later sections we will study the more general laser rate equations that permit us to predict just how the steady-state oscillation level will increase with pumping power and explain in detail how the gain and the population inversion are limited or saturated at their threshold values.

MAGNITUDE CONDITION: LASER
CAVITY Q PARAMETERS

■ The magnitude portion of the basic laser oscillation condition (1) is

$$r_1 r_2 e^{2[\alpha_m(\omega)-\alpha_0]L} = 1 \tag{2}$$

which may be rewritten as

$$\alpha_m = \alpha_0 + (2L)^{-1} \ln \frac{1}{r_1 r_2} \tag{3}$$

From earlier chapters, the laser gain coefficient may be related to a maser or molecular Q_m parameter for the laser medium by

$$Q_m \equiv \frac{\omega \times \text{stored energy per unit length}}{\text{laser power emission per unit length}} = \frac{n_0 \omega}{2\alpha_m c} \tag{4}$$

Therefore we are led to rewrite the laser oscillation condition in the form

$$Q_m = \frac{n_0 \omega}{2\alpha_m c} = \frac{n_0 \omega}{2\alpha_0 c + (c/L) \ln (1/r_1 r_2)} \tag{5}$$

The right-hand factor in Eq. (5) depends only on passive laser cavity properties such as α_0, L, and r_1 and r_2. Therefore we are led to define a cavity quality factor Q_c for the laser cavity as

$$Q_c \equiv \frac{n_0\omega}{2\alpha_{0c} + (c/L)\ln(1/r_1r_2)} \tag{6}$$

With this definition of the cold-cavity Q_c (without laser action) the basic laser oscillation condition (2) or (3) takes on the very simple form

$$Q_c = Q_m \tag{7}$$

which simply states that the gain (or negative loss) in the laser cavity as measured by the maser Q_m must just exactly balance the positive cavity losses as measured by the usual cavity Q_c of the laser cavity.

The laser oscillation condition is converted to the simple and reasonable form of Eq. (7), provided that the most general form for the cavity Q_c of the optical cavity is taken to be

$$Q_c = \frac{n_0\omega}{2\alpha_{0c} + (c/L)\ln(1/r_1r_2)} = \frac{2\pi n_0 L}{\lambda}\frac{1}{2\alpha_0 L + \ln(1/r_1r_2)} \tag{8}$$

This is indeed a realistic and meaningful definition of the cavity Q_c, even in the limits of low mirror reflectivities or large internal cavity losses (see Appendix E). For small losses, the general cavity Q_c definition (8) may be connected with the simpler approximate cavity Q_c definition in Chap. 5 by noting that the one-way power transmission down the laser cavity may be written (given internal losses but no laser action) as

$$e^{-2\alpha_0 L} \approx 1 - 2\alpha_0 L = 1 - \delta_0 \tag{9}$$

Hence $\delta_0 = 2\alpha_0 L$ is the fractional power loss per one-way pass, or per bounce, due to the internal losses. If the fractional power losses δ_1 and δ_2 due to each mirror reflection are also defined as

$$R_1 = r_1{}^2 = 1 - \delta_1 \qquad R_2 = r_2{}^2 = 1 - \delta_2 \tag{10}$$

then for small mirror losses (high-reflectivity mirrors, $R \approx 1$) a valid approximation is

$$\ln\frac{1}{r_1r_2} = \frac{1}{2}\ln\frac{1}{R_1R_2} \approx \tfrac{1}{2}(\delta_1 + \delta_2) \qquad \delta_1, \delta_2 \ll 1 \tag{11}$$

With these small-loss approximations, the general expression (8) may be converted to essentially the same Q_c expression as in Chap. 5 (differing only in the added n_0 factor),

$$Q_c \approx \frac{2\pi n_0 L}{\lambda}\frac{1}{\delta_0 + (\delta_1 + \delta_2)/2} = \frac{2\pi n_0 L}{\lambda}\frac{1}{\delta} \tag{12}$$

where $\delta \equiv \delta_0 + (\delta_1 + \delta_2)/2$ is the average power loss per bounce due to all loss and output-coupling mechanisms. For values of loss per bounce less than 20 percent this approximate form for Q_c may be used, while for larger losses the exact expression (8) should be employed.

We will also need later the cavity lifetime or cavity energy-decay time due to losses, τ_c, given by

$$\frac{1}{\tau_c} = \frac{\omega}{Q_c} = \frac{c}{n_0 L}\left(2\alpha_0 L + \ln\frac{1}{r_1 r_2}\right) \tag{13}$$

which may be written in the form

$$\tau_c \approx \frac{1}{\delta}\frac{n_0 L}{c} = \frac{T}{\delta} \tag{14}$$

where $T \equiv n_0 L/c$ is the one-way transit time down the cavity length and δ is again the total power loss per pass from all causes. The energy in the cavity makes $\sim 1/\delta$ bounces before it decays by a factor of $1/e$.

The length L of a laser cavity will typically be somewhere between 10 cm and 1 m, while the wavelength λ of visible light is around 5×10^{-7} m. Therefore the Q_c of a typical laser cavity at visible-light frequencies will be in the range

$$Q_c \sim \frac{10^6 - 10^7}{\delta} \sim 10^7 - 10^9 \qquad \text{for } \delta \sim 0.01 \text{ to } 0.1 \tag{15}$$

There is sometimes an intuitive idea that a cavity with a loss of 10 percent per bounce must have a Q_c value of ~ 10; this is obviously not the case. Although 10 percent of the energy may be lost on every bounce, it takes L/λ cycles to complete one bounce, and hence the Q_c is higher by 2π times this factor. The one-way transit time T for a typical laser cavity will be in the range of ~ 0.3 to 3 nsec, and hence, from Eq. (14), the energy-decay time for the cavity will be

$$\tau_c \sim \frac{3 \times 10^{-9} - 3 \times 10^{-10}}{\delta} \text{ sec}$$

$$\sim 0.3 \text{ } \mu\text{sec to 3 nsec} \qquad \text{for } \delta \sim 0.01 \text{ to } 0.1 \tag{16}$$

This will be a very large number of cycles at the laser frequency—approximately $L\delta/\lambda$ cycles. Optical Q values, even for very lossy cavities, are typically very large.

THRESHOLD POPULATION INVERSION ■ We can next relate the laser gain necessary to obtain oscillation to the population inversion on the laser transition required to produce this gain. From Chaps. 2 and 5, the laser amplification coefficient at the center frequency of a lorentzian atomic transition may be written as

$$\alpha_m(\omega_a) = \frac{3}{8\pi^2}\frac{(\mathcal{N}_2 - \mathcal{N}_1)_v \lambda^2}{n_0^2 \, \Delta f_a \, \tau_{\text{rad}}} \tag{17}$$

where

$$(\mathcal{N}_2 - \mathcal{N}_1)_v = \text{inverted population difference per unit volume in laser material}$$
$$n_0 = \text{index of refraction of laser material}$$
$$\Delta f_a = \text{atomic linewidth of laser transition}$$
$$\tau_{\text{rad}} = \text{radiative lifetime}$$

(The corresponding expression for a gaussian atomic line is identical, except that it is multiplied by the factor $\sqrt{\pi \ln 2} \approx 1.48$.) Since the laser oscillation condition (2) or (3) may be written as

$$\alpha_m = \frac{n_0 \omega}{2 Q_c c} = \frac{n_0}{2c}\frac{1}{\tau_c} \tag{18}$$

the population inversion density required for laser oscillation may be obtained from

Eqs. (17) and (18) as

$$\Delta \mathcal{N}_v = (\mathcal{N}_2 - \mathcal{N}_1)_v = \frac{4\pi^2}{3} \frac{\Delta f_a}{f_a} \frac{\tau_{\text{rad}}}{\tau_c} \left(\frac{n_0}{\lambda}\right)^3 \tag{19}$$

Several important conclusions are immediately apparent. First, the required inversion is lowered by a narrow atomic linewidth Δf_a and by a long cavity lifetime τ_c; that is, one wants low cavity losses. It is also lowered by a short radiative lifetime τ_{rad}, since this implies a strongly allowed transition with a good atomic response. However, this condition is usually more than counterbalanced by the fact that much more pumping power is needed to obtain a given inversion on a transition with a short relaxation time. Indeed, a major conclusion of Sec. 10-1 is that population inversion is likely to be achieved, if at all, primarily on those transitions having *long* radiative lifetimes. Finally, there is the very basic limitation that the population inversion required for oscillation increases more or less as the inverse third power of the laser wavelength λ (depending in part on how other quantities, such as the linewidth and τ_{rad}, change with wavelength). In general, therefore, long-wavelength infrared-spectrum lasers are fairly easy to achieve; short-wavelength visible-spectrum and particularly ultraviolet-spectrum lasers are much harder to make; very-short-wavelength X-ray or gamma-ray lasers have yet to be achieved at all.

To gain some feeling for the size of population inversion required, let us consider some typical numerical examples. For example, for the ruby laser transition with the laser rod at room temperature, the appropriate parameters have values of order

$$\Delta f_a \approx 150 \text{ GHz} = 1.5 \times 10^{11} \text{ Hz}$$
$$f_a = 4.3 \times 10^{14} \text{ Hz}$$
$$\tau_{\text{rad}} = 4.3 \text{ msec} \tag{20}$$
$$\tau_c = 6 \times 10^{-9} \text{ sec} \qquad (L = 5 \text{ cm}, \delta = 5\% \text{ loss per bounce})$$
$$\frac{\lambda}{n_0} = \frac{6943 \text{ Å}}{1.76} = 4 \times 10^{-5} \text{ cm}$$

and this gives for the required threshold inversion

$$(\mathcal{N}_2 - \mathcal{N}_1)_v \sim 5 \times 10^{16}/\text{cm}^3 \tag{21}$$

Now, the total density of Cr^{3+} ions in a typical ruby laser crystal is $\mathcal{N} \approx 10^{19}/\text{cm}^3$. Hence the fractional degree of inversion required for oscillation is very small, about 5 parts in 1000. Unfortunately, because ruby is a three-level system, half of all these 10^{19} atoms must be lifted from the ground state to the upper laser level in order to attain the small excess of $\sim 5 \times 10^{16}$ in the upper level that is needed for population inversion and sufficient gain for laser action.

Many of the four-level rare-earth laser systems have parameters comparable to those in Eq. (19) for ruby, and hence have threshold population inversion densities of the same order of magnitude. However, because these are four-level systems, the fractional number of atoms that will have to be lifted from the ground state into the upper laser level is, of course, very much smaller than in the ruby case.

As another, rather different numerical example, consider the He-Ne laser transition at 6328 Å, for which the appropriate values are approximately

$$\Delta f_a = 1500 \text{ MHz} = 1.5 \times 10^9 \text{ Hz}$$
$$f_a = 4.74 \times 10^{14} \text{ Hz}$$
$$\tau_{\text{rad}} = 7 \times 10^{-7} \text{ sec} \qquad (22)$$
$$\tau_c = 10^{-7} \text{ sec} \qquad (L = 60 \text{ cm}, \ \delta = 2\% \text{ loss per bounce})$$
$$\lambda = 6328 \text{ Å} = 6.3 \times 10^{-5} \text{ cm}$$

Note that the atomic linewidth here is very much narrower, the radiative lifetime is considerably shorter, and the cavity lifetime is considerably longer (i.e., a longer cavity with smaller losses per bounce). As a result, the required population inversion density is very much smaller than in the solid-state example; that is,

$$(\mathcal{N}_2 - \mathcal{N}_1)_v \sim 1.3 \times 10^9/\text{cm}^3 \qquad (23)$$

The much smaller inversion density required in typical gas lasers is fortunate, if not essential, since the available densities of atoms in gases are, of course, very much less than in solids. Also, the number of excited levels over which these atoms will be dispersed when the material is pumped is typically much larger in gases than in solids, so that there may be less inversion created for a given amount of pump excitation. In many typical cases higher-Q cavities (i.e., longer cavities with higher mirror reflectivities) are required for gas lasers than for solid-state lasers, at least in the visible frequency range.

LASER PUMPING REQUIREMENTS

■ For continuous laser oscillation the population inversion we have been discussing must be continuously maintained by the pumping process against all decay mechanisms. Atoms lifted by the pumping process into the upper laser level will decay with some overall lifetime τ_{total} based on all the relaxation mechanisms present (this decay time is equivalent to what we called τ_3 in the four-level model or τ_2 in the three-level model). In addition, the population inversion in the presence of laser oscillation is continually being depleted by the effects of the laser action itself. Each photon of optical signal energy generated by the laser requires the equivalent of one downward stimulated transition of an atom from the upper to the lower laser level.[1]

To calculate the amount of pump power required to maintain continuous laser oscillation in even a rather idealized case, let us consider a nearly ideal four-level type of laser with an upper-laser-level population $\mathcal{N}_2$. Decay of atoms from this upper level occurs at a rate $(d/dt)\mathcal{N}_2 = -\mathcal{N}_2/\tau_{\text{total}}$ as a result of relaxation processes, in addition to the loss of atoms due to the transitions stimulated by laser action. For continuous steady-state laser action the pumping process must lift atoms upward at the same total rate at which they decay downward. Since lifting each atom to the upper laser level requires an amount of energy hf_p, where f_p is some effective pumping frequency $\geq f_a$, the absolute minimum pump power per unit volume, P_p, required to maintain the upper-level population in the laser medium is

$$P_p \geq \frac{\mathcal{N}_{2v} h f_p}{\tau_{\text{total}}} \qquad (24)$$

With the use of Eq. (19), this may be written as

$$P_p \geq \frac{\mathcal{N}_{2v}}{\mathcal{N}_{2v} - \mathcal{N}_{1v}} \frac{f_p}{f_a} \frac{\tau_{\text{rad}}}{\tau_{\text{total}}} \left[\frac{4\pi^3}{3} \frac{h \Delta f_a}{\tau_c} \left(\frac{n_0}{\lambda}\right)^3 \right] \qquad (25)$$

---

[1] Note that since $\mathcal{N}_{\text{upper}}$ is decreased by 1 and $\mathcal{N}_{\text{lower}}$ is increased by 1 in this process, the population difference $\Delta \mathcal{N}$ is actually decreased by 2 for each stimulated transition.

The first three factors on the right-hand side of Eq. (25) are all unity or greater, depending on how close to ideal the laser system is. For minimum pump power the lower laser level should have negligible population, $\mathcal{N}_{1v} \to 0$ (owing to fast decay out of this level), so that all of the upper-level population $\mathcal{N}_{2v}$ is useful in creating inversion. The ratio of the pumping-energy gap to the laser-energy gap, f_p/f_a, will be at least unity in all lasers, and may be ~ 2 in typical lasers. The ratio τ_{rad}/τ_{total} has a minimum value of unity when the decay of the upper laser level is purely radiative and purely on the laser transition itself, so that $\tau_{total} = \tau_{rad}$. Note that in this case the expression for the required overall pump-power density becomes independent of the upper-level lifetime τ_{rad}. A transition with a longer radiative lifetime has a weaker response, and so requires a larger threshold population inversion from Eq. (19); but with a long lifetime $\tau_{total} = \tau_{rad}$ less pump-power input is required to maintain a given inversion.

The fundamental parameters in the pump-power requirement appear in the square brackets at the end of Eq. (25). Evidently, narrow atomic linewidth and long cavity lifetime (high Q_c) are needed to achieve laser action with minimum pumping power, and the minimum pumping power required unavoidably increases somewhat as the laser transition frequency cubed (or possibly worse, depending on how Δf_a and τ_{rad} change for higher-frequency laser transitions). Again, shorter-wavelength lasers become increasingly harder to obtain.

If the three initial factors in Eq. (25) are all given their idealized values of unity for simplicity, then a hypothetical four-level solid-state laser system having the typical parameter values given in (20) will have a minimum pump-power density in the laser crystal of

$$P_p \sim 3 \text{ W/cm}^3 \tag{26}$$

where $\Delta f_a = 1.5 \times 10^{11} \text{ Hz}$
$\tau_c = 6 \times 10^{-9} \text{ sec}$
$\lambda/n_0 = 4000 \text{ Å}$

A three-level gas laser system having the parameters given in (22) will have a predicted minimum pump-power density of

$$P_p \sim 0.5 \text{ mW/cm}^3 \tag{27}$$

where $\Delta f_a = 1.5 \times 10^9 \text{ Hz}$
$\tau_c = 10^{-7} \text{ sec}$
$\lambda = 6328 \text{ Å}$

However, it must be emphasized that these calculations of pump power required do not take into account that portion of the pump input that is wasted in lifting atoms up to other excited levels having no useful connection with the laser levels, or that portion of the total electric power input to a typical laser that is dissipated simply in heating up the laser components or in other inefficient uses. In fact, these unproductive channels absorb by far the greater part of the total pump power input in most practical lasers. Aside from a few exceptional cases (such as the semiconductor injection laser with efficiency ~ 60 percent at low temperatures and the CO_2 gas laser with efficiency >30 percent in carefully designed lasers), overall laser-power efficiencies are typically extremely low (<1 percent).

Note that in the ruby laser system in particular the factor $\mathcal{N}_{2v}/(\mathcal{N}_{2v} - \mathcal{N}_{1v})$ in Eq. (25) becomes very large because half of all the Cr^{3+} ions in the crystal must first be pumped up before the relatively small population inversion needed for laser action can be attained. The required pump-power density for ruby then becomes extremely large—~ 500 W/cm^3. To give some idea of the various practical factors involved in the overall pumping efficiency of an optically pumped solid-state laser, Table 10-1 shows the estimated conversion efficiencies for various steps in the overall pumping process (from electric power input to laser output) in a very carefully engineered, continuously operating ruby laser. For a similarly engineered solid-state laser of the four-level type, the final overall efficiency might be increased to several percent, rather than the ~ 0.1 percent of the three-level ruby case.

AN EXPERIMENTAL RESULT ■ We will consider here only one experimental result which illustrates fairly directly at least some of the preceding analytical results. Consider a pulsed, optically pumped, four-level laser system which is pumped (starting from rest) with a pump flash that is intense but of short duration compared to the fluorescent lifetime of the laser system. From the discussions of Sec. 10-1, we may view this pump flash as quickly lifting a certain number of atoms into the upper laser level, from where these atoms decay with the fluorescent lifetime (or faster, if laser action occurs). The population inversion at the end of the pump flash will be directly proportional to the integrated pumping rate during the flash, i.e., to the total energy input to the pumping flashlamp.[1]

From Eq. (3), the threshold condition for laser oscillation to occur just at the end of the pumping flash is

$$2\alpha_{mT}L = 2\alpha_0 L + \ln \frac{1}{r_1 r_2}$$

where α_{mT} is the maximum value of laser gain reached at the end of the pump flash. But from Eq. (17), this gain coefficient is directly proportional to the population inversion reached at that point, and this is proportional in turn to the flashlamp energy input. Thus

$$\alpha_{mT} = \text{const} \times \Delta \mathcal{N}_T = \text{const} \times E_T$$

where E_T is the flashlamp energy input and the subscript T refers in each case to the

---

[1] This is true only for a pump flash short compared to the level decay time, so that negligible decay occurs during the pump flash itself. Also, in practice correction factors may be necessary because the light output from a pulsed flashlamp is usually not exactly linear in the electric energy input to the lamp.

TABLE 10-1

Pumping efficiency of a mercury-arc-pumped cw ruby laser

Conversion of electrical power input to light output in ruby pumping bands	$\sim 25\%$
Pump light transfer efficiency from lamp to laser rod (due to imperfect cavity reflectivity and focusing)	$\sim 80\%$
Fraction of incident pump light actually absorbed by rod	$\sim 4\%$
Power quantum efficiency of absorbed pump light†	$\sim 50\%$
Laser output-coupling efficiency: useful output compared to internal losses plus useful output	$\sim 30\%$
OVERALL PUMPING EFFICIENCY ABOVE THRESHOLD	$\sim 0.12\%$

† Quantum efficiency as defined in the text, multiplied by f/f_p, so as to give ratio of energies instead of just excited atoms per pump photon absorbed.

SOURCE: From W. Evtuhov and J. K. Neeland, *J. Appl. Phys.*, **38**:4051 (September, 1967).

value needed to just reach laser threshold. Thus threshold energy input E_T for the pulsed laser is given as a function of the internal attenuation coefficient α_0 and the laser-mirror reflectivities R_1 and R_2 by

$$2\alpha_{mT}L = 2\alpha_0 L + \ln \frac{1}{r_1 r_2} = \text{const} \times E_T \qquad (28)$$

or, in reverse order,

$$E_T = \text{const} \times \left(2\alpha_0 L + \ln \frac{1}{r_1 r_2}\right) = E_{T0} + \frac{E_{T0}}{4\alpha_0 L}\ln \frac{1}{R_1 R_2} \qquad (29)$$

where E_{T0} is the minimum possible threshold energy that can be obtained with mirrors that are 100 percent reflective.

Figure 10-9 shows experimental results for threshold pump energy E_T in joules[1] versus the quantity $\ln (1/R_1 R_2)$ obtained with mirrors of different reflectivity values R_2 on one end of a typical Nd-glass laser rod 1.5 cm in diameter and 15 cm long, pumped by two xenon-filled linear flashlamps in a double-elliptical pump enclosure. The variation of E_T with $\ln (1/R_1 R_2)$ is linear, as predicted by the analysis. Note also that by measuring the pump energy intercept E_{T0} ($\sim$250 joules in this case) and the slope of the E_T-vs.-[$\ln (1/R_1 R_2)$] curve it is possible to determine the internal-loss coefficient in the laser rod. The data indicate an internal-power-loss coefficient for this glass sample of $2\alpha_0 \approx 0.007$ cm^{-1}, in reasonable agreement with direct attenuation measurements on the same glass. (It is found that in this glass the attenuation coefficient α_0 is due largely to direct absorption by the host glass at the laser wavelength $\lambda = 1.06\mu$, rather than to any scattering losses, which are negligible.)

■ The laser-threshold analysis above may also be used to find the threshold dc current necessary to obtain laser action in the semiconductor diode-injection type of laser. In this case we may suppose that the active laser volume consists of a broad, thin diode-junction region of area A and very small thickness d, as shown in Fig. 10-10. The laser mirrors are formed by the dielectric-air interfaces at two ends of this broad, flat cavity.

INJECTION-LASER THRESHOLD CURRENT

[1] The threshold energy E_T is measured by gradually increasing the voltage applied to a capacitor bank which is discharged through the flashlamps and observing the lowest voltage value at which laser oscillation first appears. There is inevitably some scatter and variation from shot to shot in such data.

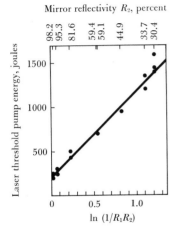

FIG. 10-9 The threshold pulsed pump energy required to just reach laser-oscillation threshold for a pulsed Nd-glass laser plotted against the mirror reflectivity R_2 on one end (top scale) and the analytical parameter $\ln (1/R_1 R_2)$ (bottom scale). [Data taken from M .E. Vance, "Measured internal losses and output energies of neodymium glass lasers," *Appl. Opt.*, **6**:775 (April, 1967).]

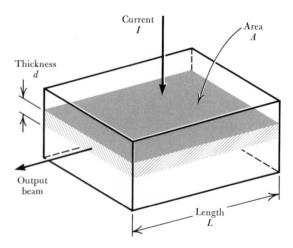

FIG. 10-10   Geometry of the active laser volume in a diode-injection semiconductor junction type of laser.

The upper- and lower-level populations in this case consist of electrons in the lowest levels of the conduction band and the highest levels of the valence band, respectively, in the junction region of the *p-n* diode. If we assume for simplicity the ideal condition $(N_2 - N_1)_v \approx N_{2v}$, then the number density of conduction-band electrons in the junction region is also N_{2v}, and the total number of such electrons that must be maintained in the conduction band in the entire junction volume is $N_{2v}Ad$. If these electrons decay down to the valence band with lifetime τ_2, with each such decay requiring the transfer of one new electron charge e into the junction region, the required total current flow into the junction to maintain the upper-state population is

$$I = \frac{N_{2v}Ade}{\tau_2} \tag{30}$$

Since this current flows in through the broad area A of the junction, the required threshold current density in the junction is, from Eqs. (13) and (19),

$$J = \frac{I}{A} = \frac{4\pi^2}{3} \frac{\Delta f_a}{f_a} \frac{\tau_{\text{rad}}}{\tau_c} \left(\frac{n_0}{\lambda}\right)^3 \frac{de}{\tau_2}$$

$$= \frac{4\pi^2}{3} \frac{\tau_{\text{rad}}}{\tau_2} \frac{n_0^2 \, \Delta\lambda_a}{\lambda_a^4} \frac{ced}{L} \left(2\alpha_0 L + \ln \frac{1}{r_1 r_2}\right) \tag{31}$$

where the second line is expressed in wavelength instead of frequency units so that it will have the same form in which it usually appears in the literature on injection lasers. The ratio τ_2/τ_{rad}, often called the *quantum efficiency*, measures the fraction of injected conduction-band electrons that decay by purely radiative light emission compared to the total decay by both radiative and nonradiative processes.

As a numerical illustration of Eq. (31), typical parameter values for a GaAs injection laser operated at low temperatures are

$$\begin{aligned}
&\tau_{\text{rad}} \approx \tau_2 \qquad \text{quantum efficiency} \to 1 \\
&n_0 = 3.6 \qquad \lambda_a = 8400 \text{ Å} \qquad \Delta\lambda_a = 200 \text{ Å} \\
&\text{Junction thickness: } d \approx 1 \, \mu = 10^{-4} \text{ cm} \\
&\text{Junction length: } L \approx 0.3 \text{ mm} = 3 \times 10^{-2} \text{ cm} \\
&\text{Air-dielectric reflectivities: } R_1, R_2 \approx 0.32
\end{aligned} \tag{32}$$

The scattering/absorption loss α_0 is negligible (at low temperatures). The threshold current density and the total diode current for a typical junction 0.3 mm long and 0.1 mm wide, $A = 3 \times 10^{-4}$ cm², will then be

$$J \sim 120 \text{ A/cm}^2 \quad \text{or} \quad I \approx 35 \text{ mA} \tag{33}$$

Experimental results for real GaAs injection lasers are in good agreement with these calculations at liquid-helium temperatures. However, for temperatures $T \geq 60°\text{K}$ the threshold current density for laser action is found to increase as $\sim T^3$ because of increased absorption in the bulk GaAs material in and around the junction region, increased thermal population of the lower laser level, and other factors. The measured threshold currents at room temperature are therefore larger than the above values by a factor of ~ 100—several amperes in typical cases.

■ An alternate way of expressing laser amplification coefficients and finding the population inversion needed for laser oscillation is the *transition cross section* for an atomic transition. This cross section is often used as a convenient way of measuring the strength of a transition used for laser action. Consider a traveling-wave beam of radiation which is carrying total power P, say in the z direction. Let the power be uniformly distributed over the beam cross-sectional area A, so that the power density in the transverse plane is P/A. Suppose that a small black (totally absorbing) disk of cross-sectional area σ is placed in this beam. The average power absorbed by this disk will be $\Delta P = (\sigma/A)P$. If the beam contains a randomly dispersed collection of many such disks with density N_v per unit volume, as shown in Fig. 10-11, the total number of disks in a small unit length Δz of the beam will be $N_v A \, \Delta z$, and the total power absorbed in the length Δz by these disks will be

ALTERNATE FORMULATION: TRANSITION CROSS SECTION

$$-\Delta P = (N_v A \, \Delta z)\frac{\sigma}{A}P = N_v \sigma P \, \Delta z \tag{34}$$

Taking the limit of small Δz converts $\Delta P/\Delta z$ to the differential form[1]

$$\frac{dP}{dz} = -N_v \sigma P \tag{35}$$

[1] We are assuming that there are sufficient disks per unit volume that the absorption is essentially smooth and uniform throughout the beam, but that the disks are not so numerous or so large that they block each other or absorb all the beam power with just a few disks.

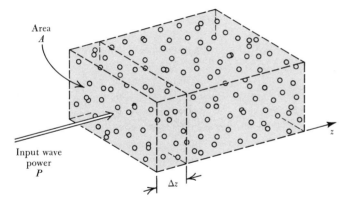

Area A

Input wave power P

z

Δz

FIG. 10-11   To develop the concept of transition cross section, we view each individual atom as a small black absorbing (or emitting) disk with a capture area or cross section σ for an incident wave of radiation.

The usual equation for the power attenuation in a beam passing through an absorbing medium with (voltage) absorption coefficient α is just

$$\frac{d}{dz}P = -2\alpha P \tag{36}$$

Thus in this purely classical picture we make the identification

$$2\alpha = \mathcal{N}_v \sigma \tag{37}$$

for the power-absorption coefficient of a beam passing through a medium containing a density $\mathcal{N}_v$ of scatters having individual cross-sectional areas σ (note that the cross-sectional area A of the beam itself completely drops out of this result).

Suppose now that, instead of the hypothetical absorbing disks of Fig. 10-11, the beam of radiation passes through a similar collection of atoms which have an atomic transition at or near the wave frequency. There is again an absorption (or possibly an emission) of power from the wave by the atoms. We can describe this by supposing that each atom is like a small absorbing disk with a cross-sectional area σ chosen so that the actual power absorbed by the atom equals the power that would be absorbed by an ideal black disk of the same cross section.

In the case of a quantum atomic transition, however, power absorption is proportional, not to the total number (or number density) of atoms, but to the population difference on the transition in question. Therefore in setting up the quantum analogy for the absorbing-disk case we replace the number density in Eq. (37) by the population-difference density for the atomic transition. The transition cross section σ_{12} for a laser transition (or generally for any atomic transition) between, say, levels E_1 and E_2 is defined by the expression analogous to Eq. (37),

$$2\alpha_m(\omega) = (\mathcal{N}_2 - \mathcal{N}_1)_v \sigma_{12}(\omega) \tag{38}$$

With the aid of Eq. (17) this becomes

$$\sigma_{12} = \frac{2\alpha_m(\omega_a)}{(\mathcal{N}_2 - \mathcal{N}_1)_v} = \frac{3}{4\pi^2} \frac{\lambda_a{}^2}{n_0{}^2 \, \Delta f_a{}^2 \, \tau_{\text{rad}}} \tag{39}$$

This is the value of the cross section for a signal tuned to the peak of the atomic transition. For frequencies away from line center the effective cross section $\sigma_{12}(\omega)$ will be decreased in exactly the same fashion as the atomic transition's absorption lineshape.

The cross section for a given laser transition provides a convenient single parameter for expressing the strength of that transition, or for describing how strongly the individual atoms are excited by an applied signal. It is particularly interesting to note that if a transition is broadened only by radiative lifetime broadening, so that $2\pi \, \Delta f_a \, \tau_{\text{rad}} \equiv 1$ in Eq. (39), then with $n_0 = 1$ the cross section takes on the maximum possible value for radiatively broadened transition,

$$\sigma_{12} = \frac{3\lambda^2}{2\pi} \approx \frac{1}{2}\lambda^2 \tag{40}$$

Under these ideal conditions an atom has a transition cross section on the order of a wavelength in diameter. The apparent size of the atom as seen by an incident light beam can be, for example, $\sigma_{12} \sim (5000 \text{ Å})^2$ for an optical transition, even though the physical size of the atom (as measured by the radius of the Bohr orbit of the outermost electron, for example) is typically only a few angstroms or so.

The cross section of an atomic transition decreases in size as the atomic linewidth is increased by any broadening effects such as nonradiative damping, doppler broadening, or thermal broadening. This corresponds exactly to the decrease in peak susceptibility with increasing linewidth that was discussed in earlier chapters. The cross sections of real laser transitions are usually considerably smaller than the optimum value of Eq. (40). For example, the measured cross section for the Nd^{3+} laser transition in a typical Nd-glass laser material is $\sigma \approx 3 \times 10^{-20}$ cm^2 (≈ 0.02 Å diameter) at room temperature, while the value for the Nd^{3+} ion in Nd YAG is $\sim 3 \times 10^{-19}$ cm^2. The transition cross section for the 6943-Å laser transition in ruby is $\sigma \approx 2 \times 10^{-20}$ cm^2 at room temperature and increases substantially at lower temperatures because of the rapid decrease in the ruby transition linewidth with cooling (see Fig. 9-10).

Given the cross section for a laser transition and the inverted population density in the laser material, the laser gain coefficient and gain per unit length can be immediately evaluated from Eq. (38). For example, the decibel gain of a wave passing through a length L of inverted laser material may be written as

$$G_{\mathrm{dB}}(\omega) = 4.34(\mathcal{N}_2 - \mathcal{N}_1)_v \sigma_{12}(\omega) L \tag{41}$$

The same transition cross section applies equally well to a transition in either absorption or emission, of course, and all these expressions may also be used (with a change of sign in the population difference and the coefficient α) to measure loss on an absorbing (noninverted) transition. This makes the transition cross section an easily measurable parameter in many cases, particularly when the population difference can be determined from thermal-equilibrium conditions and the loss or absorption per unit length can then be measured by straightforward techniques.[1]

The threshold population inversion needed for laser oscillation can also be written, from Eqs. (3), (18), and (38), in the particularly simple forms

$$(\mathcal{N}_2 - \mathcal{N}_1)_v \geq \frac{2\alpha_0 + (1/L) \ln (1/r_1 r_2)}{\sigma_{12}} = \frac{n_0}{\sigma_{12} c \tau_c} \tag{42}$$

The last of these expressions has the interesting physical interpretation that the required inversion density is just one atom per amount of volume equal to the transition cross section times the distance traveled by light in one cavity decay time.

Finally, note that the magnified apparent size or capture area of an atom with a radiatively broadened transition, as expressed by Eq. (40), has a direct classical analog in the effective receiving cross section, or capture area, of an ordinary radio antenna. Any small radio antenna, such as a small dipole antenna, even one very much smaller than half an operating wavelength in all its dimensions, will have an effective cross section or capture area for an incoming radio wave of roughly λ^2, where λ is the radio wavelength involved.[2] In fact, the excitation of voltages and currents in the dipole antenna by the incident radio wave is very much like the excitation of an induced polarization in an atom by an incident wave at or near any transition frequency, as we stressed in the classical-electron-oscillator discussions of Chap. 2. Also, the response of an atomic transition will have directional characteristics, with nulls in the transition cross section for waves arriving from certain directions or with certain polarizations

---

[1] See, for example, Refs. 10-9 and 10-10.

[2] Provided that the antenna is low loss and properly impedance-matched to its output line.

and broad receiving lobes or maxima of the cross section in other directions. These directional characteristics are ordinarily dipolelike for simple electric-dipole-type atomic transitions but can become somewhat more complicated when magnetic-dipole effects and/or degenerate atomic transitions are taken into account.

10-3 LASER OSCILLATION CONDITIONS: OSCILLATION FREQUENCY AND FREQUENCY PULLING

The basic condition for steady-state oscillation in an elementary laser system such as that in Fig. 10-8 is that the net complex round-trip gain be exactly unity; that is,

$$r_1 r_2 e^{2[\alpha_m(\omega) - \alpha_0]L} e^{-2j[\beta_0(\omega) + \Delta\beta_m(\omega)]L} = e^{-jq\pi} \qquad \text{for } q \text{ an integer} \tag{1}$$

In Sec. 10-2 we saw how the magnitude part of this complex expression determines the laser gain coefficient $\alpha_m(\omega)$ necessary for laser oscillation, and hence the required population inversion in the laser material and the minimum pumping power necessary to reach the oscillation threshold. In this section we will consider the phase angle part of Eq. (1). As we will see, the requirement that the phase angles on opposite sides of Eq. (1) be equal determines the exact frequency at which the laser will oscillate, including the usually small but still noticeable pulling of the exact oscillation frequency when the laser cavity resonance and atomic transition frequencies are not exactly coincident.

BASIC OSCILLATION-PHASE CONDITION ■ The condition that the phase angles on both sides of Eq. (1) be equal may be written as

$$\beta_0(\omega) L + \Delta\beta_m(\omega) L = \frac{n_0 \omega L}{c} + \frac{1}{2} \frac{n_0 \omega L}{c} \chi'(\omega) = q\pi \tag{2}$$

where $\beta_0(\omega) = n_0 \omega/c$ is the propagation constant in the laser medium, without the effects of the laser transition itself (but including the background index of refraction n_0 of the laser medium if it is greater than unity), and $\Delta\beta_m(\omega) = \frac{1}{2}\beta_0(\omega)\chi'(\omega)$ is the added phase shift due to the reactive susceptibility χ' of the laser transition. The integer q is the axial-mode index, $\sim 10^5$ to 10^6 in typical laser cavities.

Solving Eq. (2) for ω determines the exact oscillation frequency $\omega = \omega_{osc}$ of the laser. The cold-cavity resonance frequency ω_q for the qth axial mode of the laser cavity in the absence of laser action is given by

$$\frac{n_0 \omega_q L}{c} = q\pi \tag{3}$$

or

$$\omega_q \equiv q \frac{\pi c}{n_0 L} \tag{4}$$

Thus the basic phase condition (2) becomes[1]

$$\omega + \tfrac{1}{2}\omega\chi'(\omega) = \omega_q \tag{5}$$

[1] We are assuming here that n_0 is constant with frequency (i.e., nondispersive) at least to the extent that $\partial n_0(\omega)/\partial\omega \ll n_0/\omega_q$. If this is not the case, a dispersion correction must be included in the above frequency-pulling calculation. However, the general nature of the frequency-pulling effects remains the same, and the dispersion correction, if any, is always very small, except in semiconductor lasers where it can be significant.

If the cavity frequency ω_q is not located exactly at the atomic line center, where $\chi'(\omega) = 0$, then the $\Delta\beta_m(\omega)$ or $\chi'(\omega)$ term will cause ω to be pulled away from ω_q by a small amount. Since the $\chi'(\omega)$ term is in all cases only a small correction term, so that ω is only pulled away from ω_q by a small amount at most, and since $\chi'(\omega)$ does not vary too rapidly with ω, Eq. (5) may be solved approximately, to first order in the frequency pulling, by evaluating $\chi'(\omega)$ at the known axial-mode frequency $\omega = \omega_q$ instead of the initially unknown exact oscillation frequency $\omega = \omega_{osc}$. The oscillation frequency is then given to a very good approximation by

$$\omega = \omega_{osc} \approx \omega_q - \tfrac{1}{2}\omega_q\chi'(\omega_q) \tag{6}$$

The second term on the right-hand side is the frequency-pulling term.

The general nature of this frequency-pulling term is illustrated in Fig. 10-12, which shows the phase shift for one pass down the laser cavity plotted against ω. The basic propagation factor $\beta_0(\omega) = n_0\omega/c$ gives a straight line with slope n_0/c which intersects the resonance value $q\pi$ at the axial-mode cavity resonance frequency $\omega = \omega_q$. The general form of the added phase shift $\Delta\beta_m(\omega) = \tfrac{1}{2}\beta_0\chi'(\omega)$ due to the laser transition is shown along the ω axis and is also added to the β_0 straight line to give the total phase shift (solid line). Note that $\Delta\beta_m(\omega) = 0$ exactly at the atomic transition frequency ω_a and has opposite signs above and below $\omega = \omega_a$.

The shifted or pulled oscillation frequency ω_{osc} is determined by the point at which the total-phase-shift curve given by $\beta_0(\omega)L + \Delta\beta_m(\omega)L$ intercepts the $q\pi$ value necessary to satisfy the phase condition (2). Note that this frequency lies between ω_q and ω_a; that is, the oscillation frequency is pulled[1] away from the cold-cavity resonance

---

[1] In some cases with a very broad low-Q_c cavity resonance and a very sharp high-Q_a atomic transition it may be more appropriate to say that ω_{osc} is pulled away from ω_a and toward ω_q.

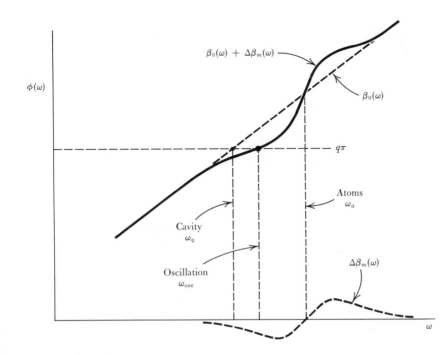

$\phi(\omega)$

$\beta_0(\omega) + \Delta\beta_m(\omega)$

$\beta_0(\omega)$

$q\pi$

Atoms
ω_a

Cavity
ω_q

Oscillation
ω_{osc}

$\Delta\beta_m(\omega)$

ω

FIG. 10-12   A single-pass phase shift down a laser cavity versus optical frequency ω, with and without the atomic transition's phase-shift contribution $\Delta\beta_m(\omega)$ included, to illustrate the frequency-pulling effect in a laser oscillator.

frequency ω_q toward the atomic transition frequency ω_a. (Try redrawing Fig. 10-12 with $\omega_q > \omega_a$ instead of $\omega_q < \omega_a$ to see that the previous statement is equally true in this case.)

FREQUENCY-PULLING
EXPRESSION FOR A
LORENTZIAN TRANSITION

■ The frequency-pulling effect becomes particularly simple for an atomic transition with a lorentzian response. The laser-gain coefficient and laser phase shift in this case may both be expressed in simple form as

$$\alpha_m(\omega) = \alpha_{m0}\frac{1}{1 + [2(\omega - \omega_a)/\Delta\omega_a]^2}$$

$$\Delta\beta_m(\omega) = \alpha_{m0}\frac{2(\omega - \omega_a)/\Delta\omega_a}{1 + [2(\omega - \omega_a)/\Delta\omega_a]^2} = \alpha_m(\omega)\frac{2(\omega - \omega_a)}{\Delta\omega_a}$$

$$(7)$$

From here on we will write the cold-cavity frequency for whatever axial mode we are considering as ω_c (for *cavity*) rather than ω_q, so that $n_0\omega_c L/c = q\pi$. In general this cavity frequency may not be located exactly at the atomic line center; that is, $\omega_c \neq \omega_a$. Phase condition (2) may then be written, from (7), as

$$\frac{n_0\omega L}{c} + 2\alpha_m(\omega)L\frac{\omega - \omega_a}{\Delta\omega_a} = \frac{n_0\omega_c L}{c} \tag{8}$$

which can be manipulated to the form

$$\frac{n_0\omega}{2\alpha_m(\omega)c}(\omega - \omega_c) + \frac{\omega}{\Delta\omega_a}(\omega - \omega_a) = 0 \tag{9}$$

Now, from Eqs. (5) and (7) of Sec. 10-2, the steady state gain requirement for laser oscillation is

$$Q_m = \frac{n_0\omega}{2\alpha_m(\omega)c} = Q_c \tag{10}$$

where the laser-gain coefficient $\alpha_m(\omega)$ must clearly be the gain value evaluated at the frequency ω at which the oscillation is going to occur. Also, the factor $\omega/\Delta\omega_a$ in Eq. (9) is just the atomic linewidth $Q = Q_a$. Therefore Eq. (9) takes the especially simple form

$$Q_c(\omega - \omega_c) + Q_a(\omega - \omega_a) = 0 \tag{11a}$$

or

$$\omega = \omega_{\text{osc}} = \frac{Q_c\omega_c + Q_a\omega_a}{Q_c + Q_a} \tag{11b}$$

This very widely used expression can also be derived in a great many other ways, such as starting from a lumped-circuit cavity model such as Fig. 5-5 and solving for the exact oscillation frequency.

Result (11) again says that the oscillation frequency will lie between the cavity and atomic frequencies ω_c and ω_a, as illustrated in Figs. 10-12 and 10-13, and closer to whichever resonance has the higher Q value. If the cavity Q_c is much higher than the linewidth Q_a (as is usually the case in most, although not all, laser oscillators), then Eq. (12) may be recast in the form

$$\omega_{\text{osc}} = \omega_c + \frac{Q_a}{Q_c + Q_a}(\omega_a - \omega_c)$$

$$\approx \omega_c + \frac{Q_a}{Q_c}(\omega_a - \omega_c) \qquad Q_a \ll Q_c \tag{12}$$

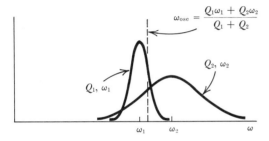

$$\omega_{\mathrm{osc}} = \frac{Q_1\omega_1 + Q_2\omega_2}{Q_1 + Q_2}$$

FIG. 10-13   In any doubly resonant system, such as a resonant cavity plus resonant atoms, the actual oscillation frequency is intermediate between the two different resonance frequencies and closer to whichever one has the higher Q value.

The oscillation frequency ω_{osc} is close to the axial-mode frequency ω_c but is slightly pulled toward the atomic transition frequency ω_a. If, however, the atomic transition happens to be very much sharper than the cavity resonance, then (11) is better put into the opposite form

$$
\begin{aligned}
\omega_{\mathrm{osc}} &= \omega_a + \frac{Q_c}{Q_a + Q_c}(\omega_c - \omega_a) \\
&\approx \omega_a + \frac{Q_c}{Q_a}(\omega_c - \omega_a) \qquad Q_c \ll Q_a
\end{aligned}
\tag{13}
$$

In this case the oscillation occurs essentially at the atomic frequency ω_a, but pulled slightly toward the cavity frequency ω_c. The ammonia-maser microwave frequency standard is a practical example in which the NH_3 atomic transition is enormously sharper than the microwave cavity response even for the highest-Q cavities available. Hence the oscillation frequency stays very close to the unchanging atomic frequency ω_a, as desired in a frequency standard. Any inadvertent detuning of the microwave cavity, $\omega_c \neq \omega_a$, will, however, still cause a frequency-pulling effect. This frequency pulling, although it is small (since it is reduced by the ratio Q_c/Q_a), may still be an important error term in a very-high-accuracy frequency standard.

■ For typical laser devices, in which Q_c is usually much greater than Q_a, the ratio Q_a/Q_c is a measure of the pulling effect of the atomic transition, as shown by Eq. (12). Note, for example, that for several axial modes within a single atomic transition all the axial modes are pulled inward toward the atomic line center, and, from Eq. (12), the amount by which each axial mode is pulled is directly proportional to its initial distance from line center. As a result, the spacing between adjacent axial-mode oscillations is reduced by the same frequency-pulling factor; that is,

$$
f_{q+1} - f_q \approx \left(1 - \frac{Q_a}{Q_c}\right)\frac{c}{2n_0 L} \qquad Q_c \gg Q_a
\tag{14}
$$

The observed frequency difference or beat frequency between adjacent axial modes will be less than the cold-cavity axial-mode spacing $c/2n_0 L$ by the amount of the frequency-pulling factor.

Table 10-2, which gives the expected amounts of frequency pulling for several typical laser systems, illustrates examples of both weak and strong frequency pulling. Thus the 6328-Å He-Ne laser generally requires such a high-Q_c cavity that the frequency pulling correction is only ~0.25 percent in the example shown (i.e., a change of ~600 kHz in the 250-MHz axial-mode spacing). The 3.39-μ He-Ne laser, by contrast, has such high gain per unit length that a very short, high-loss, low-Q_c cavity may be used, with a pulling factor of ~30 percent. Note that if the cavity frequency ω_c

TYPICAL NUMERICAL VALUES

TABLE 10-2
Some typical examples showing
the magnitude of the frequency-
pulling effects in practical lasers

Type of Laser	He–Ne 6328 Å	He–Ne 3.39 μ	Ruby* 300°K	Ruby* 4°K
f_a	4.7×10^{14}	8.85×10^{13}	4.3×10^{14}	4.3×10^{14}
Δf_a	1.5×10^9	2.8×10^8	1.5×10^{11}	3×10^9
Cavity length L, cm	60	10	5	5
Loss/pass δ, %	5	20	20	20
Cavity Q_c	1.2×10^8	$\sim 10^6$	4×10^6	4×10^6
Atomic Q_a	3×10^5	3×10^5	3×10^3	1.5×10^5
Q_a/Q_c	0.0025	0.3	7.5×10^{-4}	0.04

*Mirrors directly on the laser rod.

in such a laser is tuned across the atomic linewidth while the laser is oscillating—for example, by tuning the length L of the laser cavity with a piezoelectric crystal behind one laser mirror—the actual oscillation frequency ω_{osc} will tune at only ~70 percent of the rate predicted for the cavity resonance itself. Figure 10-14 illustrates this effect, which can readily be observed in high-gain low-Q_c lasers such as the He-Ne 3.39 and He-Xe 3.51-μ lasers.

The ruby-laser examples in Table 10-2 are chosen with fairly high-transmission mirrors placed directly on the rod ends in order to lower the cavity Q_c and hence enhance the pulling effect as much as possible. The results show that the very wide atomic linewidth and low Q_a of ruby at room temperature make the pulling effect negligible at that temperature, but at low temperatures the atomic line becomes very much sharper (see Chap. 9), and the pulling effect increases to ~4 percent or more. The resulting reduction in axial-mode beat frequencies from ruby lasers at low temperature can readily be observed.

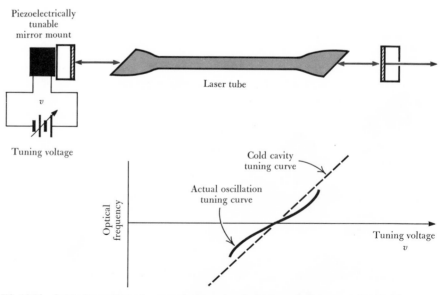

FIG. 10-14 Curves for oscillation-frequency tuning and cavity-frequency tuning versus piezoelectric voltage for a gas laser with a strong frequency-pulling effect. The tuning rate of the actual laser-oscillation frequency is reduced noticeably below the predicted tuning rate for the cold laser cavity.

■ The frequency-pulling behavior can become more complicated for an inhomogeneously broadened laser in which several modes may oscillate simultaneously, with hole burning caused by each of the separate oscillations.[1] Without going into a detailed analysis of this behavior, let us consider the most important physical concepts governing the frequency-pulling in an inhomogeneous line.

As described in Sec. 9-1, an inhomogeneous transition may be treated as the sum of individual homogeneous lines or spectral packets, each with a slightly different resonance frequency ω_a'. The total susceptibility and the total pulling effect in an inhomogeneous line will then be the summation of the contributions from all the individual packets. For example, the $\chi'(\omega)$ in Eq. (5) must be taken as the sum of the χ' effects contributed by all the different spectral packets within the overall inhomogeneous line. Each packet, since it is essentially a separate and (in the laser case) inverted homogeneous transition, will cause a small pulling effect toward itself for a laser mode on either side, just as in the homogeneous case analyzed above. The pulling effect of a given packet with resonant frequency ω_a' on a laser mode located at frequency ω is proportional to $\chi'(\omega: \omega_a')$, where

$$\chi'(\omega: \omega_a') \propto \frac{2(\omega - \omega_a')/\Delta\omega_a}{1 + [2(\omega - \omega_a')/\Delta\omega_a]^2} \tag{15}$$

and $\Delta\omega_a$ is the homogeneous packet linewidth. As shown in Fig. 10-15a, the pulling effect of a given single packet is zero at the packet frequency ω_a', rises to a maximum for frequencies one-half a homogeneous linewidth away on either side of ω_a', and then falls off rather slowly, as $\sim(\omega - \omega_a')^{-1}$, at more distant frequencies.

If no hole-burning effects occur, the total $\chi'(\omega)$ curve for an inhomogeneous line, representing the summation of all individual packets, is virtually the same as if the overall line were homogeneously broadened with the overall inhomogeneous linewidth (Fig. 10-15b). To this degree of approximation, the inhomogeneous line acts the same as an equivalent homogeneous line.

Whenever any packet is partially or completely saturated, and a hole thus burned into the line, the susceptibility contribution, and hence the frequency-pulling contribution, of that packet is reduced or eliminated in direct proportion to the degree of saturation. Hence burning a hole eliminates part or all of a packet's pulling effect. To put this another way, the hole itself may be said to have a *pushing* effect equal to the reduction in the previous pulling effect.

If, however, a single laser oscillation frequency burns only a single hole into an atomic transition, then the most strongly saturated packet in that hole, the packet located right at the oscillation frequency, has no pulling or pushing contribution (since $\chi' = 0$ for a packet exactly on resonance). Moreover, to first order, the changes in the pulling contributions from the partially saturated packets just on either side of the oscillation will be nearly equal and opposite. As a result, when a single oscillation burns a single, not too large hole in an inhomogeneous line, to first order, the pulling of that mode remains unaltered. Even in this case the inhomogeneous line still behaves like the equivalent homogeneous line (Fig. 10-15c).

One new complexity does arise even for single-mode operation in the case of doppler-broadened gas laser transitions. In this case, as already discussed in Chap. 9,

---

[1] The concepts of inhomogeneous broadening and hole burning in atomic transitions were introduced in Chap. 9.

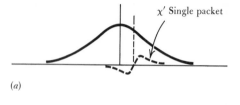

χ' Single packet

(a)

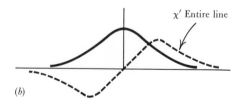

χ' Entire line

(b)

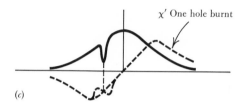

χ' One hole burnt

(c)

FIG. 10-15 Changes in $\chi'(\omega)$, and hence in frequency-pulling effects, caused by hole burning in an inhomogeneous laser transition. (a) The χ' contribution or pulling effect due to a single spectral packet. (b) Total χ' curve due to all packets, without any hole burning. (c) Burning just one hole does not change the χ' value right at the center frequency of the hole, but does change the χ' value away from the hole on either side. (d) The pushing effect of a second hole on the first oscillation frequency must, however, be taken into account.

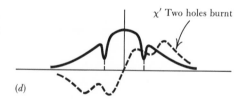

χ' Two holes burnt

(d)

a single oscillation frequency on one side of the atomic line center actually burns two holes symmetrically located on opposite sides of the line center, because of the different doppler conditions for the two oppositely traveling waves that make up the standing wave in the usual laser cavity. The pulling effect (or, more accurately, the pushing effect) of the second hole on the primary laser oscillation must then also be taken into account, as shown in Fig. 10-15d. This effect will become most evident when the primary oscillation is tuned in nearly to the atomic line center, so that the two holes are only a homogeneous linewidth or two apart. The behavior in this region is closely interrelated with the Lamb-dip behavior in the same region (see Sec. 9-4).

Finally, when one mode is already oscillating in an inhomogeneous line, and a second mode then starts oscillation at some distance away in frequency, the hole burned by the second line will cause a reduction in the pulling effect due to its packets on the first mode. In the simplest case the startup of the second mode causes the first mode's oscillation frequency to move slightly away from the second mode; i.e. there is a *repulsion* between the two modes. This general effect continues to exist, but becomes more complex in the gas-laser case, where each oscillation burns two symmetrically located holes. We must then take into account the net repulsion effect of all the holes, considering their sizes and their distance from each other.

All the effects described above are small, especially where they entail small changes in the already small primary pulling effects. However, in a cw gas laser, for example, the frequency difference between two simultaneously oscillating modes can be measured to very high precision simply by measuring the beat or difference frequency generated when the laser output falls on any sufficiently high-frequency photodetector. Very small frequency shifts in this beat frequency due to changing second-order pulling effects can then be easily detected.

As the most common illustration of this, the beat frequency at 150 MHz between adjacent axial modes is easily observed in a typical commercial He-Ne laser with a 1-m-long cavity. Perhaps 10 adjacent axial modes will be oscillating in this case, and the frequency difference, $f_{q+1} - f_q$, between each pair will be slightly different because of second-order pulling effects. The observed beat at 150 MHz will not be a clean signal, but will have random jumps and shifts over a range of ~100 kHz as the various axial modes compete with one another, turn on and off, and are slowly scanned across the atomic transition by thermal changes in the length of the laser cavity.

10-4 RATE EQUATIONS FOR A LASER OSCILLATOR

In Secs. 10-2 and 10-3 the condition for steady-state laser oscillation was used to find the threshold population inversion and the frequency-pulling effects in a laser oscillator. In this section we will develop a relatively simple set of *cavity and atomic rate equations* which can be used to describe in more detail the transient and dynamical behavior both of the atomic energy-level populations and of the cavity-mode oscillation level. Later we will employ these useful rate equations to calculate the laser power output versus pumping level, the optimum coupling to the laser for maximum power output, the transient response, or spiking behavior, observed in some lasers, and other important properties of laser oscillators.

■ Consider a laser cavity which is not in steady-state oscillation, but which at a given instant t may be operating either above or below its steady-state gain and oscillation levels. As a measure of the instantaneous signal level in the cavity, let us write $\tilde{u}(t)e^{j\omega t}$ for the instantaneous value of the signal wave traveling to the right in the cavity at an arbitrarily chosen reference plane somewhere inside the cavity, as illustrated in Fig. 10-16. The complex phasor amplitude $\tilde{u}(t)$ of this wave will in fact be varying in time, in either amplitude and/or phase, if the laser signal is not in a steady state.

LASER CAVITY NOT IN STEADY STATE

If we follow any small segment of this wave for one complete round trip inside the laser cavity, which takes a round-trip transit time $2T$, we will see this segment of the wave increase in amplitude by the factor

$$|\tilde{u}(t + 2T)| = r_1 r_2 e^{2(\alpha_m - \alpha_0)L} |\tilde{u}(t)| \tag{1}$$

where $2T = 2n_0 L/c$ is twice the one-way transit time down the laser. The signal-energy

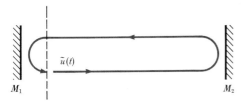

FIG. 10-16 Model for analyzing the transient signal behavior inside a laser cavity. The complex amplitude $\tilde{u}(t)$ represents the optical wave amplitude traveling to the right at a reference plane just inside the mirror M_1.

density $W(t)$ inside the laser cavity is proportional to this wave amplitude squared; that is, $W(t) = \text{const} \times |\tilde{u}(t)|^2$. Hence the increase in signal energy inside the cavity in one round trip is given by

$$W(t + 2T) = R_1 R_2 e^{4(\alpha_m - \alpha_0)L} W(t) = W(t) + \Delta W(2T) \tag{2}$$

which we can rewrite as

$$\ln\left[1 + \frac{\Delta W(2T)}{W(t)}\right] = 4\alpha_m L - 4\alpha_0 L - \ln\frac{1}{R_1 R_2} \tag{3}$$

If the net gain in energy ΔW per round trip is not too large compared to the signal energy W already there, we may use the approximation $\ln(1 + x) \approx x$ to write this as

$$\Delta W(2T) \approx \left(4\alpha_m L - 4\alpha_0 L - \ln\frac{1}{R_1 R_2}\right) W(t) \tag{4}$$

Then, dividing both sides of this equation by $2T$, using the definitions of maser Q_m and cavity Q_c, and noting that $2T$ is typically a very small time interval compared to the transient buildup times or response times of lasers, we can convert (4) to the differential equation

$$\frac{\Delta W(2T)}{2T} = \frac{dW(t)}{dt} = \left(\frac{\omega}{Q_m} - \frac{\omega}{Q_c}\right) W(t) \tag{5}$$

This is the equation of motion governing the transient buildup or decay of the laser-cavity signal level $W(t)$. According to this equation, the laser's instantaneous energy or power level must grow, decay, or remain steady according to the following conditions:

$Q_m < Q_c$ growth (buildup) with time
$Q_m > Q_c$ decay of the signal level with time
$Q_m = Q_c$ steady state, no change in signal level with time

Both these conclusions, and the differential equation itself, seem entirely reasonable and in accord with the expected behavior for any resonant system having both a positive-loss or absorptive $Q = Q_c$ and a negative-loss or amplifying $Q = -Q_m$.

CAVITY PHOTON NUMBER AND CAVITY RATE EQUATION ■ Although we could continue to develop our analysis in terms of the signal energy density $W(t)$ in the laser cavity, our equations and discussions will become more graphic and somewhat more elegant if we choose to write instead the *number of photons* $n(t)$ in the laser cavity mode. The number of photons in the laser cavity will be directly proportional to the energy in the cavity mode; that is,

$$n(t) = \text{const} \times W(t) \tag{6}$$

and we will not actually need to know the value of the proportionality constant. [If, however, $W(t)$ is interpreted as the laser signal energy per unit length, then to a first approximation, $n(t) = (L/hf)W(t)$, where L is the cavity length.]

Also, the laser gain coefficient α_m or the inverse maser Q_m of the laser medium will be directly proportional to the population difference on the laser transition; that is,

$$\frac{2\alpha_m c}{n_0} = \frac{\omega}{Q_m} = K(\mathcal{N}_2 - \mathcal{N}_1) \tag{7}$$

where the indices 2 and 1 indicate the upper and lower laser levels, and K is the proportionality constant. Using this and the relation $\omega/Q_c = \tau_c^{-1}$, we may write the differential equation for $W(t)$ in rate-equation form as

$$\frac{d}{dt}n(t) = K[\mathcal{N}_2(t) - \mathcal{N}_1(t)]n(t) - \tau_c^{-1}n(t) \tag{8}$$

This rate equation expresses the rate of growth or decay of the number of laser photons as determined by the instantaneous populations on the laser transition and the losses in the laser cavity. The first, or $K(\mathcal{N}_2 - \mathcal{N}_1)$, factor represents the growth of the signal in time due to stimulated emission if the laser transition is inverted (or the decay due to net stimulated absorption if it is not inverted), and the τ_c^{-1} factor represents the signal-energy decay due to the combination of internal cavity losses plus cavity output coupling. The level populations $\mathcal{N}_1(t)$ and $\mathcal{N}_2(t)$ are themselves functions of time, under the combined influences of pumping, relaxation, and stimulated transition terms.

Note again the confusion that can arise from indiscriminate use of the photon concept, particularly in situations where the wave behavior of light is significant. The "photon" rate equation in this section is not intended to add in any way to the photon concept. All that we are doing here is writing an essentially classical equation for the rate of change of the stored energy in a resonant circuit with positive and negative losses, and then choosing to measure this signal energy in units of size hf which we call "photons." This is a convenient energy unit to use because it also happens to be the maximum energy which can be obtained from a single atom. The significance of the photon concept need not be carried any further than this, at least not at the present moment.

Also, note that by writing an equation for the transient response of the signal *energy* in the cavity, we get a rather simple real first-order differential equation, but at the price of losing, or at least hiding, any information about the complex amplitude and particularly the *phase* of the laser signal. If we are interested only in the laser's signal-energy level or power output, then the photon rate equations (5) or (8) offer a particularly simple and useful method of analysis, as we will see in the following sections. However, if we want to keep track of the instantaneous phase, or frequency, or complex amplitude of the laser signal—or if several laser signals are present simultaneously—then the cavity rate-equation approach is not adequate, and we must go to a more complex circuit equation for the laser cavity. We will develop such a laser circuit equation in Sec. 10-9.

■ Suppose an inverted population is established in a laser cavity with no laser signal present initially, but with the laser gain exceeding the cavity losses. Then a laser oscillation will be started in the cavity starting by noise (we can never say that there is absolutely no initial signal in the cavity, because some initial noise excitation is always present). Equations (5) or (8) predict that the initial growth of this laser signal should be exponential with time, i.e., that the signal amplitude plotted on a logarithmic scale should increase linearly with time.

Figure 10-17 shows a particularly clean experimental verification of just such exponential signal growth in an He-Ne 6328-Å laser for two different pumping levels. In these experiments the He-Ne laser tube was excited while the beam path inside the laser cavity was blocked by a fast-opening shutter to prevent laser oscillation from starting (the shutter consisted of a small elastic rod bent over to block the laser beam inside the cavity, and then suddenly released to unblock the cavity). While the cavity was blocked the pumping was sufficient to make the unsaturated laser gain exceed the

EXPERIMENTAL ILLUSTRATION OF LASER TRANSIENT BUILDUP

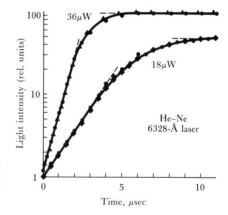

FIG. 10-17   Experimental results showing the exponential transient buildup of laser oscillations in a 6328-Å He-Ne laser cavity for two different values of pumping level, and hence of exponential growth rate. [From G. K. Born, "The growth of laser oscillations," *Appl. Phys. Letters*, **12**:46 (Jan. 15, 1968).]

normal cavity losses by a significant amount. When the cavity was suddenly unblocked, the signal level grew exponentially (from noise), as predicted.[1] This growth continued until the signal level became large enough to begin saturating the atomic transition and reducing the laser gain down toward its steady-state-oscillation level (which must, of course, just equal the total cavity losses). The saturation process accounts for the slowing down of the growth rate and the eventual change to a steady signal level shown by both curves in Fig. 10-17.

The figure shows results for two different pumping levels in the laser tube, leading to different values of initial growth rate (or unsaturated gain) and steady-state power output. Of course, as we saw in Fig. 10-7, if we pump *too* hard on this type of laser, the eventual result will be that both the unsaturated gain and the steady-state power output begin to *decrease* instead of increase with further increases in the pumping level.

NEXT STEPS IN THE DERIVATION

■ Despite its partial verification by this experimental result, the rate equation in the form given by Eq. (8) is still not adequate for a complete description of laser action in a laser cavity mode. To develop a complete rate-equation description for laser action, several further important steps are needed:

1. We must add to the cavity rate equation the necessary atomic rate equation(s) to describe the dynamics of the level populations on the laser transition.
2. We must introduce from quantum theory certain necessary spontaneous-emission terms into both the cavity and atomic rate equations.
3. We must then expand our analysis to account for the fact that there are actually multiple cavity modes within the atomic linewidth in any realistic laser cavity.
4. We must combine all these features to obtain an evaluation of the coupling coefficient K appearing in the rate equations.

We will now undertake each of these steps in order.

ATOMIC RATE EQUATIONS

■ From Chap. 6, we know that the atomic energy-level populations in a laser will be governed by rate equations of the form

$$\frac{d}{dt}N_2(t) = -W_{12}(t)N_2(t) + W_{12}(t)N_1(t)$$

$$+ \text{ relaxation terms } + \text{ pumping terms} \quad (9)$$

[1] Results are from Ref. 10-2. Note that the initial noise level is actually extremely small, and there are many decades of earlier signal buildup not seen in Fig. 10-17 because the earlier parts of the signal are too weak to be detected readily.

with a similar expression for the lower laser level $N_1(t)$. The relaxation terms and pumping terms in these equations will be different for each type of atomic laser system, and for the moment we need not worry about their detailed form. However, we do need to note that the stimulated transition probability W_{12} appearing in the stimulated-emission part of these equations is directly proportional in magnitude to the internal signal energy density in the laser cavity, i.e., to $W(t)$ or to the photon number $n(t)$. Hence we may write

$$W_{12}(t) \equiv K'n(t) \tag{10}$$

and the general form of the atomic rate equation becomes

$$\frac{d}{dt} N_2(t) = -K'n(t)N_2(t) + K'n(t)N_1(t) + \text{relaxation} + \text{pumping}$$

$$= -K'n(t)[N_2(t) - N_1(t)] + \text{relaxation} + \text{pumping} \tag{11}$$

The initial terms on the right-hand side are clearly the stimulated-emission-absorption terms, and K' is some as yet unknown proportionality constant.

Now, from conservation of energy, whenever an atom drops from the upper to the lower laser level owing to a stimulated-emission process, the number of photons in the cavity mode must increase by one.[1] This process is described in the cavity rate equation by the term $(d/dt)n = +KnN_2$ and in the atomic rate equation by the term $(d/dt)N_2 = -K'N_2n$. But the energy flows will be equal only if these terms in the separate rate equations are equal, and this will be true, as it must be, only if

$$K' \equiv K \tag{12}$$

that is, the constants K and K' in the photon and atomic rate equations must be identically the same quantities. (Note that N_1 and N_2 in these equations must mean the *total number* of lower- and upper-level atoms in the laser cavity, rather than the number *densities*.)

Thus there is really only one unknown proportionality constant or coupling constant K in the cavity and atomic rate equations. With the additions to be made in the next several paragraphs, these rate equations will form a coupled set of equations which fully determine the dynamics of a laser oscillator.

■ Spontaneous emission is a fundamental process in all quantum systems and is especially important as a relaxation process in atomic systems. Spontaneous emission can be predicted, in the most basic analysis, only by starting with a fully quantum-mechanical analysis not only of the atoms, but also of the radiation with which the atoms interact. Hence we cannot give any real derivation of the origin of spontaneous emission here. We can only assert that spontaneous emission exists and then describe its effects (we will see the close relationship between spontaneous emission, thermal noise, and blackbody radiation in the following chapter, however). Fortunately, the effects caused by spontaneous emission can be introduced into the cavity and atomic rate equations in a very simple way.

As a part of the downward atomic relaxation from level 2 (or from any other

SPONTANEOUS EMISSION

---

[1] Once again, single atoms do not in fact make isolated jumps between levels, and stimulated emission is really more than just causing an atom to make such a jump (see Appendix A). However, the crude description above is, for our present purposes, an acceptable way of summarizing the energy flow in the stimulated-emission process.

excited atomic level), some atoms in level 2 will drop to level 1 by *spontaneous* emission of photons of energy into the cavity resonant mode, thereby increasing the photon number $n(t)$ by a corresponding amount. This spontaneous emission of energy from the atoms to the cavity is separate from and in addition to the *stimulated*-emission transitions already included in Eqs. (8) and (11). The rate at which this spontaneous emission occurs is directly proportional to the number of atoms N_2 that are in the upper level and available to emit, but is completely independent of the already existing photon number n. To describe this we include in the rate equations a *spontaneous-emission coefficient* K_{spon} of the general form

$$\frac{d}{dt} n(t) = -\frac{d}{dt} N_2(t) = +\frac{d}{dt} N_1(t) = K_{spon} N_2(t) \tag{13}$$

Another basic point about spontaneous emission is that the rate at which spontaneous emission takes place into any single cavity mode is always just equal to the rate at which stimulated emission would take place into that mode if it contained a net signal energy or photon number of exactly one photon. That is, the spontaneous rate $K_{spon} N_2$ will be exactly the same as the stimulated rate KnN_2 in which the photon number has been set equal to $n = 1$. Therefore we have the very basic result

$$K_{spon} \equiv K \tag{14}$$

Because the stimulated and spontaneous coefficients are always equal, the combined stimulated-plus-spontaneous-emission terms in both the atomic and the cavity rate equations may be written in the general forms

$$\frac{d}{dt} n(t) = -\frac{d}{dt} N_2(t) = +\frac{d}{dt} N_1(t) = \underset{\text{stimulated}}{Kn(N_2 - N_1)} + \underset{\text{spontaneous}}{KN_2}$$

$$= K(n + 1)N_2 - KnN_1 \tag{15}$$

Note that if the atoms spontaneously radiate photons in the atomic rate equations, then the cavity mode must receive these photons in the cavity rate equation. Also, the extra factor of $+1$ appearing in the N_2 terms is often referred to as the *extra photon*.

CAVITY MODES AND MODE DENSITY
■ In analyzing optical masers (although usually not low-frequency or microwave masers) we must also take into account the fact that any optical cavity of larger than microscopic size will support an enormous number of resonant modes. Now, the optical resonator modes described in Chap. 8, including even the higher-order transverse modes, all travel primarily in the axial direction. These modes represent, in fact, only a small fraction of all the possible resonant modes traveling in all possible directions inside an optical cavity. Of course, only the axially traveling modes are likely to be low-loss or high-Q_c modes, but the other modes exist nonetheless.

Consider some general cavity of arbitrary shape and of size large, at least compared to an optical wavelength. Such a cavity will have some lowest-frequency resonant mode, perhaps at a frequency down around the microwave range, or at least at a frequency where the cavity dimensions are comparable to the resonant wavelength (or half-wavelength, perhaps). Then there will be another resonant mode at some slightly higher frequency, and at increasing frequencies more and more higher-order resonant modes.[1]

---

[1] See any textbook on electromagnetic theory or microwaves for examples of the resonant-cavity mode frequencies in typical cavity shapes.

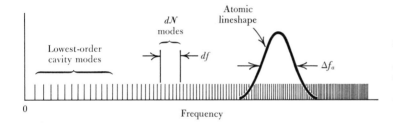

FIG. 10-18 The dense spectrum of resonant-mode frequencies for any optical cavity of dimensions large compared to an optical wavelength. There will be dN such resonant modes within any little frequency range df, and a very large number of resonances lying within the atomic linewidth Δf_a.

At successively higher frequencies, where the cavity dimensions become large compared to the resonant wavelengths, the resonant modes become very closely spaced and form a dense collection of cavity resonant frequencies. Figure 10-18 illustrates in schematic fashion the dense spectrum of resonant modes that can be expected, with many such resonant modes running through and falling within a typical atomic-transition linewidth. The high-Q, primarily axial modes of Chap. 8 are only a small fraction of all these modes. It can be shown quite generally that the number of resonant modes dN for any cavity of total cavity volume V whose resonant frequencies will fall in a narrow frequency range df about a center frequency f is given by

$$dN = \frac{8\pi V}{(\lambda/n_0)^3} \frac{df}{f} = \frac{8\pi n_0^3 f^2 V \, df}{c^3} \tag{16}$$

This expression depends only on the total volume of the cavity and is entirely independent of the cavity shape, the boundary conditions at the cavity walls, and similar factors. It can be derived, however, simply by counting the appropriate number of resonant frequencies for some simple cavity shape, such as a rectangle or cylinder, for which the exact mode frequencies are known from microwave cavity theory.

A very important number that will appear in the following analyses is the *total number of cavity modes for a laser cavity of volume V whose resonant frequencies will lie within the full atomic linewidth Δf_a of the atomic transition.* From Eq. (16), this number, which is often denoted by the symbol p, is given by

$$p = \frac{8\pi n_0^3 V}{\lambda^3} \frac{\Delta f_a}{f_a} = \frac{8\pi V f^2 \, \Delta f_a}{(c/n_0)^3} \tag{17}$$

For any practical laser cavity p is an enormous number. Table 10-3 gives sizes of p for some typical laser cavities of different types. The injection-laser diode, with its extremely small cavity volume, is a somewhat special case but still has $p \sim 10^6$. Most other types of lasers have values of $p \sim 10^9$ to 10^{12}—an enormous number of potentially available modes in which laser action might occur.

■ Each separate cavity mode in a multimode laser cavity is essentially independent of and uncoupled from all the other cavity modes, except for the fact that all the cavity

MULTIPLE-CAVITY-MODE RATE EQUATIONS

TABLE 10-3

	He–Ne 6328-Å laser	Ruby laser rod 300°K	GaAs injection-laser diode
Cavity length L	1 m	7.5 cm	0.3 mm
Cavity diameter	3 mm	1 cm	$1 \times 50 \, \mu$
Atomic linewidth	1.5 GHz	150 GHz	8500 GHz (200 Å)
n_0	1	1.76	3.6
p	$\sim 2 \times 10^9$	$\sim 8 \times 10^{11}$	$\sim 7 \times 10^5$

modes are coupled to the common laser atomic system. As a result, if each separate cavity mode is labeled by an index i, a separate cavity rate equation can be written for the photon number $n^i(t)$ in each mode, with the same atomic populations $\mathcal{N}_1(t)$ and $\mathcal{N}_2(t)$ in each case. The rate equation for each cavity photon number will have the general form derived above, that is,

$$\frac{d}{dt} n^i(t) = K^i[n^i(t) + 1]\mathcal{N}_2(t) - K^i n^i(t)\mathcal{N}_1(t) - n^i(t)/\tau_c{}^i$$

$$i = 1, 2, 3, \ldots \quad (18)$$

Note that spontaneous emission has been included, and that each different mode will in general have a different value of cavity lifetime $\tau_c{}^i$ and coupling coefficient K^i. The cavity lifetime will be longest for the lowest-loss or axially traveling type of modes and will be very short for the vast majority of higher-order and nonaxial modes, since these modes generally have very high losses out the open sides of a normal laser cavity. The coupling parameter K^i will be largest for those modes whose resonant frequencies are at the center of the atomic resonance and will decrease to a negligible value for modes well outside the atomic linewidth. In fact, K^i should vary with the cavity mode frequency ω_i essentially like the atomic lineshape or gain factor $\chi''(\omega_i)$. If the atomic transition has a preferred type of field polarization for maximum response (as most such transitions do), then the value of K^i will also vary depending on how well the polarization of the mode fields matches the optimum polarization for the transition.

At the same time, the atomic rate equations for $\mathcal{N}_1(t)$ and $\mathcal{N}_2(t)$ must include the *total* effects of *all* the cavity modes on the atomic populations. The stimulated and spontaneous effects of all the cavity photon densities $n^i(t)$ must be considered as acting on the atoms in parallel. Figure 10-19 illustrates schematically the general form of the interactions between the atoms and the multiple cavity modes. The atomic rate equations will then have the general form

$$\frac{d}{dt}\mathcal{N}_1(t) = \sum_i K^i n^i(t)[\mathcal{N}_2(t) - \mathcal{N}_1(t)] + \sum_i K^i \mathcal{N}_2(t)$$

$$+ \text{ nonradiative relaxation} + \text{ pumping}$$

$$(19)$$

$$\frac{d}{dt}\mathcal{N}_2(t) = -\sum_i K^i n^i(t)[\mathcal{N}_2(t) - \mathcal{N}_1(t)] - \sum_i K^i \mathcal{N}_2(t)$$

$$+ \text{ nonradiative relaxation} + \text{ pumping}$$

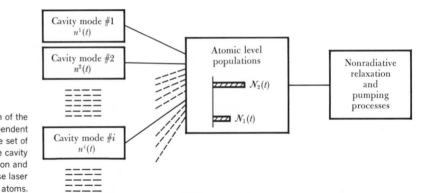

FIG. 10-19 A schematic diagram of the interactions between the many independent cavity resonant modes, showing the set of laser atoms interacting with all these cavity modes and the nonradiative-relaxation and pumping process also acting on these laser atoms.

Figure 10-20 shows a more specific two-energy-level model that might be used to write the nonradiative-relaxation and pumping terms in more specific form.

In general, these two atomic rate equations must be combined with the nearly infinite set of cavity rate equations ($\sim 10^6$ to 10^{10} equations) to specify fully the behavior of a laser oscillator. Fortunately, in practical cases we need the cavity rate equations for only one, or at most only a few, of the lowest-loss cavity modes from among the set of all possible cavity modes. This reduction is possible because only these few favored or lowest-loss modes will build up photon numbers $n^i(t)$ that are significant, while all the other modes will generally have photon numbers that remain at unity or less (as we will see in more detail after Sec. 10-8).

■ When an atom spontaneously goes from level 2 to level 1 by emitting a photon into one or another of the available cavity modes, this represents a process of *purely radiative relaxation* for that atom. In fact, the next major point is that the summation of all such spontaneous emissions from the atoms into all the available cavity modes is really *the same thing as* the total spontaneous emission, or the total purely radiative relaxation, of the atoms on the $2 \rightarrow 1$ transition.

Most laser cavities have open sides, so that the cavity volume must be viewed as bounded by the end mirrors plus imaginary side walls located at the outer edges of the laser rod, laser tube, or laser material. The exact choice of location of these imaginary side walls is not important. Indeed, in the optical case any arbitrary large volume filled with atoms can be considered to be a cavity, with a cavity resonant-mode density expressed by Eq. (16), even though this volume may have no reflecting walls at all. In any of these situations, most if not all the resonant modes of the cavity will be very lossy. Any energy placed in the modes (for example, as a result of spontaneous emission) will rapidly leak out through the open walls of the cavity and be radiated away in all directions.

Thus as the atoms spontaneously emit energy into the cavity resonant modes, this energy is in turn radiated out of the cavity in all directions. An observer looking toward the cavity or the atoms can see this radiation (with some appropriate detector if the wavelengths involved are not in the visible region). To describe this in one way, the atoms spontaneously emit energy into the cavity modes and excite them in noiselike fashion, and the modes then leak or radiate energy out in all directions at the same rate. To describe this same physical process in another way, each atom spontaneously emits fluorescent radiation into all directions, and the observer looking toward the atoms simply sees some of this spontaneous emission or radiative relaxation.

These two descriptions are really just alternative ways of describing exactly the same physical phenomenon. Spontaneous emission by the atoms into all the available (and lossy) cavity modes is exactly the same thing as atomic radiative relaxation or fluorescent emission into all available directions. In mathematical terms, the total relaxation rate, radiative plus nonradiative, of atoms from level 2 down to level 1 may be expressed in either of the alternative forms

$$\left[\frac{d}{dt} N_2(t) \right]_{2 \to 1} = \text{spontaneous emission} + \text{nonradiative relaxation}$$

$$= -\left(\sum_i K^i \right) N_2(t) - \frac{N_2(t)}{\tau_{\text{nonrad}}}$$

$$= -\left[\frac{N_2(t)}{\tau_{\text{rad}}} + \frac{N_2(t)}{\tau_{\text{nonrad}}} \right] \tag{20}$$

RADIATIVE VERSUS NONRADIATIVE ATOMIC RELAXATION

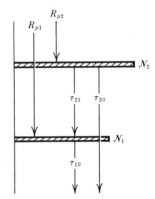

FIG. 10-20   A moderately detailed model for the laser atomic level populations, showing some of the possible pumping and relaxation rates into and out of the upper and lower laser levels.

The purely radiative decay on the $2 \rightarrow 1$ transition is then just the summation of all the $K^i N_2$ terms, and we can make the very important identification that

$$\frac{1}{\tau_{\text{rad}}} \equiv \sum_i K^i \tag{21}$$

This establishes an important connection between the K^i coefficients, which are parameters both of the cavity and of the atoms, and the atomic radiative lifetime τ_{rad}, which is really an atomic parameter only, entirely independent of the cavity.

EVALUATION OF THE COUPLING COEFFICIENT K

■ We can now use the preceding relation to evaluate the coupling coefficient K. The cavity modes i of an optical cavity will all have their energy distributed more or less uniformly through the cavity volume occupied by the laser atoms. Hence all the cavity modes should interact equally well with the laser atoms, except for the atomic-lineshape response factor of the atoms and, possibly, effects due to differing polarizations of the mode fields. If, for example, the atomic transition has a lorentzian response, we can expect that the K^i coefficients for different modes having different resonant frequencies ω_i will all be of the general form

$$K^i = \alpha_i \frac{K_0}{1 + [2(\omega_i - \omega_a)/\Delta\omega_a]^2} \tag{22}$$

where α_i is a *polarization factor* measuring how well the actual polarization of the fields of a particular mode matches up with the optimum polarization needed to excite the strongest atomic response per unit amount of laser signal energy density, and K_0 is the value of K^i for a strongly interacting mode located at the atomic line center.

In laser materials such as gases the atoms may be described as being randomly oriented in all directions, and there is no polarization dependence in the overall response of the laser material (at least, not unless some orienting influence such as a dc magnetic field is applied to the material). In this case the polarization factor may be taken to be $\alpha_i = 1$ for all modes. In single-crystal laser materials the individual atoms may have a definite orientation axis with respect to the crystal axes. The polarization factors for individual modes in this case may range from zero (for modes with exactly the wrong polarization to excite any atomic response) to a maximum of about 3 (for modes with exactly the optimum polarization). It can be shown, although we will not do so here, that in this case the average response, averaged over all modes, will be about one-third of the maximum response, or $\langle \alpha_i \rangle = 1$ in this case. Therefore, in the absence of more specific information, we can say only that α_i is a dimensionless parameter that may vary from zero to as much as 3 (in anisotropic crystalline materials), with an average value over all modes of unity.

We wish now to evaluate the summation of K^i over all modes as in Eq. (21), using the general form of Eq. (22) for K^i. The lorentzian form in Eq. (22) can be integrated over all frequencies, but as a simpler way to get a first-order approximate answer we can simply say that K^i will be close to the optimum value $K^i \approx K_0$ for all those modes within about one atomic linewidth Δf_a centered at $f = f_a$, while $K^i \approx 0$ for all modes farther away from the atomic resonance. Using this approximation plus the averaged value of unity for α_i, we obtain

$$\sum_i K^i \approx K_0 \times \frac{p \text{ modes}}{\text{within } \Delta f_a} = pK_0$$

$$= \frac{8\pi n_0^3 V}{\lambda^3} \frac{\Delta f_a}{f} K_0 = \frac{1}{\tau_{\text{rad}}} \tag{23}$$

where $p \equiv (8\pi n_0{}^3 V/\lambda^3)(\Delta f_a/f_a)$ is the number of cavity modes within the atomic linewidth, as defined earlier. We then obtain for the K^i value of a mode at or near the atomic line center

$$K^i \approx \alpha_i K_0 \approx \frac{\alpha_i}{p\tau_{\mathrm{rad}}} \approx \alpha_i \frac{\lambda^3}{8\pi n_0{}^3 V} \frac{f_a}{\Delta f_a \tau_{\mathrm{rad}}} \qquad (24)$$

This important result expresses the coupling coefficient K in terms of measurable cavity and atomic parameters. More exact calculations show that this is indeed a very good approximation, and we will be able to make good use of this result in later sections.
■ One major conclusion we will reach later is that in any cavity mode that is below threshold, and hence not oscillating, the photon number n^i remains small, usually $n^i \ll 1$. The contribution of any such mode to the atomic rate equations (11) or (19) through *stimulated* emission is then also small. Furthermore, the contribution to the N_1 and N_2 equations caused by *spontaneous* emission into all the many below-threshold modes is automatically taken care of simply by including a $-N_2/\tau_{\mathrm{rad}}$ term in the atomic rate equations. Therefore the cavity rate equations for all these below-threshold modes supply no useful information, and we need not write them.

SINGLE-CAVITY-MODE APPROXIMATION

The photon number n^i will become large enough to be significant only in those few preferred cavity modes having low enough losses, or long enough cavity lifetimes $\tau_c{}^i$, that these modes reach or exceed the laser oscillation threshold. In simplified or idealized cases, especially with homogeneously broadened lines and carefully designed laser cavities, there may be only a single preferred mode that has a slightly lower loss and a slightly lower laser threshold than all the other modes. If this is the case, then it is necessary to write out only the one cavity rate equation for that mode. The mode index i may be dropped, and only the single cavity rate equation for the photon density $n(t)$ in that particular mode need be written out.

The complete set of cavity-plus-atomic rate equations then reverts to the simplified and manageable form

$$\frac{d}{dt}n = K(N_2 - N_1)n + KN_2 - \frac{n}{\tau_c}$$

$$\frac{d}{dt}N_2 = Kn(N_2 - N_1) + \text{total relaxation} + \text{pumping} \qquad (25)$$

$$\frac{d}{dt}N_1 = -Kn(N_2 - N_1) + \text{total relaxation} + \text{pumping}$$

Note that the spontaneous emission into the single preferred cavity mode is included in the cavity rate equation for that mode, but the spontaneous emission of the atoms into all the cavity modes is taken care of simply by absorbing this effect into the total-relaxation terms for the atomic populations. We will examine some of the most important properties of this simplified single-mode situation in the following sections.

Let us review briefly some of the approximations and idealizations in this general rate-equation approach to laser dynamics. In the atomic rate equations we are neglecting the *phase information* in the atomic response, as well as various *higher-order nonlinear effects* that may arise with very narrow atomic lines and strong applied signals. We have not included the possibility of *spatial variations* in the inverted-population density or possible changes in this spatial distribution with time caused by time-and-space-varying saturation. Also, in describing the energy-level populations by single numbers N_1 and N_2 we are assuming that the atomic transition is *homogeneously broadened,* or at least acts as if it were. We also neglect other effects that can become important in special situations, such as the *scattering of energy* from one cavity mode into others, and the general time variation in cavity-mode parameters that occurs during laser action because the laser cavity vibrates, heats up, or otherwise changes with time. Finally, there is the approximation in representing the cavity signal by only a photon rate equation, and not a complex *circuit equation*—an approximation we will seek to remove in the final section of this chapter.

10-5   STEADY-STATE SOLUTIONS: SATURATION AND LASER-POWER OUTPUT

In this section we will apply the laser rate equations derived in the preceding section to predict the laser-power output versus pump-power input for an idealized single-mode laser oscillator and to explain various other aspects of laser oscillation and saturation.

SIMPLIFIED SINGLE-MODE LASER MODEL

■ As we noted at the end of the preceding section, under ideal conditions one preferred laser cavity mode may have significantly lower loss, and hence a significantly lower threshold inversion requirement, than any of the other cavity modes. As a result, with a homogeneous laser transition, only this one mode will ever be able to reach threshold in the steady state, and only this one mode will acquire any significant number of photons. It is then necessary to write only a single cavity rate equation in order to keep track of the number of photons $n(t)$ in this one preferred mode.

Also, it will simplify our initial analysis, without changing the basic character of the results, if we assume an idealized two-level atomic system as in Fig. 10-21, in which level 1 has such rapid relaxation to lower energy levels that its population remains negligible, $N_1 \approx 0$, under all conditions and in which there is pumping at a rate R_p into the upper laser level 2 only. With these approximations, the laser is governed by the two coupled cavity-plus-atomic rate equations

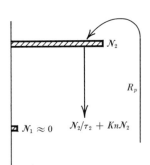

FIG. 10-21   A simplified model for the laser atomic system. The downward relaxation out of the lower laser level is assumed to be sufficiently fast that $N_1 \approx 0$ at all times.

$$\frac{d}{dt} n(t) = K[n(t) + 1] N_2(t) - \frac{n(t)}{\tau_c} \tag{1a}$$

$$\frac{d}{dt} N_2(t) = -Kn(t)N_2(t) - \frac{N_2(t)}{\tau_2} + R_p \tag{1b}$$

where τ_2 is the total lifetime of the upper laser level due to all decay mechanisms. Because of the product terms $n(t)N_2(t)$, these equations are basically nonlinear, but their solutions, at least in the steady-state case, are still straightforward.

STEADY-STATE SOLUTIONS: BEHAVIOR BELOW THRESHOLD

■ By setting the time derivatives $d/dt = 0$ in both equations, we may obtain the interconnected steady-state solutions to these two basic equations. Thus the steady-state solution to Eq. (1a) may be written in the two alternative ways

$$n = \frac{N_2}{(K\tau_c)^{-1} - N_2} = \frac{N_2}{N_{2,\text{th}} - N_2} \tag{2a}$$

$$N_2 = \frac{1}{K\tau_c} \frac{n}{n+1} = N_{2,\text{th}} \frac{n}{n+1} \tag{2b}$$

and Equation (1b) yields the two alternative forms

$$N_2 = \frac{R_p \tau_2}{1 + K\tau_2 n} \tag{3a}$$

$$n = \frac{R_p \tau_2 - N_2}{K\tau_2 N_2} \tag{3b}$$

It is useful to examine these expressions to obtain some general understanding of the expected behavior.

First of all, it is obvious from Eq. (2a) that there is a critical, or *threshold, value* of the upper-level population N_2 given by

$$N_{2,\text{th}} \equiv \frac{1}{K\tau_c} = \frac{p\tau_{\text{rad}}}{\alpha\tau_c} \tag{4}$$

For populations well below this value, $N_2 \ll N_{2,\text{th}}$, the cavity photon number is small, $n \ll 1$. As the population approaches this threshold value, $N_2 \to N_{2,\text{th}}$, the photon number grows large and in fact diverges, $n \to \infty$. This behavior is illustrated in Fig. 10-22a.

Equation (2b)—which is, of course, really the same equation as Eq. (2a)—also makes clear that as $n \to \infty$ the upper-level population N_2 in the steady state can never exceed, and in fact can never even quite reach, the threshold value $N_{2,\text{th}}$. This point is illustrated by replotting Fig. 10-22a in the alternative form of N_2 versus n as in Fig. 10-22b.

There are, in fact, two general regimes of operation for the laser described by these equations: *below threshold* and *above threshold*. Below threshold the cavity photon number remains small. Equation (3a) then indicates that as long as the cavity photon number remains small and $K\tau_2 n \ll 1$, the upper-level population N_2 increases directly with the pumping rate, $N_2 \approx R_p \tau_2$. By substituting this result for N_2 back into Eq. (2a) we can obtain the approximate below-threshold values of both the population and the photon number,

$$N_2 \approx R_p \tau_2 \approx \frac{R_p}{R_{p,\text{th}}} N_{2,\text{th}}$$

$$n = \frac{N_2}{N_{2,\text{th}} - N_2} \approx \frac{R_p}{R_{p,\text{th}} - R_p} \qquad R_p < R_{p,\text{th}} \tag{5}$$

FIG. 10-22   An idealized single-mode, single-level laser model under steady-state conditions: (a) cavity photon number n versus inverted atomic population N_2 and (b) inverted population versus photon number.

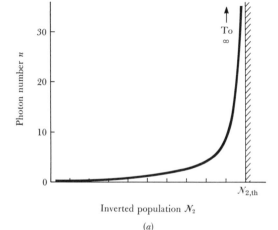

Photon number n

Inverted population N_2

(a)

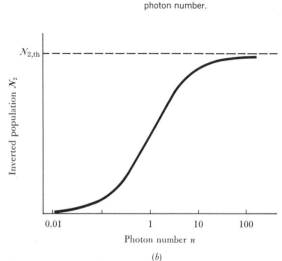

Inverted population N_2

Photon number n

(b)

where the threshold pumping rate $R_{p,\text{th}}$ is defined by

$$R_{p,\text{th}} = \frac{N_{2,\text{th}}}{\tau_2} = \frac{1}{K\tau_c\tau_2} = \frac{p\tau_{\text{rad}}}{\alpha\tau_2\tau_c} \tag{6}$$

This is the pump rate which would be required to make N_2 just reach the threshold value $N_{2,\text{th}}$ if it continued to follow the below-threshold approximation right up to threshold.

The atomic rate equation (1b) shows that the upper laser level loses atoms both as a result of relaxation, through the term $-N_2/\tau_2$, and as a result of stimulated emission, through the term $-KnN_2$. The second term in the denominator of Eq. (3a) is, in fact, just the ratio of these two processes; i.e.,

$$K\tau_2 n = \frac{\text{stimulated-emission rate}}{\text{relaxation rate}} = \frac{\alpha\tau_2}{\tau_{\text{rad}}}\frac{n}{p} \tag{7}$$

The relaxation-time ratio $\alpha\tau_2/\tau_{\text{rad}}$ will always be unity or lower, since $\alpha \approx 1$ and τ_2 is at least as fast, and possibly much faster, than τ_{rad}. Since p is always a very large number, we can conclude that the above ratio will always be much smaller than unity—that is, that simulated emission will remain small compared to relaxation—until the photon number n becomes a very large number, $n \sim p$. This in turn will not occur until the laser is essentially right at or above threshold. In other words, the below-threshold approximations will remain valid, and the photon-stimulated transition rate will remain negligible compared to the ordinary relaxation rate in the atomic rate equation, right up to the point of threshold.

LASER OSCILLATION ABOVE THRESHOLD

■ Under steady-state conditions the upper-level population can approach, but can never exceed or even quite reach, the threshold value $N_{2,\text{th}}$, as illustrated in Fig. 10-22, even though the pumping rate R_p reaches and even greatly exceeds the threshold value $R_{p,\text{th}}$. The essential characteristics of the above-threshold regime, when $R_p > R_{p,\text{th}}$, are then that the level population does approach very closely to its limiting value, $N_2 \approx N_{2,\text{th}}$, and the cavity photon number becomes very large. The stimulated-emission term in Eq. (1b) and the saturation term in the denominator of Eq. (3a) then do become significant. From Eqs. (2b), (3b), and (6), we have the above-threshold approximate solutions,

$$N_2 \approx N_{2,\text{th}}$$
$$n \approx \frac{1}{KN_{2,\text{th}}}(R_p - R_{p,\text{th}}) = \frac{\tau_c N_{2,\text{th}}}{\tau_2}\left(\frac{R_p}{R_{p,\text{th}}} - 1\right) \qquad R_p > R_{p,\text{th}} \tag{8}$$

These results, together with the below-threshold results, are shown as a function of the pumping rate R_p in Fig. 10-23. The primary results here are obviously that the inverted population level N_2 saturates in the above-threshold regime at just the threshold value, while the laser oscillation level or photon number n rises linearly with the increase in pumping rate R_p above threshold. The sudden (very) large increase in the cavity photon number and in the resulting laser output at the threshold point is the essence of laser oscillation.

Every electronic oscillator, including a laser oscillator, in order to begin oscillating from noise initial conditions, must initially have an unsaturated gain slightly larger than its total losses. The steady-state level of oscillation of any oscillator is then determined by some sort of saturation mechanism in the oscillator. Either there is a

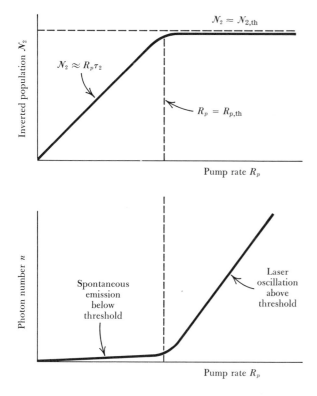

FIG. 10-23   The cavity photon number n and the inverted atomic population N_2 of Fig. 10-22 plotted separately as functions of the laser-pumping rate R_p for the same idealized single-mode and single-level laser model.

loss mechanism that increases with the signal level, as in a simple audio oscillator stabilized by a lamp whose resistance increases as the lamp is heated by the oscillation signal, or else there must be some form of gain saturation (reduction in gain) caused by clipping or overloading in the amplifying mechanism at higher signal levels. In a laser oscillator the latter situation occurs. At pumping levels above threshold, which would otherwise make the inverted population $N_2 > N_{2,\text{th}}$ and make the laser gain exceed the cavity losses, the laser oscillation level increases until the oscillation "burns up" excited atoms through stimulated emission at a rate which just balances the supply rate of excited atoms through pumping minus relaxation. The net round-trip gain in the laser cavity is then stabilized at exactly unity. Note in particular that in this case Eq. (3a) shows that for a fixed pumping rate R_p the upper-level population, and hence the gain in the laser medium, saturates with increasing signal level n in the form

$$\text{Saturated gain} = \text{const} \times N_2 = \text{const} \times \frac{1}{1 + K\tau_2 n}$$

$$= \text{unsaturated gain} \times \frac{1}{1 + n/n_{\text{sat}}} \qquad (9)$$

This simple form for the signal-induced saturation of a laser transition recurs constantly in laser analyses based on the rate-equation approach. We might note as an aside that in some laser analyses the general form for the gain saturation is written instead as

$$\text{Saturated gain} \approx \text{unsaturated gain} \times (1 - n/n_{\text{sat}}) \qquad (10)$$

While the form of Eq. (10) may be sometimes simpler to use, Eq. (9) is certainly more basic, and also much more correct when the depth of saturation is large.

In general, the most important point to be drawn from this discussion is that it is the balance between the competing processes of pumping and stimulated laser emission that is responsible for stabilizing the laser oscillation level, determining the laser-power output, saturating the gain down to equal the losses in steady state, and otherwise determining several other important properties of laser oscillators.

THE LASER THRESHOLD REGION

■ As we will see in more detail in Sec. 10-7, close examination shows that the threshold for laser oscillation is not a perfectly discrete point, below which there is no laser output and above which laser oscillation suddenly and discontinuously starts. Rather, as shown in Fig. 10-23, there are some spontaneous and even some stimulated photons in the favored laser cavity mode even below threshold, and there is some output power in the laser's output beam in this regime. Also, both the photon number and the population change smoothly and continuously with the pump level R_p as the pump rate is increased up to and through the threshold value. Still, in any practical case the transition in the laser operation at or near threshold is extremely large and extremely sharp, so that the apparent behavior at threshold is virtually discontinuous. The plot of photon number versus R_p in Fig. 10-23 is, in fact, misleading in its picture of the relative amplitudes below and above threshold. The below-threshold numbers should be indicated on a scale with units on the order of $n \sim 0.1$ to 1 or 10, and the above-threshold numbers should be plotted on a scale with units $n \sim p$, where $p \sim 10^6$ to 10^{10} in typical lasers. Thus on any correct linear plot where the above-threshold values remained on scale, the below-threshold values would be so small as to be invisible. The below-threshold values of n are exaggerated in Fig. 10-23 for purposes of illustration.

In any real laser minute adjustments in the pump level R_p near threshold will cause extremely large increases in laser output as the pump level goes from just below to just above threshold. In most practical cases the laser output below threshold is so weak as to be undetectible with ordinary equipment, and the laser output then appears to turn on discontinuously, or suddenly break into oscillation, as threshold is reached. The basic spectral character of the laser output will also change very sharply just at the threshold point. In the below-threshold region the laser signal is really only slightly amplified spontaneous emission or noise, and the laser signal will have the statistical characteristics of a narrowband gaussian random-noise process. The spectral width of this noise is on the same order as the lineshape of the atomic transition, narrowing somewhat as the laser approaches threshold, but still quite wide. Of course, none of this behavior is evident in the rate-equation analysis above, which does not reveal anything about the spectral or phase characteristics of the laser signal.

Just at or very slightly above threshold, however, the sudden very large increase in laser signal level is accompanied by an equally sharp change in the detailed statistical and spectral character of the laser output. The laser signal changes from essentially amplified noise to a true sinusoidal-amplitude-stabilized or constant-amplitude oscillation. The spectrum of the laser signal also suddenly becomes very much narrower, by a very large factor. The laser output is now a single-frequency or virtually monochromatic oscillation, rather than simply a very narrowband noise process. The laser output above threshold, in ideal cases, comes very close to being a perfectly monochromatic and constant-amplitude optical sine wave.

STEADY-STATE POPULATION INVERSION

■ If we combine the threshold population given by Eq. (4) with the value of p from Eq. (17) of Sec. 10-4, we obtain for the required steady-state population inversion in the laser cavity

$$N_{2,\text{th}} = \frac{p\tau_{\text{rad}}}{\alpha\tau_c} = \frac{8\pi V}{\alpha} \frac{\Delta f_a}{f_a} \frac{\tau_{\text{rad}}}{\tau_c} \left(\frac{n_0}{\lambda}\right)^3 \tag{11}$$

or for the inverted population density

$$\frac{N_{2,\text{th}}}{V} = \frac{8\pi}{\alpha} \frac{\Delta f_a}{f_a} \frac{\tau_{\text{rad}}}{\tau_c} \left(\frac{n_0}{\lambda}\right)^3 \tag{12}$$

But this result, obtained through the rate-equation approach of Sec. 10-4, is exactly the same as the population-inversion requirement obtained in Eq. (19) of Sec. 10-2, except for an unimportant difference in the numerical coefficient in front. If we set the polarization coefficient α in Eq. (12) (which we really did not include in Sec. 10-2) equal to its maximum value of ~ 3, then the two different expressions for threshold inversion differ numerically by only ~ 50 percent, and this 50 percent difference can be traced back to the approximation made in deriving Eqs. (23) and (24) of Sec. 10-4 without actually integrating all modes over the lorentzian atomic lineshape.

In general, the good agreement obtained above can be taken as strong support for all the various steps by which we introduced spontaneous emission, summed over spontaneous emission into all cavity modes, evaluated the K coefficients, and derived the cavity and atomic rate equations in Sec. 10-4.

■ The oscillation-power output from a laser is, of course, an important parameter to calculate, and the power output from our idealized single-mode laser above threshold can be expressed in a particularly instructive form. If a laser cavity mode with cavity lifetime τ_c contains n photons, the total photon-decay rate from this mode due to all cavity loss mechanisms is $-n/\tau_c$, and therefore the total power being delivered by this laser mode into all forms of loss (including output coupling) is

SINGLE-MODE LASER-POWER OUTPUT

$$P_{\text{laser}} = \frac{nhf}{\tau_c} \tag{13}$$

The *useful* power emerging in the laser's output beam will be equal to or less than this total power output, depending on whether output coupling is the dominant loss term for the laser cavity, or whether there are other unwanted cavity loss mechanisms. If $\tau_c = \tau_{c,\text{total}}$ is the *total* cavity lifetime due to all loss mechanisms, and $\tau_{c,\text{out}}$ is the value this lifetime would have if only the output coupling were present, then the useful power output in the output beam from the laser cavity is really

$$P_{\text{laser}} = \frac{\tau_{c,\text{total}}}{\tau_{c,\text{out}}} \frac{nhf}{\tau_{c,\text{total}}} \leq \frac{nhf}{\tau_{c,\text{total}}} \tag{14}$$

since $\tau_{c,\text{total}} \leq \tau_{c,\text{out}}$. For optimum power output it is important to keep the unwanted cavity losses (absorption, scattering, imperfect optical surfaces, etc.) small compared to the useful output coupling, as we will analyze in more detail in the following section.

For the moment let us use the ideal expression (13), since it represents the full oscillation power delivered to all loss sources in any case. Then it is also useful to calculate that in a laser cavity containing N_2 excited-state atoms with relaxation lifetime τ_2, the total rate of atomic decay due to relaxation is $-N_2/\tau_2$, and the total rate of fluorescent power emission due to this relaxation is

$$P_{\text{fluor}} = \frac{N_2 hf}{\tau_2} \approx R_p hf \qquad R_p < R_{p,\text{th}} \tag{15}$$

Here we are interpreting *fluorescence* in an expanded sense to include both the purely radiative decay mechanisms, which yield true fluorescence, and any nonradiative decay mechanisms that may be present, which channel energy into mechanisms other than true fluorescent radiation. In any event, Eq. (15) represents power supplied by the pump to the atoms and then passed along by the atoms to the surroundings.

Below threshold the fluorescent emission given by (15), since it is proportional to N_2, should increase linearly with pump power in our simple model. However, at and above threshold, where N_2 saturates, the total fluorescent emission and decay into all cavity modes plus all nonradiative mechanisms should saturate at the value

$$P_{\text{fluor}} = P_{\text{fluor,th}} \equiv \frac{N_{2,\text{th}}hf}{\tau_2} = R_{p,\text{th}}hf \qquad R_p > R_{p,\text{th}} \tag{16}$$

But by using Eq. (8), we can also write the above-threshold laser-power output in the form

$$P_{\text{laser}} = \frac{N_{2,\text{th}}hf}{\tau_2}\left(\frac{R_p}{R_{p,\text{th}}} - 1\right) = P_{\text{fluor,th}}\left(\frac{R_p}{R_{p,\text{th}}} - 1\right) \tag{17}$$

Figure 10-24 shows, on the *same absolute scales,* the total fluorescent or decay-power output both below and above threshold, and the total laser-power output above threshold.

The primary feature of this result is that below threshold all the pumping excitation to the upper laser level goes into the decay mechanisms, which either simply heat up the surroundings via nonradiative decay or else create incoherent fluorescent emission which emerges from the laser in all directions and at all frequencies within the atomic linewidth. Because this decay, or at least the purely radiative part of it, is divided among all the possible cavity modes $n \approx p$, the radiated energy per cavity mode is extremely small, and the amount of power emitted into a given direction and into a small frequency range is also extremely small. But beginning at threshold, *all* the additional pump excitation above threshold (in our simple model) goes entirely into the *one* preferred or oscillating mode. Hence the level of excitation of this one preferred mode becomes enormous ($\sim p$ times larger) compared to all other cavity modes. As a consequence, all the additional power output emerges from this one mode, in essentially a single output direction and at essentially a single output frequency. The fluorescent and decay-power output into all other directions and frequencies saturates at and above threshold, and the single oscillating mode bleeds off all the additional pump input. At $R_p = 2 \times R_{p,\text{th}}$, for example, the coherent laser output in the one

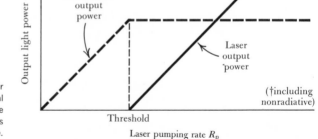

FIG. 10-24   The total fluorescent and nonradiative-decay power from the idealized laser model (heavy dashed line) and the total laser-oscillation power from the same laser plotted against the input pump power or pumping rate to the laser, with both curves plotted to the same scale.

preferred oscillating mode equals the total incoherent decay output into all the p other modes plus the nonradiative-decay routes.

This dramatic channeling of all the additional pumping excitation above threshold into just one (or, more typically, into a few) oscillating mode is a primary feature of laser oscillation. This general behavior and the very large magnitude of the mode number p are the primary reasons for the enormous brightness and coherence of the laser oscillator compared to any other type of incoherent or thermal light source. In actual lasers other decay mechanisms and routes may be present, and the behavior may not be as ideal as in our simplified single-mode model, but these lasers will still have this general property of directing a significant amount of the excitation above threshold into just a few oscillating modes, which become very greatly enhanced over all the other modes in the laser cavity.

■ The linear dependence of laser output on pump input above threshold predicted by our simple model applies surprisingly well to many real lasers, particularly optically pumped solid-state lasers, even though they may not satisfy all the assumptions used in our analysis. Figure 10-25 shows, by way of example, the laser-power output versus pump-power input for two different solid-state lasers, a CaF_2-U^{3+} laser at $\lambda = 2.61\ \mu$ pumped by a xenon-arc lamp, and a typical YAG-Nd^{3+} laser at $\lambda = 1.06\ \mu$ pumped by a tungsten-filament lamp. Both these lasers may actually operate in both multiple axial and multiple transverse modes at higher pump levels. The curvature of the YAG laser's power-output curve in the region between the actual threshold and the linearly extrapolated threshold (dashed line) can be understood by observing that the YAG rod actually first begins oscillating in a narrow filament mode at the center of the rod, where the pumping light is somewhat greater due to a focusing effect in the rod itself. As the pumping is increased, the region of laser action broadens out to include the entire rod cross section, after which the power output increases linearly with further increases in pump power.

EXPERIMENTAL
DEMONSTRATION

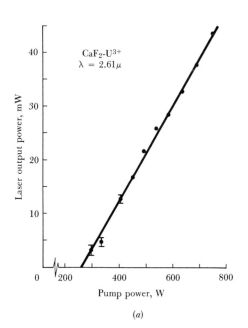

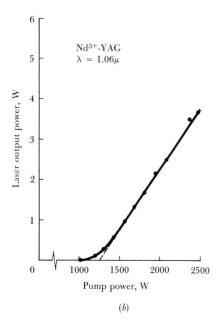

FIG. 10-25 Two experimental results for typical solid-state optically pumped laser oscillators, illustrating the linear (or nearly linear) increase in oscillation-power output versus pump-power input above threshold, as predicted in Fig. 10-24.

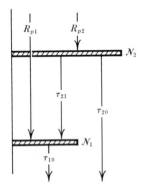

FIG. 10-26 A somewhat more
detailed two-level model for use in
a laser rate-equation analysis.

■ To extend our general conclusions concerning laser oscillation and laser-power output versus pumping rate to more general laser models, consider the more detailed two-level laser atomic system shown in Fig. 10-26. We still assume a single cavity mode, but we now assume a combination of pumping plus relaxation from above into both the laser levels 1 and 2, as well as relaxation from level 2 to level 1, and downward relaxation from both 2 and 1 to still lower levels. The three necessary laser rate equations then become

$$\frac{d}{dt} n = K(N_2 - N_1)n + KN_2 - \frac{n}{\tau_c} \tag{18a}$$

$$\frac{d}{dt} N_1 = Kn(N_2 - N_1) + \frac{N_2}{\tau_{21}} - \frac{N_1}{\tau_{10}} + R_{p1} \tag{18b}$$

$$\frac{d}{dt} N_2 = -Kn(N_2 - N_1) - \frac{N_2}{\tau_{21}} - \frac{N_2}{\tau_{20}} + R_{p2} \tag{18c}$$

The steady-state photon number now becomes, from Eq. (18a),

$$n = \frac{N_2}{(K\tau_c)^{-1} - (N_2 - N_1)} = \left(\frac{N_2}{N_2 - N_1}\right) \times \frac{N_2 - N_1}{(N_2 - N_1)_{th} - (N_2 - N_1)} \tag{19}$$

We write this in the particular form given by the second equality because the second factor can then be identified with the amount of regenerative amplification in the laser cavity. (The first factor in this expression will also be found later to be a significant quantity in determining the amount of spontaneous noise emission per unit gain from an atomic system.) There is now clearly a threshold population difference given, as before, by

$$(N_2 - N_1)_{th} \equiv (K\tau_c)^{-1} = \frac{p\tau_{rad}}{\alpha\tau_c} \tag{20}$$

When the actual population difference approaches this threshold value, the cavity photon number again becomes very large, $n \to \infty$.

The below-threshold values for the populations N_1 and N_2 can also be readily found from Eqs. (18b) and (18c) with the assumption that the stimulated-emission terms $\pm Kn(N_2 - N_1)$ in these equations will be negligible compared to the relaxation terms below threshold. These results, together with Eq. (19), readily yield the *below-threshold* solutions for population difference and photon number versus pumping rate,

$$N_2 - N_1 \approx (N_2 - N_1)_{th} \frac{R_p}{R_{p,th}} \qquad R_p < R_{p,th} \tag{21}$$

$$n \approx \frac{N_2}{N_2 - N_1} \frac{R_p}{R_{p,th} - R_p}$$

Here for simplicity the pumping rates into the upper and lower laser levels have been written as $R_{p2} \equiv R_p$ and $R_{p1} \equiv \xi R_p$ (for ξ dimensionless), and the threshold pump level is

$$R_{p,th} \equiv \frac{1}{K\tau_c\tau_2} \frac{1}{1 - \tau_{10}/\tau_{21} - \xi\tau_{10}/\tau_2} \tag{22}$$

Except for the $N_2/(N_2 - N_1)$ factor in front of n and the more complex definition of $R_{p,\text{th}}$, these below-threshold results are the same as in our earlier, simpler analysis. Note that in this case $R_{p,\text{th}}$ depends rather critically on both the relaxation-time ratios and the differential pumping ratio ξ (which should be as small as possible). For some values of these parameters population inversion cannot be achieved at all on this transition at any pump level ($R_{p,\text{th}} \to \infty$ or < 0).

Now, in the above-threshold regime the same arguments as before require that $N_2 - N_1 \approx (N_2 - N_1)_{\text{th}}$ for steady-state oscillation. From this and some algebra, it can be shown that the *above-threshold* results become

$$N_2 - N_1 \approx (N_2 - N_1)_{\text{th}}$$

$$n \approx \frac{1}{1 + \tau_{10}/\tau_{20}} \frac{\tau_c(N_2 - N_1)_{\text{th}}}{\tau_2}\left(\frac{R_p}{R_{p,\text{th}}} - 1\right) \qquad R_p > R_{p,\text{th}} \qquad (23)$$

The expression for photon number now has a somewhat more complex term in front than in the earlier idealized case, but the basic feature of the earlier result is still retained: the photon number n, and hence the laser-power output above threshold, both increase linearly with the pumping rate above threshold, and thus above threshold a sizable fraction of the additional pump excitation is channeled into oscillation in the single preferred oscillating mode rather than the many other nonoscillating modes. The general conclusions we may draw from the very simplest single-mode and single-level laser model do furnish at least a general guide to the behavior of more realistic and complex laser systems.

10-6   OPTIMUM LASER OUTPUT COUPLING

The amount of output coupling from the laser cavity that will provide the maximum laser power is an important consideration in designing a practical laser oscillator. If the amount of output coupling is too large—if, for example, the output mirror has too large a transmission factor, and hence too little reflectivity—then the total cavity losses will exceed the available laser gain, and the laser will not oscillate at all. If the output coupling is very small or zero, then all the available laser power will go into the internal laser cavity losses and essentially none into useful power output. Between these two extremes, there is an optimum output coupling to achieve maximum useful power output. The calculation of this optimum output coupling is a good demonstration of the further usefulness of the laser rate equations developed in Sec. 10-4.

■ For a first analysis let us consider a simple single-mode laser cavity having a fractional power loss per bounce $\delta = \delta_0$ due to internal cavity losses, plus an additional power loss per bounce $\delta = \delta_e$ due to external output coupling, so that the total cavity losses are $\delta = \delta_0 + \delta_e$. For simplicity we will assume that all the external coupling δ_e occurs through the output mirror on one end of the laser cavity, with 100 percent reflectivity for the other laser mirror, as shown at the top of Fig. 10-27.

ELEMENTARY ANALYSIS

In the absence of laser action (for example, with the laser mirrors removed or the laser cavity blocked) the laser medium will have a small-signal or unsaturated gain per pass which we write as[1] $\delta_{m0} = 2\alpha_{m0}L$. As soon as the laser begins oscillating and develops some signal energy, which we will denote by $W(t)$, inside the laser cavity,

---

[1] Strictly speaking, we are assuming that $\delta \ll 1$ for all the losses and gains per bounce involved in this derivation; see Sec. 10-2.

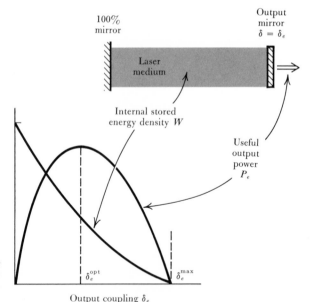

FIG. 10-27   A simple laser model for use in calculating the optimum output coupling, and the resultant variation of internal stored energy and useful external power output with the output-coupling factor δ_e.

this unsaturated gain is reduced by saturation effects. In a great many cases we may relate the saturated gain δ_m and the unsaturated gain δ_{m0} by the simple expression

$$\delta_m = \delta_{m0} \frac{1}{1 + W(t)/W_{\text{sat}}} \tag{1}$$

where δ_m is the saturated-signal gain (*power* gain) per pass and W_{sat} is by definition the signal energy level inside the laser cavity that will reduce the saturated gain to half its unsaturated value. The quantity W_{sat} is a property of the laser material and is dependent on various atomic parameters, including the laser pumping level as well as the mode volume of the laser cavity. It can either be calculated or, if necessary, measured for a given laser material.

With these loss and gain parameters, the net change in internal signal level per bounce is given by

$$\Delta W(T) = [\delta_m - (\delta_0 + \delta_e)]W(t)$$
$$= \left[\delta_{m0} \frac{1}{1 + W(t)/W_{\text{sat}}} - (\delta_0 + \delta_e)\right]W(t) \tag{2}$$

By setting this net change equal to zero for steady-state operation, we can solve for the steady-state signal energy density W_{st} that is necessary to saturate the laser gain down to where it exactly equals the total laser losses, or

$$W_{\text{st}} = \frac{\delta_{m0} - (\delta_0 + \delta_e)}{\delta_0 + \delta_e} W_{\text{sat}} \tag{3}$$

But, since δ_e gives the fraction of this cavity signal energy that is coupled out per bounce, or per time interval $T = n_0 L/c$, the useful power into the external output beam from the laser at steady state is given by

$$P_e = \delta_e T W_{\text{st}} = \frac{n_0 L W_{\text{sat}}}{c} \frac{\delta_e(\delta_{m0} - \delta_0 - \delta_e)}{\delta_0 + \delta_e} \tag{4}$$

The lower sketch in Fig. 10-27 illustrates how this external power output P_e varies with the amount of output coupling δ_e for typical fixed values of the internal cavity losses δ_0 and the unsaturated laser gain δ_{m0}. If the output coupling is greater than the maximum allowable value, $\delta_e > \delta_{e,\max} \equiv \delta_{m0} - \delta_0$, then the total losses exceed the laser gain, and the laser does not oscillate at all. As the output coupling is reduced into the oscillating range, the laser begins oscillating, and for smaller external coupling the internal signal energy W_{st} steadily increases because the *total* cavity loss is steadily decreasing. But the *fraction* of W_{st} that gets coupled out as useful output power also decreases directly as δ_e, even though W_{st} itself is rising. As a result, there is an optimum value of external coupling, $\delta_{e,\text{opt}}$, that gives the maximum available power output.

The optimum output coupling is evaluated, as usual, by setting $\partial P_e / \partial \delta_e = 0$ and solving for $\delta_{e,\text{opt}}$. The resulting optimum output coupling is

$$\delta_{e,\text{opt}} = \sqrt{\delta_{m0}\delta_0} - \delta_0 \tag{5}$$

and the maximum power output with this optimized coupling is then

$$P_{e,\max} = \frac{n_0 L W_{\text{sat}}}{c} (\sqrt{\delta_{m0}} - \sqrt{\delta_0})^2 \tag{6}$$

Reducing the internal cavity losses δ_0 to a small fraction of the unsaturated laser gain δ_{m0} is obviously important for obtaining the maximum power output, as inspection of Eq. (6) will show. In certain gas lasers where the unsaturated laser gain may be only a few percent per pass, it is important (but also quite difficult) to reduce the internal losses caused by scattering, imperfect Brewster-angle surfaces, poor mirrors, and poor surface polishing down to the smallest possible value if the best power output is to be obtained.

It is somewhat interesting to note that in the (unrealistic) case of identically zero internal losses, $\delta_0 \equiv 0$, the maximum power output is predicted to be obtained with *zero* output coupling—i.e., maximum power output with no output coupling. The explanation for this unusual result is, of course, that, from Eq. (3), if the internal losses are really zero, then the internal stored energy W_{st} will go up toward infinity with decreasing δ_e faster than the output fraction of this stored energy goes down toward zero.

■ Very clean experimental confirmation of the simple analysis above has been obtained by using a standard He-Ne laser oscillator with different output mirrors and different amounts of added internal loss to test the theory.[1] Figure 10-28 shows, on the left, theoretical power output versus output-mirror percent transmission, given an unsaturated laser gain of $\delta_{m0} = 12$ percent per pass, with various values of the internal loss per pass δ_0. On the right, experimental values for external power output, obtained with four different output mirrors of known transmission and three different values of internal cavity loss, are shown for comparison. The agreement is clearly very good between theory and experiment.   **EXPERIMENTAL CONFIRMATION**

■ Our first analysis was based on a fixed value for the unsaturated gain, and presumably for the laser pumping rate. Let us now develop a more detailed analysis of optimum output coupling, taking into account variation in the laser pumping rate. It proves most convenient to work with cavity decay rates γ defined by $\gamma \equiv 1/\tau$, where τ is an   **MORE DETAILED ANALYSIS**

[1] See Ref. 10-7.

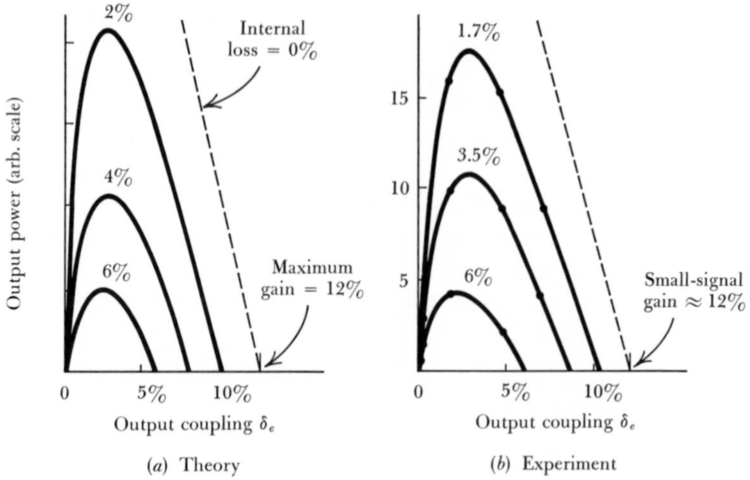

FIG. 10-28 (a) Theoretical variation of laser-power output with external coupling for different amounts of internal cavity loss, with all other laser parameters fixed. (b) Experimental results for a 6328-Å He-Ne laser oscillator, in good agreement with this theory. [From P. Laures, "Variation of the 6328 Å gas laser output power with mirror transmission," *Phys. Letters,* **10**:61 (May 15, 1964).]

appropriate cavity decay time. In particular, the total cavity decay rate γ_c can be written, from earlier results, as

$$\gamma_c \equiv \frac{1}{\tau_c} = \frac{c}{n_0 L} \left(\ln \frac{1}{r_1} + \ln \frac{1}{r_2} + 2\alpha_0 L \right)$$

$$= \gamma_e + \gamma_0 \tag{7}$$

The laser output through one of the end mirrors, say, the r_1 mirror, may be considered as the useful output coupling and described by the external-coupling decay rate $\gamma_e \equiv (c/n_0 L) \ln (1/r_1)$. The internal cavity losses α_0 plus the output through the other mirror are then lumped together as the unwanted internal losses, described by an internal-loss decay rate $\gamma_0 \equiv (c/n_0 L)[\ln (1/r_2) + 2\alpha_0 L]$.

In the preceding section we used the laser rate equations to derive an expression for the cavity photon number n as a function of the pumping rate and other laser parameters for a simple laser model (the cavity photon number is, in fact, essentially the same as the cavity signal energy W just discussed and behaves with the laser parameters in the same way). The results of Sec. 10-5 had essentially the same form using either a very idealized or a more realistic two-level laser model. Therefore for maximum simplicity let us use the most idealized of our earlier results here. From Eqs. (17) and (14) of Sec. 10-5, the useful laser output is given by

$$P_e = \frac{\gamma_e N_{2,\text{th}}}{\gamma_c \tau_2} \left(\frac{R_p}{R_{p,\text{th}}} - 1 \right) \tag{8}$$

Both $N_{2,\text{th}}$ and $R_{p,\text{th}}$ in this expression are themselves dependent on the cavity decay rate γ_c. Therefore we must go back still further, to Eqs. (4) and (6) of Sec. 10-5, to obtain the more basic form

$$P_e = \frac{\gamma_e hf}{\gamma_c K \tau_2 \tau_c} (K \tau_2 \tau_c R_p - 1) = \frac{\gamma_e hf}{K \tau_2} \left(\frac{K \tau_2 R_p}{\gamma_e + \gamma_0} - 1 \right) \tag{9}$$

This expression now gives the useful laser power P_e as a function of the external coupling γ_e, the internal cavity losses γ_0, and the laser pumping rate R_p.

This general result can be manipulated into a number of different forms, depending on which parameters we wish to emphasize. Without defining any new parameters, we can find that the optimum output coupling to maximize P_e is given by

$$\gamma_{e,opt} = \sqrt{K\tau_2 R_p \gamma_0} - \gamma_0 \tag{10}$$

A vital point here is that the optimum coupling is different for different levels of pump excitation R_p applied to the laser material. The laser can be designed with an optimum output mirror for only one particular pumping level, since the optimum coupling changes for different R_p. The maximum power output as a function of R_p, given optimized coupling at each value of R_p, is then

$$P_{e,max} = R_p hf \left[1 - \left(\frac{\gamma_0}{K\tau_2 R_p} \right)^{1/2} \right]^2 \rightarrow R_p hf \qquad \text{for } R_p \gg \frac{\gamma_0}{K\tau_2} \tag{11}$$

For large enough R_p compared to the quantity $\gamma_0/K\tau_2$, this says that the power output approaches the ideal limit $P_{e,max} \rightarrow R_p hf$; i.e., every atom lifted to the upper laser level by the pump is converted into one photon of useful laser-power output.

One useful way of manipulating the general expression (9) is to define the minimum pump-power quantity by

$$R_{p,min} \equiv \frac{\gamma_0}{K\tau_2} \tag{12}$$

This parameter is the absolute minimum pumping rate at which laser oscillation is just attained if the external coupling to the laser is reduced to a negligible value, $\delta_e \ll \delta_0$, so that the total loss in the laser cavity has its minimum possible value. Then, for any finite value of external coupling the general power-output expression may be written in the form

$$P_e = \frac{\gamma_e/\gamma_0}{1 + \gamma_e/\gamma_0} \left[R_p - \left(1 + \frac{\gamma_e}{\gamma_0} \right) R_{p,min} \right] hf \tag{13}$$

Obviously, as the external coupling γ_e increases, the laser pumping threshold increases according to the expression $R_{p,th} = (1 + \gamma_e/\gamma_0)R_{p,min}$. The optimum output coupling may then be written as

$$\gamma_{e,opt} = \left(\frac{R_p}{R_{p,min}} \right)^{1/2} \gamma_0 - \gamma_0$$

$$\rightarrow \left(\frac{R_p}{R_{p,min}} \right)^{1/2} \gamma_0 \qquad \text{for } R_p \gg R_{p,min} \tag{14}$$

and the resulting maximum power output is given by

$$P_{e,max} = \left[1 - \left(\frac{R_{p,min}}{R_p} \right)^{1/2} \right]^2 R_p hf$$

$$\rightarrow R_p hf \qquad \text{for } R_p \gg R_{p,min} \tag{15}$$

It is clear that the best laser action requires low enough internal losses, and hence a low enough value of $R_{p,min}$, together with a high enough pumping rate R_p at the laser's normal operating point that the condition $R_p \gg R_{p,min}$ can be achieved. The optimized output coupling for this condition will then be external coupling substantially larger than internal losses, in fact by approximately the ratio $\gamma_e/\gamma_0 \approx (R_p/R_{p,min})^{1/2}$.

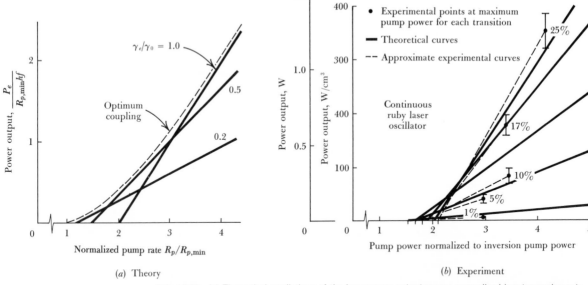

(a) Theory

(b) Experiment

FIG. 10-29 (a) Theoretical predictions of the laser-power output versus normalized input pumping rate for different fixed values of external coupling (solid lines), with all other laser parameters held fixed. The maximum power output, with a separately optimized external coupling value for each pumping level, is indicated by the dashed line. (b) Experimental results for power output versus pumping rate in a cw ruby laser, showing good agreement with the theoretical predictions. Solid lines are theoretical predictions and dashed lines are the corresponding experimental values. For simplicity only the final experimental point along each dashed line is shown. [From V. Evtuhov and J. K. Neeland, "Power output and efficiency of continuous ruby lasers," *J. Appl. Phys.*, **38**:4051 (September, 1967).]

To illustrate the general character of these results, Fig. 10-29a shows the normalized useful output power from a laser oscillator, $P_e/(R_{p,\min}hf)$ plotted against the normalized pumping rate $R_p/R_{p,\min}$. The straight lines indicate the power output as a function of pumping input for various fixed values of the output coupling relative to the internal cavity losses. These curves would be directly applicable to a given laser with no change except in the external coupling (e.g., the percent transmission of the output mirror) between the different curves, with laser-power output and pump-power input plotted on the same scales for each curve. Note that increasing the value of output coupling produces a higher pumping threshold, and also reduces the laser-power output for values of R_p not too far above that threshold. However, larger output coupling also means a steeper slope for the curve of output versus pump rate, and hence higher power output at higher values of R_p. The dashed line is the curve of maximum power output, given optimized coupling at each value of R_p, as given by Eq. (15). It thus represents an upper bound for the family of fixed-coupling straight lines, of which three examples are shown in the figure.

EXPERIMENTAL CONFIRMATION   ■ Figure 10-29b shows a set of experimental results that correspond almost directly to the theoretical curves shown in Fig. 10-29a. These experimental results were obtained on a continuously operating (cw) ruby laser, pumped by a mercury-arc lamp in a small elliptical cavity.[1] The rate equations necessary to analyze a three-level laser system such as ruby are significantly more complex than those for the simple two-level model discussed above. However, the final conclusions concerning power output versus

[1] See Ref. 10-5.

external coupling and pump rate are essentially the same for either case. The solid lines in Fig. 10-29b thus show the theoretical results for the three-level ruby system, and the dashed lines represent measured experimental results. Since the measured points all fell accurately along straight lines as a function of pumping power input, only the largest experimental point has been plotted for each output coupling value. The different output couplings were obtained by changing the output coatings on the laser-cavity output mirror to get different reflection and transmission values, as indicated. The experimental curves are all in good agreement with the related theoretical curves, except for the case of 10 percent output coupling, where the experimental values are somewhat low. However, other measurements indicated that the mirror coating in this case may have been of inferior optical quality. In general, the results shown may be taken as a remarkably good confirmation of our simple theoretical analysis.

The calculation of power output versus pump input and versus the amount of external coupling, and the calculation of the optimum external coupling, rapidly become more complicated when we begin to take into account possible oscillation in multiple modes simultaneously, laser transitions with very high gain per pass, inhomogeneously broadened laser transitions with their differing saturation characteristics (see Chap. 9), or other more complex but possibly more realistic laser situations. A number of such calculations have been carried out and reported in the literature.[1]

10-7   THE LASER THRESHOLD REGION

Perhaps the most interesting region of laser behavior from a theoretical standpoint is the oscillation threshold region. In this region an extremely minute change in the rate of pump excitation can cause the laser's mode of operation to change dramatically from the below-threshold condition, where the atoms reemit the pumping excitation more or less equally and spontaneously into all available cavity modes, to the above-threshold or oscillating condition, where all further pump excitation is channeled into only one or a few oscillating laser modes. In this section we will examine in closer detail the behavior of a laser in the threshold transition region, using an idealized single-mode laser model to simplify the analytical expressions as much as possible.

■ From Sec. 10-4, the coupled rate equations for the cavity photon number and the upper-level atomic population in an idealized single-mode laser, given one preferred lowest-loss cavity mode and very fast relaxation from the lower atomic level, are

SINGLE-MODE LASER MODEL: EXACT SOLUTION

$$\frac{d}{dt}n = K(n + 1)N_2 - \frac{n}{\tau_c}$$
$$\frac{d}{dt}N_2 = -KnN_2 - \frac{N_2}{\tau_2} + R_p$$

(1)

Setting $d/dt = 0$ in both these equations leads to the pair of coupled steady-state relationships

$$n = \frac{N_2}{(K\tau_c)^{-1} - N_2}$$
$$N_2 = R_p\tau_2 \frac{1}{1 + K\tau_2 n}$$

(2)

[1] See especially Refs. 10-1, 10-8, 10-12, 10-13, 10-19, and 10-20.

In Sec. 10-5 we made appropriate approximations to these expressions in order to obtain approximate solutions for n and N_2 as functions of the pumping rate R_p in both the below-threshold and above-threshold regions. However, it is also easy to obtain a single *exact* expression for either one of these quantities, say, for the photon number n, as a function of the pumping rate R_p simply by eliminating the other quantity, N_2, between the pair of coupled equations in (2). In fact, the exact result for the cavity photon number n is just

$$n = \frac{1}{2K\tau_2}\left[\left(\frac{R_p}{R_{p,\text{th}}} - 1\right) + \sqrt{\left(\frac{R_p}{R_{p,\text{th}}} - 1\right)^2 + \frac{4R_p}{K\tau_2 R_{p,\text{th}}}}\right] \tag{3}$$

an expression that is fully correct both above and below and exactly at threshold.

To express this result in a slightly simpler form we may define the dimensionless pump rate, normalized with respect to threshold, by

$$r \equiv \frac{R_p}{R_{p,\text{th}}} \tag{4}$$

Hence $r = 1$ exactly at threshold. The combination $(K\tau_2)^{-1}$ may also be rewritten as

$$\frac{1}{K\tau_2} = \frac{\tau_{\text{rad}}}{\tau_2}\frac{p}{\alpha} \tag{5}$$

For simplicity we can assume $\alpha = 1$ and $\tau_2 = \tau_{\text{rad}}$ and just write p for this quantity. The exact solution for the photon number n as a function of the normalized pump rate r can then be written in the apparently simple but surprisingly interesting form

$$n = \frac{p}{2}\left[(r - 1) + \sqrt{(r - 1)^2 + \frac{4r}{p}}\right] \tag{6}$$

The behavior of this expression is our major concern in this section.

THRESHOLD-REGION BEHAVIOR   ■ A remarkable change occurs in the numerical value of the rather innocuous appearing expression (6) when the normalized pumping rate changes from a value $r = 1 - \delta r$ just very slightly below threshold to a value $r = 1 + \delta r$ just very slightly above threshold, where $\delta r \ll 1$ in both cases. To illustrate this, Fig. 10-30 gives a carefully plotted curve of n versus r from Eq. (6) for the particular case of a cavity mode number $p = 10^{10}$. This curve shows the cavity photon number increasing suddenly at threshold from $\sim 10^3$ to 10^8 within a range of pump variation that is narrower than the width of the line in the plot, despite the use of a greatly expanded scale for the pump rate r and a greatly compressed logarithmic scale for the photon number n. This dramatic change in cavity photon number, and hence in laser-power output, right at threshold is fundamental to all types of laser oscillators and is very important in understanding the ability of a laser to channel most of its power output into only a single or a few cavity modes despite the presence of an enormous number of potentially active cavity modes.

In order to examine this behavior more carefully, we may note first that the photon number has the approximate magnitude $n \sim 1$ in the region below threshold and $n \sim p$ in the region above threshold. Hence the large size of the cavity mode number p is of primary importance. We can also note that exactly at threshold the photon number is given by

$$n = \sqrt{p} \qquad r = 1 \tag{7}$$

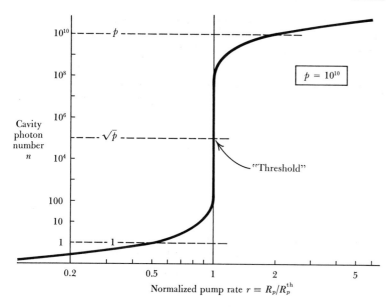

FIG. 10-30 A curve of cavity photon number n (or laser-power output) versus normalized pumping rate r from the exact solution to the rate equations for the idealized single-mode single-level laser model. Note the different logarithmic scales along the horizontal and vertical axes.

that is, the geometric mean of the below- and above-threshold values. This point is not a particularly useful point in any experimental sense, however, since there is no independent way of calibrating r to determine when the pump rate is exactly at threshold. In any event, the n-vs.-r characteristic is so extraordinarily steep at this point that we cannot hope to adjust the pump excitation to obtain stable operation exactly at the threshold point in any real laser. The derivative of photon number with normalized pumping rate at the threshold point is given, in fact, by

$$\frac{d}{dr}n \approx \frac{p}{2} \qquad r = 1 \tag{8}$$

Thus for $p = 10^{10}$ a change in normalized pumping rate of only $\delta r \sim 10^{-5}$ will lead to a change in laser power output of $\delta n \sim 10^{+5}$ at threshold.

A second significant point is that the below-threshold and above-threshold approximations derived in Sec. 10-5 actually provide extremely exact approximations essentially right up to threshold on the lower side and right down to threshold on the upper side. Because of the very large value of p in typical cases, the quantity $(r - 1)^2$ inside the radical sign in Eq. (6) will be large compared to the quantity $4r/p$ for all values of r except right at the threshold value $r = 1$. Therefore Eq. (6) may be expanded in the below-threshold region into the form

$$n = \frac{p}{2}\left[(r - 1) + (1 - r)\sqrt{1 + \frac{4r}{(1 - r)^2 p}}\right]$$

$$\approx \frac{r}{1 - r}\left[1 - \frac{r}{(1 - r)^2 p} + \cdots\right] \qquad r = 1 - \delta r \tag{9}$$

and in the above-threshold region into the form

$$n = \frac{p}{2}\left[(r - 1) + (r - 1)\sqrt{1 + \frac{4r}{(1 - r)^2 p}}\right]$$

$$\approx p(r - 1)\left[1 + \frac{r}{(1 - r)^2 p} + \cdots\right] \qquad r = 1 + \delta r \tag{10}$$

The leading term in each of these expansions is just the approximate form derived for that region in Sec. 10-5, $n \approx r/(1 - r)$ below threshold and $n \approx (r - 1)p$ above threshold. The first-order correction term for both these expressions is given by the same factor, $r/(1 - r)^2 p$ compared to unity. This correction factor becomes significant only when $r \to 1$. For example, to determine how close we must come to threshold before this correction factor becomes as large as, say, a 1 percent correction, we may write

$$\frac{r}{(1 - r)^2 p} \approx \frac{1}{(1 - r)^2 p} = \frac{1}{100} \tag{11}$$

and solve for the deviation from threshold,

$$(1 - r) = \sqrt{\frac{100}{p}} = 10^{-4} \tag{12}$$

Thus for our example of $p = 10^{10}$ we can come to within $\delta r = 10^{-4}$, or 0.01 percent of threshold, from either side before the errors in the below-threshold or above-threshold approximations become as large as even 1 percent.

SIGNIFICANCE OF THRESHOLD BEHAVIOR
■ This leads to several interesting conclusions. The power output from a laser oscillator in the below-threshold region is usually so weak as to be below the minimum detectible level for normal laser detectors. Therefore, as a practical matter, no output from the laser will be detected below threshold. At threshold the laser will appear to suddenly "break into oscillation" as the pump excitation is turned up to the threshold point and above. However, there is definitely a finite power output from the laser mode even *below* threshold, with substantially more photons in the preferred cavity mode than in other modes with higher losses and higher thresholds. In careful experiments with sufficiently sensitive detectors this below-threshold power output has been not only detected, but studied in some detail.

The threshold pump rate required for a given cavity mode is directly proportional to the loss rate of that cavity mode. Suppose two cavity modes share exactly the same set of laser atoms in a homogeneous atomic transition. If one mode has a slightly lower loss, and hence a slightly lower laser threshold, than the other, the lower-loss mode will reach threshold first. It will build up a very large above-threshold photon number while the higher-loss, and thus slightly less preferred, mode is still below threshold with a very small below-threshold photon number. Once the preferred mode reaches threshold, further increases in pumping rate will not increase the upper-level population N_2 because this quantity saturates sharply at its threshold value as soon as the first mode reaches threshold. Hence the second mode, even though it may be only slightly more lossy, is doomed to remain forever below threshold, regardless of any increase in pumping rate, with only an insignificant photon number compared to the strongly oscillating mode.

The extreme sharpness of the threshold behavior is the key to the rather astonishing fact that, at least in carefully designed lasers, oscillation can be made to occur in a single controlled cavity mode even though there may be some 10^8 to 10^{10} other cavity modes in which it might occur. In fact oscillation in a single axial mode, and also in a single transverse-mode pattern, can be obtained, with reasonable care, in many practical and commercially available lasers. Oscillation in a single *transverse*-mode pattern can almost always be obtained in any standard laser by placing inside the laser cavity a *mode-control iris* which increases the cavity losses for all the transverse modes higher than the lowest-order one. Oscillation in only a single *axial* mode, and hence at only a single oscillation frequency, is generally more difficult to achieve.

Multiple-axial-mode oscillations occur in many real lasers primarily because many laser transitions are not homogeneously broadened. Laser oscillation at one frequency burns a hole in the transition at that frequency but does not saturate the gain across the entire atomic linewidth. Other oscillations can then begin, at slightly higher pumping rates, on other axial modes within the overall inhomogeneously broadened linewidth. Multiple oscillations may also occur if different cavity modes occupy different mode volumes, or at least only partially overlapping mode volumes, within the laser cavity. Different modes can then make use of partially different sets of atoms within the cavity. Oscillation in one mode does not saturate the gain for all the atoms as seen by another mode, and with further pumping additional modes can also reach threshold and break into oscillation.

Note again the differing character of the laser "oscillation" in the below-threshold and above-threshold regions. Below but close to threshold, the laser's output signal is essentially highly amplified narrowband gaussian noise, representing atomic spontaneous emission or quantum noise that has been linearly amplified by the regenerative laser amplification in the cavity. The net gain per round trip inside the laser cavity is still less than unity, although very close to unity, and so in the usual sense the laser is not oscillating. The cavity will, however, have a finite photon number and a finite power output that is considerably above the quiescent value without any laser action. The observed output will have all the amplitude and phase fluctuations characteristic of random noise, although this noise will become very narrowband as the threshold is approached from the lower side.

There is a smooth but rapid changeover in the characteristics of the laser when it passes through the threshold region. The details of this changeover require a rather complex analysis, and we will only say here that the transition is nearly as sudden as the sudden change in average power output at threshold. Above threshold, the laser's output signal becomes a true amplitude-stabilized coherent oscillation, or a smooth optical-frequency sine wave. There is a very small amount of random amplitude and phase, or frequency jitter, in this sine wave, owing to the spontaneous emission in the laser atoms and to mechanical vibrations and microphonics in the laser, fluctuations in power supply, and the like. Still, the laser's overall spectral width is extremely small, and the output is, to a very high degree of approximation, a nearly ideal sinusoidal oscillation, like that generated by any other high-quality electronic oscillator at any other frequency.

■ The sudden, sharp onset of laser oscillation observed in any practical laser as the discharge current or the pumping intensity is turned up provides at least a qualitative verification of our laser threshold predictions. Detailed measurements of the laser behavior near, and particularly below, threshold in any usual laser are extremely difficult to make. The emission below threshold is too weak to be detected with the usual measuring apparatus, and the threshold itself is so sharp that the microphonics and noise in any normal laboratory smear out and obscure the true threshold behavior very near the threshold.

Nonetheless, with much care given to shielding and isolation of the experimental apparatus, various measurements have been made on lasers both below and above threshold, usually with small, stable, single-mode 6328-Å He-Ne lasers. The best such observations include measurements of photon numbers to within a factor of 2 just

EXPERIMENTAL CONFIRMATION

above and just below threshold, as well as over a considerable range on either side of the threshold. These measurements have all yielded results in excellent agreement with theoretical predictions.

One particularly simple type of laser in which the power output can be observed as the pumping rate passes through threshold is the semiconductor injection laser. Because of the very small active cavity mode volume in this laser, the mode number p is somewhat smaller than in other lasers, although the small mode volume is offset to some extent by a very wide atomic linewidth. For a smaller value of p the threshold transition is not as sharp. Also, because of the efficient pumping but comparatively high threshold in the injection laser, it is easier than in other lasers to observe the spontaneous fluorescent output from the laser cavity below threshold. As an example, Fig. 10-31a shows the measured light output versus pumping input (which in this case is the injected dc current) for a GaAs injection-laser diode operated in cw fashion at liquid-helium temperature (4.2°K). It is obvious that this curve is at least generally similar to our theoretical result, with a sharp rise in output by several orders of magnitude at threshold. Detailed comparisons of theory and experiment are not possible here because the injection laser is really a multiple-mode rather than single-mode type of laser. Also, the light output observed below threshold is not simply the light output from a single cavity mode, but represents the total output from a fairly large number of cavity modes, all of which are coming close to threshold from below.

Figure 10-31b is a plot of the output spectrum (output intensity versus wavelength) for another, similar injection-laser diode at two very slightly different currents or pumping levels, one just below and one just above threshold. Note that the difference in pump rates between these two curves is ~1 percent. In the below-threshold curve at least seven resolvable axial cavity modes can be seen, each of which is coming close enough to threshold at this pumping level, so that it is beginning to contain appreciably more photons than the average cavity mode. Therefore each peak represents an observable below-threshold power output in that particular axial mode (although this probably includes a large number of different transverse modes for each such axial mode). Then, with a very slight increase in pumping rate, the most favored

FIG. 10-31 (a) Experimental data for light output versus pumping current input to a cw GaAs diode-injection laser at 4.2°K. This experimental result may be compared to the theoretical curve of Fig. 10-30. (b) Spectrum of the light output versus wavelength for a similar (but not the same) injection laser at two slightly different values of injection current, just below and just above threshold. [From G. K. Born, "The growth of laser oscillations," *Appl. Phys. Letters,* **12**:46 (Jan. 15, 1968).]

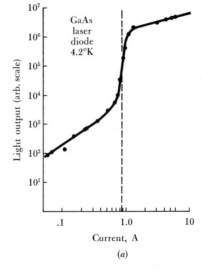

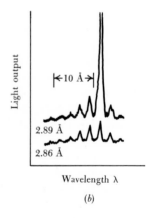

of these axial modes—the one closest to the atomic line center—reaches threshold and breaks into a very much stronger and narrower oscillation. The other modes, meanwhile, are still below threshold and are changed very little by the slight increase in pumping rate. The resolution of these measurements is much too limited to provide any detailed test of the theory of laser threshold, but Fig. 10-31b should still give at least a rough indication of the sudden increase in power in the favored mode and the sudden change in output spectral characteristics that occur in a laser oscillator just at the threshold point.[1]

10-8   LASER AMPLITUDE FLUCTUATIONS AND SPIKING

Although the laser rate equations are dynamic equations for the laser's photon number and atomic level populations as functions of time, so far in this chapter we have considered only the steady-state behavior of the laser and the steady-state solutions to the laser rate equations. Let us now consider some aspects of the transient or dynamic behavior of a laser oscillator, as predicted by the time-varying solutions to these equations.

The most notable transient effect in many laser oscillators, particularly in most solid-state laser oscillators, is the phenomenon of *spiking*. In ruby and many other solid-state lasers, the laser oscillation is not continuous, but occurs instead in large, quasi-random bursts of laser output, or *spikes*, as illustrated in Fig. 1-29. This spiking behavior, which represents a form of relaxation oscillation of the envelope of the laser output, can be predicted with reasonable accuracy from a simple rate-equation transient analysis, and we will use it as the primary example in discussing transient rate-equation solutions.

■ As before, we will simplify the algebra in our analysis as much as possible by using the simplest possible single-mode, single-level laser model, for which the laser rate equations are

LASER RATE EQUATIONS AND SPIKING

$$
\begin{aligned}
\frac{d}{dt} n(t) &= K n(t) N_2(t) + K N_2(t) - \frac{n(t)}{\tau_c} \\
\frac{d}{dt} N_2(t) &= -K n(t) N_2(t) - \frac{N_2(t)}{\tau_2} + R_p(t)
\end{aligned}
\tag{1}
$$

These are nonlinear equations: the product term $n(t) N_2(t)$ appears in both of them. Therefore simple analytical expressions for the transient solutions are not obtainable. Solutions to specific problems must be found by numerical (computer) solution, by graphical methods, or by making appropriate approximations, such as piecewise linearization or linearization for small fluctuations about the steady-state solutions.

The spiking behavior observed in many lasers can be described with reasonable accuracy by the above rate equations (or more complicated rate equations if necessary for more complicated laser systems). However, we will merely describe the large-spiking region of laser behavior, and then discuss an approximate linearized solution for the limiting case of small spiking fluctuations about the steady-state limiting behavior.

Suppose that the laser pumping rate $R_p(t)$ is suddenly turned on from zero to a steady value considerably above the threshold value for laser oscillation. Then, as shown in the lower curve of Fig. 10-32, the upper-level atomic population N_2 will

[1] The experimental results are from Ref. 10-4. Similar results are reported in more detail in Ref. 10-15.

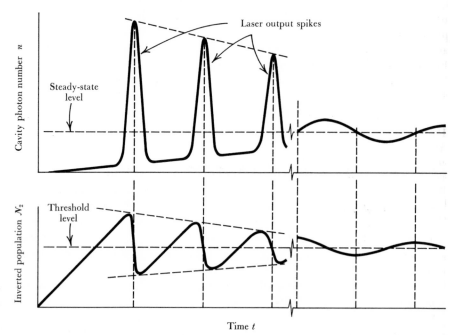

FIG. 10-32 The spiking behavior of a simple laser oscillator when the pump power is suddenly turned on at time $t = 0$.

begin to build up toward, and then past, the oscillation threshold value $N_{2,\text{th}}$. Although under steady-state oscillation conditions N_2 can never exceed $N_{2,\text{th}}$, under transient conditions the pump can raise N_2 above the threshold level, because no laser oscillation has yet been built up and no laser photon number n yet exists to pull N_2 back down by means of stimulated emission.

The laser oscillation level or photon number n does not begin to build up from noise, in fact, until after N_2 passes $N_{2,\text{th}}$, so that the net round-trip gain in the laser exceeds unity. Then, however, because N_2 is considerably in excess of $N_{2,\text{th}}$, the oscillation level will actually build up very rapidly to a value of n considerably in excess of the steady-state value of n appropriate for the particular pumping level R_p.

But then, when $n(t)$ becomes very large, the rate of depletion of the upper-level atoms due to stimulated emission becomes correspondingly large, in fact considerably larger than the pumping rate R_p. As a result, the upper-level population $N_2(t)$ passes through a maximum and begins to decrease rapidly, driven downward by the large oscillation level. The population $N_2(t)$ is, in fact, driven back below the threshold level $N_{2,\text{th}}$; the net gain in the laser cavity becomes less than unity, and so the existing oscillation in the laser cavity begins to die out.

To complete the cycle of this relaxation process, once the oscillation level has died out below the proper steady-state level, the stimulated-emission rate again becomes small. At this point the pumping process can begin to build the population level N_2 back up toward and through the threshold value again. This causes the generation of another burst of laser action, and the system can again go through a repeat performance of the same or a very similar cycle.

For the pumping rates, cavity lifetimes, and atomic lifetimes characteristic of most solid-state lasers (but not most gas lasers), the result of this process is a repeated sequence of short, but intense, pulses or spikes of laser output, as in the upper curve of Fig. 10-32 (these curves are intended only to illustrate the basic process and are not drawn to scale). The rate equations (1), or more complicated equations if necessary, can be solved numerically by either digital or analog computation to produce curves similar in general character to Fig. 10-32. From the stability theory of nonlinear systems, it can be shown that, for the rate equations (1) at least, the spikes will become successively smaller, and the overall spiking behavior will gradually damp down toward the steady-state behavior in which $N_2(t)$ and $n(t)$ approach their steady-state non-fluctuating values. However, the rate at which the spiking behavior will die out is slow in many real solid-state lasers. Furthermore, the mechanical and thermal shocks and disturbances present in many real lasers act to continually reexcite the spiking behavior and keep it from damping out. Hence many lasers, especially the ruby laser,[1] will spike continuously even in supposedly cw operation, without ever damping down to the steady state. It is possible, however, in carefully controlled experiments, to increase the damping rate in various ways and observe the predicted damping of the spikes.

■ A good demonstration of the rate equations, which also provides a considerable amount of useful information, is an analysis of the spiking behavior in the limiting case where the fluctuations have damped down almost, but not quite, to steady state. The rate equations can then be linearized and solved analytically by considering only small fractional fluctuations about the known steady-state solutions. To linearize the equations, we write the photon number $n(t)$ and the level population $N_2(t)$ in the form

LINEARIZED SMALL-SIGNAL APPROXIMATION

$$
\begin{aligned}
n(t) &= n_0 + \Delta n(t) \qquad \Delta n \ll n_0 \\
N_2(t) &= N_0 + \Delta N(t) \qquad \Delta N \ll N_0
\end{aligned}
\tag{2}
$$

where the steady-state values n_0 and N_0 are the above-threshold steady-state solutions we derived in Sec. 10-5 and 10-7 and the quantities $\Delta n(t)$ and $\Delta N(t)$ are the deviations from steady state, assumed to be small compared to the steady-state values. The steady-state values themselves are

$$
\begin{aligned}
N_0 &= N_{2,\text{th}} = (K\tau_c)^{-1} \\
n_0 &= \frac{\tau_c N_{2,\text{th}}}{\tau_2}\left(\frac{R_p}{R_{p,\text{th}}} - 1\right)
\end{aligned}
\tag{3}
$$

If the deviations from steady state are in fact small compared to these values, then in writing out the rate equations we may eliminate the nonlinear part of the product term by using the approximation

$$
\begin{aligned}
n(t)N_2(t) &= [n_0 + \Delta n(t)][N_0 + \Delta N(t)] \\
&= n_0 N_0 + n_0 \Delta N(t) + N_0 \Delta n(t) + \{\Delta n(t)\,\Delta N(t)\}
\end{aligned}
\tag{4}
$$

The final term, in braces, is the product of two small quantities and can be neglected in relation to the other terms in the expression. Also, since we are dealing with an oscillating laser, we may assume that $n(t) \gg 1$ at all times; hence we may neglect the spontaneous term $KN_2(t)$ in relation to the stimulated term $Kn(t)N_2(t)$ in the cavity rate equation. The linearized equations that govern the small deviations from steady state may then be written as

$$
\begin{aligned}
\frac{d}{dt}\Delta n(t) &= \left(KN_0 - \frac{1}{\tau_c}\right)\Delta n(t) + Kn_0\,\Delta N(t) \\
\frac{d}{dt}\Delta N(t) &= -KN_0\,\Delta n(t) - \left(Kn_0 + \frac{1}{\tau_2}\right)\Delta N(t)
\end{aligned}
\tag{5}
$$

[1] Ruby must also be described by a more complex three-level set of rate equations than Eqs. (1).

and these linearized equations are solvable by well-known methods. The transient solutions to these equations will give the residual spiking behavior in the region where the spiking has damped down to small, damped sinusoidal fluctuations about steady state, as illustrated in the right-hand part of Fig. 10-32.

Before we carry out these solutions, it is convenient to define the normalized pumping rate above threshold, as before, by

$$r \equiv \frac{R_p}{R_{p,\text{th}}} \tag{6}$$

and to write the steady-state quantities in the form

$$KN_0 = \frac{1}{\tau_c}$$
$$Kn_0 = \frac{r-1}{\tau_2} \tag{7}$$

The linearized equations then take on the simpler, final form

$$\frac{d}{dt}\Delta n(t) = \frac{r-1}{\tau_2}\Delta N(t)$$
$$\frac{d}{dt}\Delta N(t) = -\frac{1}{\tau_c}\Delta n(t) - \frac{r}{\tau_2}\Delta N(t) \tag{8}$$

We may assume that the small deviations $\Delta n(t)$ and $\Delta N(t)$ will vary with time as e^{st}. The secular equation for the normal modes or the natural values of s is then given by the determinant

$$\begin{vmatrix} s & -(r-1)/\tau_2 \\ 1/\tau_c & s + r/\tau_2 \end{vmatrix} = 0 \tag{9}$$

or

$$s^2 + \frac{r}{\tau_2}s + \frac{r-1}{\tau_2\tau_c} = 0 \tag{10}$$

The roots of this equation, or the values of s that characterize the transient behavior of the system, are

$$s = s_1, s_2 = -\frac{r}{2\tau_2} \pm \sqrt{\left(\frac{r}{2\tau_2}\right)^2 - \frac{r-1}{\tau_2\tau_c}} \tag{11}$$

The transient behavior is then of the form

$$\Delta n(t) \propto A_1 e^{s_1 t} + A_2 e^{s_2 t} \tag{12}$$

with a similar expression for $\Delta N(t)$.

We need to consider the nature of the transient roots s_1 and s_2. In many common gas lasers both the upper-level lifetime τ_2 and the cavity lifetime τ_c are short and not too different from each other. The transient behavior then consists either of two rapidly decaying exponentials or of a rapidly damped sinusoidal oscillation in the envelope. In either case the main point is that the transient behavior is rapidly damped, which means that little or no spiking behavior will be observed. (In particular, if the decay time is rapid and the turn-on of the pumping mechanism has a finite rise time, then the quantities in Fig. 10-32 may rise smoothly to their steady-state values with virtually no spiking or transient overshoot at all.)

However, in typical solid-state lasers the metastable upper-state lifetime τ_2 is very much longer than the cavity lifetime τ_c. The transient roots must then be written in the form

$$s_1, s_2 = -\frac{r}{2\tau_2} \pm j \sqrt{\frac{r-1}{\tau_2\tau_c} - \left(\frac{r}{2\tau_2}\right)^2} = -\gamma_s \pm j\omega_s \tag{13}$$

where the spiking decay rate and the natural spiking frequency are given by

$$\gamma_s \equiv \frac{r}{2\tau_2}$$

$$\omega_s \equiv \sqrt{\frac{r-1}{\tau_2\tau_c} - \left(\frac{r}{2\tau_2}\right)^2} \tag{14}$$

$$\approx \sqrt{\frac{r-1}{\tau_2\tau_c}} \qquad \tau_2 \gg \tau_c$$

The transient fluctuations in the cavity photon number and the upper-level population will then be decaying sinusoids of the general form

$$\Delta n(t) \propto e^{-\gamma_s t} \sin(\omega_s t + \phi_s)$$
$$\Delta \mathcal{N}(t) \propto e^{-\gamma_s t} \cos(\omega_s t + \phi_s) \tag{15}$$

with amplitudes and phase angles determined by the initial conditions of the problem. Regardless of the phases, however, note that the photon number and the level population will be $90°$ out of phase, as we would expect from the physics of the situation. ■ For a typical numerical example we can consider a solid-state laser with a cavity TYPICAL NUMERICAL VALUES lifetime $\tau_c = 10^{-8}$ sec and a metastable upper-state lifetime $\tau_2 = 500$ μsec $= 5 \times 10^{-4}$ sec, pumped at 50 percent above threshold, or $r = 1.5$. The spiking frequency, in conventional units, and the decay time for the spiking envelope will then be

$$f_s \equiv \frac{\omega_s}{2\pi} \approx 50 \text{ kHz}$$

$$\tau_s \equiv \gamma_s^{-1} \approx 1.5 \text{ msec} \tag{16}$$

Experimental measurements on solid-state lasers such as the Nd-YAG laser are generally in quite good agreement with this type of simple theory; moreover, the spiking rate and decay rate will vary with the pumping level r in essentially the same manner as predicted by the analysis.

The expressions above apply directly only to four-level lasers, or only to those four-level lasers in which the lower-level decay rate is fast. The rate equations for a three-level ruby laser are different in their detailed structure from Eqs. (1), and the final results analogous to Eqs. (11) to (15) are also different in detail. However, the same general ideas and the same technique of linearization about the steady-state values apply equally well in the three-level and other cases. The results for the ruby case predict a more highly resonant and less strongly damped spiking behavior, and real ruby lasers, in agreement with this prediction, almost always show a strong and nearly undamped spiking in their output. This general approach to the spiking problem is sometimes referred to as the *Statz-deMars approach*, since this group studied the problem in some detail (Ref. 10-16). A great many other analyses of spiking have also appeared in the literature—more, perhaps, than are really useful, since spiking is more troublesome nuisance than a particularly interesting phenomenon to be studied in any great detail.

■ There are very few new ideas without some interesting history behind them, and spiking was well known at considerably lower frequencies long before it was observed and studied (quite independently) in lasers. In close analogy to a laser, a simple RC audio oscillator also has an amplification mechanism, combined with a power-dependent saturation mechanism, and a feedback mechanism whose round-trip phase is strongly frequency dependent. The saturation or gain-reducing mechanism in the audio-frequency RC "laser" is a variable resistance in the feedback loop, usually consisting of a small lamp bulb whose temperature and resistance change with the average signal power in the loop, so as to reduce the loop gain as the power level goes up.

This system is also similar to the solid-state-laser case in that the time constant of its gain or saturation mechanism (the thermal time constant of the lamp) is long compared to the decay time of the oscillator or laser circuit or cavity. As a result, we can predict and, in appropriate cases, readily observe a strong envelope spiking behavior in the output of such audio oscillators, with an envelope variation that may look almost exactly like the corresponding spiking envelope in a laser oscillator. Actually, in most audio oscillators there is also some weaker but fast-acting saturation behavior caused by nonlinear distortion in the electronic amplifier stages themselves, and this saturation, equivalent to a short τ_2, usually acts to eliminate the spiking. However, on occasion, either by design or by accident, an audio oscillator is built with a highly linear, distortion-free amplifier section. Such an oscillator shows the spiking effects very strongly.[1]

■ The basic technique of linearizing the nonlinear rate equations by considering small deviations about the steady state can be applied to other problems of interest in lasers. Suppose, for example, that we want to modulate the output of a laser oscillator by modulating the pump power applied. We may write

$$R_p(t) = R_{p0} + \Delta R_p(t) \qquad \Delta R_p \ll R_{p0} \tag{17}$$

where R_{p0} is the average pump power applied and $\Delta R_p(t)$ is a small modulation signal. If the depths of modulation of $\Delta R_p(t)$ and of the resulting fluctuations in $n(t)$ and $\mathcal{N}_2(t)$ are not too large, then they may be analyzed by the linearized set of equations

$$\frac{d}{dt} \Delta n(t) - \frac{(r-1)}{\tau_2} \Delta \mathcal{N}(t) = 0$$

$$\left(\frac{d}{dt} + \frac{r}{\tau_2}\right) \Delta \mathcal{N}(t) + \frac{1}{\tau_c} \Delta n(t) = \Delta R_p(t) \tag{18}$$

These equations may be solved by Laplace transformation or by any other of the standard techniques for coupled linear differential equations. Since the transient response of the laser system is a rather lightly damped resonance at the spiking frequency ω_s, at least for "spiky" types of lasers, it should not be surprising that the modulation response of the laser shows a strong resonance peak for sinusoidal input modulation at modulation frequencies ω near the spiking frequency ω_s. We might also consider modulating a laser by modulating the cavity losses or the output coupling. Again, linearized equations can be used where appropriate, and the same comments about resonance apply.

[1] For a full analysis and description of this behavior see Ref. 10-11.

■ The technique of *Q*-switching a laser (Chap. 1) can be considered as a kind of stimulated single-spike behavior of the laser. While we will not take up any of the details here, in many cases the dynamics of laser *Q* switching can also be described very well by the laser rate equations. The linearized approach is usually not useful here, because the range of dynamic variation is large, but the rate equations for $n(t)$ and $\mathcal{N}_2(t)$ can still be solved by computer simulation or by piecewise linearization of the rate equations.

10-9   A LASER LUMPED EQUIVALENT CIRCUIT

Earlier in the chapter we used a cavity rate equation for the number of signal photons to analyze the dynamics of the signal in a laser cavity. Such a photon rate equation can be very useful, as we have seen, for analyzing the transient buildup of oscillations in a laser cavity mode, for calculating the steady-state oscillation level and the variation of laser output with external coupling, and for analyzing spiking and other transient disturbances in a laser oscillator. The use of a photon rate equation is a simplification, however. The price of this simplification is that the rate-equation approach only keeps track of the signal *energy* in the cavity and discards all information concerning the signal *phase* or the complex phasor amplitude of the signal.

In some situations we need to keep track of both the amplitude and the phase of the signal in a laser cavity mode. This is the case, for example, when an external signal is applied to the laser cavity and we wish to study its amplification and phase shift, or when several signals at slightly different frequencies are simultaneously present in the same cavity mode and interference effects between these signals are important, or when we want to study not only the amplitude, but also the phase and frequency fluctuations of a laser signal. For these purposes the cavity rate-equation approach is not adequate, and we must go back to a more accurate and detailed (but really only slightly more complicated) *circuit analysis* of the cavity behavior.

In this section we will go through a simple derivation to obtain the basic circuit equation necessary to describe both the amplitude and the phase of the laser cavity signal in a single selected laser cavity mode. This equation will turn out to be a first-order differential equation for the complex phasor amplitude of the laser signal, rather than the purely real first-order differential equation obtained in the photon rate-equation approach. This equation for the laser signal is generally called the *circuit equation*, because it is very similar in form to the differential equation for the voltage or current in a lumped electric circuit. In fact, we will also show in this section how the laser circuit equation can be interpreted so as to replace the laser cavity model by the simple and perhaps more familiar model of a lumped resonant equivalent circuit.

■ Let us represent the wave amplitude of the given single laser cavity mode—and by this we mean a single transverse and axial mode of the laser cavity—by a complex phasor amplitude $\tilde{u}e^{j\omega t}$. The complex wave amplitude $\tilde{u}$ may represent, for example, the positive-traveling wave at a reference plane just inside the laser mirror M_1, as shown in Fig. 10-33a. We also assume that there may be an external wave $\tilde{u}_e$ which is mode-matched to the selected cavity mode and incident on mirror M_1 from outside, as in Fig. 10-33a.

These wave amplitudes are defined so that the power carried by the wave is just the wave amplitude squared, or

$$P = |\tilde{u}|^2 \qquad P_e = |\tilde{u}_e|^2 \tag{1}$$

$\tilde{u}_e(t) \longrightarrow$ $\tilde{u}(t)$

M_1 M_2

(a) Laser model

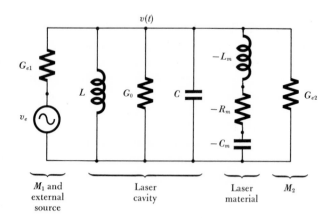

$v(t)$

G_{e1} L G_0 C $-L_m$
v_e $-R_m$ G_{e2}
                                    $-C_m$

M_1 and   Laser   Laser M_2
external   cavity   material
source

(b) Lumped equivalent circuit

FIG. 10-33 (a) Model for developing a laser-cavity circuit equation. (b) A lumped equivalent circuit that can have the same circuit equation and hence can replace the laser-cavity model for purposes of analysis.

where P is the power carried by the wave flowing in the indicated direction inside the laser cavity. The complex amplitudes $\tilde{u}$ and $\tilde{u}_e$ may both be slowly varying functions of time, $\tilde{u}(t)$ and $\tilde{u}_e(t)$, since the laser may be operating in a transient condition or the external signal $\tilde{u}_e(t)$ may be modulated in amplitude or phase. However, we will assume that these amplitudes are always slowly varying, in the sense that

$$\left| \frac{d^2}{dt^2} \tilde{u} \right| \ll \omega \left| \frac{d}{dt} \tilde{u} \right| \ll \omega^2 |\tilde{u}| \tag{2}$$

Now, the total wave amplitude $\tilde{u}(t + 2T)$ passing through the reference plane at the instant $t + 2T$ must be equal to the total wave amplitude $\tilde{u}(t)$ that passed through that plane one round-trip transit time $2T$ earlier, multiplied by the net round-trip gain g_{rt} for a wave in the cavity, plus the added wave amplitude $t_1 \tilde{u}_e(t + 2T)$ being transmitted through the external mirror at that same instant; that is,

$$\tilde{u}(t + 2T) = g_{rt}\tilde{u}(t) + t_1\tilde{u}_e(t + 2T)$$
$$= \tilde{u}(t) + \Delta\tilde{u}(2T) \tag{3}$$

where $\Delta\tilde{u}(2T)$ represents the net change or increment in the wave amplitude $\tilde{u}$ during the time interval $2T$. The round-trip gain in Eq. (3) is given by

$$g_{rt} = r_1 r_2 \exp\left(-2\alpha_0 L - 2j\beta_0 L\right) \exp\left(+2\Gamma_m L\right) \tag{4}$$

where the propagation factor Γ_m due to the laser transition itself will be, for a lorentzian transition,

$$\Gamma_m(\omega) = \alpha_m(\omega) + j\,\Delta\beta_m(\omega) = \frac{n_0\omega}{2Q_{m0}c}\frac{1}{1 + 2j(\omega - \omega_a)/\Delta\omega_a} \tag{5}$$

All the symbols in these expressions are as defined in earlier chapters.

Equation (3) may be rewritten as

$$\ln\left[1 + \frac{\Delta\tilde{u}(2T)}{\tilde{u}(t)} - \frac{t_1\tilde{u}_e(t + 2T)}{\tilde{u}(t)}\right] = \ln g_{rt}$$

$$= -\left(2\alpha_0 L + \ln\frac{1}{r_1 r_2}\right) - j[2\beta_0(\omega)L - q2\pi] + 2\Gamma_m(\omega)L \qquad (6)$$

Note that an arbitrary integer multiple of 2π may always be added to the imaginary part of such a complex logarithm, as in the $-jq2\pi$ term, to bring the net phase angle within the range $-\pi$ to π. In the cases of interest to us, both the second and the third terms in the argument of the first logarithm will be small compared to unity, and the approximation $\ln(1 + x) \approx x$, $|x| \ll 1$, may be used to rewrite (6) in the form

$$\frac{\Delta\tilde{u}(2T)}{2T} = \frac{2\Gamma_m L - 2\alpha_0 L - \ln(1/r_1 r_2) - 2j(\beta_0 L - q\pi)}{2T}\tilde{u}(t)$$

$$+ \frac{t_1}{2T}\tilde{u}_e(t + 2T) \qquad (7)$$

We then define or identify the following cavity parameters:

Round-trip transit time: $2T = \dfrac{2n_0 L}{c}$

Cold-cavity frequency: $\omega_c = q\dfrac{\pi c}{n_0 L}$

Cavity internal losses: $\dfrac{\omega}{2Q_0} = \dfrac{c\alpha_0}{n_0}$ (8)

Cavity external coupling: $\dfrac{\omega}{2Q_e} = \dfrac{c}{2n_0 L}\left(\ln\dfrac{1}{r_1} + \ln\dfrac{1}{r_2}\right)$

$$= \frac{\omega}{2Q_{e1}} + \frac{\omega}{2Q_{e2}}$$

Total (loaded) cavity losses: $\dfrac{\omega}{2Q_c} = \dfrac{\omega}{2Q_0} + \dfrac{\omega}{2Q_e}$

Off-resonance frequency term: $\dfrac{2[\beta_0(\omega)L - q\pi]}{2T} = \omega - \omega_c$

Then, provided that the net fractional change in $\tilde{u}(t)$ per round trip is not too great, we may replace the discrete quantity $(2T)^{-1}\Delta\tilde{u}(t)$ by the differential rate of change $(d/dt)\tilde{u}$ and write

$$\frac{\Delta\tilde{u}(2T)}{2T} = \frac{d\tilde{u}}{dt} = \left[-\frac{\omega}{2Q_c} - j(\omega - \omega_c)\right.$$

$$\left. + \frac{\omega}{2Q_m}\frac{1}{1 + 2j(\omega - \omega_a)/\Delta\omega_a}\right]\tilde{u}(t) + \frac{t_1}{2T}\tilde{u}_e(t) \qquad (9)$$

Since we are really assuming, in fact, that $\tilde{u}(t)$ and $\tilde{u}_e(t)$ change only slowly, even in comparison with the round-trip time $2T$, we have also, as a valid approximation, replaced $\tilde{u}_e(t + 2T)$ by $\tilde{u}_e(t)$ in Eq. (9).

Equation (9) is then, in fact, essentially the desired circuit equation for the laser cavity, at least within the various approximations used in this derivation. The successive terms on the right-hand side can readily be identified as giving the total cavity losses due to internal losses and scattering plus mirror output coupling, the phase-shift term that will be present if the signal frequency ω is not exactly at the cavity resonance ω_c, the laser interaction term including both gain and added-phase-shift effects, and finally, the driving term corresponding to any external wave $\tilde{u}_e$ that may be present.

If the input mirror M_1 is assumed to be lossless (or its losses, if any, are absorbed in the internal loss term α_0), then we may write $R_1 = r_1{}^2 = 1 - t_1{}^2 = 1 - \delta_1$, and hence the mirror transmission is $t_1 = \delta_1{}^{1/2}$. With some minor rearrangements, the circuit equation (9) can then be put into the final form

$$\frac{d}{dt}\tilde{u} = \left\{\left(\frac{\omega}{2Q_m(\omega)} - \frac{\omega}{2Q_e}\right) - j\left[(\omega - \omega_c) + \frac{Q_a}{Q_m(\omega)}(\omega - \omega_a)\right]\right\}\tilde{u}$$

$$+ \frac{2}{\delta_1{}^{1/2}}\frac{\omega}{2Q_{e1}}\tilde{u}_e \quad (10)$$

where by $Q_m(\omega)$ we mean the frequency-dependent value

$$\frac{1}{Q_m(\omega)} \equiv \frac{1}{Q_{m0}}\frac{1}{1 + [2(\omega - \omega_a)/\Delta\omega_a]^2} \quad (11)$$

Equation (10) is then the final form of the laser circuit equation, within the approximations made here.

EVALUATION OF THE CAVITY   ■ The cavity circuit equation (10) can be criticized, with some justification, for being
CIRCUIT EQUATION   a somewhat confusing mixture of *time-varying* quantities, such as $\tilde{u}(t)$ and $(d/dt)\tilde{u}$, with *sinusoidal steady-state* quantities and concepts, such as $Q_m(\omega)$ and the general concept of $\tilde{u}$ as a complex phasor amplitude to be multiplied by $e^{j\omega t}$. These two approaches are intermingled in order to retain the general idea of essentially sinusoidal-wave behavior for the cavity signals, with all the associated and useful sinusoidal concepts, while still permitting slow but otherwise arbitrary transient time variations for the complex amplitudes of the sinusoidal signals. The resulting mixed equation gives answers which are admittedly approximations, but which still describe the transient responses of the laser signal with more than sufficient accuracy in most situations of practical interest.

Before we discuss certain aspects of the circuit equation further, it may be useful to apply it to a few simple situations to illustrate some of its properties. Let us consider first the case of steady-state laser oscillation at the steady oscillation frequency ω_{osc} (from Sec. 10-3), assuming for the moment no externally injected signal and no transient variations, so that $\tilde{u}_e = 0$ and also $(d/dt)\tilde{u} = 0$. The general form of Eq. (10) makes it apparent that if $\tilde{u}(t)$ is to have neither exponential growth nor decay in amplitude, then the same steady-state gain condition discussed in Sec. 10-2 must apply; that is

$$\frac{\omega}{2Q_m(\omega)} - \frac{\omega}{2Q_c} \equiv 0 \quad (12)$$

or $Q_m(\omega) = Q_c$ at the frequency ω of the steady-state oscillation [note that Eq. (12) is only a steady-state oscillation condition, and not a general requirement, especially in the transient case]. Now, in this case there is no externally injected signal to define a signal frequency ω, and we may not know in advance exactly the correct value of

$\omega \equiv \omega_{\mathrm{osc}}$ at which the laser oscillates. There is therefore some uncertainty in choosing the value of ω to use in writing the laser signal as $\tilde{u}(t)e^{j\omega t}$. Inspection of Eq. (10) makes it clear, however, that the phase variation with time of $\tilde{u}(t)$ will also be identically zero if we select ω to be the value which makes

$$(\omega - \omega_c) + \frac{Q_a}{Q_m(\omega)}(\omega - \omega_a) = 0 \tag{13}$$

Combined with (12), this immediately gives

$$\omega = \frac{Q_c\omega_c + Q_a\omega_a}{Q_c + Q_a} \equiv \omega_{\mathrm{osc}} \tag{14}$$

This is, of course, just the frequency-pulled oscillation frequency of Sec. 10-3. Thus Eq. (10) contains at least as a start the steady-state oscillation conditions of Secs. 10-2 and 10-3.

We should note next that the exact choice of the basic frequency ω to use in writing the laser signal as $\tilde{u}(t)e^{j\omega t}$ is not critical, and need not agree with (14), so long as the ω value used is reasonably close to the actual laser signal frequency ω_{osc}. In the case just discussed, if we initially choose a value of $\omega = \omega_{\mathrm{osc}} + \Delta\omega$, where $\Delta\omega$ is some arbitrary offset, then the circuit equation (10) will automatically yield the answer that $\tilde{u}(t) \simeq \tilde{u}_0 e^{-j\,\Delta\omega\,t}$, or that the complete laser signal is

$$u(t)e^{j\omega t} \simeq \tilde{u}_0 e^{-j\,\Delta\omega\,t}e^{j\omega t} = \tilde{u}_0 e^{j\omega_{\mathrm{osc}}t}$$

In other words, the circuit equation automatically gives $\tilde{u}(t)$ the necessary phase variation $-j\,\Delta\omega\,t$ to compensate for an arbitrary initial choice of $\omega \neq \omega_{\mathrm{osc}}$.

Consider next the case in which a cw external signal $\tilde{u}_e e^{j\omega_e t}$, with $\omega_e \simeq \omega_c$, is injected into a laser cavity in the below-threshold condition, and we wish to find the resulting amplified steady-state signal $\tilde{u}$ inside the laser cavity. In this case we clearly should choose the ω in Eq. (10) to be just the externally injected frequency ω_e, since all signal components present will be at that frequency. The steady-state form of (10), with $(d/dt)\tilde{u} = 0$, will then become

$$\left[\left(\frac{\omega_e}{2Q_e} - \frac{\omega_e}{2Q_m}\right) + j\frac{Q_m + Q_a}{Q_m}(\omega_e - \omega_c')\right]\tilde{u} = \frac{2}{\delta^{1/2}}\frac{\omega}{2Q_{e1}}\tilde{u}_e \tag{15}$$

where $\omega_c' \equiv (Q_m\omega_c + Q_a\omega_a)/(Q_m + Q_a)$ is the pulled cavity resonance frequency, as in Chap. 5. The internal laser signal will then be given by

$$\frac{\tilde{u}}{\tilde{u}_e} = \frac{1}{\delta^{1/2}}\frac{Q_e}{Q_{e1}}\frac{1}{(1 - Q_e/Q_m) + 2j(Q_e/Q_m)(Q_m + Q_a)(\omega_e - \omega_c')/\omega_e} \tag{16}$$

The resonance amplification of the external signal shown by this result, with $\tilde{u}/\tilde{u}_e \to \infty$ as $Q_m \to Q_e$ and $\omega_e \to \omega_c'$, is essentially the same as the regenerative traveling-wave amplification discussed in Chap. 5.

Finally, consider briefly the situation where an external signal $\tilde{u}_e e^{j\omega_e t}$ is applied to a laser already oscillating at frequency ω_{osc}. This case arises, for example, when we attempt to injection-lock the signal in an oscillating laser with an externally injected signal. In this situation it must be considered that two separate signal components, injected plus self-oscillating, may be simultaneously present in the single cavity mode. Therefore $\tilde{u}(t)$ must be written as the sum of two terms; for example,

$$\tilde{u}(t)e^{j\omega t} = \tilde{u}_1(t)e^{j\omega_e t} + \tilde{u}_2(t)e^{j\omega_{osc} t} \tag{17}$$

where $\tilde{u}_1$ is due to the injected signal and $\tilde{u}_2$ represents the self-oscillation. The choice of the reference frequency ω to use in expanding $\tilde{u}(t)e^{j\omega t}$ is again arbitrary here. However, the best choice for simplifying the results may be to choose ω equal to the free-running oscillation frequency ω_{osc}. The total signal $\tilde{u}(t)$ is then written as

$$\tilde{u}(t) = \tilde{u}_1(t)e^{j(\omega_e - \omega_{osc})t} + \tilde{u}_2(t) \tag{18}$$

and this form is then substituted into all the $\tilde{u}(t)$ terms in Eq. (10). Note that the total $\tilde{u}(t)$ expression in (18) can still be termed slowly varying, as required by approximation (2), since any injected signal, to be significant, will have to be at a frequency ω_e close to the natural resonance frequency ω_{osc} of the laser, and hence $\omega_e - \omega_{osc} \ll \omega_e$ or ω_{osc}. We will not attempt to carry this analysis further, since the main point here is that $\tilde{u}(t)$ in many situations of interest may contain two, or even more, frequency components, in which case it must be written in a form like Eq. (18).

In all these cases the cavity circuit equation (10) must be combined with the appropriate atomic rate equation(s), such as Eq. (19) of Sec. 10-4 or (18) of Sec. 10-5, to make a complete dynamical analysis of the laser. In particular, if the inverted-population difference $\Delta \mathcal{N}(t)$ on the laser transition is varying with time, as governed by some rate equation, then the Q_m parameters in Eqs. (10) and (11) will be given by

$$[Q_{m0}(t)]^{-1} = const \times \Delta \mathcal{N}(t) \tag{19}$$

and so Q_m itself must also be considered as a (slowly) *time-varying* parameter. In the simplest cases $\Delta \mathcal{N}(t)$ will be governed by a rate equation of the form

$$\frac{d}{dt} \Delta \mathcal{N}(t) = -K_1 |\tilde{u}(t)|^2 \Delta \mathcal{N}(t) - \frac{\Delta \mathcal{N}(t) - \Delta \mathcal{N}_{small-sig}}{T_1} \tag{20}$$

where $\Delta \mathcal{N}_{small-sig}$ is the small-signal value of inverted population difference obtained with the laser pump on but with no strong laser signals present. The $-K_1 |\tilde{u}(t)|^2 \Delta \mathcal{N}(t)$ term represents the stimulated-emission terms, or the saturation of $\Delta \mathcal{N}(t)$ toward zero by the laser cavity signals, and the remaining terms represent the recovery of $\Delta \mathcal{N}(t)$ toward $\Delta \mathcal{N}_{small-sig}$ due to laser pumping plus relaxation processes. Note that $|\tilde{u}(t)|^2$ gives the variation in power level with time of the laser signal, or essentially the variation of the photon number $n(t)$ in the cavity. If two or more signal components are present, as in Eq. (18), or if the laser is in a transient condition, then $|\tilde{u}(t)|^2$ will indeed vary with time, but always with a slow variation in the sense of this section.

In many cases the combination of the cavity equations (10) and (11) plus the atomic equations (19) and (20) is all that is needed for a more or less complete analysis of a laser problem. Equations (10) and (11) describe how the laser signal $\tilde{u}(t)$ varies as determined by the cavity and atomic parameters, especially $\Delta \mathcal{N}(t)$ or $Q_m(t)$, while Eqs. (19) to (20) describe how $\Delta \mathcal{N}(t)$ and $Q_m(t)$, respectively, vary as determined by the pumping and signal parameters, especially $\tilde{u}(t)$. The analysis then becomes the mathematical problem of finding the slowly varying solutions to these equations. Strictly speaking, these equations, especially (11), are accurate only for homogeneously broadened laser transitions. However, with perhaps some slight extensions, they also supply good first-order approximate solutions to many inhomogeneous laser problems.

Note that there is one important assumption hidden in all of this analysis. In representing the interaction with the laser transition by a simple gain (and phase-shift) factor, as in Eqs. (4) and (5), we are implicitly neglecting any short-term ac transients in the atomic response itself. That is, we are neglecting the kind of transients with time constant T_2 that will occur in the transient solution of the classical electron-oscillator model of Chap. 2, for example, and we are assuming that the sinusoidal atomic polarization will follow the quasi-sinusoidal laser signal with no significant delay. This is equivalent to assuming that the atomic linewidth is broad, and hence the atomic transient response time T_2 is short compared to the time scale of the slow time variations in this problem. This assumption is valid in many cases but will fail for narrow atomic lines. When it fails seriously, then the only resort is to go to a still more detailed analysis in which both the cavity and the atoms are described by complex "circuit" type of equations. We will not attempt such a derivation here.[1]

Note also that the pairs of equations (10) and (11) and (19) and (20) are *nonlinear* equations. Hence when two or more signal frequency components are present, as in (18), we can expect still further but generally weaker signals to appear as intermodulation products at sum and difference frequencies. Therefore it may be necessary to add still further components to an expansion such as (18) to analyze the intermodulation effects in the system.

It should be emphasized that the cavity equation (10) describes only the signals in a single transverse and axial mode of the laser cavity. If signals are present simultaneously in several laser cavity modes, a separate circuit equation must be written for *each* such cavity mode, each with its own separate resonant frequency and other parameters. Since all the cavity modes share the same atomic system, as diagramed in Fig. 10-19, if several modes are active, then the signals from all the modes must be summed to find the total laser intensity $|\tilde{u}(t)|^2$ to use in an atomic rate equation such as Eq. (20).

■ The lumped electric circuit shown in Fig. 10-33b is a doubly resonant circuit with a negative-impedance branch which should be familiar from earlier chapters. The basic circuit equation for this network is

LUMPED EQUIVALENT CIRCUIT

$$G_{e1}v_e(t) = G_c v(t) + C\frac{d}{dt}v(t) + \frac{1}{L}\int v(t)\,dt + i_m(t) \tag{21}$$

where $v_e(t)$ is the external applied voltage, $v(t)$ is the voltage across the main network, the total cavity conductance (internal loss G_0 plus external couplings G_{e1} and G_{e2}) is $G_c = G_0 + G_e = G_0 + G_{e1} + G_{e2}$, and $i_m(t)$ is the current flowing through the shunt laser-material branch consisting of $-L_m$, $-R_m$, and $-C_m$. Assuming that $v_e(t)$ and $v(t)$ are basically sinusoidal at frequency ω, we write these quantities as

$$v(t) = \tilde{u}(t)e^{j\omega t} \qquad v_e(t) = \tilde{u}_e e^{j\omega t} \tag{22}$$

where the phasor amplitudes $\tilde{u}(t)$ and $\tilde{u}_e(t)$ are assumed to be slowly varying and governed by the same approximation in Eq. (2) as before. Within this approximation, the integral term in (21) may be repeatedly integrated by parts to generate a sequence like

$$\int v(t)\,dt = \int \tilde{u}(t)e^{j\omega t}\,dt = \frac{1}{j\omega}\tilde{u}(t)e^{j\omega t} - \frac{1}{j\omega}\int \frac{d\tilde{u}(t)}{dt}e^{j\omega t}\,dt$$
$$= \frac{1}{j\omega}\tilde{u}(t)e^{j\omega t} + \frac{1}{\omega^2}\frac{d\tilde{u}(t)}{dt}e^{j\omega t} + \frac{1}{\omega^2}\int \frac{d^2\tilde{u}(t)}{dt^2}e^{j\omega t}\,dt \tag{23}$$

[1] A derivation that proceeds from the basic quantum equations to various forms of circuit and rate equations is summarized in Ref. 10-14.

Since each successive term in the resulting sequences is reduced by one further power of the frequency ω compared to the slow time variation of $\tilde{u}(t)$, we will keep only the first two terms and drop the final integral in the third line of the above equation.

We also assume that the current $i_m(t)$ through the laser material branch will be related to the sinusoidal voltage $v(t)$ across the branch by

$$v(t) = \tilde{u}(t)e^{j\omega t} = -\left[R_m + j\left(\omega L_m - \frac{1}{\omega C_m}\right)\right] i_m(t) \tag{24}$$

or

$$i_m(t) = -\frac{\tilde{u}(t)e^{j\omega t}}{R_m + j\left(\omega L_m - \frac{1}{\omega C_m}\right)}$$

$$\approx -\frac{1}{R_m}\frac{\tilde{u}(t)e^{j\omega t}}{1 + 2j(\omega - \omega_a)/\Delta\omega_a} \tag{25}$$

where the connection between the real laser transition and the equivalent circuit branch is established by

$$\omega_a{}^2 = (L_m C_m)^{-1} \qquad Q_a = \frac{\omega_a}{\Delta\omega_a} = \frac{\omega_a L_m}{R_m} \tag{26}$$

Note that any transient response behavior of the current in the $(-R_m, -L_m, -C_m)$ branch has *not* been included here. That is, we have assumed that the sinusoidal $i_m(t)$ follows the quasi-sinusoidal $v(t)$ according to strict steady-state sinusoidal formulas, even though $v(t)$ itself is not in general a perfectly steady sinusoidal voltage. The approximation made here is exactly the same as the approximation concerning the laser-material response in the cavity case above.

Equation (21) now becomes

$$[1 + (\omega^2 LC)^{-1}]\frac{d\tilde{u}}{dt} = \left\{\left[\frac{1}{R_m C}\frac{1}{1 + 2j(\omega - \omega_a)/\Delta\omega_a} - \frac{G_c}{C}\right]\right.$$
$$\left. -j[\omega - (\omega LC)^{-1}]\right\}\tilde{u} + \frac{G_{e1}}{C}\tilde{u}_e \tag{27}$$

To connect this with the laser cavity case we define the parameters

Cavity frequency: $\omega_c{}^2 = (LC)^{-1}$

Loaded-cavity-loss Q: $Q_c = \frac{G_c}{\omega C}$

Maser Q: $Q_{m0} = \frac{1}{\omega R_m C}$

External Q: $Q_{e1} = \frac{G_{e1}}{\omega C} \qquad Q_e = \frac{G_e}{\omega C}$

$$\tag{28}$$

and we make the near-resonance approximations

$$1 + \frac{1}{\omega^2 LC} = \frac{\omega^2 + \omega_c{}^2}{\omega^2} \approx 2$$

$$\omega - \frac{1}{\omega LC} = \frac{(\omega + \omega_c)(\omega - \omega_c)}{\omega} \approx 2(\omega - \omega_c) \tag{29}$$

Equation (26) then becomes, finally,

$$\frac{d\tilde{u}(t)}{dt} = \left\{ \left[\frac{\omega}{2Q_m(\omega)} - \frac{\omega}{2Q_c} \right] - j \left[(\omega - \omega_c) + \frac{Q_a}{Q_m(\omega)} (\omega - \omega_a) \right] \right\} \tilde{u}(t)$$
$$+ \left[\frac{\omega}{2Q_{e1}} \right] \tilde{u}_e(t) \quad (30)$$

But, this is exactly the same form as the laser circuit equation (10), with $Q_m(\omega)$ defined as in (11). Hence for purposes of analysis the lumped-circuit model of Fig. 10-33a is an essentially exact equivalent circuit for the laser-cavity models of Fig. 10-8 or 10-33a and can replace them. We obtained essentially this same result in earlier chapters.

We will not pursue the use of the cavity circuit equation or of the lumped equivalent circuit further in this chapter. However, the circuit model of Fig. 10-33b can be very useful as an analytical model and also as a guide to understanding the analytical results in many practical laser calculations.

PROBLEMS

10-1. It is possible in theory (although not very likely in practice) to have a three-level laser system in which the laser action takes place on the $3 \to 2$ rather than the $2 \to 1$ transition (no such real system is known). Suppose that level 3 in such a system is long-lived or metastable, level 2 has a short relaxation time to the ground state, and the system is optically pumped on the $1 \to 3$ transition. Carry through the rate-equation analysis necessary to find the population inversion on the $3 \to 2$ transition as a function of pumping power, and add the appropriate curve for this system to the other two cases in Fig. 10-4.

10-2. In an idealized three-level system such as that for ruby, let the pump power be suddenly turned on to a constant value $W_p > W_{p,\text{th}}$ at time $t = 0$. There will then be a finite time delay τ_d before the three-level system can reach inversion so that the first burst of laser action can build up. Find an expression for the time delay τ_d to reach inversion as a function of $W_p/W_{p,\text{th}}$, where $W_{p,\text{th}}$ is the minimum value to just reach inversion after infinite delay, and plot the normalized delay τ/τ_d versus $W_p/W_{p,\text{th}}$, where τ is the upper-laser-level lifetime.

10-3. In a somewhat more exact model of the ruby laser than Fig. 10-3, the ground level E_1 is split into two separate but very closely spaced levels by a zero-field splitting (Chap. 1), and the upper laser level E_2 is also split into the two so-called R_1 and R_2 levels, separated by $\Delta E/hc \approx 39$ cm^{-1}. The relaxation between these two levels is so rapid that we can assume that the relative populations of the two levels will remain fixed in the appropriate Boltzmann ratio $e^{-\Delta E/kT}$ even during laser pumping and laser oscillation. Since the Boltzmann ratio is not negligible here, the R_2 population is smaller than the R_1 population by a significant amount, and the R_1 rather than the R_2 transition will always oscillate unless special steps are taken (the ground-state splitting is much smaller, and the Boltzmann difference there may be ignored).

Taking these level splittings into account, but otherwise making the same idealized three-level assumptions as in the text, calculate the population difference from the R_1 level to either of the ground levels as a function of the pumping power. Also develop an expression for pulse-pumped gain compared to unpumped absorption analogous to Eq. (33) of Sec. 10-1, but with the level splitting and Boltzmann effects taken into account.

10-4. What is the optical power-generation density (i.e., the optical power generated per unit volume) in a typical injection-laser diode junction at threshold, at 4°K, and at 300°K? If just 1 percent of this power were absorbed and converted to heat in the junction volume, what would be the rate of temperature rise in the GaAs material?

10-5. Obtain a simple expression valid in the small-cavity-loss approximation for the cold-cavity bandwidth of a laser cavity in terms only of the cavity's axial-mode spacing and its fractional power loss per bounce.

10-6. An He-Ne laser has a doppler-broadened gain profile with a linewidth $\Delta f_a = 1500$ MHz. The laser discharge in a typical tube diameter will have a midband gain coefficient $\alpha_m = 2.5 \times 10^{-3}$ cm^{-1}. Suppose that a laser is to use mirrors with 100 percent and 97 percent reflectivity at the two ends, and that internal cavity losses are negligible. While the laser is running, its exact mode frequencies will undoubtedly change with time due to thermal expansion, etc., so that the axial modes will be scanned (i.e., will drift) across the atomic-gain profile. Find the allowable range of cavity (and discharge) lengths such that during such drifts the laser will always oscillate in one or two axial modes, but three-axial-mode oscillation can never occur.

10-7. The cavity for a certain 6328-Å He-Ne laser is 1 m long and has mirrors with $R = 100$ percent on one end and $R = $

98 percent on the other. Internal cavity losses are negligible. If the steady-state power output of this laser is 35 mW, what is the steady-state photon number in the oscillating cavity mode? Suppose the transverse-mode pattern of this cavity is approximately 1 mm in diameter, with a roughly uniform transverse distribution instead of the more usual gaussian distribution. What is the power density, in watts per square centimeter, carried by the two traveling waves propagating in each direction inside the laser cavity? What is the optical E field strength associated with this power density?

10-8. Suppose that in the laser of Prob. 10-7 the population difference on the laser transition is suddenly pumped up from zero to an inverted value 1.1 times as large as the oscillation threshold value. If the inversion is held at this greater-than-threshold value, how long will it take for the photon density inside the laser cavity to grow from an initial level of $\sim$1 noise photon/cavity mode to the steady-state photon number calculated in Prob. 10-7?

10-9. Verify the optical cavity mode density $(d/df)N$ of Eq. (16) in Sec. 10-4 for one or more simple cavity shapes, such as a rectangle or a cylinder, using the resonant-mode formulas for microwave resonant cavities.

10-10. If the gain-saturation expression Eq. (1) of Sec. 10-6 is approximated in the form $(1 + W/W_{\text{sat}})^{-1} \approx (1 - W/W_{\text{sat}})$, the nonlinear cavity rate equation for the buildup of laser oscillation, as in Fig. 10-17, can be solved exactly, and both the initial exponential buildup and the bending over to a steady final value can be described by a single expression. Try to find this closed analytic solution and compare it to the experimental data shown in Fig. 10-17.

10-11. Consider a Q-switched ruby laser in which the output mirror has $R = 70$ percent and the opposite mirror is switched from $R = 8$ percent to $R = 100$ percent in essentially zero switching time. The ruby rod is 10 cm long and 1 cm in diameter, with $N = 10^{19}$ ions/cm³. Internal scattering causes an attenuation $\alpha_0 = 0.01$ cm^{-1}. The upper-level decay is purely radiative, with $\tau_{\text{rad}} = 4.3$ msec and $\Delta f_a = 300$ GHz.

Suppose the Q-switched mirror is switched from low to high reflectivity at the instant when the population inversion is just on the verge of reaching oscillation threshold for the low reflectivity value. Calculate the buildup rate for the Q-switched oscillation signal in the cavity after switching. Can you also estimate the peak value to which the laser pulse will rise, and thus the total time delay from the mirror switching until the output pulse occurs?

10-12. Develop expressions that will relate the oscillation-power output above threshold to the total laser fluorescent and decay power below and above threshold, in the general fashion of Fig. 10-24, but with the more detailed two-level atomic model of Fig. 10-26. Assume some representative values for relaxation-time ratios and for R_{p1}/R_{p2}, and plot curves analogous to those in Fig. 10-24. Discuss the differences between the idealized case of Fig. 10-24 and the more realistic results you obtain.

10-13. To gain some insight into multimode oscillations in a laser, consider a cavity having *two* preferred cavity modes, whose losses differ by some moderate amount, say, 10 percent. As a rough model for either spatial inhomogeneity or partially overlapping hole burning in the laser transition, assume that the laser atoms are divided into three groups: those seen only from one cavity mode, those seen only from the other mode, and those seen from both modes. All the atoms are pumped equally, and all other appropriate simplifying assumptions are made.

Devise the proper set of laser rate equations for this system, and attempt to solve these to find the oscillation-power outputs in the two modes as the pump level is raised so that first one and then the other mode comes above threshold (assume that each mode is either well above or well below threshold at any given pumping level, and ignore the photon density in either mode when it is below threshold). Explore the resulting behavior for various values of the cavity loss ratio and of the population distribution between the modes (i.e., for different degrees of sharing of atoms between the two modes). *Note:* It may be possible to solve this problem analytically by assuming at various pumping levels that both, one, or neither of the modes oscillates, or numerical solutions with the aid of a computer may be needed.

10-14. Show that the results of Fig. 10-29 for output power versus output coupling may also be expressed in the simple forms

$$p = \frac{r_1 - 1}{r_1}(r - r_1) \qquad p_{\max} = (r^{1/2} - 1)^2$$

where

$$p \equiv P_e/R_{p,\min}hf \quad r \equiv R_p/R_{p,\min} \quad r_1 \equiv R_{p,\text{th}}/R_{p,\min}$$

with $R_{p,\text{th}}$ the threshold pump rate for the particular external coupling employed at any instant.

10-15. Consider a laser cavity containing a saturable two-level laser material with a peak gain $+\alpha_m$ or $+\gamma_m$ and a saturation coefficient $W_{\text{sat}} = W_m$ as defined in Eq. (1) of Sec. 10-6, and also containing a saturable two-level *absorbing* medium with a peak absorption $-\alpha_0$ or $-\gamma_0$, which also saturates in the fashion of Eq. (1), but with a different $W_{\text{sat}} = W_0$. Assume that the laser cavity may also have external coupling γ_e but, for simplicity, no other internal losses except the saturable losses just described. Analyze the laser-power output as a function of external coupling for this case, including the optimum external coupling and the maximum output power available. Compare your results with the case of nonsaturable internal cavity losses for different values of W_0/W_m.

10-16. Consider the same situation as in Prob. 10-17, but with the particular conditions that $\gamma_0 > \gamma_m$ and $W_0 < W_m$. Such a system obviously cannot build up to oscillation initially from noise, since the low-level loss exceeds the gain. If it is somehow raised to a high enough signal level, however, can it maintain a steady oscillation? At what power level? Could this system potentially serve as a bistable optical computer device, or a *laser flip-flop?*

10-17. When a laser beam is passed through certain nonlinear optical crystals, some of the laser power can be converted to second-harmonic radiation at twice the frequency, or half the wavelength, of the fundamental beam. Since this second-harmonic generation is a nonlinear process, the amount of light converted to the second harmonic is proportional to the fundamental signal strength *squared,* and the conversion efficiency thus increases with increasing fundamental signal level (see Chap. 13).

To increase the second-harmonic conversion in this situation the nonlinear crystal is sometimes placed inside the cavity of an oscillating laser, where the fundamental signal field strength or power density is significantly higher than in the external beam outside the laser. By placing such a crystal inside an Nd-YAG laser cavity, for example, and using laser mirrors that are 100 percent reflecting for the usual laser oscillation frequency but 100 percent transmitting for the second harmonic, a large fraction of the laser power normally taken out at the fundamental wavelength $\lambda = 1.06\mu$ can be obtained instead at the more useful visible (green) wavelength $\lambda = 5300$ Å.

Because the harmonic power extracted is proportional to fundamental signal energy density squared, the harmonic power output P_2 extracted in this fashion can be represented by adding a new term $(dn/dt)_{harmonic} = -K_2 n^2 = -P_2/hf$ to the cavity photon rate equation. The objective in this problem is to calculate the harmonic coupling coefficient K_2 that will give maximum harmonic power output from a given laser (the value of the coefficient K_2 will depend on the nonlinearity coefficient of the nonlinear crystal, the nonlinear crystal length, and similar factors). Using the simple laser saturation law, Eq. (1) of Sec. 10-6, calculate P_2 as a function of K_2 and of the total fundamental losses in the laser cavity. Also compute the harmonic conversion efficiency, defined as the ratio of the harmonic output power to the fundamental power that could be obtained from the same laser with optimum output coupling. Maximize these quantities with respect to K_2. Discuss the sensitivity of these results to variations in K_2 away from its optimum value.

10-18. Repeat Prob. 10-17, but use the complete rate equations for an idealized single-cavity, single-level laser system. Discuss the variation of P_2 and of harmonic efficiency with R_p as well as with the other parameters.

10-19. The laser-threshold discussion of Sec. 10-7 describes the exact variation of the cavity photon number n as the laser passes through threshold. Complete the discussion by considering the exact variation of the upper-laser-level population N_2 through the threshold region in the same case. Use accurate plots and/or analytical expressions as necessary to make clear the detailed behavior of N_2 versus R_p, especially in the close-to-threshold region.

10-20. Extend the threshold discussion of Sec. 10-7 by considering an idealized laser system in which just *two* preferred laser cavity modes, with very nearly the same losses, share the same single-level atomic system. Write the necessary rate equations, using all the simplifying single-level and other assumptions of Sec. 10-7, and attempt to find exact or approximate solutions for the two cavity photon numbers versus pumping rate. Consider particularly the population in the second (more lossy) mode as the first mode goes through and above threshold. Note also whether there are any significant changes in the general behavior when the difference in mode losses becomes very small. If so, how small, in terms of p?

10-21. The pump power in an operating Nd-YAG laser is suddenly increased by a small amount ΔR_p at $t = t_0$ from its previous steady-state value of R_{p0}, with $\Delta R_p \ll R_{p0}$. Evaluate the resulting transient and steady-state changes in the laser-power output and the upper-laser-level populations for $t > t_0$.

10-22. Using the lumped laser cavity model and strictly lumped-circuit equations and concepts, show that in such a lumped-circuit model with $f_c \neq f_a$ the frequency at which circuit oscillation will first occur is given by exactly the same oscillation-frequency-pulling expression as for the traveling-wave-laser case in Sec. 10-3.

REFERENCES

10-1. F. T. Arecchi, C. A. Sacchi, and A. Sona, "Optimization of power and energy output in a laser," *Alta Frequenza,* **32**:183 (1963).

10-2. G. K. Born, "The growth of laser oscillations," *Appl. Phys. Letters,* **12**:46 (Jan. 15, 1968).

10-3. R. F. Broom, "Room temperature operation of gallium arsenide lasers," *Phys. Letters,* **4**:330 (May 15, 1963).

10-4. W. E. Engeler and M. Garfinkel, "Temperature effects in coherent GaAs diodes," *J. Appl. Phys.,* **34**:2746 (September, 1963).

10-5. V. Evtuhov and J. K. Neeland, "Power output and efficiency of continuous ruby lasers," *J. Appl. Phys.,* **38**:4051 (September, 1967).

10-6. J. E. Geusic and H. E. D. Scovil, "A unidirectional traveling-wave optical maser," *Bell Syst. Tech. J.,* **41**:1371 (July, 1962).

10-7. P. Laures, "Variation of the 6328 Å gas laser output power with mirror transmission," *Phys. Letters,* **10**:61 (May 15, 1964).

10-8. P. A. Miles and I. Goldstein, "Effects of output coupling on optical masers," *IEEE Trans. Electron. Devices,* **ED-10**:314 (September, 1963).

10-9. J. K. Neeland and V. Evtuhov, "Measurement of the laser transition cross section for Nd^{3+} in yttrium aluminum garnet," *Phys. Rev.,* **156**:244 (April 10, 1967).

10-10. D. F. Nelson and M. D. Sturge, "Relation between absorption and emission in the region of the *R* lines of ruby," *Phys. Rev.,* **137A**:A1117 (Feb. 15, 1965).

10-11. B. M. Oliver, "The effect of μ-circuit nonlinearity on the amplitude stability of *RC* oscillators," *Hewlett-Packard J.,* **11**(8-10):1 (April–June, 1960).

10-12. W. Rigrod, "Gain saturation and output power of optical masers," *J. Appl. Phys.,* **34**:2602 (September, 1963).

10-13. W. Rigrod, "Saturation effects in high-gain lasers," *J. Appl. Phys.,* **36**:2487 (August, 1965).

10-14. J. H. Shirley, "Dynamics of a simple maser model," *Am. J. Phys.,* **36**:949 (November, 1968).

10-15. P. P. Sorokin, J. D. Axe, and J. R. Lankard, "Spectral characteristics of GaAs lasers operating in 'Fabry-Perot' modes," *J. Appl. Phys.,* **34**:2553 (September, 1963).

10-16. H. Statz and G. A. deMars, "Transients and oscillation pulses in masers," in C. H. Townes, (ed.), *Quantum Electron,* p. 530, Columbia University Press, New York, 1960.

10-17. M. E. Vance, "Measured internal losses and output energies of neodymium glass lasers," *Appl. Optics* **6**:775 (April, 1967).

10-18. A. D. White and E. I. Gordon, "Excitation mechanisms and current dependence of population inversion in He-Ne lasers," *Appl. Phys. Letters,* **3**:197 (Dec. 1, 1963).

10-19. A. Yariv, "Theory of power output and optimum coupling in laser oscillators," in P. Grivet and N. Bloembergen, (eds.), *Quantum Electronics III,* p. 1055, Columbia University Press, New York, 1963.

10-20. A. Yariv, "Energy and power considerations in injection and optically pumped lasers," *Proc. IEEE,* **51**:1723 (December, 1963).

SPONTANEOUS EMISSION AND NOISE

The first atomic phenomenon discussed in Chap. 1 was a spontaneous-emission process—the visible spontaneous emission radiated on certain transitions by excited He atoms. In all the succeeding chapters, however, we were concerned chiefly with stimulated rather than spontaneous transitions, that is, with the induced responses of atomic transitions rather than with their noise-emission properties. It is now time to go back and consider spontaneous emission and the resulting atomic noise phenomena.

We will begin by adding appropriate spontaneous-emission or noise terms to the atomic and cavity rate equations developed in Chaps. 6 and 10. From these terms we will then be able to deduce many important consequences concerning spontaneous emission, thermal noise, and blackbody radiation in electric circuits, transmission lines, and microwave and optical cavities.

By extending these results in a straightforward way to the very interesting domain of inverted atomic populations and negative temperatures, it will be possible to understand the basic source of maser noise and to predict the noise properties of all types of laser and maser devices. We can then apply these results to such topics as the noise properties of microwave maser amplifiers (and other ultralow-noise microwave systems generally), as well as the noise properties and noise limitations of optical maser (laser) amplifiers.

As we will see, such apparently diverse phenomena as radiative damping, spontaneous emission, optical fluorescence, thermal noise and thermal emission, Johnson-Nyquist resistor noise, blackbody radiation, brownian motion, and laser and maser noise are really only different aspects of the same basic physical principles. These topics are not only closely related, but all represent essentially the same physical phenomena. We will attempt in this chapter to unify all these topics and to show how they fit into a single framework.

11-1   SPONTANEOUS EMISSION

Because all the phenomena mentioned above are really the same, we can choose any one of them as a starting place from which to derive all the others. Regardless of which we choose, at some point quantum mechanics must be brought in to explain (or at least to predict) the existence of any of these processes. Hence it will make our discussions most orderly if we begin with spontaneous emission and introduce the necessary quantum results. All the other phenomena can then be easily derived from this starting point.

INSERTING THE "EXTRA PHOTON"

■ The simplest possible, but very general, model for discussing spontaneous emission is a single lossless cavity mode or resonant mode coupled to a collection of two-level atoms, as in Fig. 11-1. The energy in the resonant mode is $W = n\hbar\omega_c$, where $\omega_c = 2\pi f_c$ is the cavity frequency and n is the number of photons in the mode. The populations of the atomic energy levels are N_1 and N_2. The atomic rate equation for the level populations (without spontaneous emission) is then

$$\frac{d}{dt}N_2 = -KnN_2 + KnN_1 - w_{21}N_2 + w_{12}N_1 = -\frac{d}{dt}N_1 \tag{1}$$

and the cavity rate equation governing the buildup or decay of the cavity energy due to stimulated interaction with the atoms is

$$\frac{d}{dt}n = -K(N_2 - N_1)n \tag{2}$$

In these equations K is the coupling factor measuring the strength of the coupling between the cavity mode and the atoms, and w_{21} and w_{12} are the relaxation transition probabilities representing the coupling of the atoms to a surrounding thermal bath.

The rate equations above are obtained from classical or semiclassical analyses, which take into account the quantum nature of the atoms themselves, including their quantum energy levels, but do not take into account any quantum properties of the cavity mode or the signal fields. In a rigorous quantum treatment, however, we must treat as a quantum system not only the atoms, but also the cavity resonant mode and its associated field quantities. Such a quantized-field analysis is beyond the scope of

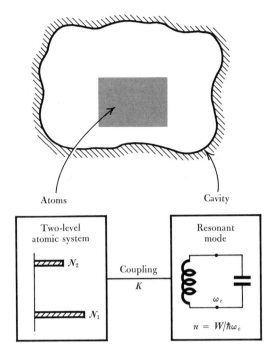

Atoms   Cavity

FIG. 11-1   Schematic representation of a single resonant mode or cavity mode coupled to a two-level atomic system.

this book. All we can do here is state and then make use of the results of such a fully quantum-mechanical analysis.

In brief, a rigorous quantum analysis will treat each cavity mode as a quantized harmonic oscillator, and the signal fields of a resonant mode will be treated much like the position and velocity (or momentum) quantities in a quantized simple harmonic oscillator. Then, when these quantized signal properties are added to the cavity-atom analyses, the major change is the appearance in the above rate equations of a new term, which represents spontaneous emission from the upper-level atoms into the cavity mode. With this added term, the atomic rate equation becomes

$$\frac{d}{dt} N_2 = \underset{\text{extra photon}}{-K(n+1)N_2} + KnN_1 - w_{21}N_2 + w_{12}N_1$$

$$= \underset{\substack{\text{stimulated}\\\text{emission}}}{-Kn(N_2 - N_1)} \underset{\substack{\text{spontaneous}\\\text{emission}}}{- KN_2} \underset{\text{relaxation}}{- w_{21}N_2 + w_{12}N_1} \tag{3}$$

At the same time, the cavity rate equation becomes

$$\frac{d}{dt} n = \underset{\text{extra photon}}{-KN_1 n} + KN_2(n+1) = \underset{\substack{\text{stimulated}\\\text{emission}}}{-K(N_1 - N_2)n} + \underset{\substack{\text{spontaneous}\\\text{emission}}}{KN_2} \tag{4}$$

The net effect of spontaneous emission is to add an extra factor of $+1$ to the number of photons n in the downward transition term, the term involving the upper-level population N_2, in both rate equations. This factor is sometimes referred to as the *extra photon,* for obvious reasons. However, no such extra-photon term appears in the transition terms in the opposite direction, the N_1 terms.

The atomic rate equation may also be written in the form

$$\frac{d}{dt}\,N_2 = -\,W_{12}(N_2 - N_1) - \underset{\text{spon}}{W}_{\text{spon}}N_2 - w_{21}N_2 + w_{12}N_1 \tag{5}$$

$$\underset{\substack{\text{stimulated}\\\text{emission}}}{} \qquad \underset{\substack{\text{spontaneous}\\\text{emission}}}{} \qquad \underset{\text{relaxation}}{}$$

where W_{12} is the stimulated transition rate between levels 1 and 2 caused by applied signals and W_{spon} is a spontaneous downward emission rate from level 2 to level 1 independent of any applied signals. The basic features of spontaneous emission are now apparent and can be summarized as follows:

1.　Spontaneous emission appears only in a *quantized field analysis,* in which the signal mode as well as the atoms are treated quantum-mechanically.

2.　Spontaneous emission appears in the atomic rate equation as a *downward transition rate from level 2,* directly proportional to the upper-level population N_2 and independent of any applied-signal fields. The energy released by the spontaneous emission goes into the energy of the resonant mode.

3.　The rate of spontaneous emission from the atoms into the signal mode is exactly equal to the downward stimulated transition rate *that would be caused by an applied signal in that mode having an energy of exactly one quantum.* That is, the spontaneous-emission probability W_{spon} is numerically equal to the stimulated transition probability W_{12} that would be caused by a signal with an energy of one photon in that resonant mode. One consequence of this is that when the stimulated transition probability into a particular signal mode is small or zero, due to a small interaction constant or oscillator strength for that particular case, then the spontaneous emission into that mode will also be small or zero.

4.　In Eqs. (3) to (5) the transition terms have been separated rather arbitrarily into *stimulated* and *spontaneous* terms, where the stimulated terms are those that are the same as in the usual semiclassical rate-equation results. Although the stimulated and spontaneous terms may be separated in this fashion, it is important to realize that they both emerge out of the same rigorous quantum analysis and are thus inextricably tied together. The separation is a convenient simplification and is used in many situations, but the two effects really come out together from the rigorous analysis and are not basically different mechanisms.

　　　The spontaneous-emission probability for any situation can thus be calculated by first calculating the stimulated transition probability, using an appropriate semiclassical method of analysis, and then adding an additional downward-only transition rate equal to the downward stimulated transition rate that would be caused by a signal of one photon. Again, this additional transition rate occurs in the downward direction only.

THERMAL EQUILIBRIUM　■ Spontaneous emission is closely linked to thermal noise and blackbody radiation. Suppose that the cavity of Fig. 11-1 is in thermal equilibrium, so that $N_1 = \overline{N}_1$ and $N_2 = \overline{N}_2$, where we will use overhead bars in this chapter to indicate values at thermal equilibrium. Assume for simplicity that the atoms are in strong enough contact with a heat bath at temperature T that N_1 and N_2 remain fixed at their thermal-equilibrium values despite any energy exchanges with the cavity mode.

　　　The number of photons in the signal mode as a function of time, starting with any arbitrary initial condition $n(t = 0)$, will be given by the solution of Eq. (4) as

$$n(t) = \overline{n} + [n(t = 0) - \overline{n}]e^{-K(\overline{N}_1 - \overline{N}_2)t}$$

$$\rightarrow \overline{n} \qquad t \rightarrow \infty, \; \overline{N}_1 > \overline{N}_2, \; T > 0 \tag{6}$$

The number of photons tends asymptotically toward a thermal-equilibrium value $\bar{n}$, which is the value such that the net rate of change in the number of photons is identically zero; that is,

$$\frac{dn}{dt} = -K(\overline{\mathcal{N}}_1 - \overline{\mathcal{N}}_2)\bar{n} + K\overline{\mathcal{N}}_2 \equiv 0 \tag{7}$$

The thermal-equilibrium number of photons in the signal mode is thus given by the simple expression

$$\bar{n} = \frac{K\overline{\mathcal{N}}_2}{K(\overline{\mathcal{N}}_1 - \overline{\mathcal{N}}_2)} = \frac{1}{\overline{\mathcal{N}}_1/\overline{\mathcal{N}}_2 - 1} \tag{8}$$

But since the thermal-equilibrium populations are related by the Boltzmann ratio,

$$\frac{\overline{\mathcal{N}}_2}{\overline{\mathcal{N}}_1} = e^{-hf/kT} \tag{9}$$

the thermal-equilibrium photon number must be given by

$$\bar{n} = \frac{1}{e^{hf/kT} - 1} \tag{10}$$

This is one of the most important results in this chapter. It gives the average number of photons present in a quantized harmonic oscillator or quantized normal mode of any sort at thermal equilibrium, as predicted by quantum-statistical mechanics. When a harmonic oscillator or a resonant mode of any sort is coupled to a system of atoms at thermal equilibrium (or to any other kind of heat bath) the combination of stimulated and spontaneous emission always acts to bring the harmonic oscillator or resonant mode to thermal equilibrium at the same temperature, with an average number of photons, or a mean occupation number, in the resonant mode given by expression (10). Note that this result is completely independent of the coupling coefficient K; that is, the equilibrium value is independent of the strength of the coupling between the resonant mode and the heat bath, as we would expect. The coupling strength enters only in determining how rapidly the mode will come to equilibrium, starting from a nonequilibrium initial value.

The average thermal energy in the signal mode at thermal equilibrium is

$$W = \bar{n}hf = \frac{hf}{e^{hf/kT} - 1}$$

$$\approx kT \qquad \frac{hf}{kT} \ll 1 \tag{11}$$

In the classical limit of high temperature and/or low frequency, $hf \ll kT$, the number of thermal photons in the mode becomes large, and the energy per mode is given by the familiar classical expression kT. In the high-frequency or optical limit $hf \gg kT$, the number of photons per mode becomes $\approx e^{-hf/kT}$, very much less than unity.

It should also be clear that even if the resonant mode is initially in its lowest quantum energy state, with $n = 0$ and no signal photons present, so that there can be no stimulated transitions, spontaneous emission from the atoms will still cause the resonant mode to become heated up, and the number of photons will be increased to the thermal-equilibrium value $\bar{n}$.

■ The expression (10) for the average number of photons per mode at thermal equilibrium is a very general result and applies equally to simple harmonic oscillators, microwave or optical cavity modes, resonant modes in electric circuits, or to any individual normal mode in a linear system, whether the system is mechanical, electrical, or some other type. It can be derived in a more general fashion without introducing atoms or spontaneous emission, and because of the importance of the result, we will briefly examine this derivation as background information.

Consider either a large ensemble of many identical resonant systems in thermal equilibrium, on each of which we make a single energy measurement, or else a large number of repeated measurements made at separate times on a single such resonant system while it remains in thermal equilibrium. The systems we consider are in thermal equilibrium at a temperature T, which means they must be at least weakly coupled to some outside heat bath, also at that temperature. None of the details of this outside coupling need be known, and the strength of the coupling is irrelevant here, provided only that some such coupling must exist.

Now, the instantaneous energy of a resonant mode in thermal equilibrium is a fluctuating quantity with a fairly wide range of variation (except in the limiting case of $T \to 0°K$), so that either of the sets of measurements above will exhibit a fairly large variation. What we seek is the *average* thermal energy, or the average of this set of measurements, whether this is an *ensemble* average over a large number of similar systems or a *time* average of repeated measurements on a single system. Since this is a quantum derivation, each individual energy measurement will yield one of the allowed quantum energy measurements for a simple harmonic oscillator,[1] $E_n = nhf$, where $n = 0, 1, 2, \ldots$ (see Appendix A). But from Boltzmann's principle, the relative probability of finding the resonant mode in a particular energy state E_n under thermal-equilibrium conditions is

$$\text{prob } E_n = e^{-E_n/kT} \tag{12}$$

Therefore the average energy value over a long series of measurements will be

$$\bar{E} = \frac{\sum \text{prob } E_n \times E_n}{\sum \text{prob } E_n}$$

$$= \frac{hf \sum_{n=0}^{\infty} n(e^{-hf/kT})^n}{\sum_{n=0}^{\infty} (e^{-hf/kT})^n} = \frac{hf}{e^{hf/kT} - 1} \tag{13}$$

This is the same as

$$\bar{n} = \frac{\bar{E}}{hf} = \frac{1}{e^{hf/kT} - 1} \tag{14}$$

which is, of course, the same result obtained earlier.

Note that the eventual coming of the system to thermal equilibrium implies the presence of some sort of *loss or coupling to the outside world* or to a set of atoms, although

---

[1] The energy levels of a harmonic oscillator are often written as $E_n = (n + \frac{1}{2})hf$, but the zero-point energy $\frac{1}{2}hf$ is neither of fundamental significance nor important for the present discussion, and so we will ignore the factor of $\frac{1}{2}$.

the details of this coupling are not important. Also, the result above is the *average* energy of the mode in thermal equilibrium; the instantaneous energy will fluctuate rather widely about this average value following the Boltzmann probability distribution. ■ Instead of starting from a quantum calculation of spontaneous emission and using it to derive the thermal-equilibrium photon number, we might also start from the thermal-equilibrium photon number just derived and use it to prove the necessity of spontaneous emission. Since this approach is sometimes useful and yields some insight, let us quickly carry it out. Consider again the cavity-plus-atoms model of Fig. 11-1 at thermal equilibrium, without spontaneous emission included, so that the atomic rate equation becomes

$$\frac{d}{dt}N_2 = -K\bar{n}\overline{N}_2 + K\bar{n}\overline{N}_1 - w_{21}\overline{N}_2 + w_{12}\overline{N}_1 \overset{?}{=} 0 \qquad (15)$$

It is assumed known from Boltzmann's principle that $\overline{N}_2/\overline{N}_1 = e^{-hf/kT}$ and that $\bar{n} = (e^{hf/kT} - 1)^{-1}$. Therefore there is a definite and finite absorptive population difference $\overline{N}_1 - \overline{N}_2$ in the atoms in the cavity at thermal equilibrium, and also a definite amount of average signal energy $\bar{n}hf$ in the signal fields in the cavity under the same condition. The signal fields will then induce a net stimulated response proportional to $\bar{n}(\overline{N}_1 - \overline{N}_2)$ in the atoms, and there will be a corresponding net power absorption by the atoms from the signal fields. But this means a continuing net power transfer from the cavity fields to the atoms, and the existence of such a continued net power transfer violates the assumption of detailed balance at thermal equilibrium. If it persists, in fact, the resonant mode will cool down because of its continuing loss of energy, while the atoms (or their surrounding heat bath) will warm up.

To balance the energy flow from cavity fields to atoms there must be a matching energy flow from atoms to cavity fields in the form of a spontaneous emission. To ensure equilibrium, the net change in $\overline{N}_2$ (or in $\overline{N}_1$, or in $\bar{n}$) due to stimulated plus spontaneous transitions must be identically zero, or

$$\frac{d}{dt}\overline{N}_2 = -K\bar{n}\overline{N}_2 + K\bar{n}\overline{N}_1 + \left(\frac{d}{dt}\overline{N}_2\right)_{\text{spon}} \equiv 0 \qquad (16)$$

This requires that at thermal equilibrium

$$\left(\frac{d}{dt}\overline{N}_2\right)_{\text{spon}} = K\bar{n}\overline{N}_2 - K\bar{n}\overline{N}_1 = -K\bar{n}\left(\frac{\overline{N}_1}{\overline{N}_2} - 1\right)\overline{N}_2 = -K\overline{N}_2 \qquad (17)$$

which, of course, agrees exactly with our earlier statements.

The only remaining point is to argue that if spontaneous emission occurs at a rate proportional to $\overline{N}_2$ under conditions of thermal equilibrium (under which $\overline{N}_2$ can vary widely for different temperature values), then it is not unreasonable to suppose that the same spontaneous-emission process will continue to occur, and will continue to be proportional to the instantaneous value of N_2, even when the atoms are not in thermal equilibrium. That is, we assume that

$$\left(\frac{d}{dt}N_2\right)_{\text{spon}} = -KN_2 \qquad (18)$$

is the general spontaneous-emission term valid in all situations, thermal equilibrium or not.

RESISTOR NOISE IN AN
ELECTRIC CIRCUIT

■ To show how our results thus far may be applied to a simple electric-circuit problem, we will now use them to derive the Johnson-Nyquist noise formula for the thermal-noise current appearing in parallel with a conductance in thermal equilibrium (or the noise voltage appearing in series with a resistance in thermal equilibrium). Figure 11-2 shows a simple parallel-resonant electric circuit which has a single resonant mode. From the preceding discussions, this mode will have a thermal-noise energy at thermal equilibrium, which must in this case be in the form of reactive stored energy in the capacitance C and inductance L. If the mean-square voltage across the circuit and current through the inductance are $\overline{v_C^2}$ and $\overline{i_L^2}$, respectively, then the total circuit energy will be

$$\overline{W} = \frac{1}{2} C\overline{v_C^2} + \frac{1}{2} L\overline{i_L^2} = \frac{hf}{e^{hf/kT} - 1} \tag{19}$$

For a high-Q resonant circuit the two electrical stored-energy terms will be equal, so that

$$\overline{v_C^2} = \frac{1}{C} \frac{hf}{e^{hf/kT} - 1} \tag{20}$$

will be the mean-square voltage across the circuit. This will be a noiselike ac voltage, and for a high-Q circuit will be restricted to frequency components close to the resonant frequency $(2\pi LC)^{-1}$ of the circuit.

To account for this mean-square circuit voltage in purely electrical terms, a thermal-noise current source $\overline{i_n^2}$ can be introduced into the circuit as shown in Fig. 11-2. More precisely, this is a noise current source providing a mean-square noise current $\overline{di_n^2}(f)$ in any narrow frequency range df centered at f, or a noise-current spectral density $\overline{di_n^2}(f)/df$. For the moment this noise-current source is not specifically associated with any of the circuit elements C, L, or G.

The increment of mean-square voltage $\overline{dv_C^2}$ across the circuit due to the noise-current source $\overline{di_n^2}$ will be

$$\overline{dv_C^2}(f) = \frac{\overline{di_n^2}(f)}{|\tilde{Y}(f)|^2} = \frac{\overline{di_n^2}}{G^2 + (2\pi fC - 1/2\pi fL)^2} \tag{21}$$

where $\tilde{Y}(f)$ is the shunt admittance of the circuit. The total mean-square voltage across the circuit will then be

$$\overline{v_C^2} = \int d\overline{v^2}(f) = \int_0^\infty \frac{\overline{di_n^2}(f)}{df} \frac{df}{G^2 + (2\pi fC - 1/2\pi fL)^2} \tag{22}$$

If the circuit has a reasonably high Q, it will not be unreasonable to suppose that the spectral density of the noise current source is constant across the narrow bandwidth of the resonant circuit (which is the only region where $\overline{dv_C^2}$ has any appreciable value).

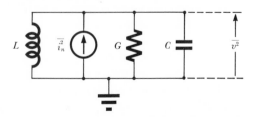

FIG. 11-2   A lumped resonant circuit at thermal equilibrium, including a thermal-noise current generator.

With this assumption, the mean-square circuit voltage becomes

$$\overline{v_C{}^2} = \frac{\overline{di_n{}^2}}{df} \int_0^\infty \frac{df}{R^2 + (2\pi fC - \frac{1}{2}\pi fL)^2} = \frac{\overline{di_n{}^2}}{df} \frac{1}{4GC} \tag{23}$$

If this is equated to the thermal-equilibrium value, the noise-current source that is to account for the thermal noise must have the value

$$\overline{di_n{}^2} = \frac{4Ghf\,df}{e^{hf/kT} - 1}$$
$$\approx 4GkT\,df \qquad hf \ll kT \tag{24}$$

This expression depends only on the conductance G and is totally independent of the capacitance C or inductance L. Hence it is reasonable to associate this thermal-noise current source entirely with the conductance G.

The result above is, in fact, just the standard Johnson-Nyquist result for the thermal-noise current source in parallel with a conductance, or the thermal-noise voltage source in series with a resistance. Converting the parallel current source to a series voltage source with a resistance $R = G^{-1}$ yields

$$\overline{dv_n{}^2} = \frac{4Rhf\,df}{e^{hf/kT} - 1}$$
$$\approx 4kTR\,df \qquad hf \ll kT \tag{25}$$

which may be a more familiar form to some readers.

We will return to this general topic later, but this result can be taken as a derivation of Johnson-Nyquist noise from spontaneous emission, or conversely, as a derivation of the average energy in a resonant mode, with Johnson-Nyquist noise as the source. Note that in either case the results are independent of the Q of the circuit, so that we can, for example, take the limit of $Q \to \infty$ and claim that the results apply equally well to a lossless circuit.

■ In the rate-equation developments of earlier chapters it was noted that, although the signal-stimulated transition probability W_{12} between two levels is the same in either direction, the upward and downward relaxation transition probabilities w_{12} and w_{21} are related by the Boltzmann ratio

RATE-EQUATION RELAXATION TERMS

$$\frac{w_{12}}{w_{21}} = e^{-(E_2 - E_1)/kT} \tag{26}$$

With the introduction of spontaneous emission, it is now possible to give a simple explanation for this apparent difference.

The relaxation transition probabilities w_{12} and w_{21} are the result of interactions between the atoms and their thermal surroundings. The thermal surroundings, depending on the specific case, may be the electromagnetic radiation modes of the volume containing the atoms in the case of primarily radiative relaxation, or they may be the vibrational modes of the crystal or solid containing the atoms in the case of primarily nonradiative relaxation processes. In either case, however, the interaction between atoms and surroundings may be regarded as the summation of stimulated plus spontaneous interactions between the atoms and the usually very large number of normal modes or vibrational modes of the surroundings.

These interactions may, in fact, be described by rate equations exactly like those we have developed. If the many possible modes of the thermal surroundings are labeled by an index i, the relaxation terms in the rate equation may be written more specifically as

$$-w_{21}N_2 + w_{12}N_1 = -\sum_i K_i(m_i + 1)N_2 + \sum_i K_i m_i N_1 \tag{27}$$

where m_i is the number of photons (or phonons) in the ith mode of the surroundings. These modes include the extra photon, and each of the relevant modes will have a different value of coupling coefficient K_i. If the surroundings are assumed to be in thermal equilibrium at temperature T, however, all the modes will have the same average number m_i of photons (or of phonons, for lattice modes), the thermal-equilibrium value

$$m_i = \overline{m}_i = \frac{hf}{e^{hf/kT} - 1} \tag{28}$$

It is obvious that the upward and downward relaxation rates must stand in the Boltzmann ratio, for

$$\frac{w_{12}}{w_{21}} = \frac{\displaystyle\sum_i K_i \overline{m}_i}{\displaystyle\sum_i K_i(\overline{m}_i + 1)} = \frac{\displaystyle\sum_i K_i}{\displaystyle\sum_i K_i} \frac{\overline{m}_i}{\overline{m}_i + 1} = e^{-hf/kT} \tag{29}$$

The relaxation transition probabilities stand in the Boltzmann ratio because, as we have elected to write them, the relaxation transition probabilities w_i include both the thermally stimulated and the spontaneous transition probabilities caused by the surrounding modes to which the atoms relax.

However, the stimulated transition probability W_{12}, as we have written it, includes only stimulated transitions, and the spontaneous emission into the signal mode is added in separately as a separate W_{spon} term. It is reasonable to do this, especially in computing stimulated responses caused by applied signals which typically contain a great many photons, so that the small spontaneous-emission effects of the one extra photon are of no significance in the stimulated terms. It becomes necessary to include the spontaneous emission in the signal mode only in computing the noise performance of a maser amplifier in very low-signal situations, or possibly in fluorescence experiments where atoms are excited into some upper atomic level and the resulting fluorescence output is used to observe some of the important transition frequencies in the atomic system.

In brief, the basic physics of the atom–normal-mode interactions involved in either the signal rate-equation terms or the relaxation rate-equation terms are precisely the same. However, we choose to separate out the stimulated and the spontaneous terms in the former case and not to do so in the latter case simply because of the different uses that are made of the signal and the relaxation terms in applying the rate equations.

11-2 BLACKBODY RADIATION AND NOISE IN ELECTRIC CIRCUITS

Within every transmission line, waveguide, microwave or optical cavity, or any kind of electromagnetic structure at thermal equilibrium there will be noise voltages and currents or noiselike E and H fields at all frequencies, corresponding to the thermal energy in these circuit elements at equilibrium. This thermal energy is often referred to as the *blackbody radiation density* in these elements. In this section we will derive the blackbody radiation density for one-dimensional and three-dimensional cases and use the results to explain thermal noise emission in electric circuits, transmission lines, and hot bodies.

■ Consider a long but arbitrary length L of a single-mode transmission line, as shown in Fig. 11-3. By *single-mode* we mean that the line only propagates (or at least we only take account of) a single mode of propagation in the line; for example, the mode on a two-wire or coaxial transmission line, or a single selected TE_{mn} or TM_{mn} mode in a waveguide.[1] Now, regardless of how this line is actually terminated at its ends or what actual fields are present along the line at any instant, the field variation along the line inside any given segment of length L at any given instant can always be written as a summation of the form [2]

ONE-DIMENSIONAL BLACKBODY RADIATION

$$e(z) = \sum_{q=1}^{\infty} E_q \sin \frac{q2\pi z}{2L} = \sum_{q=1}^{\infty} E_q \sin \frac{2\pi z}{\lambda_q} \tag{1}$$

where the wavelength λ_q is given by

$$\frac{q\lambda_q}{2} = L \tag{2}$$

But, a wavelength λ_q along the line corresponds to the axial-mode frequency ω_q, where

$$\omega_q \equiv 2\pi f_q = q2\pi \frac{c}{2L} \tag{3}$$

In other words, the fields inside a length L of the line at any instant can always be written as a superposition of the axial modes that would be resonant if the line segment were terminated with mirrors (or were short-circuited) at each end.

The key argument in the derivations of this section is that if the fields in a given transmission line, or circuit, or electromagnetic structure can be expanded in a set of resonant modes or normal modes, then the thermal-equilibrium fields in that same

---

[1] If the line actually propagates several different transverse modes, as in a waveguide well above cutoff, the following derivation applies independently to each different mode of propagation in the line.

[2] To prove this, consider the instantaneous E-field pattern $e(z)$ at time t in a section of line between $z = 0$ and $z = L$. Fold this same field pattern over about $z = 0$ to fill the region between $z = 0$ and $z = -L$, and then change its sign so that $e(-z) = -e(z)$. Expand the resulting field pattern between $-L \leq z \leq L$ in a Fourier series in z. Since the pattern is odd, only sine terms will be needed, and since the expansion region is of length $2L$, this will be the fundamental wavelength in the Fourier expansion. The field pattern in $0 \leq z \leq L$ has then been expanded in the terms $\sin(q2\pi z/2L)$, corresponding to the resonant-mode patterns at frequencies $\omega_q = q2\pi(c/2L)$.

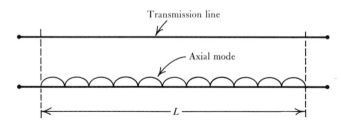

FIG. 11-3   Schematic of a long section of single-mode transmission line.

system can be found by assuming that each normal mode is thermally excited with the average thermal energy per mode derived in the previous section. For example, since the modes in a length L of transmission line are spaced by $f_q = c/2L$, which can be very small if L is many wavelengths long, the number of modes dN contained in a frequency range df is (see Fig. 11-4)

$$dN = \frac{df}{c/2L} = \frac{2L}{\lambda}\frac{df}{f} \tag{4}$$

This is the total number of modes needed to describe fully all the fields or voltages in the line within the length L and within the frequency band of width df centered at f. The total thermal energy density in the line at thermal equilibrium (no external signals applied) is then given by

$$\text{Thermal energy per unit length} = \frac{\text{no. of modes} \times \text{energy per mode}}{\text{length } L}$$

or

$$dW_n = \bar{n}hf\,dN = \frac{2Lhf}{LC}\frac{df}{e^{hf/kT} - 1}$$

$$= \frac{2}{\lambda}\frac{hf}{e^{hf/kT} - 1}\frac{df}{f} \tag{5}$$

where dW_n is the average thermal energy or noise energy per unit length per frequency bandwidth df in the line at equilibrium. This result is independent of what sorts of terminations may be connected onto the line at either end, or what sorts of losses may be present in the line, provided only that the terminations, the losses, and the line are all in thermal equilibrium at the same temperature T.

Because variations are assumed along only one direction, or because there is only one significant position coordinate z in the situation, the expression above is generally referred to as the *one-dimensional blackbody radiation density*. We will consider three-dimensional blackbody radiation in large volumes shortly.[1]

TRANSMISSION-LINE NOISE
WAVES

■ The thermal energy in the line at equilibrium may also be viewed as a collection of noise standing waves or as noise traveling waves moving in both directions along the line. From the latter viewpoint, since there should be no preference for either direction at equilibrium, the average noise power flow in either direction at any point along the line should be given by

$$\text{Noise-power flow in one direction} = \frac{1}{2} \times \frac{\text{energy per unit length}}{\text{energy velocity}}$$

[1] The single-resonant-circuit result of Sec. 11-1 might be called *zero-dimensional* blackbody radiation.

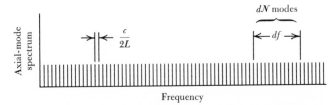

FIG. 11-4   The resonant-mode frequencies of a segment of line of length L.

or

$$dP_n = \frac{hf\,df}{e^{hf/kT} - 1}$$

$$\approx kT\,df \qquad hf \ll kT \tag{6}$$

This is the average power carried by those noise waves within bandwidth df moving to the right or to the left at any plane along the line, as shown in Fig. 11-5. Of course, there is no net power flow along the line at thermal equilibrium, since the average power flows are equal and opposite.

It should perhaps be emphasized here that these noise fields and noise waves are perfectly real and measurable quantities. The noise voltage on a line can be measured, for example, by bridging a high-impedance high-sensitivity rms voltmeter across the line, as shown in Fig. 11-6a. Of course, the voltmeter must have sufficient sensitivity to measure the generally small noise voltages from the line without losing them in the voltmeter's own internal noise. To measure the traveling-wave components separately, directional couplers can be used as in Fig. 11-6b, or the line can be opened at the measurement point and a circulator inserted to separate the oppositely traveling waves for measurement by low-noise receivers, as in Fig. 11-6c.

If the transmission line propagates many different waves or modes, as for example the many higher-order TE_{mn} and TM_{mn} modes that propagate in a waveguide well above cutoff, then this discussion applies separately and independently to each such propagating mode. For example, the total noise power in the waveguide will be the sum of the separate noise powers, given by Eq. (6), in each separate mode.

■ Suppose that the transmission line above, with a characteristic impedance Z_0, is actually terminated in a matched resistance $R = Z_0$ at one end, as shown in Fig. 11-7, with the line and resistance in thermal equilibrium. The resistance, being a matched or reflectionless termination, will then absorb and dissipate all the energy in the noise waves traveling to the left at the left end of the line. But to maintain thermal equilibrium conditions the resistance must also generate and transmit out to the right into the transmission line the same amount of thermal-noise power on the average.

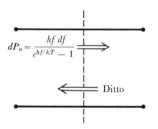

FIG. 11-5 The noise power propagating in either direction at any point along a transmission line in thermal equilibrium at temperature T.

JOHNSON-NYQUIST NOISE IN RESISTANCES

FIG. 11-6 Three different methods for measuring the noise voltages or waves on a transmission line or in a waveguide of any sort. (a) A high-impedance voltmeter connected across the line to measure the noise voltages without loading down or disturbing the line. (b) Directional couplers to tap off a small fraction of the energy traveling in each direction for measurement by sensitive receivers, with little effect on the line itself. (c) A circulator with reflecting terminations on the side arms, to separate the two waves traveling in opposite directions, so that a probe receiver can be used to measure either wave separately.

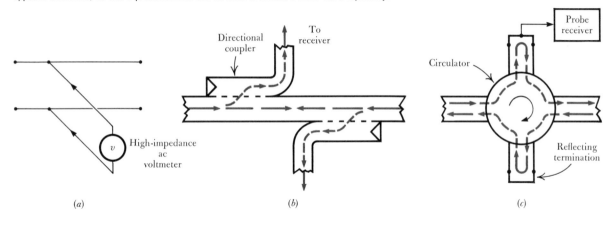

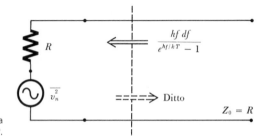

FIG. 11-7   A transmission line of characteristic impedance Z_0 terminated in a matched resistive load $Z_0 = R$.

To account for this noise generation a noise voltage source $\overline{v_n^2}$ is often associated with the resistance R, as shown in Fig. 11-7. The noise power that this noise voltage source must deliver to the transmission line is given by

$$dP_n = \frac{d\overline{v_n^2}}{4R} = \frac{hf\,df}{e^{hf/kT} - 1} \tag{7}$$

and this says that the noise voltage source must have the value

$$d\overline{v_n^2} = \frac{4Rhf\,df}{e^{hf/kT} - 1}$$

$$\approx 4kTR\,df \qquad hf \ll kT \tag{8}$$

where $d\overline{v_n^2}$ is the mean-square noise voltage contributed by those frequency components of the (white) noise source within the narrow bandwidth df. This noise voltage is the *Johnson-Nyquist thermal-noise voltage* associated with the resistance R. In this chapter it will become apparent that associated with every loss or dissipation mechanism at temperature T there will always be a thermal-noise-generating mechanism, so that every lossy or absorbing element will also radiate or emit thermal noise. The Johnson-Nyquist noise voltage is one way of representing this noise-generating property for the simple case of a lumped resistance R.

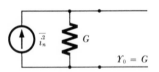

FIG. 11-8   The series noise voltage source of Fig. 11-7 transformed into a parallel noise current source.

As a Thévenin equivalent, the noise voltage $\overline{v_n^2}$ in series with a resistance R can be replaced by a noise current source $\overline{i_n^2}$ in parallel with a conductance $G \equiv R^{-1}$, as shown in Fig. 11-8. This noise current source will have the mean-square value

$$d\overline{i_n^2} = \frac{4Ghf\,df}{e^{hf/kT} - 1}$$

$$\approx 4GkT\,df \qquad hf \ll kT \tag{9}$$

which is the same as derived in the previous section with a single-resonant-mode tuned circuit model.

The Johnson-Nyquist noise voltage is again a real and entirely measurable voltage, as can be determined by connecting a sufficiently sensitive voltmeter across the terminals of any resistance and measuring the rms noise voltage as a function of temperature. Indeed, the Johnson-Nyquist noise formula is so named because it was first obtained by Johnson in 1928 strictly from experimental results, and then derived theoretically by Nyquist the same year with an approach very similar to that used here.

NOISE FROM TRANSMISSION-LINE TERMINATIONS   ■ Consider next a transmission line with a mismatched termination $Z = R + jX$ (or $Y = G + jB$), as shown in Fig. 11-9. What noise power will this mismatched termination, with $Z \neq Z_0$, deliver to the transmission line? If the same noise voltage $\overline{v_n^2}$ is associated with the resistance R, the noise power generated and delivered by the noise voltage source to the transmission line, in the form of an outgoing noise wave on the transmission line, will be (from simple circuit theory)

$$\text{Noise power delivered to line} = \frac{Z_0}{|Z + Z_0|^2} \overline{v_n^2} \tag{10}$$

But, from transmission-line theory, the power-reflection coefficient as viewed into the termination Z from the transmission line Z_0 is

$$|\tilde{\rho}|^2 = \left| \frac{Z - Z_0}{Z + Z_0} \right|^2 \tag{11}$$

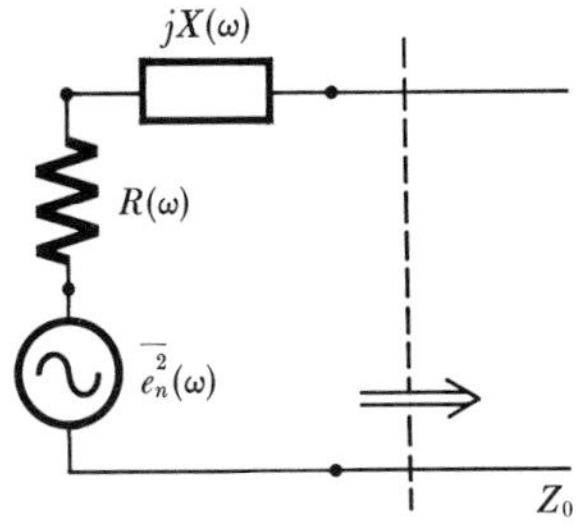

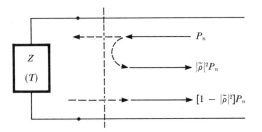

FIG. 11-9   A mismatched transmission line with $Z \neq Z_0$ (how much power will the noise voltage source deliver to the outgoing wave in the transmission line?).

Therefore, with a little algebraic manipulation the noise power delivered by the mismatched termination to the line can also be written in the form

$$\text{Noise power delivered to line} = (1 - |\tilde{\rho}|^2) \frac{hf\,df}{e^{hf/kT} - 1}$$

$$\approx (1 - |\tilde{\rho}|^2)\,kT\,df \qquad hf \ll kT \tag{12}$$

This result, although it is derived from the specific model of Fig. 11-9, is really a very much more general result, which can be derived in a general way without using any specific model for the termination.

■ Figure 11-10 shows the general case. A transmission line, or a wave-propagating system of any sort, is terminated in an arbitrary mismatched termination characterized only by its power reflection coefficient $|\tilde{\rho}|^2$ and its temperature T. At thermal equilibrium a noise power P_n is incident upon the termination in the form of traveling noise waves coming from the right. Of this noise power, a fraction $|\tilde{\rho}|^2$ is reflected back to the right and a fraction $1 - |\tilde{\rho}|^2$ is absorbed in the termination.

In thermal equilibrium the net power flow from line to termination, or vice versa, must be zero on the average. The same total noise power P_n must flow out to the right in the transmission line as comes in from the right. This can be the case only if the termination itself generates and sends out into the line a certain amount of internally generated noise power sufficient to balance the equation

$$\text{Noise generated} + \text{noise reflected} = \text{noise incident} \tag{13}$$

or

$$\text{Noise generated} + |\tilde{\rho}|^2 P_n = P_n \tag{14}$$

Thus the general result is

GENERAL MISMATCHED TERMINATION

FIG. 11-10   General model for noise generation in a mismatched transmission-line termination at temperature T.

$$\text{Noise generated} = (1 - |\tilde{\rho}|^2) \frac{hf \, df}{e^{hf/kT} - 1}$$

$$\approx (1 - |\tilde{\rho}|^2) \, kT \, df \qquad hf \ll kT \tag{15}$$

for any kind of termination with reflection coefficient $|\tilde{\rho}|^2$ and temperature T.

This result is very important and general, applying equally well to voltage waves on a two-conductor transmission line, waveguide waves in waveguides of any shape, optical waves propagating through free space, acoustic waves propagating in solids or liquids, or any other kind of propagating and energy-carrying wave. Note that a purely reactive termination, such as a lossless inductance or capacitance connected across a transmission line, will have a reflection coefficient $|\tilde{\rho}|^2 = 1$, so that such a termination will generate no outgoing noise wave. Noise generation is associated only with resistive or lossy elements, not with purely reactive elements. In fact, any termination that is 100 percent reflecting, such as a polished mirror or a complete short circuit, will generate or radiate no outgoing noise, no matter how hot the termination is. In the terms used in optics, $|\tilde{\rho}|^2$ is the reflectivity of the termination and $1 - |\tilde{\rho}|^2$ is the emissivity, and for any optical surface the basic rule is

$$\text{Emissivity} = 1 - \text{reflectivity} \tag{16}$$

The amount of noise generation from a termination depends only on the temperature of the termination and its impedance, and not in any way on the details of its internal construction. In a resistive termination, for example, the noise generation does not depend on whether the resistance is a carbon-film resistor or a wire-wound resistor, or possibly a complex network of resistances, or a resonant circuit tuned to resonance so that it looks purely resistive, or possibly even a collection of absorbing two-level atoms (as we will discuss very shortly). It is also understood that the termination will continue to radiate the same amount of thermal noise given by Eq. (15), according to its own temperature T, even if the line and the termination are no longer in thermal equilibrium, so that the balance in Eq. (13) no longer holds. In other words, we derive the necessary thermal-emission expression for the termination by using a thermal-equilibrium argument, but then we assert that the noise generated by the termination should depend only on the internal properties (temperature and reflection coefficient) of the termination, and so this noise generation should remain the same even if the transmission line becomes hotter or cooler than the termination.

Finally, careful use of the general transmission-line approach to noise generation can avoid certain meaningless questions that arise when the Johnson-Nyquist resistance-noise-voltage approach is used, particularly in negative-resistance circuits. In Figs. 11-7 and 11-9, for example, it appears that the noise voltage $\overline{v_n^2}$ associated with the resistance R can not only deliver power to an external load connected to the resistance R, but can also deliver thermal-noise power to the resistance R itself. If the resistance R is connected into certain kinds of negative-resistance amplifiers, this power can become quite large, and in any event it is not clear just how to interpret the idea of thermal-noise power delivered by a resistance to itself (does this power heat the resistance, for example?).

This situation can always be clarified by supposing, for purposes of analysis, that an arbitrary length of transmission line of characteristic impedance $Z_0 = R$ is connected into the network in front of the resistance R, as shown in Fig. 11-11. The impedance into the terminals of this matched line from the rest of the network will be

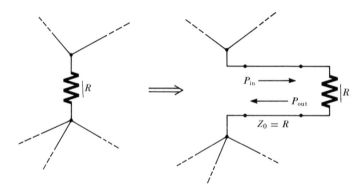

FIG. 11-11   For purposes of analysis, any resistance connected into a network, as at the left, can have a short segment of transmission line with the same characteristic impedance connected in front of it, as at the right. The circuit performance will be entirely unchanged, and questions of power delivered to or generated by the resistance become clearer.

just $Z = R$ at all frequencies, regardless of the length of line inserted (including a vanishingly small line). Hence the network's performance so far as both signal and noise are concerned will be totally unchanged by the insertion of the line. Now, however, instead of using the noise voltage $\overline{v_n{}^2}$ of Eq. (8), we can unambiguously identify the noise generated by the resistance as the noise radiated by the matched termination ($|\tilde{\rho}|^2 = 0$) down the inserted line segment toward the rest of the network. When this outgoing wave reaches the terminals where the line connects to the rest of the network, some of the noise may be reflected back toward the resistor. In fact, if the network contains negative-resistance elements, the reflection coefficient as viewed from the resistance toward the rest of the network may have magnitude greater than unity, so that the outgoing noise emitted by the resistance R comes back to the resistance greatly amplified. Our main point here is simply that by the device of inserting a fictitious, arbitrary length of transmission line it becomes clear where the noise comes from and what happens to it owing to interactions in the circuit. As a basic model, the concept of a termination with an associated outgoing noise wave source given by Eq. (15) is more general and useful than the idea of a resistance with an associated noise voltage source given by Eq. (8).

■ As another example of the basic principle that noise generation always accompanies loss mechanisms, we can consider thermal-noise generation in lossy transmission lines. Figure 11-12a represents a lossy wave-propagating system, such as a waveguide with lossy walls, in which the losses are at temperature T. The wave-attenuation coefficient in the system is α, so that a wave propagating to the right attenuates with distance in the form $v(z) \propto e^{-\alpha z}$.

NOISE GENERATION IN LOSSY TRANSMISSION LINES

Now, in the lossy-waveguide example we might expect the resistive losses in the waveguide walls to generate noise voltages or to radiate thermal-noise energy into the waveguide mode (or modes) in some fashion. To put this more generally, if the power carried by a wave on the system at plane z is $P(z)$, then the change in power between planes z and $z + dz$ may be written as

$$dP(z) \equiv P(z + dz) - P(z)$$

$$= \underset{\text{absorption}}{-2\alpha P(z)\, dz} + \underset{\substack{\text{thermal-noise} \\ \text{generation}}}{dP_n} \tag{17}$$

where dP_n is the thermal-noise power that may be generated and added into the propagating wave by the line losses in the length dz. But at thermal equilibrium the average

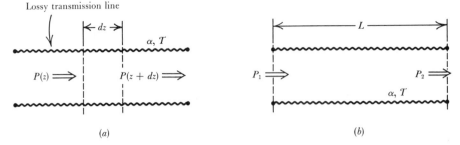

Fig. 11-12   (a) A lossy transmission line or (b) a finite length L of such a lossy line.

noise power per bandwidth df traveling in either direction must have the same value at every point along the line,

$$P_n(z) = P_n(z + dz) = \frac{hf\,df}{e^{hf/kT} - 1}$$

$$d\bar{P}(z) = 0 \tag{18}$$

This cannot mean that all the waves passing through point z reach the point $z + dz$, since there is attenuation between these points which attenuates thermal-noise waves as well as any other signal or noise waves. Rather, in a lossy line the absorption of noise wave energy by the losses at thermal equilibrium must be just balanced by the generation and emission of new noise waves into the line, at a rate per unit length given by

$$dP_n = 2\alpha P_n = 2\alpha \frac{hf\,df}{e^{hf/kT} - 1}\,dz$$

$$\approx 2\alpha kT\,df\,dz \qquad \text{if } hf \ll kT \tag{19}$$

We also assume, as before, that this noise generation is a basic property of the losses themselves, independent of the actual power in the line, so that this expression will still describe the noise generation by the losses even when the line itself is no longer in thermal equilibrium.

The general equation for the variation of signal and noise power along the lossy line then becomes

$$\frac{d}{dz}P(z) = -2\alpha P(z) + 2\alpha \frac{hf\,df}{e^{hf/kT} - 1} \tag{20}$$

If this is integrated over a length L, as in Fig. 11-12b, the net power transmission in passing through the lossy line section is

$$\mathcal{L} \equiv e^{-2\alpha L} \tag{21}$$

and the total output power P_2, noise plus signal, given an input power P_1 to the line section, is

$$\underset{\text{output}}{P_2} = \underset{\substack{\text{attenuated} \\ \text{input}}}{\mathcal{L}P_1} + \underset{\substack{\text{thermal noise generated} \\ \text{in line}}}{[1 - \mathcal{L}]\,\frac{hf\,df}{e^{hf/kT} - 1}} \tag{22}$$

Depending on what is connected to the line, the input power P_1 may itself be a mixture of signals and noise. In any event, this input power will be attenuated, and will also have added to it additional thermal-noise emission from the wall losses, as given by the second term in Eq. (22). The temperature T to be used in this second term is, of course, the physical temperature of the wall losses themselves, in the case there may be several temperatures associated with the overall system.

One basic point here is that a system, however hot it may be, cannot radiate if it cannot absorb. When light waves pass through a hot material, for example, the emissivity of the material at any wavelength is related to the absorption in the material at that wavelength in exactly the same fashion as the dependence on $\mathcal{L}$ in Eq. (22). For example, a piece of quartz heated to a temperature at which any other material would be red hot and glow very brightly will remain transparent; hence even at very elevated temperatures the heated quartz sample will emit very little radiation and will be visually indistinguishable from an unheated sample. As another example important in laser applications, the gases in a flashlamp used for laser pumping can be heated to a high temperature but will not radiate pumping light effectively unless the gases are also strongly absorbing ($\mathcal{L} \to 0$) at the wavelengths of interest. Thus in evaluating a flashlamp design for pumping lasers it is necessary to know the transparency of the gas discharge at the pump wavelengths of interest, as well as the temperature of the gas during the discharge.

■ Let us consider now a large volume V of arbitrary shape—large in the sense that all dimensions correspond to many wavelengths at frequencies of interest, as illustrated in Fig. 11-13a—and derive the blackbody radiation density that will be present in this volume at thermal equilibrium. To carry out this derivation we can view the volume V as a resonant electromagnetic cavity. Such a cavity, regardless of its shape, will have a lowest resonant mode and associated resonance frequency, and then at higher frequencies a series of higher-order mode resonances, as illustrated in the resonant-mode spectrum of Fig. 11-13b. At frequencies well above the lowest-order mode, the spectrum of these higher-order resonant modes will become very densely populated, and we are interested primarily in frequencies high enough (or volumes large enough) that there are a large number of such resonant modes within any reasonably narrow frequency range[1] df (see also page 417 and Fig. 10-18).

It can be shown that for a volume large compared to a wavelength in all dimensions the number of possible resonant modes dN in volume V within a frequency range

---

[1] At low frequencies, where only a few modes are present, the thermal-noise fields in the cavity should be represented by using the lumped resonant model of Fig. 11-1 or Fig. 11-2 for each mode separately, rather than by summing over many modes, as in this section.

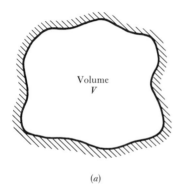

(a)

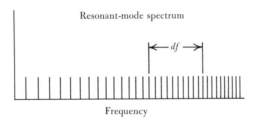

Resonant-mode spectrum

Frequency

(b)

FIG. 11-13 (a) A large cavity or enclosure, with total volume V and dimensions large compared to a wavelength at the frequencies of interest. (b) Resonant-mode spectrum of the same cavity.

df is given by[1]

$$dN = \frac{8\pi V}{\lambda^3} \frac{df}{f} = \frac{8\pi f^2 V \, df}{c^3} \qquad (23)$$

This three-dimensional mode number may be compared with the one-dimensional mode number of Eq. (4). It can also be proved, as in the one-dimensional case, that any arbitrary field distribution within the volume V at any instant can be expanded as a summation in the resonant cavity modes of the volume.

From this, we again make the argument that to find the thermal-noise fields, or the thermal energy density, within the volume V at thermal equilibrium, we must simply suppose that each of the resonant modes or normal modes appropriate to the volume is excited to an average energy level, as derived in Sec. 11-1. That is, the total thermal energy in the volume V will be

$$\text{Total thermal energy} = \frac{\text{no. of resonant}}{\text{modes}} \times \frac{\text{thermal energy}}{\text{per mode}} \qquad (24)$$

In the more usual definition of blackbody radiation density, this expression is divided by the volume V to get the average thermal energy per unit volume, or

$$dW_n = \text{thermal energy per unit volume} = \frac{\text{no. of modes}}{\text{volume } V} \times \text{energy per mode}$$

$$= \frac{8\pi f^2 \, df}{c^3} \frac{hf}{e^{hf/kT} - 1} = \frac{8\pi}{\lambda^3} \frac{hf}{e^{hf/kT} - 1} \frac{df}{f} \qquad (25)$$

This is the standard expression for the blackbody radiation density inside any enclosure in thermal equilibrium at temperature T.

PRINCIPLES OF BLACKBODY RADIATION

■ Having shown how this result may be derived, let us consider the physical principles involved, without giving any further analytical results. First of all, this blackbody radiation density or thermal energy per unit volume represents real and measurable E and H fields in the volume, at least at any temperature greater than $T \rightarrow 0°$K. The mean-square E or H fields at any point in the volume within a frequency bandwidth df may be calculated by equating the energy density W_n to the standard expressions $\frac{1}{2}\epsilon_0|\tilde{E}|^2$ and $\frac{1}{2}\mu_0|\tilde{H}|^2$ for electromagnetic energy density. These fields may be measured by inserting a probe or an antenna into the volume, as in Fig. 11-14, and connecting the antenna to a sufficiently sensitive receiver or detector.

The fields are noiselike in that the amplitude and phase of each mode fluctuates randomly with time (note that the thermal-energy expressions give only the *average* thermal energy per mode), so that a measuring antenna or any other measuring apparatus will measure only a certain amount of noise power per unit bandwidth. The fields have exactly the same character as if each mode were excited independently by an independent noise generator of the correct average power level.

The blackbody radiation density present at thermal equilibrium depends only on the temperature of the surroundings, and not on the nature of the surroundings, the

[1] One way to prove this is to consider a rectangular volume, and to make a careful count of all the possible TE_{mnq} and TM_{mnq} modes of a rectangular cavity having their resonant modes within a given frequency range. A volume of arbitrary shape can then be approximated by a series of rectangular boxes. Also, the cavity derivation can be repeated with the modes of a cylindrical cavity used to verify that the mode density depends only on cavity volume and is shape independent.

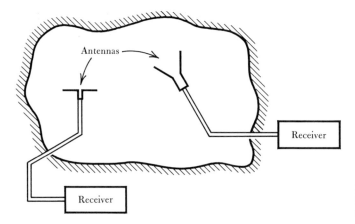

FIG. 11-14 Antennas or probes placed inside the large enclosure can detect and measure the electromagnetic fields of the thermal blackbody-radiation density.

location of the surrounding walls, their reflectivity, and so forth. This point can lead to some apparent paradoxes. If the volume is surrounded by perfectly absorbing, or black, walls at temperature T, it is clear that the thermal radiation emitted by these walls will account for the thermal energy within the enclosure; hence the name *blackbody* radiation density. The walls will, of course, also absorb radiation incident upon them from the volume, thus keeping the system in balance. Suppose, however, that the volume is surrounded by what are claimed to be perfectly reflecting walls, with 100 percent reflectivity, but still at temperature T, while the internal volume is initially cold. Since perfectly reflecting walls, by Eq. (15) or Eq. (16), cannot radiate into the volume, there appears to be no way in which the hotter temperature T of the surroundings can be communicated to the enclosed volume. The answer to this apparent paradox is that no *perfectly* reflecting surface is really possible. The surroundings are bound to have some slight amount of absorption, and hence some slight amount of emission, however small this may be. But with any emissivity at all, the enclosure will eventually come to the same thermal equilibrium independently of the emissivity value, although the time required to reach equilibrium will be longer the weaker the thermal contact between the enclosure and the surrounding walls, or the higher the reflectivity of the surrounding walls.

The fields in a given enclosure at thermal equilibrium may equally well be viewed as standing waves in standing-wave cavity modes or as traveling waves moving in all possible directions and with all possible polarizations. Indeed, the heat radiation from any surface, and Planck's law governing the magnitude and spectral distribution of this heat radiation, may be derived simply by supposing that such a surface is part of the boundary of the volume V and balancing the blackbody radiation incident upon the surface with the equal and opposite radiation that the surface must emit.

A similar thermal-balance argument can be applied to the antennas of Fig. 11-14. Suppose that these antennas are connected, not to a receiver, but to a matched termination at the same temperature as the volume V. Then this termination will radiate energy according to Eq. (15) down the antenna line, and this energy will be transmitted out the antenna into the volume. At the same time the antenna will be picking up or receiving an exactly equal amount of thermal energy from the blackbody radiation in the volume V and delivering it to the termination. From the requirement that these two energies balance, certain basic properties about the integrated cross sections of antennas can be derived. Also, as viewed from along the feed line toward the antenna, the antenna will appear to be a load or termination, with whatever reflection coefficient is given by its design, and with an effective or apparent temperature just equal to the temperature of the volume into which the antenna is radiating.

11-3 MASER NOISE IN NEGATIVE-RESISTANCE ELECTRIC CIRCUITS

For finite-energy-level atomic systems, the existence of negative temperature values is a straightforward, and in fact unavoidable, extension of thermodynamics (see Appendix B). In this section we will see how the noise behavior of negative-resistance maser elements and maser devices can be obtained from similar straightforward extensions of thermal-noise concepts to the fascinating world of negative atomic resistances with negative atomic temperatures.

NOISE IN NEGATIVE-RESISTANCE ELEMENTS

■ Suppose that a cavity or a tuned circuit containing absorbing atoms is represented by a tuned circuit with a parallel conductance G, as in Fig. 11-15. From the results of the previous section, this conductance at temperature T will be accompanied by a noise current generator $\overline{di_n^2}$ with the value

$$\overline{di_n^2} = 4G\,\frac{hf\,df}{e^{hf/kT} - 1} \tag{1}$$

as shown in Fig. 11-15. Now, if this resistance or conductance is caused by absorption on an atomic transition, then the value of the conductance in the circuit will be directly proportional to the population difference on this transition; i.e.,

$$G = K(\mathcal{N}_1 - \mathcal{N}_2) \tag{2}$$

At the same time, since the appropriate temperature for the conductance is obviously the atomic temperature of these same atoms, we have

$$\frac{1}{e^{hf/kT} - 1} = \frac{1}{\mathcal{N}_1/\mathcal{N}_2 - 1} = \frac{\mathcal{N}_2}{\mathcal{N}_1 - \mathcal{N}_2} \tag{3}$$

Combining these results, we find for the total dependence of the noise current source on the atomic energy-level populations

$$\overline{di_n^2} = \text{const} \times (\mathcal{N}_1 - \mathcal{N}_2) \times \frac{\mathcal{N}_2}{\mathcal{N}_1 - \mathcal{N}_2} = \text{const} \times \mathcal{N}_2 \tag{4}$$

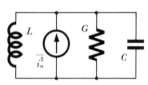

FIG. 11-15 Model for noise generation in a negative conductance.

In other words, the magnitude of the noise current generator is directly proportional to the number of atoms *in the upper energy level* $\mathcal{N}_2$ *only*, in exactly the same fashion as the spontaneous noise emission from a collection of atoms.

In fact, the discussions of Sec. 11-2 together with this little derivation make it apparent that the Johnson-Nyquist noise current generator associated with the atomic conductance and the spontaneous emission in the atoms themselves are not merely similar, but are really both exactly the same physical phenomenon described in different ways. Johnson-Nyquist noise in a resistance *is* the spontaneous emission of the atoms in the resistance.

Now, if the noise current generator is proportional only to the upper-level population $\mathcal{N}_2$ and is independent of the population difference, there is no reason that this same noise current generator should not continue to be valid—in fact, it *must* continue to be valid—even if the atomic system is converted into a maser amplifier, so that the absorption changes over to maser amplification instead. The upper-level population N_2 always remains finite and positive, and the amount of associated spontaneous noise emission always behaves in the same way, regardless of whether the population difference on the transition remains positive and absorbing or negative and maser amplifying.

To show this more directly, let us write down the noise expressions and assume that the atomic transition is indeed converted from an absorbing condition to an inverted or amplifying transition—perhaps simply by turning on the maser pumping source, whatever it may be. Then the conductance in the circuit changes over to the negative value

$$G = K(N_1 - N_2)$$
$$= -G_m \qquad N_2 > N_1 \tag{5}$$

Since the population is inverted, the temperature of the atomic system takes on the negative value

$$T = \frac{hf}{k} \ln \frac{N_1}{N_2}$$
$$= -T_m \qquad N_2 > N_1 \tag{6}$$

The second factor in the noise-current expression also changes over to a negative value, which can be written in the form

$$\frac{1}{e^{hf/kT} - 1} = \frac{N_2}{N_1 - N_2}$$
$$= -\frac{N_2}{N_2 - N_1} = -\frac{1}{1 - e^{-hf/kT_m}} \tag{7}$$

Therefore combining these expressions still leads to the positive noise-current-source expression

$$\overline{di_n^2} = \frac{4Ghf\,df}{e^{hf/kT} - 1} = \frac{4G_m hf\,df}{1 - e^{-hf/kT_m}}$$
$$\approx 4(-G_m)(-kT_m)\,df \qquad \frac{hf}{kT_m} \ll 1 \tag{8}$$

This result is a specific example of the general principle that we wish to develop in this section: a *negative* atomic conductance (or resistance) at a *negative* atomic temperature always leads to the presence of a *positive* noise-generation source; or

$$\text{Negative } G \text{ or } R + \text{negative } T = \text{positive } \overline{v_n^2} \text{ or } \overline{i_n^2} \tag{9}$$

In line with this, Eqs. (5) and (6) make it apparent that in maser atomic systems negative resistance and negative temperature always go together; one does not occur without the other.

■ If the lumped circuit of Fig. 11-15 is regarded as the equivalent circuit for a maser amplifier, then the noise performance of this amplifier can readily be evaluated. In fact, the noise performance of any kind of lumped circuit containing negative maser resistances can be evaluated in a very general way as follows. Figure 11-16 shows schematically what is intended to be any sort of lumped electric circuit containing one or more negative maser conductances $-G_m$ all at the same negative temperature $-T_m$.

NOISE IN NEGATIVE-RESISTANCE AMPLIFIERS

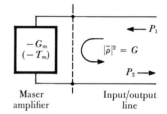

FIG. 11-16   General schematic of a reflection-type maser amplifier for noise-analysis purposes.

This circuit may also include the negative reactances associated with the maser material, as well as other positive reactances for broadbanding purposes or whatever. It is assumed, however, that there are no other resistances or positive-loss elements at positive temperatures in the circuit, so that the negative temperature $-T_m$ is the only significant thermodynamic temperature for the circuit.

If the resistances and temperature in the network were positive, the relationship between input signal P_1 and output signal plus noise P_2 for this network would be, as derived in the preceding section,

$$P_2 = |\tilde{\rho}|^2 P_1 + (1 - |\tilde{\rho}|^2)\frac{hf\,df}{e^{hf/kT} - 1} \tag{10}$$

But there is really no reason this same derivation and the above expression should become invalid even if the resistances and their temperature become negative. In the latter case the reflection coefficient will become greater than unity, and we can speak of it instead as the gain of the network; that is,

$$|\tilde{\rho}|^2 = G = \text{power gain} \qquad |\tilde{\rho}|^2 > 1 \tag{11}$$

At the same time, the factor containing the Boltzmann ratio also becomes negative,

$$\frac{hf\,df}{e^{hf/kT} - 1} = -\frac{hf\,df}{1 - e^{-hf/kT_m}} \qquad T = -T_m \tag{12}$$

With these substitutions, the output power (amplified input plus added noise) becomes

$$P_2 = GP_1 + (G - 1)\frac{hf\,df}{1 - e^{-hf/kT_m}}$$

$$\approx GP_1 + (G - 1)kT_m\,df \qquad \text{if } \frac{hf}{kT_m} \ll 1 \tag{13}$$

The second term represents, of course, the thermal or spontaneous-emission noise added to the amplified signal by the reflection-type maser amplifier. It is this added noise that gives the maser amplifier a noise figure greater than unity, as we will discuss shortly.

As is the case in most amplifier devices, the noise introduced by the amplifier is proportional to the amplifier power gain minus 1, $G - 1$. The factor -1 enters this expression for the following reason. Consider a perfectly reflecting termination; such a termination acts as an "amplifier" with a gain of unity, $G = 1$, since it simply passes the signal through without either amplification or attenuation. We would not expect any added noise in this case, and the factor of $G - 1 = 0$ for $G = 1$ ensures that this will in fact be true. Of course, most common high-gain amplifiers will have $G \gg 1$, and the approximation that $G - 1 \approx G$ is commonly made in this limit.

Note also that the excess noise in any little frequency range df centered at a given frequency f is proportional to the gain $G(f) - 1 \approx G(f)$ at that particular frequency. Therefore the spectral profile of the random noise appearing in the output of a high-gain amplifier will have the same lineshape as the power-gain-vs.-frequency profile of the amplifier itself (minus unity). This is really just another way of saying that the spontaneous-emission lineshape or fluorescent lineshape of an atomic transition will be the same as the absorption or gain lineshape of the transition. Moving away from the amplifier center frequency, the gain, and hence the noise emission per unit bandwidth, decreases.

■ Let us next apply the noise expressions for a lossy transmission line to the negative-resistance negative-temperature case, in very much the same way, to obtain exactly the same noise expressions for a traveling-wave type of maser amplifier. In Sec. 11-2 we saw that in a lossy transmission line having voltage-attenuation coefficient α and temperature T (of the losses), the noise power generated and radiated into the traveling wave in either direction, per length dz, is given by

NOISE IN TRAVELING-WAVE MASER AMPLIFIERS

$$dP_n = 2\alpha \frac{hf\,df}{e^{hf/kT} - 1}\,dz \qquad (14)$$

Now, the derivation of this expression given in Sec. 11-2 cannot be extended to the negative-temperature case, because there is no steady-state thermal-noise power flow in a negative-loss transmission line. That is, the steady-state average power flow at every point along the line in thermal equilibrium must be

$$P_n = \frac{hf\,df}{e^{hf/kT} - 1}$$
$$\approx kT\,df \qquad hf \ll kT \qquad (15)$$

but this expression becomes negative, and hence meaningless, for negative temperatures.

However, the noise power generated per incremental length by line losses, as given by Eq. (14), is readily seen to be directly proportional to the upper-level population N_2 in those cases where the line loss is caused by absorption on an atomic transition. That is, where the line loss α is due to an atomic transition, and the significant line temperature T is therefore the atomic temperature, the noise power generated per unit length has the functional dependence upon N_1 and N_2 of

$$dP_n \propto \frac{\alpha}{e^{hf/kT} - 1} \propto \frac{N_1 - N_2}{N_1/N_2 - 1} \propto N_2 \qquad (16)$$

Therefore we can identify this noise power added per unit length with the spontaneous emission of the atoms, and we can also argue that this expression for noise generation per unit length should continue to be equally good (that is, dependent on N_2 in the same way) even if the population difference in the line becomes inverted, and the line becomes a traveling-wave maser amplifier with a negative absorption and a negative temperature. In the inverted-maser case we simply make the two inversions

$$\alpha = K(N_1 - N_2) = -\alpha_m \qquad (17)$$

and

$$T = \frac{hf}{k} \ln \frac{N_1}{N_2} = -T_m \qquad (18)$$

and the added noise power per unit length in the maser case becomes

$$dP_n = (-2\alpha_m) \frac{hf\,df}{e^{-hf/kT_m} - 1}\,dz$$

$$= +2\alpha_m \frac{hf\,df}{1 - e^{-hf/kT_m}}\,dz \tag{19}$$

The basic differential equation for power growth along the line then becomes

$$\frac{d}{dz}P(z) = +2\alpha_m P(z) + 2\alpha_m \frac{hf\,df}{1 - e^{-hf/kT_m}} \tag{20}$$

If this is integrated over a total length L, the resulting single-pass power gain G is given by

$$G = e^{+2\alpha_m L} > 1 \tag{21}$$

and the resulting total power output becomes

$$P_2 = GP_1 + (G-1)\frac{hf\,df}{1 - e^{-hf/kT_m}}$$

$$\approx GP_1 + (G-1)kT_m\,df \qquad \text{if } \frac{hf}{kT_m} \ll 1 \tag{22}$$

This traveling-wave result is, of course, exactly the same as expression (13) for the reflection-type maser amplifier, with the total output consisting of the amplified input plus an added noise that is given by the excess gain $G - 1$ times the factor involving the negative temperature T_m of the maser atoms.

EQUIVALENT NOISE INPUT AND MINIMUM DETECTIBLE SIGNAL ■ Both the above derivations are based on an ideally lossless maser amplifier, in the sense that there are no cavity losses or ohmic line losses in the amplifiers to lower the gain performance or increase the noise generation. It can be shown that any such losses will always make the noise performance of a maser amplifier worse than the results derived above (see Prob. 11-6). It can also be shown more generally that no linear phase-preserving amplifier of any kind—that is, no amplifier that amplifies input signals linearly without destroying knowledge of the phases of spectral components—can have a noise performance better than these ideal maser results. As one proof that no better amplifier is possible, note that if such an amplifier were available the accuracy of the measurements it made would exceed by a large amount the limits set by the uncertainty relationship of quantum mechanics.

The second term in the amplifier noise expressions (13) and (22) represents added-noise output that is generated by noise processes (specifically, spontaneous emission) that take place inside the maser amplifier itself. This added-noise output is present even if the input power P_1 at the input to the amplifier is zero; for example, even if the input is simply a termination or source impedance cooled to $T = 0°K$. However, it is sometimes convenient to treat the added amplifier noise as if the amplifier itself were noiseless and the added noise were caused by an additional or equivalent input noise power $P_{n,eq}$ added to the actual power input P_1 at the input port of the amplifier. (As we have noted before, the input power P_1 may itself be a mixture of coherent signals, of noise from some thermal source that we are trying to measure, and/or of unwanted noise power from the background or from the source impedance.)

The equivalent noise input power $P_{n,eq}$ needed to account for the noise generation in the amplifier itself can be obtained by writing the total amplifier output in the form

$$P_2 = G\left(P_1 + \frac{G-1}{G}\frac{hf\,df}{1 - e^{-hf/kT_m}}\right) = G(P_1 + P_{n,\text{eq}}) \tag{23}$$

The equivalent noise input power itself is then given by

$$P_{n,\text{eq}} = \frac{G-1}{G}\frac{hf\,df}{1 - e^{-hf/kT_m}}$$

$$\approx \begin{cases} kT_m\,df & kT_m \gg hf \\ hf\,df & kT_m \ll hf \end{cases} \quad G \gg 1 \tag{24}$$

Figure 11-17 is a plot of this expression versus kT_m/hf. There are two limiting cases depending upon whether $kT_m/hf \gg 1$ or $\ll 1$.

It is apparent that if the atomic temperature T_m in a maser amplifier can be reduced, at first the noise generation in the amplifier will be reduced proportionately. As the population sketch for the linear region in Fig. 11-17 shows, in this region reducing the atomic temperature gives better noise performance essentially by providing a larger inverted population difference $N_2 - N_1$ for a given amount of noise-creating or spontaneously emitting upper-level population N_2. To put this another way, there is more gain per unit spontaneous emission (or less spontaneous emission per unit gain) as T_m is reduced.

However, this improvement in noise performance with decreasing T_m no longer continues once the maser's negative temperature magnitude is reduced below $T_m \sim hf/k$ (as a reminder, at $f = 10$ GHz this means $hf/k = 0.5°$K, and at $f = 5 \times 10^{14}$ Hz or the visible-light range this gives $hf/k = 25,000°$K). Below this temperature essentially all the atoms are frozen into the upper energy level—or perhaps it would be more accurate to say that they are all heated or boiled up into the upper energy level—and further reductions in T_m change neither the inverted population difference $(=N_2)$ nor the amount of noise generation $(\propto N_2)$.

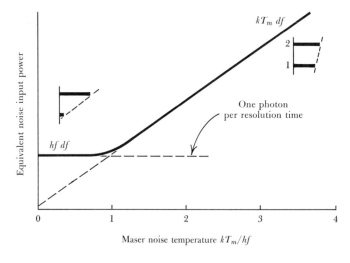

FIG. 11-17 The equivalent noise input power for an ideally lossless maser amplifier is $kT_m\,df$ for $kT_m \gg hf$ and $hf\,df$ for $kT_m \ll hf$.

For an ideal maser amplifier in this limiting case, which is the optimum case, the equivalent noise input power within a bandwidth B is

$$P_{n,\text{eq}} = hfB \qquad T_m \ll \frac{hf}{k} \tag{25}$$

We assume that the amplifier has a useful amplification bandwidth B within which it detects signals, so that we have replaced the incremental frequency range df by the full amplifier bandwidth B. Now, according to the sampling theorem of communication theory, in order to fully describe the most general sort of signal occupying a full bandwidth B we need just $2B$ samples of that signal per second, or two samples every $1/B$ sec. To put this another way, the signal of bandwidth B can be fully described by measuring its phase and amplitude, say, once every $1/B$ sec, and no more information than this can be contained in the bandwidth B. Thus the time interval $1/B$ is often referred to as the *sampling time* or *resolution time* of an amplifier or signal channel of bandwidth B. Then the above result says that the equivalent input noise power for a perfect maser amplifier is equal to *one photon per amplifier resolution time*.

The minimum input signal power that can readily be detected with an amplifier is often defined, rather arbitrarily, as an input power just equal to the equivalent input noise power of the amplifier; that is, $P_{1,\text{min}} = P_{n,\text{eq}}$. This is, of course, the signal input that will just double the output power from the amplifier compared to the output power due to noise alone, and this doubling should be readily observable on an output meter, an oscilloscope, or other indicating device. We may conclude, then, that the minimum detectible signal power for a perfect maser amplifier is just one input photon per amplifier resolution time, or B photons/sec. Of course, by using various filtering and signal-processing techniques on the output of the amplifier we can actually detect the presence of input signals very much weaker than this, but all such techniques require that the output signal be integrated over some period of time long compared to the amplifier resolution time, so that they severely limit the rate at which new information can be transmitted over the resulting channel.

AMPLIFIER NOISE TEMPERATURE ■ Another way of describing the equivalent input noise power to a maser amplifier, or other low-noise amplifier, is find the temperature an additional passive thermal source connected to the input of the amplifier must have for that source to radiate the amount of power $P_{n,\text{eq}}$ into the amplifier input. If we call this temperature T_{eq}, then its value will be given by the relationship

$$\frac{hf\,df}{e^{hf/kT_{\text{eq}}} - 1} = P_{n,\text{eq}} = \frac{hf\,df}{1 - e^{-hf/kT_m}} \tag{26}$$

which reduces to

$$T_{\text{eq}} = \frac{hf}{k \ln\left(2 - e^{-hf/kT_m}\right)}$$
$$\approx \begin{cases} T_m & hf \ll kT_m \\[2mm] \dfrac{hf}{k \ln 2} & hf \gg kT_m \end{cases} \tag{27}$$

In other words, for a maser amplifier with $hf \ll kT_m$, as is usually the case for microwave solid-state amplifiers, the equivalent input temperature is just equal to the inverted atomic temperature T_m of the maser. As T_m is reduced, the amplifier's noise performance gets better. Conversely, in the limit $hf \gg kT_m$, which is usually the case for optical maser amplifiers, the equivalent input temperature is $T_{eq} \approx hf/k$, and we note once again that for a frequency f in the visible-light region this equivalent temperature is about $hf/k \sim 25,000°\mathrm{K}$.

■ Suppose that the input power to an amplifier consists just before reaching the **AMPLIFIER NOISE FIGURE** amplifier input of a wanted signal with signal power S_1 plus accompanying noise power N_1, so that the total incident power is $P_1 = S_1 + N_1$, and the signal-noise ratio in the input signal *before* reaching the amplifier is

$$\left(\frac{S}{N}\right)_{\mathrm{in}} = \frac{S_1}{N_1} \tag{28}$$

Then the output from the amplifier will consist of the amplified input signal and noise plus the added amplifier noise, or $P_2 = G(S_1 + N_1 + P_{n,eq})$, and the signal-noise ratio in the amplifier *output* will be

$$\left(\frac{S}{N}\right)_{\mathrm{out}} = \frac{GS_1}{GN_1 + GP_{n,eq}} \tag{29}$$

Before masers and other specialized low-noise amplifiers became important, most conventional amplifiers at radio and microwave frequencies received their input signals from sources whose temperature was usually close to room temperature; and therefore the accompanying noise power N_1 in the input to these amplifiers in almost all cases consisted of thermal noise kT_sB coming from a source at room temperature, $T_s \approx 300°\mathrm{K}$. Therefore the conventional definition of *noise figure* F for an electronic amplifier was established as the ratio of the input signal-noise ratio to the output signal-noise ratio, with the input noise consisting of thermal noise from a source at room temperature. Combining this definition of noise figure with the definition of equivalent input noise temperature for an amplifier leads to

$$F \equiv \frac{(S/N)_{\mathrm{in}}}{(S/N)_{\mathrm{out}}} = 1 + \frac{T_{eq}}{300°\mathrm{K}} \qquad T_s = 300°\mathrm{K} \tag{30}$$

The noise figure F is a pure number or ratio, and is often expressed in decibels, since it is essentially a ratio of powers. Now, a well-designed maser amplifier (or a cooled parametric amplifier) may have an equivalent input noise temperature $T_{eq} = 10°\mathrm{K}$ or less. The noise figure in this case will then be $F = 1.03 = 0.14$ dB. In the limit of very low noise figures, which means $F \to 1$, the equivalent input noise temperature T_{eq} becomes a more direct and useful way of expressing the noise capabilities of an amplifier than the conventional noise figure F. Therefore the noise behavior of masers and other similar amplifiers is usually specified in terms of equivalent input noise temperature, rather than noise figure. Note particularly that when a low-noise amplifier is being used to measure the thermal radiation from a source, or for some similar radiometric application, then the minimum source temperature that can be detected with a signal-noise ratio of unity is just the equivalent input noise temperature; that is, $T_{s,\min} = T_{eq}$ will give $S/N = 1$ in the amplifier output (and further signal processing can then be used as necessary to improve this ratio).

11-4   NOISE PROBLEMS IN PRACTICAL MASER AMPLIFIERS

Microwave maser amplifiers find important practical applications as sensitive receiver preamplifiers for use in deep-space communications and telemetry, radio astronomy, satellite communications, and certain special microwave radar systems. In this section we will discuss some of the practical problems involved in obtaining and applying very-low-noise maser amplifiers in the low-frequency limit, $hf \ll kT_m$. These concepts are useful even if the microwave solid-state maser is supplanted by the cooled parametric amplifier or other ultralow-noise microwave device, as is now happening to some extent, since most of these ideas apply generally to any sort of low-noise microwave system.

Optical maser or laser amplifiers have yet to find any practical applications in optical receiving systems, but the future possibility of such uses is not entirely remote. There are certain special concepts that apply particularly to the noise behavior of optical maser amplifiers which operate in the high-frequency limit, $hf \gg kT_m$. In the final part of this section we will discuss some of the special features of the noise behavior of an optical maser (laser) amplifier.

NOISE EFFECTS OF INTERNAL
MASER LOSSES

■ In deriving the maser noise performance in the preceding section, we assumed ideal maser amplifiers with no internal ohmic losses. The presence of such losses will always cause the noise performance of an amplifier to deteriorate. The noise performance of a cavity maser amplifier with internal losses can be analyzed by the complete equivalent circuit of Fig. 11-18, which includes both the maser negative conductance $-G_m$ at temperature $-T_m$, with its associated Johnson-Nyquist noise current generator, as derived earlier in this chapter, and a positive cavity-loss conductance G_c at a positive cavity (or bath) temperature T_c, also with its thermal-noise current source. The reactive effects of the maser material have been included for completeness. The total internally generated noise of the cavity maser amplifier caused by the two noise sources can be computed and compared with the gain performance of the maser amplifier by means of this equivalent circuit. This calculation is straightforward and will not be carried out here (see Prob. 11-6).

Instead of considering the lossy-cavity case in detail, we will discuss here the noise performance of a traveling-wave maser amplifier with internal losses. This case indicates equally well the nature of the deterioration in noise performance caused by internal losses in a maser amplifier.

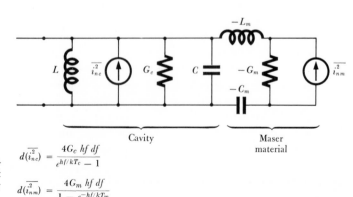

Cavity   Maser material

FIG. 11-18 Complete equivalent circuit for a cavity-maser amplifier, including cavity losses. The equivalent noise sources associated with both the inverted maser material and the cavity losses have also been included.

$$d(\overline{i_{nc}^2}) = \frac{4G_c \, hf \, df}{e^{hf/kT_c} - 1}$$

$$d(\overline{i_{nm}^2}) = \frac{4G_m \, hf \, df}{1 - e^{-hf/kT_m}}$$

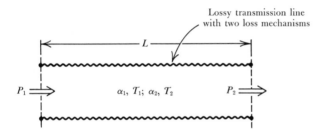

L

$P_1 \Rightarrow$ $\alpha_1,\ T_1;\ \alpha_2,\ T_2$ $P_2 \Rightarrow$

FIG. 11-19   A transmission-line section with two different loss mechanisms, α_1 and α_2, at two different temperatures, T_1 and T_2, respectively.

■ As a general model for a traveling-wave maser amplifier with internal losses, we may consider the transmission-line model of Fig. 11-19, which is assumed to have two different loss mechanisms with loss coefficients α_1 and α_2 at two different temperatures T_1 and T_2 (this might be, for example, a waveguide with lossy walls at one temperature, filled with a lossy medium held at another temperature). The lossy-transmission-line discussion of Sec. 11-2 should make it clear that each of these loss mechanisms independently absorbs power from any waves propagating in the line, and also independently radiates noise into the waves propagating in the line. The differential equation governing the flow of power in one direction down the line is then

LOSSY TRANSMISSION LINE WITH TWO LOSSES

$$\frac{d}{dz} P(z) = -2(\alpha_1 + \alpha_2) P(z) + \left(2\alpha_1 \frac{hf\, df}{e^{hf/kT_1} - 1} + 2\alpha_2 \frac{hf\, df}{e^{hf/kT_2} - 1} \right) \qquad (1)$$

The net transmission through a section of the line of length L is

$$\mathcal{L} = e^{-2(\alpha_1 + \alpha_2)L} \qquad (2)$$

and by solving the differential equation (1) the relation of power input to power output from such a section is found to be

$$P_2 = \mathcal{L}P_1 + (1 - \mathcal{L})\left(\frac{\alpha_1}{\alpha_1 + \alpha_2} \frac{hf\, df}{e^{hf/kT_1} - 1} + \frac{\alpha_2}{\alpha_1 + \alpha_2} \frac{hf\, df}{e^{hf/kT_2} - 1} \right) \qquad (3)$$

Note that the noise contributions of each loss term are weighted by the relative amounts of loss and that the result (3) reduces to the single-loss result (22) of Sec. 11-2 if the two losses have the same temperature.

To adapt this general result to the case of lossy traveling-wave masers we need only consider one of the loss mechanisms, say, α_1, as a positive, possibly ohmic, loss mechanism α_0 at a positive temperature T_0, and consider the other loss mechanism α_2 as a negative-loss, or maser-gain, coefficient $-\alpha_m$ at a negative temperature $-T_m$, so that

$$\begin{matrix} \alpha_1 \to \alpha_0 & T_1 \to T_0 \\ \alpha_2 \to -\alpha_m & T_2 \to -T_m \end{matrix} \qquad (4)$$

The maser-gain coefficient will presumably be larger than the loss coefficient, so that the net traveling-wave gain G (maser gain minus ohmic losses) will be

$$\mathcal{L} = G = e^{2(\alpha_m - \alpha_0)L} \geq 1 \qquad (5)$$

Direct substitution of these quantities into the general expression (3) then yields the result

$$P_2 = GP_1 + (G-1)\left(\frac{\alpha_m}{\alpha_m - \alpha_0}\frac{hf\,df}{1 - e^{-hf/kT_m}} + \frac{\alpha_0}{\alpha_m - \alpha_0}\frac{hf\,df}{e^{hf/kT_0} - 1}\right)$$

(6)

In the low-frequency limit appropriate to microwave maser amplifiers, the equivalent input noise power of the amplifier becomes

$$dP_{n,\mathrm{eq}} = \frac{G-1}{G}\left(\frac{\alpha_m}{\alpha_m - \alpha_0}kT_m\,df + \frac{\alpha_0}{\alpha_m - \alpha_0}kT_0\,df\right) = kT_{\mathrm{eq}}\,df$$

(7)

and the equivalent input noise temperature of the amplifier may be written as

$$T_{\mathrm{eq}} = \frac{\alpha_m}{\alpha_m - \alpha_0}T_m + \frac{\alpha_0}{\alpha_m - \alpha_0}T_0 = T_m + \frac{\alpha_0}{\alpha_m - \alpha_0}(T_m + T_0)$$

(8)

The last equality in particular should make it clear that internal losses always cause a deterioration of the noise performance, and in a situation where the maser gain and the internal losses are very nearly the same, so that $\alpha_m \geq \alpha_0$, the noise performance of the resulting amplifier can become very bad indeed. The physical reason for this, of course, is that there has to be much more inverted population, with its accompanying spontaneous emission, in the maser amplifier in order to cancel out the ohmic losses and achieve the same gain as could be achieved with fewer maser atoms if the losses were not present.

The expression for the noise in a lossy-cavity maser amplifier will have the same general character as these results, although the detailed algebraic expression will be somewhat different. As a general rule, internal losses in a maser amplifier should not have a serious effect on maser noise performance as long as the maser gain is, say, four or five times larger than the internal loss, unless the internal losses are at a temperature very much larger than the magnitude of the maser's negative temperature $-T_m$.

NOISE EFFECTS OF INPUT-LINE LOSSES

■ Probably the most serious practical limitation on the overall noise performance of any genuinely ultralow-noise radio or microwave amplifier is noise generation in the signal-input line caused by small losses in the line. Consider a mixture of signal and noise, $P_1 = S_1 + N_1$, which passes through an input line at temperature T_1 having an attenuation coefficient α_1 (or a total transmission $\mathcal{L}_1$) before entering a maser or other low-noise amplifier, as shown in Fig. 11-20. Then the input power P_1' actually reaching the input to the maser amplifier is given by

$$\begin{aligned}P_1' &= e^{-2\alpha_1 L}P_1 + (1 - e^{-2\alpha_1 L})kT_1\,df\\ &\approx P_1 + 2\alpha_1 LkT_1\,df\\ &= S_1 + N_1 + 2\alpha_1 LkT_1\,df \qquad 2\alpha_1 L \ll 1\end{aligned}$$

(9)

If the input-line losses are less than about 0.5 dB—and the losses should be this small

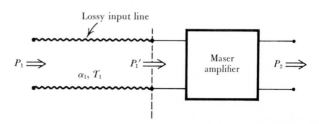

FIG. 11-20 A maser (or other low-noise amplifier) preceded by a lossy input line with loss coefficient α_1 and temperature T_1.

or smaller if there is to be any point in using an ultralow-noise amplifier—then the original input signal and noise powers are transmitted through the input line essentially unattenuated, but there is an additional thermal-noise contribution given by

$$k(2\alpha_1 L T_1) \, df \approx k\left(\frac{\mathcal{L}_{dB}}{4.34}\right) T_1 \, df \tag{10}$$

where $\mathcal{L}_{dB}$ is the decibel loss of the input line.

The figures in Chap. 7 show a number of practical microwave maser amplifiers. In general, there must be a signal-input line in such a maser which runs at least from the top of the liquid-helium Dewar down to the maser amplifier itself. This line must be made of some material, such as stainless steel or thinly silver-plated ceramic, chosen for minimum heat transfer into the liquid-helium bath. However, such lines designed for poor heat conduction often also have poor electrical conduction, i.e., large electrical losses. Thus such a line is likely to have a loss of least $\mathcal{L}_{dB} \sim 0.1$ dB, and this loss is likely to be concentrated in the warmer portions of the line, where the line temperature is closer to room temperature, $T_1 \approx 300°\text{K}$. However, from Eq. (10), the noise contributed by a small room-temperature loss may be written as

$$k\left(\frac{\mathcal{L}_{dB}}{4.34}\right) T_1 \, df \approx k(7°\text{K}) \, df \qquad \mathcal{L}_{dB} = 0.1 \text{ dB}, \, T_1 = 300°\text{K} \tag{11}$$

In other words, the effective input temperature of the maser amplifier is increased by $\sim7°\text{K}$ for each 0.1 decibel of room-temperature loss in front of the maser.

It is very difficult to reduce the total loss of a maser's input line (and the associated waveguide or coaxial connections) below about 0.1 dB, and the resulting thermal noise is usually the predominant noise source in the overall noise performance of real maser amplifiers. Also, if the maser is to be connected to a receiving antenna, there should obviously be a minimum length of room-temperature waveguide or coaxial line connecting the antenna and the maser. This is why the maser, despite the fact that it is a bulky, awkward package, is often mounted directly at the focus of a large dish antenna, as in Fig. 7-26a. The "sugar-scoop" antenna of Fig. 7-26b has the considerable advantage of providing a very direct antenna-to-maser connection along with a convenient physical location for the maser receiver.

■ Antenna characteristics affect the noise performance of a maser receiver in other   ANTENNA NOISE
ways. First, the antenna itself should be very low loss; i.e., it should transmit all the energy received to the maser without losses in the antenna surface. Conversely, any power sent into the antenna should all be radiated, and none should be absorbed by the antenna. Small losses in the antenna itself have exactly the same effect as losses of the same size in the antenna feed line.

Second, suppose that the antenna is pointed at the cold sky, but that it has side lobes or back lobes which are 20 dB down from the main lobe (a factor of 100 in sensitivity), but which are pointed at the warm ground. The amount of thermal noise picked up through these side lobes is then given by $[k\,(300°\text{K})\,df]/100 = k\,(3°\text{K})\,df$. In other words, even a small side-lobe or back-lobe level can pick up a significant amount of noise from the warm ground. Antennas to be used with ultralow-noise receiving systems must have minimum pickup in all but the main receiving lobe.

It should also be obvious that any waveguide switches, diplexing switches, filters, or other transmission-line components to be used between an antenna and a maser amplifier must have uncommonly small insertion losses, or else must be cooled to low temperatures themselves. In fact, it is not common to insert any such hardware in front of a maser amplifier unless absolutely necessary.

NOISE IN LASER AMPLIFIERS ■ The noise output in a single spatial or transverse mode from an optical maser amplifier may be written in the form

$$P_2 \approx (G - 1) \frac{hf\,df}{1 - e^{-hf/kT_m}} \approx Ghf\,df \frac{\mathcal{N}_2}{\mathcal{N}_2 - \mathcal{N}_1} \tag{12}$$

The factor $\mathcal{N}_2/(\mathcal{N}_2 - \mathcal{N}_1)$ at the end of this result has a minimum value of unity if the population inversion on the maser transition is complete (i.e., if $\mathcal{N}_1 = 0$), and in general it has a value greater than unity for real maser transitions. This factor, often called the *excess-noise factor*, may have values ranging from perhaps ~2 to 10 in typical laser materials. As noted previously, the basic factor $hf\,df$ in the noise output corresponds to one equivalent input photon per amplifier resolution time, or an amplifier equivalent input noise temperature of ~25,000°K for visible light (or ~1500°K at $\lambda = 10\,\mu$ in the infrared region). It is interesting to realize that a visible-spectrum laser amplifier with its input port pointed directly at the sun would show almost no increase in output, since the 25,000°K spontaneous emission inside the laser itself would be effectively brighter or hotter—at least within the narrow spectral bandwidth of the laser—than the 6000°K equivalent blackbody temperature of the sun at visible wavelengths.

NOISE IN MULTIPLE SPATIAL MODES ■ The most significant aspect of a typical optical maser such as that in Fig. 11-21a, however, is that the diameter of the laser tube or rod is usually large enough that the amplifier can transmit and amplify not only a single lowest-order mode, but also usually a large number of higher-order transverse modes or higher-order modes of propagation. The expression for noise output, Eq. (12), gives the noise-power output *per propagating mode,* but the total noise power coming out the end of the amplifier will be this noise power per mode times the total number of lower- and higher-order modes that can propagate in the amplifier.

A large-area detector placed at the output end of the amplifier tube will intercept and detect all this noise. Suppose that a signal is sent into the input end of the

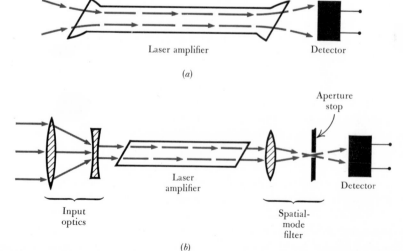

Laser amplifier   Detector

(a)

Aperture stop

Input optics

Laser amplifier

Spatial-mode filter

Detector

FIG. 11-21 (a) A laser amplifier without transverse-mode selection or control. (b) A laser amplifier with input optics to match the incoming signal into the lowest-order mode of propagation, and with a spatial-mode filter on the output to eliminate all but the lowest-order mode of propagation.

(b)

amplifier as a single propagating mode, is amplified in the usual fashion, and is then detected by the detector at the output end. This detector will pick up not only the amplified signal and the accompanying noise power in that particular mode, but the total noise from all the other modes as well. As a result, the noise performance of the amplifier in this simple arrangement appears to be very much worse than predicted by single-mode theory.

For purposes of analysis the waves propagating through a laser amplifier can be separated mathematically into a set of lowest- and higher-order modes of propagation. Depending on how the amplifier is to be used, a number of different basis sets, or sets of normal modes, may be used to expand the waves. The normal modes may be the waveguide modes of a round pipe, for example, or the gaussian-Laguerre optical beam modes introduced in Sec. 8-4. In any event, these modes can in principle be separated both analytically and experimentally by their different mode patterns inside the laser and by their different radiation patterns as they emerge from the end of the laser. Then, for most efficient use of a laser amplifier, the input signals to be amplified should be matched into a single selected mode of propagation in the laser, and the output beam from the laser should be manipulated so that only this mode and its noise is transmitted to the detector or to the next amplifying stage, with all the other unwanted and noise-carrying modes blocked off from reaching the detector.

As a practical matter, this is most easily accomplished by using pinhole spatial filtering, as shown in Fig. 11-21b. A good-quality lens is used at the amplifier output to focus the emerging waves onto a stop containing only a single pinhole aperture. This aperture is made so small that it corresponds essentially to the diffraction-limited spot size of the lowest-order mode coming through the laser tube and is located at the point to which this lowest-order mode will focus. In terms of the gaussian beams of Chap. 8, this pinhole should be $\sim 3w_0$ in diameter, where w_0 is the gaussian spot size of the mode in the focal plane of the lens (which will also be a waist for the gaussian beam). This pinhole will pass the lowest-order mode with little or no attenuation, but higher-order modes will focus to larger spots in the focal plane, which will be more or less completely blocked by the aperture. Clearly, a small amount of each mode will still leak through, but at progressively higher-order modes a steadily smaller fraction of the mode energy will pass through the aperture.

It is apparent that the adjustment and alignment of this aperture requires considerable care, since the aperture size (from the arguments of Chap. 8) is typically only a few wavelengths in diameter, and the aperture must also be positioned in the focal plane to better than this accuracy to avoid complete blocking of the desired lowest-order beam. However, experiments of exactly this type have yielded results in excellent agreement with theory. Laser amplifiers are difficult to construct, but entirely feasible should a need arise for them. Certain infrared gas lasers, for example, have extremely high gains per unit length, and it is possible that laser amplifiers will eventually prove useful as the first stages in communications systems at these wavelengths. In other experiments the mode problem in glass laser amplifiers has been solved by using as the amplifier tube a glass optical fiber of such small diameter that only a single lowest-order mode could be propagated in any case.

■ Consider now a visible-spectrum gas laser having an excess noise factor $N_2/(N_2 - N_1) = 5$ and a single-pass gain $G = 20$ dB $= 10^2$. The amplified noise emission from one end of this laser, within the narrow bandwidth of the atomic transition and within the narrow angular field of view defined more or less by the bore of

SUPERRADIANCE

the laser, is equivalent to the light emission from a thermal source with a temperature of approximately $5 \times 100 \times 25,000°K \approx 10,000,000°K$. Within a fairly narrow angular field of view and a narrow linewidth, this device will emit a semicollimated beam of semimonochromatic light in what is often referred to as *superradiant emission*. The beam emerging from the end of such a device will produce a bright monochromatic spot that appears at first glance very much like the beam from a true laser device.

The output from a superradiant laser device may be described roughly as *incoherent laser emission*. Depending on the shape of the superradiant laser tube, which is often very long and narrow, the beam will consist of some fairly small number of lowest- and higher-order transverse modes. If the beam does contain a fairly large number of transverse modes, then its far-field beam pattern will be correspondingly larger than the far-field pattern of a true single-mode laser, or its focused spot size will be correspondingly larger. Some superradiant devices, however, can even be stopped down to yield only a single lowest-order transverse mode.

In the time or frequency domains the superradiant output really consists only of highly amplified spontaneous emission or maser noise. Since there is no feedback, because of the absence of mirrors, there is no true discrete-frequency oscillation. However, because the amplification is highest at the center of the atomic line, there is some narrowing of the spectrum of the superradiant emission compared to the usual unamplified spontaneous emission. Note also that because the amount of amplification of the original spontaneous emission is large, the ratio of stimulated to spontaneously emitted energy in the output is very large.

In some instances where the full temporal and spatial coherence of a laser is not required, a superradiant source can be a useful device as well as a simple one, since no mirrors, mirror alignment, or mirror supporting structures are required. Superradiant sources have been achieved, for example, with cascaded high-gain Nd-glass lasers at $\lambda = 1.06\,\mu$ and in a large number of pulsed laser transitions which cannot run on a continuous basis, but which do give extremely high gains during the leading edge if a powerful pulse is applied to the gas mixture.

PROBLEMS

11-1. Connected to each port of an ideal three-port circulator is a matched termination, with each of the three terminations at a different temperature. Because of the properties of the circulator, it appears that in this situation the thermal noise from a colder termination can be carried one step around the circulator and delivered to a hotter termination. If so, this represents a continuous transfer of energy from a colder source to a hotter source—something that is usually said to be thermodynamically forbidden. Does this system indeed violate the second law of thermodynamics?

11-2. Two pieces of different lossy transmission line are connected together, and the outer unconnected end of each line is capped with a completely reflecting termination ($\rho = 1.0$). The two lines have loss coefficients α_1 and α_2, lengths L_1 and L_2, and temperatures T_1 and T_2, respectively. What is the net rate of energy transfer (net power flow) from one line to the other?

11-3. Repeat Prob. 11-2 for three segments of transmission line, one connected in the middle between the other two, and the outer two terminated at the outer ends, just as before.

11-4. To fill in the one remaining possible blackbody-radiation situation, consider two flat, perfectly conducting plates, placed face to face with a separation very much less than a wavelength at all frequencies of interest, but large compared to a wavelength in the other two directions, so that field variations are possible only in the two transverse coordinates. Evaluate the two-dimensional blackbody radiation density (energy per unit area) that can be expected in such a situation at thermal equilibrium.

11-5. From the results of Sec. 11-2 for three-dimensional blackbody-radiation density, evaluate the spectral density of the mean-square ac electric fields $|\tilde{E}|^2$ in a large enclosure at thermal equilibrium. Then assume that a collection of electric-dipole atoms with a specified oscillator strength and a specified lorentzian atomic linewidth are placed inside the enclosure. Calculate the total net power that this collection of atoms will absorb from the blackbody radiation fields through their absorptive susceptibility $\chi''(\omega)$ integrated over all ω, assuming that the atoms are at the same temperature as the enclosure. Show that this power will be exactly the same as the net power that will be spontaneously radiated back into the blackbody radiation fields by the atoms through their purely radiative emission processes.

11-6.   Evaluate the equivalent input noise power $P_{n,eq}$ and the equivalent input noise temperature T_{eq} of the general lossy-cavity maser circuit shown in Fig. 11-18 (make various high-gain and narrow-bandwidth approximations as necessary).

11-7.   It is possible to purchase commercial 30-MHz amplifiers, either the vacuum-tube or transistor type, having noise figures $F \leq 1.5$ dB. What is the equivalent input noise temperature T_{eq} of such an amplifier? If your answer comes out to be less than room temperature, is this possible for a device all of whose components operate at room temperature (or warmer)?

11-8.   A very-high-gain single-pass laser amplifier with a lorentzian atomic transition is being used as a superradiant light source. Write the expression for the spectral profile (power spectral density versus frequency) of the amplified spontaneous emission from this device. Find the linewidth (full width at half power) of this superradiant output as a function of single-pass gain. How much single-pass gain is required, for example, to narrow the superradiant output down to 10 percent of the atomic transition linewidth Δf_a?

11-9.   A microwave maser amplifier has an equivalent input noise temperature $T_{eq} = 4°$K for the amplifier itself, but the input line preceding it has an insertion loss of $\mathcal{L}_{dB}$ which is effectively at room temperature, $T = 300°$K. Considering the maser plus the input line as forming a single overall amplifier, find the equivalent input noise temperature T'_{eq} that applies to the overall amplifier—i.e., that is relevant to the input end of the lossy line—as a function of the line loss $\mathcal{L}_{dB}$. Include values of $\mathcal{L}_{dB}$ large enough that the small-loss approximations are no longer valid.

11-10.   Look up the *Dicke radiometer* in any available reference and summarize how this concept permits us to detect and measure a source temperature T_s that is very much smaller than the equivalent input noise temperature T_{eq} of the receiver amplifier that is used to make the measurement.

11-11.   You have just taken delivery of a commercially packaged microwave amplifier system whose equivalent input noise temperature (at the signal input connector) is claimed by the manufacturer to be $T_{eq} = 8°$K $\pm 0.5°$K and whose midband gain is said to be $G = 25$ dB ± 2. Your responsibility is to plan and carry out measurements that verify that the maser actually meets its noise specifications before you approve payment.

Describe in detail a test program that will measure the input noise temperature to the required degree of precision, using measurement techniques that you devise or that you learn of by searching the literature. Keep in mind such unpleasant facts as the limited accuracy and precision of all real measurements, the possibility that the exact maser gain may change slightly in an unknown direction owing to the slight changes in input impedance matching if input sources are interchanged, the very great difficulty in making absolute microwave power measurements with high accuracy, the fact that the impedances of many components will change drastically if they are cooled to low temperatures, the importance of even small losses in sensitive noise measurements, and similar sources of error in this measurement (which is, in fact, a particularly difficult one).

11-12.   A fairly sophisticated discussion of the design of spatial filters with two cascaded apertures for reducing the noise contribution from multiple transverse modes in a laser amplifier is given in Ref. 11-5. Consider a laser amplifier with a cylindrical bore which is to be used to amplify a signal in the form of a collimated lowest-order gaussian beam. The laser bore is substantially larger than the gaussian-beam spot size, so that the amplifier can propagate and amplify a large number of higher-order beam modes as well. Spatial noise filtering is to be accomplished by means of a single pinhole aperture and focusing lens, as in Fig. 11-21b. Analyze and discuss the expected noise performance of this system, particularly the tradeoff between the signal loss if the pinhole aperture is made too small and the excess-noise transmission if the aperture is made too large.

REFERENCES

11-1.   H. B. Callen and T. A. Welton, "Irreversibility and generalized noise," *Phys. Rev.*, **83**:34 (1951). A quantum-mechanical (but not difficult) discussion of the omnipresent relationship between loss mechanisms and noise fluctuations in linear systems of all types.

11-2.   K. K. N. Chang, "Theory of a negative resistance transmission line amplifier with distributed noise generators," *J. Appl. Phys.*, **31**:871 (May, 1960). Extension of the discussion in this chapter.

11-3.   J. B. Johnson, "Thermal agitation of electricity in conductors," and H. Nyquist, "Thermal agitation of electric charge in conductors," *Phys. Rev.*, **32**:97 and 110 (July, 1928). These two classic papers on the experimental discovery and theoretical explanation of thermal noise in resistors are still very much worth reading.

11-4.   J. W. Kluver, "Laser amplifier noise at 3.5 microns in helium-xenon," *J. Appl. Phys.*, **37**:2987 (July, 1966). Careful and detailed discussion and measurement of the noise performance of a high-gain gas laser amplifier.

11-5.   H. Kogelnik and A. Yariv, "Consideration of noise and schemes for its reduction in laser amplifiers," *Proc. IEEE*, **52**:165 (February, 1964). Discussion of the design of spatial filter apertures for reducing multiple-transverse-mode noise in laser amplifiers, and the resulting overall noise performance.

11-6.   J. R. Pierce, "Physical sources of noise," *Proc. IRE*, **44**:601 (May, 1956). A very good introductory review of thermal noise.

11-7.   R. V. Pound, "Spontaneous emission and the noise figure of maser amplifiers," *Ann. Phys.*, **1**:24 (1957). The Johnson-Nyquist noise theory applied to negative-resistance maser circuits.

11-8.   H. Rothe and K. Rupf, "Intrinsic noise temperature of the reflection maser," *IEEE J. Quantum Electron.*, **QE-2**:757 (November, 1966). A particularly careful measurement of the intrinsic noise temperature of a maser amplifier.

11-9.   A. E. Siegman, *Microwave Solid-State Masers*, McGraw-Hill, New York, 1964. For additional discussion and extensive references on the topics of this chapter see chap. 8, "Noise—in masers and in general," and chap. 9, "Practical aspects of microwave masers."

11-10.   A. Yariv and R. Kompfner, "Noise temperature in distributed amplifiers," *IRE Trans.*, **ED-8**:1 (May, 1961). Good supplementary discussions on noise in lossy transmission lines.

A ATOMS, QUANTUM ENERGY LEVELS, AND ENERGY-LEVEL POPULATIONS

In discussing the behavior of atoms and their quantum energy levels, and particularly in writing rate equations for collections of atoms, we often speak of an atom as being located in one or another of its quantum energy levels. We then say that in a collection of atoms a certain number of atoms will be located in each of the allowed quantum energy levels characteristic of that atom. In fact, however, the idea that each atom in the collection is located in some single quantum energy level is basically incorrect, even though we can obtain many correct final results with this concept. Let us examine this important point in more detail.

INDIVIDUAL ATOMS   ■ Consider first a single atom. In the language of quantum theory, the quantum state of this one atom at any instant will be made up of a *mixture* or *summation* of all the atom's characteristic energy states, in various proportions. Thus the atom's instantaneous quantum wave function $\psi(t)$ will in general be a mixture of the wave functions ψ_n appropriate to all the allowed energy levels E_n, each of these wave functions being included with a certain amplitude coefficient $a_n(t)$, so that in general

$$\psi(t) = \sum_n a_n(t)\psi_n \tag{1}$$

The coefficients a_n are complex numbers and are in general functions of time if applied signals or relaxation processes are present. The ψ_n do not depend on time. They are like a set of abstract unit vectors in a quantum-state space.

Now, according to quantum theory, if we attempt to make a measurement that will tell us in what specific energy level this atom is located at a given instant, our measuring apparatus will not give us the same answer in every such measurement, even though the state of the atom just before the measurement is made exactly the same at each trial. Rather, the measurement has some *probability* of recording that the atom is in each one of the energy levels E_n. The probability, or chance, that the apparatus will give a particular answer E_n is given by the probability factor p_n, defined by

$$p_n \equiv \text{prob } E_n = |a_n|^2 \tag{2}$$

In quantum discussions we cannot say definitely that an atom *is* in level E_n; we can only say that there is a certain probability p_n that a measurement at this instant will give the particular answer E_n. Of course, since there is 100 percent probability that the atom is in *some* energy level, it is always required that

$$\sum_{\substack{\text{all levels} \\ n}} p_n = \sum_n |a_n|^2 = 1 \tag{3}$$

Also, in special cases some of the possible a_n may be identically zero, so that those probability values are $p_n = 0$, and there is no chance that the measurement apparatus will record the atom in one of those levels. For example, in thermal equilibrium at absolute zero every atom will be frozen into the lowest allowed energy level ($n = 1$), so that $p_1 = 1$ and $p_n = 0$, $n > 1$. The measurement outcome in this case will be absolutely certain. This is not the usual or general situation, however.

ENERGY-LEVEL POPULATIONS   ■ How can this mixed quantum state for each atom be reconciled with our discussions of the number of atoms or populations N_n in various energy levels E_n? Consider a collection of a large number N of similar atoms. Each of the atoms in this collection is in its own instantaneous mixed quantum state, and we can, at least in principle, consider all the probabilities of finding each of these atoms in each of its given energy levels E_n. In real experiments, of course, we certainly do not measure each atom individually; we apply the same ac signal to all the atoms at once and observe the total response of the collection as a whole. However, let us assume separate experiments on each atom, at least for the moment.

There do exist some real experiments (for example, molecular-beam experiments) in which an atom is passed through an apparatus with one input port and several output ports. The atom then emerges from one output port or another, according to which quantum state E_n it is in (interpreted in the probabilistic way just described, the same entering atom might emerge from different ports on different trials).

Suppose we pass a large collection of similar atoms through such an apparatus, one by one, not worrying particularly about what each atom does, but only counting how many atoms in total emerge from each port. The number emerging from the E_n port we will call N_n, that is, the number of atoms in the collection that are in energy level E_n.

Each atom in the collection was initially in its own mixed quantum state, with probability p_n that it would emerge from a particular E_n port. Obviously, the total number actually emerging from the E_n output port is a rather good indicator of the *average* value of p_n over all the atoms in the collection. If this total set of measurements were to be repeated, starting with exactly the same initial collection, each individual atom would very likely make a different choice of output port in the repeated experiment. However, if the total number of atoms is large, the averaged numbers of choices, i.e., the observed numbers N_n, will be essentially the same in the repeat run of the experiment. Hence in an averaged sense N_n is the number of atoms in level E_n, and for any large collection of atoms the statistical fluctuations in measuring N_n in this fashion will be very small.

The first major point, then, is that each individual atom is really most often in a mixture of its allowed energy states, with a probabilistic significance in this mixture. But the collection as a whole can still be viewed as if, on the average, a certain number N_1 of atoms were in level E_1, a certain number N_2 were in level E_2, and so on. Clearly, the total number is the sum of these; that is,

$$\sum_n N_n = N \tag{4}$$

The (apparent) number of atoms in the collection in level E_n, namely N_n, we call the *population* of level E_n.

■ If atoms are normally in mixed states rather than specific individual energy levels, then the idea that atoms make discrete jumps between levels also requires reexamination. In fact, this concept is also not really correct, although it can also be used as a good approximation valid on an averaged basis over many atoms. Quantum theory says, to be precise, that when a signal is applied to an atom, that atom's quantum state or wave function changes or evolves *smoothly and continuously,* in accordance with a quantum-mechanical law of motion.[1] If the applied-signal frequency is near the transition frequency f_{mn} between two levels E_m and E_n, then the particular expansion coefficients $a_n(t)$ and $a_m(t)$ will change most rapidly, while all the other coefficients remain virtually constant. Hence the probabilities p_n and p_m change for that atom (and for all other atoms) as a result of the applied signal; hence in a large collection the populations N_m and N_n will also change. The net result is as if some atoms "jumped" from one level to the other, but in actuality the quantum states of all the atoms evolve and change slightly, instead of a few atoms making a complete jump from one level to another.

In the detailed quantum theory the rate and direction in which the individual quantum states evolve (from $n \rightarrow m$ or from $m \rightarrow n$) turns out to depend directly on the state mixture difference, $|a_n|^2 - |a_m|^2 \equiv p_n - p_m$. If this is averaged over all the atoms in a collection, the average response or averaged transition rate is evidently proportional to the population *difference,* $N_n - N_m$, on the transition in question. This

ATOMIC TRANSITIONS

---

[1] This law of motion is, in fact, just Schrödinger's time-dependent equation of motion.

is the third basic maser principle discussed in Chap. 1 and is perhaps the most important concept underlying this entire text.

In summary, the quantum state of any atom is normally a mixture of many energy levels, with a probabilistic interpretation to the mixture, and these quantum states evolve continuously, rather than in discrete jumps, when a signal is applied (or in the process of spontaneous emission, for that matter).

B   THERMODYNAMIC DERIVATION OF NEGATIVE TEMPERATURE

This appendix gives a thermodynamic derivation—or, more accurately, a statistical-mechanical derivation—of the temperature of a two-level atomic system which shows that the concept of negative temperature is not an artifice or a purely formal device, but a necessary and unavoidable consequence of the laws of thermodynamics and statistical mechanics. Negative temperatures are exactly as real and as meaningful in a two-level system as are positive temperatures, and a consistent derivation of the concept of temperature makes the possibility of positive and negative temperature values unavoidable.[1]

Consider a collection of N distinguishable[2] atoms, of which N_1 are in a lower energy level $E_1 = -hf/2$ and N_2 are in an upper energy level $E_2 = +hf/2$. For a given pair of populations N_1 and N_2, and hence a given total energy E, there is a large number of different, distinguishable arrangements or configurations of the atoms; i.e., there are a great many ways of selecting just which of the atoms are to be in the upper and which in the lower energy levels. Statistically speaking, for a given total energy each of the different possible configurations is equally likely. For a given energy the number of these distinguishable configurations of the system is given by

$$\Omega = \frac{N!}{N_1! N_2!} \tag{1}$$

(This is the same as the number of ways in which we can arrange N_1 red balls and N_2 white balls in $N_1 + N_2$ labeled or ordered holes.)

The thermodynamic entropy S of such a system is then, by definition, given by

$$S = k \ln \Omega \tag{2}$$

or, in the case at hand,

$$\begin{aligned} S &= k(\ln N! - \ln N_1! - \ln N_2!) \\ &= k[\ln N! - \ln N_1! - \ln (N - N_1)!] \end{aligned} \tag{3}$$

The total energy of the system, provided the arbitrary zero level for energy is midway between the levels, is

$$\begin{aligned} E &= N_1 E_1 + N_2 E_2 \\ &= \frac{Nhf}{2} - N_1 hf \end{aligned} \tag{4}$$

Figures B-1a and b show these quantities plotted against the population ratio $N_2/N =$

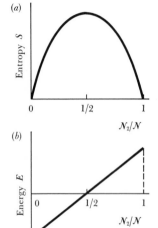

(a)

Entropy S

0   1/2   1

N_2/N

(b)

Energy E

0   1/2   1

N_2/N

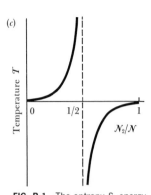

(c)

Temperature T

0   1/2   1

N_2/N

FIG. B-1 The entropy S, energy E, and thermodynamic temperature $T = (\partial S/\partial E)^{-1}$ for a collection of two-level atoms, as a function of the fractional upper-level population N_2/N.

<hr>

[1] For further discussion see especially Refs. A-1 and A-2.

[2] The atoms are distinguishable because they are located at separate and distinct positions in space, in a crystal lattice or in a gas; and each atom can be uniquely labeled by its position in space at any given time.

$1 - \mathcal{N}_1/\mathcal{N}$. Note that the entropy of the system is maximum for equal populations in the two levels. At the limits of the energy range, when all the atoms are in the upper or in the lower level, there is only one possible arrangement, and the entropy goes to zero at either limit.

Now, by a basic thermodynamic definition, the temperature of a system is related to its entropy and its energy by

$$\frac{1}{T} = \frac{\partial S}{\partial E} \tag{5}$$

In this case it is convenient to calculate this in two steps by writing

$$\frac{1}{T} = \frac{\partial S}{\partial \mathcal{N}_1} \frac{\partial \mathcal{N}_1}{\partial E} \tag{6}$$

Since the number of atoms can always be assumed to be very large, Stirling's factorial approximation may be used to write

$$n! \approx n^n e^{-n} \sqrt{2\pi n}$$

$$\frac{d(n!)}{dn} \approx n! \ln n \tag{7}$$

and the energy expression may be inverted to give

$$\mathcal{N}_1 = \mathcal{N} - \frac{2E}{hf} \tag{8}$$

Then the basic definition of temperature becomes for this case

$$\frac{1}{T} = -\frac{k}{hf} \ln \frac{\mathcal{N}_2}{\mathcal{N}_1} \tag{9}$$

This is, of course, just the Boltzmann expression for the two-level case written in inverse form. However, since $\mathcal{N}_2$ can be greater or less than $\mathcal{N}_1$ and the natural logarithm can be negative or positive, this form makes clear that the Boltzmann expression is equally valid and meaningful for either case. The derivation makes no assumptions that restrict T to only positive values. Figure B-1c shows the temperature variation on the same scale as the entropy and the energy.

Some further examination will show that this situation applies in any case where the system has a finite upper limit on its energy and the entropy must decrease to zero when all the elements of the system are raised into the upper energy level. The temperature in this case must eventually become negative for high enough energies. To repeat a point made previously, negative temperatures are always *hotter* than positive temperatures in the same system.

As mentioned in the text, the significance of negative temperatures has been dramatically confirmed by what are essentially calorimetric experiments carried out between two different systems, both of which are at negative temperatures before, during, and after the experiments.[1]

---

[1] See Ref. A-11.

C   MIRROR REFLECTION AND TRANSMISSION COEFFICIENTS

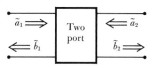

FIG. C-1 The incident and outgoing waves $\tilde{a}_i$ and $\tilde{b}_i$ at the two ports or terminals of a general two-port device (which may be a transmission-line or waveguide device, or an optical interface or partial mirror).

Consider a lossless, passive, linear two-port device such as that in Fig. C-1, with incident waves $\tilde{a}_1$ and $\tilde{a}_2$ coming into the two ports and outgoing waves $\tilde{b}_1$ and $\tilde{b}_2$ emerging from the two ports. These waves will be transmission-line waves in case the two-port device is a transmission-line device connected between two waveguides or transmission lines, and they will be quasi-plane optical waves in case the two-port device is a partially reflecting optical interface or optical mirror. The waves are assumed to be defined so that the power flow associated with each wave is $P_i = |\tilde{a}_i|^2$ or $|\tilde{b}_i|^2$, respectively.

For a linear system we must be able to obtain the two output wave amplitudes from the two input wave amplitudes from a pair of equations of the form

$$\tilde{b}_1 = \tilde{r}_{11}\tilde{a}_1 + \tilde{t}_{12}\tilde{a}_2 \qquad \tilde{b}_2 = \tilde{t}_{21}\tilde{a}_1 + \tilde{r}_{22}\tilde{a}_2 \tag{1}$$

or, in matrix notation,

$$\begin{bmatrix} \tilde{b}_1 \\ \tilde{b}_2 \end{bmatrix} = \begin{bmatrix} \tilde{r}_{11} & \tilde{t}_{12} \\ \tilde{t}_{21} & \tilde{r}_{22} \end{bmatrix}\begin{bmatrix} \tilde{a}_1 \\ \tilde{a}_2 \end{bmatrix} \tag{2}$$

The matrix defined in Eq. (2) is the scattering matrix for the two-port device. We can identify $\tilde{r}_{11}$ and $\tilde{r}_{22}$ as the reflection coefficients as viewed into the two ports and the coefficients $\tilde{t}_{12}$ and $\tilde{t}_{21}$ as the transmission coefficients from one port to the other. These are all generally complex quantities, since there is generally a phase shift associated with each coefficient.

It is a general theorem that the coefficients of a scattering matrix must be symmetrical about the diagonal, which means in this case that

$$\tilde{t}_{21} = \tilde{t}_{12} \tag{3}$$

The proof of this is beyond the scope of our discussion, but this theorem can be traced eventually to the symmetrical behavior of Maxwell's equations if we reverse either the E or the H field direction and also reverse the direction of time flow. Now, the total power leaving the two-port device can be expanded in the form

$$\begin{aligned} P_{\text{out}} = |\tilde{b}_1|^2 + |\tilde{b}_2|^2 &= (|\tilde{r}_{11}|^2 + |\tilde{t}_{12}|^2)|\tilde{a}_1|^2 \\ &\quad + (|\tilde{r}_{22}|^2 + |\tilde{t}_{12}|^2)|\tilde{a}_2|^2 + (\tilde{r}_{11}\tilde{t}_{12}^* + \tilde{r}_{22}^*\tilde{t}_{12})\tilde{a}_1\tilde{a}_2^* + cc \end{aligned} \tag{4}$$

For a lossless device the output power must always equal the input power, $P_{\text{in}} = |\tilde{a}_1|^2 + |\tilde{a}_2|^2$. Examination of Eq. (4) shows that this will be universally true, regardless of the values of the input waves $\tilde{a}_1$ and $\tilde{a}_2$, provided the scattering coefficients satisfy the relationships

$$\begin{aligned} |\tilde{r}_{11}|^2 + |\tilde{t}_{12}|^2 = |\tilde{r}_{22}|^2 + |\tilde{t}_{12}|^2 = 1 \\ \tilde{r}_{11}\tilde{t}_{12}^* + \tilde{r}_{22}^*\tilde{t}_{12} = 0 \end{aligned} \tag{5}$$

These relations are equivalent to saying that the scattering matrix of a lossless device must be what is known in matrix theory as a *unitary matrix*. It is evident from the first line that

$$|\tilde{r}_{11}|^2 = |\tilde{r}_{22}|^2 = 1 - |\tilde{t}_{12}|^2 \tag{6}$$

that is, the two reflection coefficients must have equal magnitudes, whatever their phase angles may be.

Actually, in writing the scattering coefficients for any given two-port device, we must always implicitly or explicitly choose a reference plane on each side of the device to define the point at which we measure the amplitudes, particularly the phases of the complex wave amplitudes $\tilde{a}_i$ and $\tilde{b}_i$. There may in some cases be an obvious point at which to locate these reference planes, such as the plane of the waveguide flange at each input to a waveguide device. Still, the choice of location of these planes is really arbitrary, in that we can always choose reference planes located closer in or farther out from the device. The only effect of shifting the reference planes by some fraction of a wavelength will be to add corresponding amounts of added phase shift to the waves, and hence to the scattering coefficients. The wave amplitudes must, of course, always be the same no matter at what point we measure them outside the device.

Specifically, the two reference planes can always be chosen—and it is convenient to make such a choice—such that any two of the scattering coefficients, say, $\tilde{r}_{11}$ and $\tilde{r}_{22}$, are purely real, and also both positive if desired. We can then write

$$\tilde{r}_{11} = \tilde{r}_{22} = r \tag{7}$$

The last of Eqs. (5) then simplifies to

$$\tilde{t}_{12} + \tilde{t}_{12}^* = 0 \tag{8}$$

But the only possible solution for this is for $\tilde{t}_{12}$ to be purely imaginary; that is,

$$\tilde{t}_{12} = jt \qquad t \text{ real} \tag{9}$$

With this choice of reference planes the scattering matrix for a laser mirror, or for any other type of lossless two-port junction, simplifies to the form

$$\begin{bmatrix} \tilde{b}_1 \\ \tilde{b}_2 \end{bmatrix} = \begin{bmatrix} r & jt \\ jt & r \end{bmatrix} \begin{bmatrix} \tilde{a}_1 \\ \tilde{a}_2 \end{bmatrix} \tag{10}$$

with the auxiliary condition that

$$r^2 + t^2 = 1 \tag{11}$$

The factor of j or the added $90°$ phase shift in the transmission coefficients is *unavoidable* for a lossless two-port junction with this choice of reference planes.

Of course, other choices of reference planes are equally valid, and so the above form is by no means the only possible form. For example, another reasonably simple choice is to choose reference planes such that the reflection coefficients are both purely real, but of opposite sign; that is,

$$\tilde{r}_{11} = r \qquad \tilde{r}_{22} = -r \tag{12}$$

We then have the condition

$$\tilde{t}_{12} - \tilde{t}_{12}^* = 0 \tag{13}$$

which now requires that t_{12} be purely real; that is,

$$\tilde{t}_{12} = t$$

The scattering matrix then takes on the form

$$\begin{bmatrix} \tilde{b}_1 \\ \tilde{b}_2 \end{bmatrix} = \begin{bmatrix} r & t \\ t & -r \end{bmatrix} \begin{bmatrix} \tilde{a}_1 \\ \tilde{a}_2 \end{bmatrix} \tag{14}$$

with the same auxiliary condition as above. The scattering coefficients are now all purely real, but the reflection coefficient on one side must have the minus sign.

Note that when we speak of different choices of reference planes, we are only considering variations within a total range of $\pm\lambda/4$ to go through all possible choices. But particularly at optical frequencies, we will usually not know to that precision where the "surface" of an optical mirror is. Indeed, for a multilayer dielectric mirror consisting of cascaded dielectric films each $\lambda/4$ thick, there is no obvious point to define as the mirror "surface" at all. Hence we can always say that there is *some* reference plane very near the physical surface of the mirror with reference to which the scattering matrix will take on the form (10) above, or the form (14), or any other that may be preferred. In Chap. 5 we used the form (10) for no particularly compelling reason other than that it makes the reflection coefficients real and symmetric, which is convenient. The phase-shift factors attached to the transmission coefficients jt must then be included to obtain correct results.

D   GROUP VELOCITY

The physical significance of the *group velocity* for waves on a slow-wave circuit or in any other wave-propagating system can be illustrated by the following simple example. Suppose the signal on a transmission line consists of two simultaneously propagating waves with equal amplitudes, but slightly different frequencies ω_1 and ω_2, so that the total signal on the line is

$$v(z, t) = \cos(\omega_1 t - \beta_1 z) + \cos(\omega_2 t - \beta_2 z) \tag{1}$$

where β_1 and β_2 are the propagation constants appropriate to these two frequencies. If we define the average frequency and average propagation constant by

$$\omega_0 = \frac{\omega_1 + \omega_2}{2} \qquad \beta_0 = \frac{\beta_1 + \beta_2}{2} \tag{2}$$

and the differences in these quantities between the two waves by

$$\delta\omega = \frac{\omega_1 - \omega_2}{2} \qquad \delta\beta = \frac{\beta_1 - \beta_2}{2} \tag{3}$$

then the total propagating signal may equally well be rewritten in the form

$$v(z, t) = 2 \cos(\delta\omega\, t - \delta\beta\, z) \cos(\omega_0 t - \beta_0 z) \tag{4}$$

after some elementary trigonometric manipulations.

Consider particularly the case in which ω_1 and ω_2 and β_1 and β_2 are nearly equal, so that the average values ω_0 and β_0 are much larger than the differences $2\,\delta\omega$ and $2\,\delta\beta$. Then, as illustrated in Fig. D-1, the term $\cos(\omega_0 t - \beta_0 z)$ represents a high-frequency traveling wave or "carrier" very similar to either of the two component waves taken individually. An individual cycle or wave crest of this carrier wave moves forward at a velocity such that

$$\omega_0 t - \beta_0 z = \text{const} \tag{5}$$

That is, these waves move forward at the *carrier phase velocity* v_ϕ

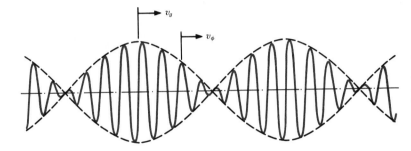

FIG. D-1 The modulated envelope or beat-note waveform produced by adding together two traveling waves of slightly different frequency. The cycles of the high-frequency, or carrier, wave move forward at the phase velocity v_ϕ, while the overall envelope (dashed line) moves forward at the group velocity v_g.

$$v_\phi = \frac{dz}{dt} = \frac{\omega_0}{\beta_0} \approx \frac{\omega_1}{\beta_1} \approx \frac{\omega_2}{\beta_2} \qquad (6)$$

given that the phase velocity is essentially constant for each of the component waves.

However, the first term in Eq. (4) above shows that the high-frequency carrier wave is multiplied by a low-frequency or long-wavelength *envelope* of the form $\cos(\delta\omega\, t - \delta\beta\, z)$, as shown by the dashed line bounding the carrier wave in Fig. D-1. This envelope results, of course, from the interference or beating between the two primary waves. The envelope itself—that is, any point on the dashed line, such as one of the crests or nulls—moves forward at a velocity such that

$$\delta\omega\, t - \delta\beta\, z = \text{const} \qquad (7)$$

Hence the forward velocity v_g of the envelope is

$$v_g = \frac{dz}{dt} = \frac{\delta\omega}{\delta\beta} \qquad (8)$$

This *envelope velocity* is not necessarily equal to, or even close to, the phase velocity of the underlying carrier wave or of the individual primary waves. If the envelope and carrier phase velocities are not equal, and the envelope velocity, for example, is slower, then an observer watching the moving waveform will see the envelope beat pattern moving forward at the envelope velocity $\delta\omega/\delta\beta$, while the high-frequency carrier cycles will appear to slide forward underneath the envelope, moving at the faster phase velocity. Individual carrier cycles will appear to emerge out of the back end of the envelope cycle, move forward through the envelope, and eventually disappear into the null at the front end of the envelope cycle.

The envelope velocity we have developed here becomes, in the general case, the *group velocity* of any kind of pulsed or modulated carrier-frequency signal on the same circuit. In general there may be not just two primary waves, but a group of many primary waves or spectral components at closely spaced frequencies about ω_0, all adding together to make up a pulse of radiation, as shown in Fig. D-2. Each frequency component of frequency ω in this signal will have a propagation constant as determined by the ω-vs.-β relationships for the circuit [this relationship may be written either as $\beta = \beta(\omega)$ or as $\omega = \omega(\beta)$]. Then, just as in the two-wave case, the carrier cycles within the pulse envelope will be seen to move forward at the average phase velocity $v_\phi \equiv \omega_0/\beta_0$ of the waves, while the pulse envelope will move forward with the group velocity v_g given by

$$v_g \equiv \frac{\partial\omega}{\partial\beta} = \left(\frac{\partial\beta}{\partial\omega}\right)^{-1} \qquad (9)$$

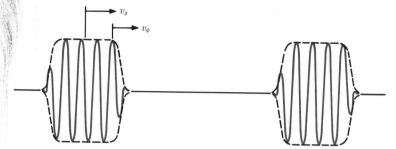

FIG. D-2 A pulse-modulated waveform. The high-frequency sine-wave cycles move at the phase velocity, while the pulses themselves move at the group velocity.

The derivative is to be evaluated at the midband frequency of the pulsed signal.

If the component waves all move at exactly the same phase velocity, so that

$$\beta(\omega) = \frac{\omega}{v_\phi} \qquad v_\phi = \text{const} \tag{10}$$

then the group and phase velocities are equal; that is,

$$v_g = \left(\frac{\partial \beta}{\partial \omega}\right)^{-1} = v_\phi \qquad v_\phi = \text{const} \tag{11}$$

and the circuit is said to be *dispersionless*. But when the phase velocity is (slightly) different for different frequencies, then the group velocity becomes

$$v_g = \left(\frac{\partial \beta}{\partial \omega}\right)^{-1} = \left(\frac{\partial}{\partial \omega}\frac{\omega}{v_\phi(\omega)}\right)^{-1} = v_\phi \frac{1}{1 - (\omega/v_\phi)(dv_\phi/d\omega)} \tag{12}$$

Depending on the slope of $dv_\phi/d\omega$, v_g may be either greater or less than v_ϕ, but v_g for a lossless electromagnetic system may never be greater than the velocity of light c.

If the dispersion of the circuit is sufficiently large (or the spectrum of the signal sufficiently wide) that the group velocity $v_g = \partial\omega/\partial\beta$ itself actually varies by a significant amount across the spectral range of the signal, then the pulse will still move forward at something like the average group velocity, but the pulse can be expected to distort or change in shape more or less gradually as it moves forward. Also, the above discussion applies rigorously only when the wave-propagating system is entirely lossless. When losses are present, and particularly when active gain is present, as in a traveling-wave maser system, a rigorous treatment of signal-pulse propagation becomes very complicated. Concepts such as *signal velocity* and *energy velocity* must be introduced, in addition to phase velocity and group velocity. However, as long as the signal gains or losses per circuit wavelength remain small, the group velocity as defined above remains a good first approximation for the velocity of a signal pulse.

E   OPTICAL CAVITY Q

In the laser analysis of Chap. 10 the cold-cavity Q of an optical cavity was given by the expression

$$Q_c = \frac{2\pi n_0 L}{\lambda}\frac{1}{2\alpha_0 L + \ln{(1/r_1 r_2)}} \tag{1}$$

where α_0 is the voltage absorption coefficient for a wave traveling down the length L of the laser cavity and r_1 and r_2 are the voltage-reflection coefficients of the cavity end mirrors. We will now see that this expression for optical cavity Q is in agreement with conventional definitions for the Q of a resonant circuit of any type.

The most general definition of the Q of a resonator, or any other element having stored energy and power loss (or gain), is

$$Q = \frac{\omega \times \text{stored energy}}{\text{power loss (or gain)}} \tag{2}$$

Since the power loss comes at the expense of the stored energy, in usual circuits this expression can be converted to the differential equation

$$-P(t) = \frac{d}{dt} W(t) = -\frac{\omega}{Q_c} W(t) \tag{3}$$

with the solution

$$W(t) = W_0 e^{-(\omega/Q_c)t} \tag{4}$$

In the optical case, because of the fact that the stored energy may not always be uniformly distributed within the optical cavity (as we will see in a simple example), the power output may not be a continuous function of time, and the cavity Q defined by a strict application of Eq. (2) may be a discontinuous and even infinite function of time. If, however, we average over one complete round-trip time $2T = 2n_0L/c$ for energy inside the cavity, then the decay of either power or stored energy in the cavity will still be in exact agreement with Eq. (4), with the cavity Q_c given by the defining expression Eq. (1).

As a specific example, suppose that the optical energy inside an optical cavity consists only of a very short rectangular pulse or packet of energy, as shown in Fig. E-1, which bounces back and forth between the two mirrors of the optical cavity. Let the length of this packet (in time) be ΔT, and suppose that at the instant just before it strikes mirror M_1 it contains an initial amount of energy W_0. The stored energy in the laser cavity and the power output from the cavity through mirror M_1 will then vary with time as shown in Fig. E-2 (there will also be interlaced power output pulses through mirror M_2, as shown by the dashed lines, as well as a continuous power loss into the absorption losses, not shown).

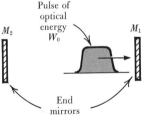

FIG. E-1 A short pulse of energy, with initial energy W_0, bouncing back and forth inside an optical cavity.

The power output in the initial pulse when the energy pulse first strikes mirror M_1 will be given by $P_0 = t_1^2 W_0/\Delta T$, where t_1^2 is the power transmission of that mirror. Then, after reflection off M_1, transmission down the laser cavity, reflection off M_2, and transmission back down the cavity, the energy left in the pulse when it returns to mirror M_1 will be

$$W(2T) = r_1^2 r_2^2 e^{-4\alpha_0 L} W_0 \tag{5}$$

and the power in the next pulse through M_1 will accordingly be $P(2T) = t_1^2 W(2T)/\Delta T$. Therefore the decay in either stored energy or power output between any two instants one complete round trip apart in time will be

$$\frac{P(2T)}{P_0} = \frac{W(2T)}{W_0} = (r_1 r_2)^2 e^{-4\alpha_0 L} \tag{6}$$

But if we equate this to Eq. (E-4) and write

$$\frac{P(2T)}{P_0} = \frac{W(2T)}{W_0} = e^{-(\omega/Q_c)(2T)} \tag{7}$$

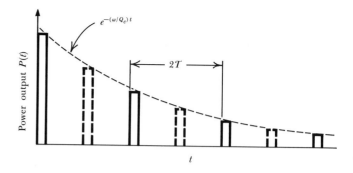

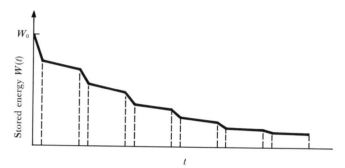

FIG. E-2   The power output through mirror M_1 and the stored energy remaining inside the cavity, both as functions of time, for the pulsed situation of Fig. E-1. The droop in the stored energy even between the output pulses is due to internal power loss to the absorption losses α_0.

then equating the right-hand sides of Eqs. (6) and (7) and taking the logarithms of both will lead to

$$\frac{\omega}{Q_c} 2T = \frac{\omega}{Q_c} \frac{2n_0 L}{c} = 4\alpha_0 L - \ln(r_1 r_2)^2 \tag{8}$$

or

$$Q_c = \frac{2\pi n_0 L}{\lambda} \frac{1}{2\alpha_0 L + \ln(1/r_1 r_2)} \tag{9}$$

which is exactly identical to the laser-derived expression, Eq. (1).

Thus Eqs. (1) or (9) provide a meaningful expression for optical cavity Q_c that is fully compatible both with laser theory and with conventional definitions of Q, and that is valid even for very large losses, so that pulses in Fig. E-2 decay very rapidly (perhaps essentially even in one pulse if the mirror reflectivity approaches zero). Of course, for small fractional losses per round trip we may use the simpler approximate expression

$$Q_c \approx \frac{2\pi n_0 L}{\lambda} \frac{1}{\delta} \tag{10}$$

where δ is the average (small) fractional power loss per one-way pass (half round trip) down the resonator due to all loss mechanisms that may be present. Note also that any initial energy distribution inside a laser cavity can always be regarded as the superposition of a large number of individual segments or pulses, as discussed in this example, and the results obtained here will then apply to each such pulse separately, with the same value of Q_c in all cases. Thus these results are quite general and independent of any assumed initial energy distribution inside the optical cavity.

REFERENCES

A-1.   D. K. C. MacDonald, *Introductory Statistical Mechanics for Physicists,* Wiley, New York, 1963. Negative temperatures are not mentioned directly, but chap. 1 and appendixes I and II are excellent reviews of the fundamental concepts that lead to negative temperatures.

A-2.   C. Kittel, *Elementary Statistical Physics,* sec. 24, "Negative Temperatures," Wiley, New York, 1958. An excellent, brief, but emphatic statement of all the major ideas involved in this subject.

A-3.   J. H. Van Vleck, "The physical meaning of adiabatic magnetic susceptibilities," *Zeit. für Phys. Chemie, Neve Folge,* **16**:358 (1958).

A-4.   B. D. Coleman and W. Noll, "Conditions for equilibrium at negative absolute temperatures," *Phys. Rev.,* **115**:262 (1959).

A-5.   C. E. Hecht, "Thermodynamic potentials for systems at negative absolute temperature," *Phys. Rev.,* **119**:1443 (1960).

A-6.   P. T. Landsberg, "Negative temperature," *Phys. Rev.,* **115**:518 (1959).

A-7.   E. M. Purcell and R. V. Pound, "A nuclear spin system at negative temperature," *Phys. Rev.,* **81**:279 (1951). A short letter showing a classic experimental recording of a system recovering (cooling down) from a negative temperature.

A-8.   N. F. Ramsey, "Thermodynamics and statistical mechanics at negative absolute temperatures," *Phys. Rev.,* **103**:20 (1956). Recommended reading for a thorough and understandable discussion of the subject.

A-9.   R. V. Pound, "Spontaneous emission and the noise figure of maser amplifiers," *Ann. Phys.,* **1**:24 (1957).

A-10.   J. Weber, "Maser noise considerations," *Phys. Rev.,* **108**:537 (1957).

A-11.   A. Abragam and W. G. Proctor, "Experiments on spin temperature," *Phys. Rev.,* **106**:160 (1957); "Spin temperature," *Phys. Rev.,* **109**:1441 (1958). A letter to the editor announcing experimental results on nuclear-spin "calorimetry" carried out at negative temperatures and a lengthy and scholarly article on the spin-temperature concept and the experiments described in the earlier letter.

A-12.   S. Ramo, J. R. Whinnery, and T. Van Duzer, *Fields and Waves in Communication Electronics,* pp. 604–609, Wiley, New York, 1965.

INDEX